CW00970113

Cambridgeshire Records Society

(Formerly Cambridge Antiquarian Records Society)

Volume 27

Published by the Cambridgeshire Records Society

Cambridgeshire Archives, The Dock, Ely, CB7 4GS

British Library Cataloguing in Publication Data

A catalogue record for this book
is available from the British Library

ISBN 978-0-904323-29-0

Agriculture in Cambridgeshire
1792 - 1815

Edited by

William Franklin

Cambridge
2022

CONTENTS

Preface i.
Abbreviations iii.
Introduction 1.
The Transcriptions 17.
Vancouver's Introduction 19.
Part I. Vancouver's Journal 21.
Part II. The Survey 99.
Vancouver's Appendix 109.
Rev. William Gooch's Survey 1811 131.
Chapter 1. Geographical State 135.
Chapter II. Property 150.
Chapter III. Buildings 150.
Chapter IV. Occupations 151.
Chapter V. Implements 157.
Chapter VI. Enclosing 160.
Chapter VII. Tillage 177.
Chapter VIII. Grass 212.
Chapter IX. Gardens and Orchards 217.
Chapter X. Woods and Plantations 218.
Chapter XI. Wastes 218.
Chapter XII. Improvements 220.
Chapter XIII. Livestock 243.
Chapter XIV. Rural Economy 251.
Chapter XV. Political Economy 256.
Chapter XVI. Obstacles to Improvement 258.
Chapter XVII. Miscellaneous Observations 258.
Arthur Young's visits to Cambridgeshire. 261.
Agricultural State of the Kingdom in February, March and April 1816 263.
Glossary 267.
Bibliography 273.

FIGURES

Figure 1. Map showing parishes omitted by Vancouver. 5.

Figure 2. Cambridgeshire Enclosure by Act of Parliament 10.

Figure 3. Vancouver's Map of the Soils of Cambridgeshire. 15.

Figure 4. Plan of the River Ouse 223.

PREFACE

Since the late eighteenth century whenever the United Kingdom has been at war parliament has turned its attention to agriculture. This has been necessary to ensure that the army could be fed and the country could also produce enough food for its population thus minimising any form of revolt from the starving poor. When country found itself at war with France between 1792 and 1815 the country was at the beginning of an Agricultural Revolution, which saw new technologies being used to enhance production and a focus upon improvement of land in a way not seen before.

Cambridgeshire at this time was a slow implementer of of new methods, despite being a neighbour of both Norfolk and Bedfordshire, both of which had champions for change. It was similarly slow in shifting from the medieval open field husbandry, with its rights of common to a newer form of husbandry based upon enclosed lands held in severalty.

This state and the changes that were just commencing can be seen in the surveys and reports of the newly formed Board of Agriculture, and the correspondence between the Board and and some of the leading agriculturalists in the county, between the close of 1792 and the beginning of 1816. It is these surveys, reports and correspondence that is the focus of this volume.

This body of information collected by the Board is of immense use to agricultural, landscape and local historians as well as those studying populations and economic conditions in the period.

William Franklin
Burwell 2022

ABBREVIATIONS

Annals	Annals of Agriculture and other Useful Arts.
B.L.	British Library
Correspondence	Correspondence with the Board of Agriculture

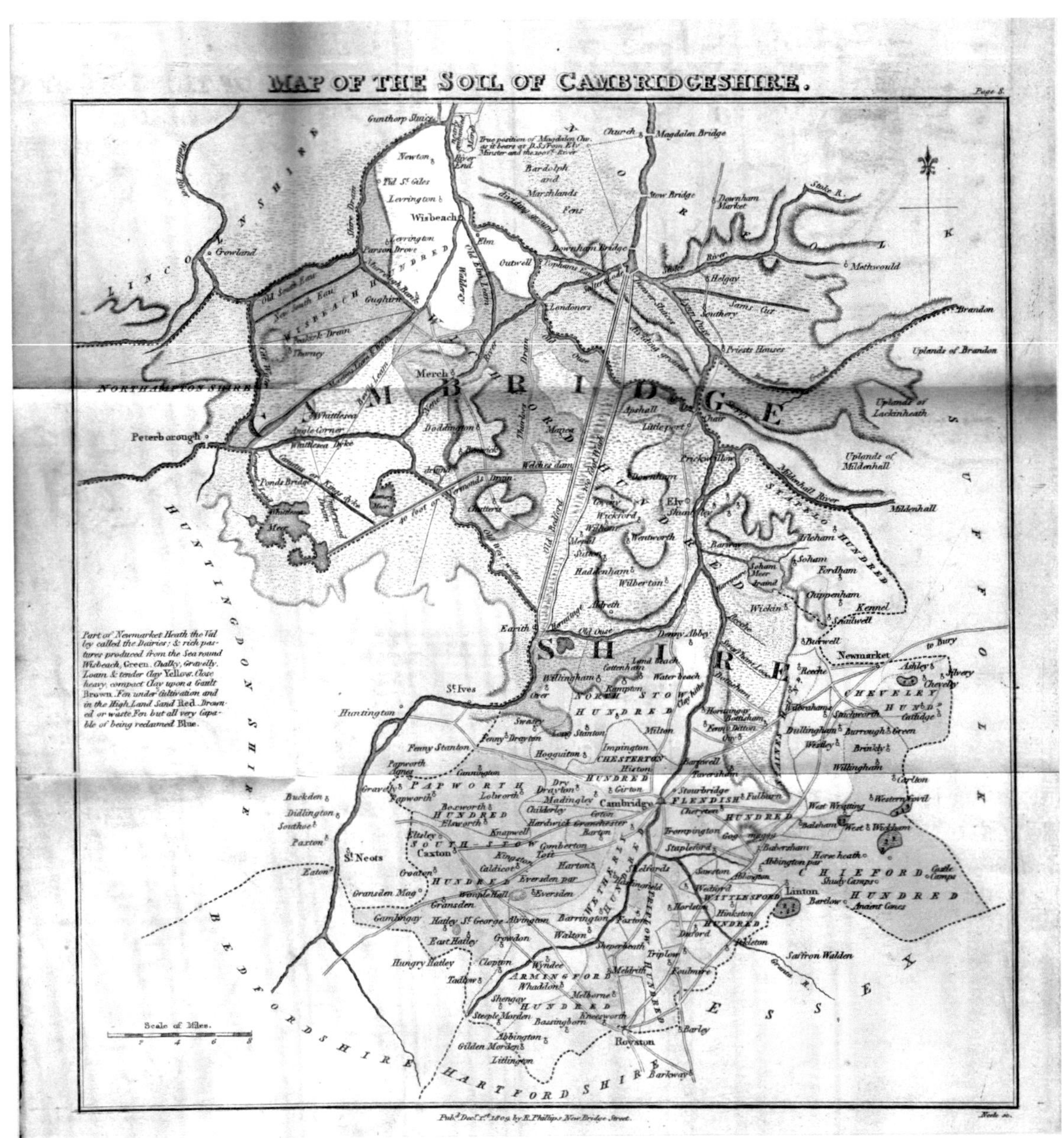

Note: This map appears at the beginning of Vancouvers survey as a fold out map and was reproduced again by the Reverend William Gooch for his survey.

Introduction

Interest in agricultural improvement had grown strongly in England during the 18th century and many forward-thinking landowners (including many of the clergy) were devising and adopting new methods, and supporting enclosure of common land. In other areas, including Cambridgeshire, farmers remained wedded to the old ways and to open field farming. A rising population and increasing poverty made increased productivity vital. War with France in 1792 made the need the greater and provided an opportunity to press for Government action to speed up change.

The publications here reprinted

The bulk of this edition is formed from the two county reports for Cambridgeshire produced for the Board of Agriculture in 1794 and 1807, with additions relating to Cambridgeshire, published either by Arthur Young or the Board of Agriculture in the period 1792-1815. While undertaking his survey, published in 1794, Vancouver also produced a report on the proposed Eau Brink Cut. That report was not usually included with his copy of the survey and was not formally published until 1811 when it was included with Arthur Young's report on the County on Huntingdon.

Publishers in the eighteenth and early nineteenth century would print out a book and often leave it unbound. The customer could then order a copy and request both a binding, card or leather and the colour of choice, and request additional items to be included in the bound copy. It is not uncommon for volumes of the period to include additional plates to the minimum called for by the author. The copy of Vancouver's report used for the transcripts in this volume is a leather-bound copy containing both Vancouver's report on Cambridgeshire and his subsequent report on the county of Essex, and included with the Cambridgeshire report is Vancouver's Eau Brink Cut report. While there is no bookplate or markings within this edition, it was probably bound for someone with interest in land in both Cambridgeshire and Essex, and as the size is larger than the standard for Board of Agriculture Reports, it was probably intended for the library of the person ordering it.[1]

The edition of Gooch's report used in this volume is a standard volume with no additions that was originally in the possession of The Royal Agricultural Society of England and bears their bookplate.

Though often used and referred to, original copies of the board of agriculture reports are mainly to be found in major college libraries, accessible only with difficulty – this edition brings the detailed info from both surveys readily to hand and provides a glossary and identification of the major players.

The Board of Agriculture

A Board of Agriculture had first been proposed by Henry Home, Lord Kames in 1776, and had gained the support of the Yorkshire-born agricultural writer and land agent William Marshall, who urged a systematic review of farming methods.[2] The increasingly influential Sir John Sinclair, MP, who saw the proper function of government as intervention or legislative action to promote welfare and economic growth, and recognised that detailed information was necessary for such intervention to be effective, pressed Prime Minister William Pitt in January 1793 for a board, with a budget of £10,000 a year. Pitt refused, but Sinclair intervened a few months later to stave off bankruptcies during the liquidity crisis caused by the war and won Pitt's support in return. On 15 May 1793, Sinclair moved in the House of Commons

> 'that His Majesty take into his consideration the advantages which might be derived from the establishment of such a board, for though in some particular districts improved methods of cultivating the soil were practised, yet in the greatest part of these kingdoms the principles of agriculture are not sufficiently understood, nor are the implements of husbandry or the stock of the farmer brought to that perfection of which they are capable.'

---

1. Typically the volumes measured 5.5 inches by 8.5 inches. This copy measures 8 inches by 10 inches.
2. Henry Home, Lord Kames, *The Gentleman Farmer. Being an attempt to Improve Agriculture by subjecting it to the Test of Rational principles* (London, Cadell 1776); G E Mingay, 'William Marshall (bap. 1745, d. 1818)', *Oxford Dictionary of National Biography* (2004)

An annual grant of £3000 was provided, and the Board for the Encouragement of Agriculture and Internal Improvement was awarded a royal charter in August 1793. Sinclair was its unpaid president and Arthur Young, to William Marshall's ire, its salaried secretary. A voluntary society rather than a branch of government, the Board comprised 31 'ordinary' members from the two houses of parliament, and 19 'official' members (officers of state, leading bishops, president of the Royal Society).[3]

The Board conducted a variety of business during its 30-year lifetime, including procuring funds for improvements (eg Elkington's land drainage system, Meikle's threshing machine), encouraging Macadam's road improvements and obtaining the removal of taxes which hampered agricultural development (eg on drainage tiles).[4] It also pressed for general enclosure legislation, leading, in watered-down format, to the General Act of 1801. In many counties, local agricultural shows were held, usually organized by local societies or clubs (there was none in Cambridgeshire) and in 1821 the Board organized the first national agricultural show. The agricultural depression of the 1820s however severely curtailed enthusiasm for the Board's work, and it was dissolved in 1822. The Board's records, which passed into the care of the Royal Agricultural Society, formed in 1838, are deposited, with those of the Society, at the University of Reading's Museum of English Rural Life.[5]

The Surveys

The Board is probably best known now for the series of county agricultural reports which it funded and published. These replaced Sinclair's initial intention of a parish-based statistical survey, addressed to clergymen, which was feared impractical, partly because of the inadequacy of the postal system, and partly from concern at 'doubts how far the public might at first approve of such inquiries until they became accustomed to them'. 80 surveys were commissioned by Sinclair in 1793 from men he termed 'very intelligent surveyors, or persons skilled in husbandry'. Whether his intention, that they be printed and circulated in draft before publication so that 'no material error can escape observation, and that every useful fact, or valuable idea, existing in the kingdom on the subject of agriculture, will be brought forward', was fulfilled seems unlikely. The job was anyway difficult enough. Every surveyor was given a list of 35 questions to answer. Sinclair, the Chairman of the Board, wanted them out by March 1794 and claimed that a surveyor could do a tour of five or six weeks for a county and that would suffice. Expenses only, of £5 to £10 per week, would be allowed, giving the surveyors time to follow their usual business pursuits.[6]

Two groups of surveys were commissioned and published, the first between 1794 and 1798, the second between 1805 and 1814. The first group was drawn up under significant time-pressure, requiring the work to be undertaken in the winter of 1793-4. Haste led in many cases to superficiality, and the reports were much criticised. The later surveys in general made good some of the deficiencies of the first, and are regarded as a valuable source. For Cambridgeshire, the opposite seems to be true. Charles Vancouver, a land agent of standing, whose report was published in 1794, was thorough in his work. He systematically rode or walked the counties he surveyed, and produced parish by parish notes, as well as corresponding with many farmers.

In 1795 it became clear to the Board that, even with extensive comments from local farmers, many of the reports were inadequate, and that for the future a common plan must be drawn up. The common plan devised by the board was for a report consisting of seventeen chapters, with subdivisions and appendices. This format was claimed to be systematic, but in reality, it was not really as systematic as it claims to be. William Marshall, himself one of the board's surveyors was not in favour of the new format, writing, "The Reports at large, seeing their bulk, and comparative smallness of the useful matter they contain, may well be deemed a heavy tax on time, if not on the purse of the agricultural public. Their voluminousness certainly debars many practical men

---

3. R. Mitchison, The Old Board of Agriculture (1793-1822). *The English Historical Review,* Vol. 74, No 290. p.43. (1959). R. Mitchison, 'Sinclair, Sir John, first baronet (1745-1835)', *ODNB* (2004) https://doi.org/10.1093/ref:odnb/25627, accessed 17 November 2021.
4. A.D. Hall, (Ed.) *English Farming Past and Present by the Right Honble. Lord Ernle.* Longmans, Green and Co. London. 5th Edition (1936). pp. 208, 366.
5. https://merl.reading.ac.uk/collections/royal-agricultural-society-of-england/ and the handlist of records there signposted. The history of the Board is recounted by Rosalind Mitchison (1959) , pp. 41- 69.
6. R. Mitchison, (1959) p.49.

from profiting by the useful parts of their contents." [7] Later in the same document he calls the new format as "silly".[8]

William Gooch, whose survey followed the new format, was published in 1811, relied much less on personal observation and more on information from named gentleman contacts and published sources. Numerous copies of Vancouver's survey survive in major collections; Gooch's survey is much rarer. [9]

The Cambridgeshire Surveyors

Charles Vancouver (1756-c.1815) was the son of Dutch parents, born in Kings Lynn, where his father was deputy collector of customs. They were it seems an adventurous family; one of his younger brothers was the explorer George Vancouver. Charles was apprenticed at an early age to a 'great farmer' in Norfolk, and in c.1776, at the age of 20, was recommended by Arthur Young to be bailiff to Lord Shelburne at Rahan, County Offaly (then King's County), Ireland. Here he gained experience in drainage, draining bog land, and by 1785 he was in Kentucky (soon to be admitted to the United States of America), supervising the drainage and settlement of a large estate. When he returned to England is unclear, but he was apparently known to Sinclair or his circle, as he was invited in 1793 to undertake surveys of Cambridgeshire and Essex (published in 1794 and 1795). In 1798 or 1799 he was in the Netherlands, where he married a cousin, Louise van Coeverden. He may have returned thereafter to the USA, but was again in England by 1806. His surveys of Devon and Hampshire were completed in 1808 and 1810. He died in Virginia, probably in 1815. [10]

William Gooch (c.1761-1813) was born in Yarmouth about 1761, listed on admission to Gonville & Caius College Cambridge in 1787, at the age of 26, as the son of a Gorleston mercer. He was ordained priest at Norwich in 1792 and became curate of Foulsham (Norfolk).[11] His subsequent history is unknown, save that by 1805 he was a proprietor of land in Swaffham Prior, that he was renting to a Samuel Hart.[12] 1807, when he completed his Cambridgeshire report, he was living in the parsonage house at Whatfield, Suffolk, where he was presumably curate. Arthur Young notes that he resided at Cockfield, Suffolk,[13] and it was here, sometime after 1807 that he was recommended by Arthur Young, his Suffolk neighbour, to John Upton, 1st Viscount Templeton as agent at Castle Upton. Gooch wrote his will near Castle Upton in January 1813, leaving all his goods to his wife, Mary, who was to be his executrix. He died in December of the same year at Douglas, Isle of Man. She declined the probate, and administration was granted in September 1814 to Viscount Templeton, his creditor. He is commemorated at St Mary's Buxhall, Suffolk together with his wife Mary, nee Hill, who died in 1836, and their youngest daughter, who had died at the age of 12 in 1814.[14] He was listed in the May 1814 edition of the Gentleman's Magazine among the lately dead, described as aged 52, late of Castle Upton, County Antrim and formerly of Whatfield parsonage, Suffolk; there is no mention of his work for the Board of Agriculture. [15]

Arthur Young (1741-1820) Born in London, Arthur Young came of a family which had owned the Bradfield Hall estate, Suffolk, since the early 1670s. After an apprenticeship in the wine trade, which he disliked, and a failed attempt to establish a career as a journalist, Young took over management of the Bradfield farm. Despite an unhappy married life, which occasioned his moving to farm briefly in Essex and then in Hertfordshire,

---

7. W. Marshall, *Review of the Northern Reports*, Longman, Hurst, Reese and Orme, London (1808), p.13.
8. Ibid, p.496.
9. Mitchison, *ODNB* cited at note 2 above; for survival see eg Cambridge University Library's *i-discover* catalogue.
10. H. S. A. Fox, 'Vancouver, Charles', *ODNB* 2004, https://doi.org/10.1093/ref:odnb/28061 accessed 27 November 2021.
11. *ACAD a Cambridge alumni database, https://venn.lib.cam.ac.uk/* accessed 26 November 2021.
12. Cambridge University Library, Doc.656, No 16. Documents relating to the Parliamentary Enclosure of Swaffham Prior. See also Add.6075 Book of proprietors for Swaffham Prior.
13. J. Gazley, Arthur Young, Agriculturalist and Traveller, 1741-1820. Some biographical sources. *Journal of the Royal Agricultural Society*, lxxxv (1925), p.417
14. J. Gazley, The Life of Arthur Young, 1741-1820, *American Philosophical Society*, 1973, pp. 489, 528-30; Prerogative Court of Canterbury will, *per* https://www.ancestry.co.uk/; memorial *per* https://www.findagrave.com/ both accessed 21 November 2021
15. Cambridge Alumni database, https://venn.lib.cam.ac.uk/, *Gentleman's Magazine* 1814, I, p.524 accessed *per* https://onlinebooks.library.upenn.edu/, both accessed 21 November 2021

Young made himself an expert on agricultural innovation, and travelled widely, in England, Ireland and abroad. By 1793, when he became secretary to the Board of Agriculture, he had acquired an international reputation, not least from the vast quantity of his writings. Between 1767 and 1774 he wrote 13 works on agriculture (as well as writing on other topics) and gained a substantial following: 11 of the 13 went into a further edition. Young was the author of six of the county surveys: Suffolk (1794); Lincolnshire (1799); Hertfordshire (1804); Norfolk (1804); Essex (1807); and Oxfordshire (1809), and it may well be he who recommended his otherwise apparently unknown neighbour, William Gooch to undertake the second survey of Cambridgeshire. In 1784 Young had launched his periodical *Annals of Agriculture,* a venture he had for some time had in mind. Of the content of the 45 issues which he edited before it ceased publication in 1808, he personally wrote roughly a quarter, and it is his accounts there, and in other works, of Cambridgeshire agriculture which provide an alternative eye upon the county, and are reproduced here alongside the Cambridgeshire surveys.

Vancouver's survey of Cambridgeshire, 1793-4

Vancouver was a diligent surveyor of the county. He attempted to visit every parish, and in the first part of his report, the Journal, he published information gathered from each parish he visited. It is not clear what districts Cambridgeshire was divided into, and he appears to have visited the fen first of all, perhaps with the intention of revising it at the end of his visits, as his Journal appears to be set out in the order in which he made his visits, commencing with Ashley cum Silverly.[16] He probably first lodged in Newmarket, and after visiting Bottisham, moved his base back to Cambridge to start again with the Wilbrahams. Presumably, he stayed in local inns, but only The Hoops in Cambridge is named.[17] He was everywhere interested to exercise his keen eye for soil types and to discuss with the farmers what he saw as he walked across the land. 'I have made it my particular care, to mix, and converse with the yeomanry of the county, and in their sedate, and sober moments, to possess myself fully of their experience, and local knowledge, and finally to ascertain the general sentiment, as to this important innovation upon the establishment of ages.' Not every parish welcomed the changes: 'A few have given an unqualified dissent', or welcomed him; distrust of a stranger was amplified by fear, when his project was understood, that it might result in increased taxation, or local disbenefit. At Wisbech, where the rector was in favour of enclosure, information was slight, he 'being unfortunately suspected to be in the interests of the rector, I was not only received coolly, but treated with great jealousy and distrust'. At Conington he reports he was 'trifled with and deceived', and it may have been deceit, too, which led local people to inform him that Graveley was in Huntingdonshire.[18] The requirement that the survey be conducted so speedily, and therefore during the winter, made for increased difficulties, especially in the fens. Manea he 'omitted through necessity', probably because the surrounding land was flooded; Coveney he apparently never found at all. There was little mapping to guide him, and he considered remedying the lack himself, by publishing a map of Cambridgeshire.[19] His practical survey work was supplemented by correspondence with landowners, to whom he apparently sent a series of questions. The answers of Edward Stone of Leverington are set out at length.[20] Where he was given information, Vancouver sets out not only soil types, but also the state of drainage, the manures used, the average yield on the largest farm and the rental value of the various land types, as well as in most cases population. The last was most frequently calculated from the number of houses and separate households, based on an average of 5 per household. He also frequently noted the poor rate, and whether tithes had been commuted at enclosure, or were paid in kind or cash. The Journal is followed by two tables, setting out parish size, population and the various acreages of cultivation, with the all-important information about rental value, the yardstick by which the Board would measure improvement.

The second part of his report, following the tables, is an analysis by subject of the information he has uncovered: arable land, enclosure, tenure, grass, crops, animals, implements of husbandry and so on.[21] Interestingly, though he included information about the (relatively little) parliamentary enclosure which had taken place, and though he quite often mentions the benefit of field (hollow) drainage systems, he does not generally note where internal drainage boards had been established, a beneficial practice which was already underway. His strong interest in drainage was however diligently employed. His initial report submission

---

16. See Parish Map on p.15
17. The address from which he signed off his paper on the fens, p126 below.
18. Ibid, p. 40, below.
19. *Sketch of a proposal to make an actual survey and publish an accurate map of the county of Cambridge. By Charles Vancouver*, London, 1793.
20. Journal, pp. 60, below
21. Survey, pp. 78, below

Figure 1. Map showing parishes omitted by Vancouver.

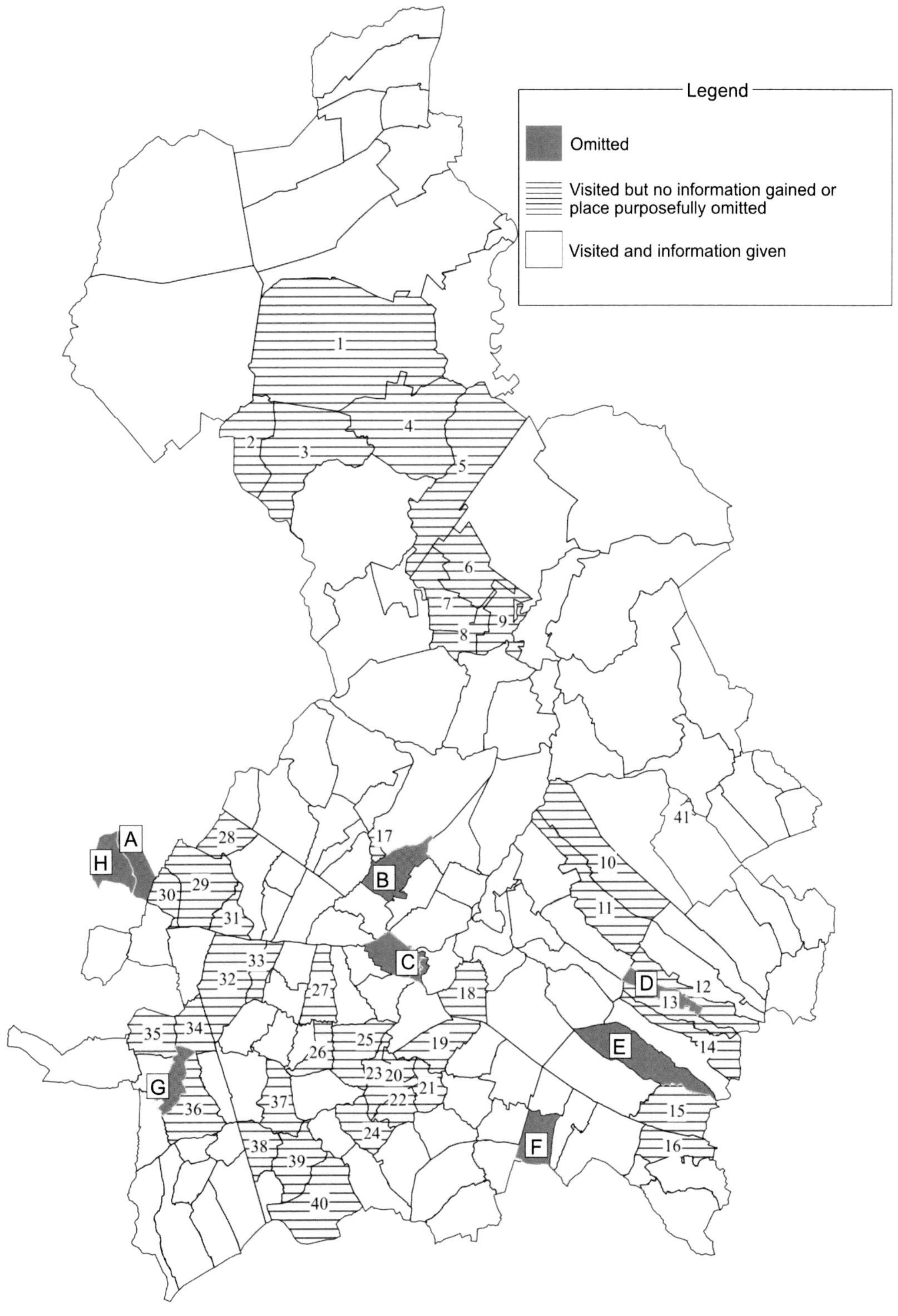

Key to figure 1.

	Parishes omitted in error		Parishes where no data gained or purposefully omitted
A	Papworth St Agnes	1	March
B	Histon	2	Benwick
C	Cambridge St Giles (west fields of Cambridge)	3	Doddington
D	Westley Waterless	4	Wimblington
E	West Wratting	5	Manea
F	Great Abington	6	Coveney
G	East Hatley	7	Witcham
H	Graveley	8	Wentworth
		9	Witchford
		10	Swaffham Prior
		11	Swaffham Bulbeck
		12	Burrough Green
		13	Brinkley
		14	Carlton cum Willingham
		15	West Wickham
		16	Horseheath
		17	Westwick
		18	Cherry Hinton
		19	Great Shelford
		20	Hauxton
		21	Little Shelford
		22	Newton
		23	Harston
		24	Foxton
		25	Haslingfield
		26	Harlton
		27	Comberton
		28	Conington
		29	Elsworth
		30	Papworth Everard
		31	Knapwell
		32	Bourn
		33	Hardwick
		34	Long Stowe
		35	Little Gransden
		36	Croydon cum Clopton
		37	Orwell
		38	Whaddon
		39	Meldreth
		40	Melbourn
		41	Landwade

appears to have included his detailed investigation of the pros and cons of the much discussed then intended legislation to dig the Eau Brink Cut, financed by a specific tax on the parishes which stood to benefit. The result of this investigation was not initially included with the Cambridgeshire report, perhaps as not of interest to the landowners and farmers in the south of the county, who formed the major market. It could though be bound in on request, as it was in the edition here reproduced. Arthur Young included it as an appendix to the Huntingdonshire report, published in 1804.

22. Returns for Ely diocese, made in 1800, are at TNA HO42/54/46 ff. 502-532, available as a digital download from the TNA website; the 1801 returns are published by the List and Index Society, vols 189, 190, 195 and 196 (Swift (P&D) Ltd, 1982-3)

William Gooch's survey of Cambridgeshire, 1807

The Government had come to appreciate, somewhat late in the day, the need for the type of information Sinclair has originally sought to uncover and had set up its own enquiries. The response to the initial Government survey of acreages and crops, directed to parish incumbents via diocesan bishops, was however far from immediate or complete; the 1801 'crop returns' were rather more so, but not immediately published.[22] Upon his re-election to the presidency of the Board in 1806 (opposition to Government policy had led to his replacement in 1798, and the work of the Board had diminished without him), Sinclair re-established the county surveys. He set out a common plan of 17 chapter headings, with subdivisions and appendices, which it was hoped would make county reports readily comparable one with another (differing only in the detail each surveyor offered). Gooch stated in his introduction that 'In drawing up this Report, my aim has been that it should nearly as possible accord with its title , and the plan for execution given by the Board.' The headings set out in the contents list for his survey demonstrate how closely he followed the plan. Only two headings are changed: 'tillage' for the Board's 'agriculture' and 'wastes' for 'drainage'), and he made good use of the invitation to make 'miscellaneous observations' as the 17th chapter.

Gooch appears mainly to have collected his information by letter or questionnaire rather than by visit, and gives the names of numerous gentlemen who provided him with information.[23] Whilst Vancouver lamented the lack of leadership in agricultural reform in the county, Gooch's introduction rejoices in change, noting the significant influence of a number of gentlemen 'a Hardwicke, an Adeane, a Tharpe, a Mortlock, a Jennyns etc'. Unlike Vancouver, who traversed the county and spoke to yeoman farmers, Gooch frequently cites the work and opinion of landowners and farmers, his correspondents. The 'great men' he named in his introduction are among those most frequently referred to. Philip Yorke, 3rd earl of Hardwicke (1757-1834), inherited the Wimpole estate on his father's death in 1790. Gooch notes (p.166) that his bailiff was a Norfolk man. The Babraham Hall estate was inherited through Anne Jones, wife of Colonel, later General, James Whorwood Adeane (1740-1802). Her father disapproved of her marriage, and on his death in 1774 he left the estate to their son, Robert Jones Adeane (1763-1823); Col Adeane certainly managed the estate during his son's minority (so to 1784) but presumably also thereafter, since it appears to be his (pre-1802) improvements which Gooch cites. John Tharp of Good Hope, Jamaica (d. 1804), purchased Chippenham Park in 1791. After 1804 the estate was managed by his second son, also John Tharp (d.1851). The family's 'manager', Shepherd, is also frequently cited. John Mortlock (d. 1816), a banker, purchased his estate in the Abingtons in 1800. The Jenyns family acquired their Bottisham estate early in the 18th century. The Rev George Leonard Jenyns (1763-1848), vicar of Swaffham Prior 1787-1848 and canon of Ely 1802-48, inherited it in 1796 and profited greatly from the 1808 inclosure. He was sometime chairman of the Board of Agriculture.[24]

Others frequently referenced were somewhat less grand: Humphrey Darnton, a tenant farmer in Babraham (d. 1803), John Edes of Wisbech (a substantial donor to the new-built girls' school in the town in 1814), the Rev Newton Charles Lane, a fellow of Christs 1785-1811, first lessee of Carlton Grange new inclosure farm from the Brand estate, 1806-14, vicar of Alveston Warwickshire 1789-1846 and rector of Ingoldsby, Lincs, 1810-46, the Rev William Leworthy (1766-1837), a Devon farmer's son educated at Caius College and vicar of Harston 1796-1837, who also farmed land in adjacent Hauxton, Mr Scott of Chatteris, Nathaniel Wedd, tenant of Anstey Hall from sometime before 1794 to c.1805, and the Rev Charles W Wedge (1781-1875), rector of Borough Green 1805-75, son of Charles, a Bottisham farmer, who in 1799 was one of the commissioners for the inclosure of Pampisford.[25] The large number of others mentioned by name are included in the index.

Like Vancouver, Gooch too complains of the difficulty of obtaining information: 'full and unreserved communication are so rarely to be met with, that there is great difficulty in collecting materials for a work of this sort'. He and Vancouver were not alone. In his (much earlier) survey of the north of England, Arthur Young noted 'my business was so very unusual that some art was requisite to gain intelligence from many farmers etc, who were startled at the first attack. I found that even a profusion of expense was often necessary to gain the ends I had in view: I was forced to make more than one honest farmer half-drunk, before I could get sober, unprejudiced intelligence.'[26]

23. See the index.
24. https://www.nationaltrust.org.uk/wimpole-estate/, Nicholas Kingsley, https://landedfamilies.blogspot.com/, both accessed 21 Nov 2021, VCH Cambs x, 375, vi, 6, x, 201.
25. VCH vi, 26, iv, 266, vi, 153 and Cambridgeshire Archives L70/35, 36, https://venn.lib.cam.ac.uk/ , VCH viii, 255, 265, Cambridgeshire Archives P130/26/1
26. A. Young, *A six months tour through the north of England,* Vol. I, xiii W. Strahan, London. (1771).

Gooch reiterates Vancouver's work on soils, lauding its completeness, and draws on Young's works and other work published by the Board, as well as offering information from published histories about the debate over the Eau Brink Cut. He demonstrates a profound interest in 'new' crops, obtaining a list of grasses from the Cambridge University Botanical Gardens, and extracts from his informants a great deal of information about farming methods and implements, as well as charting the progress of enclosure across the county. His picture remains depressing, even he has not the extent of animal disease to report which troubled Vancouver. Despite the number of 'improving' landlords he cites, including the earl of Hardwick, he laments the lack of a Coke of Norfolk and a Duke of Bedford and the leadership they provide in their own counties. Though he lauds the work of Bedford's agent at Thorney, John Wing, he appears not to have had any significant amount of information from him.

The Agricultural state of the Kingdom

Sinclair had intended to compile from the completed county surveys a report on the state of agriculture to lay before the King and Parliament. His address to the Board on 29th July 1794 had laid out an ambitious scheme of 40 chapters of observation and data, on every possible relevant topic.[27] In the subsequent 20 years, much had changed. Problems of rural poverty were greatly exacerbated by the French Wars and became of necessity a major concern. After peace was made in 1815, and despite the enactment of the first of the corn laws, conditions for farmers became ever more difficult. In April 1816, the Board wrote out to its regular correspondents with a set of nine questions:[28]

1. Are any farms in your neighborhood unoccupied by Tenants; and have Landlords in consequence, been obliged to take them into their own hands? Please state the number of farms, and their size.

2. Have any Tenants, within your knowledge, given notice to their Landlords, of quitting their farms at Lady-day, or any other period?

3. Have any farms been lately re-let at an abatement of rent; if so, what is the proportion of such abatement?

4. What circumstances, denoting the distress of the farmers, have come to your knowledge, which may not be included in the above queries?

5. Is the present distress greater on arable, or grass farms?

6. Have flock farms suffered equally with others?

7. Does the country in which you reside, suffer from a diminished circulation of paper?

8. What is the state of the labouring poor; and what is the proportion of poor-rates, compared with the years 1811 and 1812?

9. What remedies occur to you, for alleviating these difficulties?

Of the 326 responses received, 13 came from Cambridgeshire, and are set out as pp.235-239 of this edition.

Cambridgeshire in 1793

Cambridgeshire in 1793 was much as it had been two hundred years earlier. To the promotors of enclosure and agricultural change, it and Huntingdonshire were 'perhaps the two worst cultivated counties in England, lugging in their wretched common fields as proofs by which to condemn the modern agricultural system, which has scarcely crept into either'.[29] Significant change was however beginning to take place and can be charted in the two surveys and ancillary extracts published here.

---

27. *Annals*, vol 23, pp.204-09.
28. *Agricultural State of the Kingdom.* p.2.
29. *Annals,* vol 42, p.304

Enclosure

Cultivation of land in a system of open fields (usually three to five fields), where each farmer held strips in each field and followed a rotation of crops which was decided by all the strip holders, and was often inherited from long term practice, was an impediment to the experimentation with new methods which improvers saw as vital to improve crop yield. In some parts of the county, for example at Wimpole, a single landlord had consolidated his holding by buying out local owners, or offering them exchange land, but during the 18th century, this process had in other areas been accelerated by combinations of landlords in a parish joining to obtain powers under local acts of parliament to permit the open fields, and/or the parish 'waste' land, used as pasture for sheep and cattle, to be divided up and shared out as private plots. In Cambridgeshire, the adoption of parliamentary enclosure was slow; by 1793 only seven enclosure acts had been obtained. By the time Gooch's survey was published in 1811, a further 57 acts had been passed.[30] The expected improvement in crop yield was expected to produce an increase in the rental value of the land. Vancouver estimated that if Cambridgeshire's estimated 319,300 acres were enclosed the total increase would be £146,262 10s. (see Table 1.).

Table 1. Sir John Sinclair's abstract of Vancouver's figures[31]

Number of Acres.	Description of the Land.	Increased Rent per acre.			Total Increase.		
150,000	Waste and unimproved Fen	£0	10	0	£75,000	0	0
132,000	{Open and Common Field Arable Land}	0	8	0	52,800	0	0
19,800	Inferior Pasture	0	9	7	9,487	10	0
7,500	Of Upland Common	0	11	0	4,125	0	0
8,000	Of ½ yearly Meadow Land	0	10	0	4,000	0	0
2,000		0	8	6	850	0	0
319,300	At an average of 9s. per acre.				£146,262	10	0

Gooch was able to collect information from 34 of the 57 parishes where an enclosure award had been finalised. In all the rent had risen significantly, irrespective of whether tithes had been commuted under the act, for example at Pampisford and Great and Little Abington, tithes were not commuted and both rent and payment of great tithes increased.[32] Similarly, Carlton cum Willingham, where the act extinguished tithes, rents rose three fold between 1800 when the award was completed and Gooch's survey. Whether this was landowner desire to win back the costs of enclosure, or a real increase in productivity is hard to tell. If the former, it no doubt contributed to the difficulties apparent in the 1816 returns. Certainly enclosure was expensive, especially before the General Act of 1801. Young estimated an average cost of £1650.[33] However, this is an underestimate as the average calculated did not include items such as the cost of road building or drainage. In Cambridgeshire the cost of enclosing Little Wilbraham's 1,970 acres was £3,300; Great Wilbraham's 2,400 acres cost just under £3,000. The process of obtaining an act, appointing commissioners and a surveyor and then of mapping and of evaluating claims was time-consuming.[34] Even when an award was sealed there remained the physical work of dividing the land, and in many cases setting hedges. Until the hedges had grown (seven years was the estimate) livestock could not be put out, and throughout the process there was uncertainty.

Although there was a strong belief in the benefits of enclosure, both Vancouver and Gooch understood the potential detriment to smallholders when enclosure abolished the right to depasture animals on arable land once the crop had been lifted, or where common 'waste' was divided into allotments. Gooch reported that fewer animals were raised after enclosure, and noted that the act for Chatteris provided retention of some common land to meet their need.[35] Young, visiting Chatteris c.1782 observed that part of the common was enclosed and allocated to 163 houses, each receiving four acres.[36]

---

30. See figure 2. p. xi, below.
31. *Correspondence,* vol 1, appendix K, p.lvii
32. W. Gooch, p. 139.
33. Young, *General Report,* 1808, p.98
34. The process is set out in detail in J. P. Kain and others, *The enclosure maps of England and Wales* (Cambridge, 2003)
35. W. Gooch. p.78. (see page 170)
36. *Annals,* vol. 42, p.473.

Figure 2. Cambridgeshire Enclosure by Act of Parliament

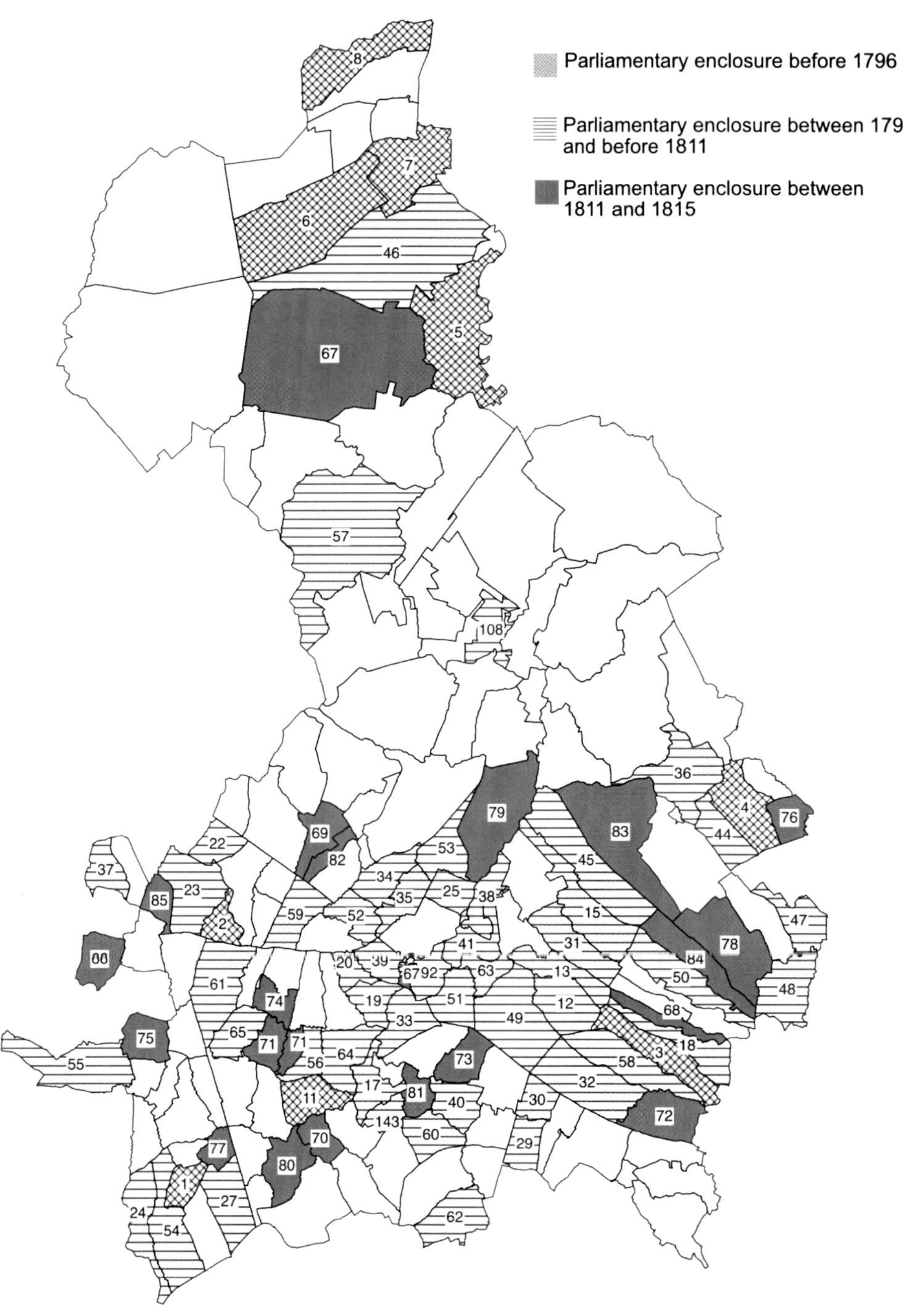

Note:- Each parish has been assigned a number based upon the date of the Act to enclose, in ascending order (see page 11).

Parish/Township Name	No on Map	Act Date
Abington Pigotts	1	1770
Knapwell	2	1775
Weston Colville	3	1777
Chippenham	4	1791
Upwell	5	1792
Wisbech St Mary	6	1793
Wisbech St Peter	7	1793
Tydd St Giles	8	1793
Newton in the Isle	9	1793
Burrough Green	10	1793
Barrington	11	1796
Great Wilbraham	12	1797
Little Wilbraham	13	1797
Longstow	14	1798
Swaffham Bulbeck	15	1798
Hauxton	16	1798
Harston	17	1798
Carlton cum Willingham	18	1799
Grantchester	19	1799
Coton	20	1799
Pampisford	21	1799
Conington	22	1800
Elsworth	23	1800
Guilden Morden	24	1800
Milton	25	1800
Benwick	26	1801
Bassingbourn	27	1801
Kneesworth	28	1801
Great Abington	29	1801
Little Abington	30	1801
Bottisham	31	1801
Balsham	32	1801
Trumpington	33	1801
Histon	34	1801
Impington	35	1801
Fordham	36	1801
Graveley	37	1802
Horningsea	38	1802
Cambridge St Giles	39	1802
Sawston	40	1802
Fen Ditton	41	1803
Cambridge St Botolph	42	1804
Cambridge St Benedict	43	1804

Parish/Township Name	No on Map	Act Date
Snailwell	44	1805
Swaffham Prior	45	1805
Elm	46	1806
Ashley cum Silverley	47	1806
Kirtling	48	1806
Dullingham	49	1806
Fulbourn	50	1806
Cherry Hinton	51	1806
Girton	52	1806
Landbeach	53	1807
Steeple Morden	54	1807
Gamlingay	55	1808
Harlton	56	1808
Chatteris	57	1809
West Wratting	58	1809
Dry Drayton	59	1809
Whittlesford	60	1809
Bourn	61	1809
Ickleton	62	1810
Teversham	63	1810
Haslingfield	64	1810
Kingston	65	1810
Croxton	66	1811
March	67	1811
Brinkley	68	1811
Longstanton All Saints	69	1811
Shepreth	70	1811
Great & Little Eversden	71	1811
West Wickham	72	1812
Stapleford	73	1812
Toft	74	1812
Little Gransden	75	1813
Kennett	76	1813
Wendy	77	1813
Woodditton	78	1813
Waterbeach	79	1813
Meldreth	80	1813
Little Shelford	81	1813
Longstanton St Michael	82	1813
Burwell	83	1814
Stetchworth	84	1814
Papworth Everard	85	1815

Maintaining fertility

Detailed attention to the fertility of the soil and the use of manure are a feature of reports to the Board of Agriculture. When animals no longer cropped the land after harvest, and when fields were no longer left fallow by rotation, land was likely to become impoverished. Several strategies were used to keep the land 'in good heart' by returning nutrients (though the science was not then understood) and organic matter to the soil. All farmers used animal dung from stables and cattle shelters, as well as family and general household waste, but the quantity available was often insufficient. Those near to Cambridge were able to purchase night-soil, or ash and soot from fireplaces. On the fen edge, at Isleham, small fish (sticklebacks) purchased at 7 pence halfpenny a barrel, were used at 20 bushels to the acre. Pigeon dung and rabbit pelts were also used, the latter purchased from as far away as Norwich. At Guilden Morden, old woollen rags were mixed with pigeon dung, oil cake dust and malt dust.[37] The effect and therefore the value of manure was generally well understood.

By the late 18th century, it was recognized that rather than leaving land as fallow, without a crop, part of it could be used without loss of fertility to grow a feed crop such as beans, peas, vetches, a grass and clover mix, or turnips for livestock. The superior feed in turn produced better quality manure, and observers noted that the yield of the following crops was increased. A sown crop on the fallow also reduced weed growth, and provided better ground cover, so that fewer nutrients were leached from the topsoil. The Norfolk rotation was much admired: in year one a field was sown with wheat, an exhausting crop. In year two it was planted with turnips, and animals, usually sheep, fed off them on the field, adding their manure, though the turnips could be lifted and carted for stall-feeding. In year three, spring corn (oats or barley) was planted. In year four, instead of being left fallow, the field was planted with a 'ley' of grasses and clover, which could be mown, grazed, or both. Weeds could be controlled by hoeing, and a variety of hoes were developed. Alternatively, an 'under crop' of grass and clover could be sown a little after oats or barley in year three. After harvest, the grass growth mixed in with the corn stubble could be left to grow in in year four, avoiding the need to plough to set a ley. Peas and beans, also nitrogen-fixing, were grown, generally as animal food.

Crops

Wheat, barley and oats were traditionally the main grains grown across the county. New varieties of wheat were being tried, and the Burwell red wheat was sold far and wide as seed. New crops included potatoes, mainly in the fens, for example at Leverington, where their importance in feeding the poor was noted. In Ely, the Rev William Metcalfe tried making potato flour, comparing the yield with wheat.[38] Carrots and parsnips were first planted in the county by Lord Hardwicke, at Wimpole. Their success was reduced by the white snail, and by the poor who stole them for food. Once harvested they were sold cheaply to the poor, and thereafter began to be grown in their gardens, alongside lettuces and radishes. Coleseed (oilseed rape) was also widely grown as animal feed, either as pasture, or processed for winter fodder, the seed crushed and pressed into cakes. The cake could also be used for fattening for market, but had to be left off three weeks before slaughter, to prevent the fat from being rank and yellow.[39] More unusually, woad (*isatis tinctoria* – a brassica) was tried at High Barns Farm, Ely. The lengthy processing it required made it less profitable than wheat, and Young rued the ploughing-up of first-rate pasture which the experiment necessitated.[40] Hemp was also grown in the fen. It was processed by being trampled in the dyke, by men working three abreast. It was purchased by merchants at the farmhouse and sold at Wisbech monthly market.[41] James Barker of Swaffham introduced tares into his farm.[42]

Livestock

Vancouver estimated that there were 153,000 sheep in the county. Neither he nor Gooch rated the native 'Cambridgeshire' breed, which was probably somewhat like the Suffolk in appearance, as highly as the

37. C. Vancouver, p.84
38. *Annals*, vol 25, p. 558
39. *The Complete Farmer: or, a general Dictionary of Husbandry, in all its branches.* Society for the Encouragment of Arts, Manufactures and Commerce. London, (1769). As a dictionary, this book is unpaginated.
40. Gooch, pp.172-5
41. Gooch, p.161
42. Gooch, p.142

imported breeds or cross-breeds. (The present Cambridgeshire sheep is a modern creation, first bred in 1979 when some native breeds were crossed with Finnish Landrace rams.) In the fens, a Lincolnshire or Leicestershire cross-bred sheep was most popular. Mr Tharp of Chippenham Hall had the first flock of South Downs in the county; when Gooch wrote, Colonel Adeane of Babraham and Mr Mortlock of Abingdon had both just switched to South Downs, selling their entire previous flocks, but such expenditure was beyond the smaller farmer. Sheep had suffered badly after the major floods in the fens and contributory river catchments in 1792, rot from the wet weather and waterlogged meadows killing many and leaving others diseased. The sorry progress of the disease being vividly described by Vancouver who also found sheep suffering from red water, gangrene and rickets.

The local breed of short-horned cattle was by 1793 being replaced by the Suffolk polled, the Craven, the short-horned Yorkshire, the Derbyshire, the Fifeshire, the Gloucester Brown and others. The fen-edge was known for its cheese production. Cottenham had a strong reputation, and Vancouver also mentions Soham's. Horses were kept for yard work and ploughing, and a few pigs were often kept. The native Cambridgeshire pig could weigh 40 stone by two years old, but a Suffolk breed was gradually replacing them. Pigeons were bred for the table in farm dove-houses, and also provided valuable dung. Gooch estimated that a typical farm could raise 1,200 pigeons a year.

Innovation and technology

Although Cambridgeshire's lack of agricultural innovation was lamented, Vancouver often notes 'two-furrow work', the sowing of seed using a seed drill (first invented 1733), though many sowed seed broadcast, or by hand dibbling, one man walking ahead with a dibbling stick, another following, placing the seed in the holes dibbled. New ploughs were being tried in some places, for example, the French plough, used to pare the surface of a field prior to burning, to eradicate wireworms and other insects. Harvesting was by scythe, the grain left to stand to dry, and then threshed by hand with threshing sticks or flails. Some wealthier farmers were investing in horse-drawn threshing machines, supposed to be more efficient, but Vancouver notes that the horse sometimes became exhausted. Mr Page, the lessee of Ely rectory farm, had a particularly large threshing machine, drawn by four horses, but which Vancouver says did the job poorly. At Wimpole, Hardwick was building a water-powered machine when Vancouver visited. Gooch does not comment on its efficiency. It is perhaps notable that the efficiency sought was improved seed yield, rather than a lower wage bill, though in a few years the threshing machine would become much-targeted by poor labourers for denying them winter work.[43]

Workers and wages

Farming remained largely a manual task. Farmers employed several farmhands and hired additional labour when the need was great, eg at harvest. There is mention of travellers employed in hoeing and 'strangers', often Irish, reaping. Perhaps surprisingly, women seem rarely to have been employed. It was noted that it was inappropriate for them to work far from home, though the reason is not given. The new crops seem more often to have called for their labour: they and children are recorded as gathering potatoes, they pulled hemp, and both flax and woad were weeded by women working on their knees, their knee pressure having the advantage of suppressing weed growth.[44] Both Vancouver and Gooch provide wage information, Gooch's the more detailed. War inevitably created labour shortages, and wages rose across the period. Farm labourers, especially those working 'as and when', remained poor. One of the reasons for the introduction of potatoes seems to have been philanthropic and as conditions worsened some farmers reported by 1816 that they were farming at a loss to keep men employed.[45]

Tithes, rents, rates and taxes

In addition to the costs of seeds, manure, feed and wages, the farmer had to cover his rent, parish rates, tithes and taxes. Vancouver's suggestion of an average annual parish poor rate in the county of 2s. 6d. in the pound

43. G.E. Mingay, *The Agricultural Revolution: Changes in Agriculture, 1650-1880.* Documents in Economic History, Black, London (1977), pp. 41-43.
44. Gooch
45. For provision of potatoes, see, *The State of the Kingdom,* (1816) pp. 69, 92, 140; for willingness to make a loss.

was questioned by Gooch, but the alarming rise to 7s. or more which the latter recorded is reflected in the mounting concern across the country at increasing poverty during the poor harvests and wartime shortages of the last years of the century and thereafter, requiring increased parish relief. Highway rates were much less onerous; Gooch notes the poor standards of maintenance of parish roads. The most contentious 'tax' in the period was the tithe. Originally one-tenth of produce, rendered to the local priest for his support, the benefit often came to be divided in the middle ages, when local churches were granted to monasteries, who took the 'rectorial' tithe for their own support, leaving a smaller amount for the vicar they provided to the parish. At the Dissolution, the rectorial tithe, together with other monastic property, was confiscated and sold off. Small farmers thus found themselves making unwelcome payments to large, often distant landowners; whilst at the same time, senior churchmen feared that tithe abolition would leave the local clergy without means of support. Local clergy, meanwhile, found that their need to press parishioners for payment soured the pastoral relationship. Though rents, poor rates, tithe and interest on capital (the last as 'opportunity cost' rather than out-payment) are noted in both surveys, neither Vancouver nor Gooch mention the burgeoning taxes imposed as the war went on. By 1814, it was estimated that farms were burdened with 171/2 percent property taxes with no abatement of the farm rent for the occupier.[46]

War, weather and prices; profit, loss and debt

The very wet years of 1792, 1795 and 1799 resulted in poor harvests across the country, and in 1804 mildew and blight severely affected crops. The wet, Vancouver noted, also caused disease in farm animals, especially sheep. Prices and grains imports from the Netherlands both rose, benefitting those farmers whose crops succeeded but creating difficulties for many. The abundant harvest of 1796 saw everyone prosper, but the advantage did not last. The Board's county surveys and other publications, and other contemporary sources provide conflicting estimates of profit. Across the period, it seems that smaller farmers saw little for their labour. By the end of the period, the larger farmer fared only slightly better. In 1816, Cambridgeshire farm failures were estimated to have left £73,000 worth of debt, with creditors unlikely to see anything back.[47] Robert Thomson, the owner of Longstowe Hall, reported 'In this neighbourhood, more tenants than I can enumerate have quitted their farms. Several of these have been taken in by the landlords, but a much greater proportion remains absolutely unoccupied'.[48] He estimated that within a few miles of Longstowe (in Croxton, Eltisley, Toseland, Yelling the Gransdens and Hatley) 8000 acres were unoccupied. John Mortlock of Abington's experience was similar: tenants started quitting in 1814, and by the beginning of 1816 'Yet scarcely a man can be found to enter upon a vacant farm' and 'in some parishes able-bodied men are paid to do nothing, that they may be kept from starving.' [49]

In the Witchford Hundred, imprisonment of farmers for unpaid debt rose from 54 in 1812-13 to 203 in 1814-15, and executions of farmers for their debt rose from 7 to 60 in the same period. The amounts owned by those imprisoned were £765 in 1812-13 and £18552 in 1814-15. [50]

46. An Agricultural Gentleman. *A Defence of the Land-owners and Farmers of Great Britain,* (1814), p.11.
47. *State of the Nation,* (1816), p.35
48. *State of the Kingdom,* (1816), p.35
49. *ibid*, p.36
50. *ibid,* p.37

Figure 3. Map of Cambridgeshire Townships 1888

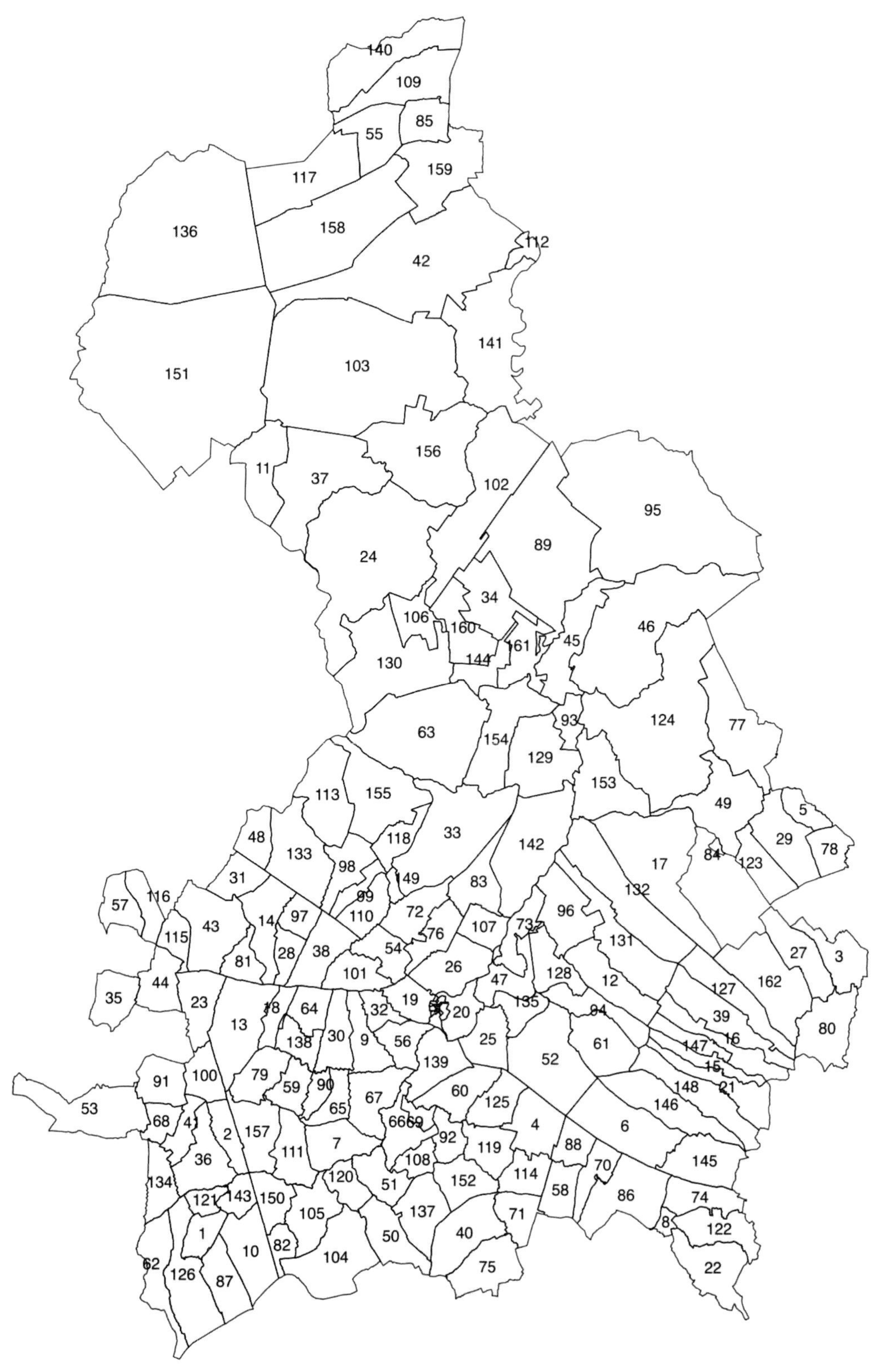

Figure 3 Legend

No	Township	No	Township	No	Township
1	Abington Pigotts	55	Gorefield	109	Newton in the Isle
2	Arrington	56	Grantchester	110	Oakington
3	Ashley cum Silverley	57	Graveley	111	Orwell
4	Babraham	58	Great Abington	112	Outwell
5	Badlingham	59	Great Eversden	113	Over
6	Balsham	60	Great Shelford	114	Pampisford
7	Barrington	61	Great Wilbraham	115	Papworth Everard
8	Bartlow	62	Guilden Morden	116	Papworth St Agnes
9	Barton	63	Haddenham	117	Parson Drove
10	Bassingbourn	64	Hardwick	118	Rampton
11	Benwick	65	Harlton	119	Sawston
12	Bottisham	66	Harston	120	Shepreth
13	Bourn	67	Haslingfield	121	Shingay
14	Boxworth	68	Hatley St George	122	Shudy Camps
15	Brinkley	69	Hauxton	123	Snailwell
16	Burrough Green	70	Hildersham	124	Soham
17	Burwell	71	Hinxton	125	Stapleford
18	Caldecote	72	Histon	126	Steeple Morden
19	Cambridge - St Giles	73	Horningsea	127	Stetchworth
20	Cambridge - St Mary the Less	74	Horseheath	128	Stow cum Quy
21	Carlton cum Willingham	75	Ickleton	129	Stretham
22	Castle Camps	76	Impington	130	Sutton
23	Caxton	77	Isleham	131	Swaffham Bulbeck
24	Chatteris	78	Kennett	132	Swaffham Prior
25	Cherry Hinton	79	Kingston	133	Swavesey
26	Chesterton	80	Kirtling	134	Tadlow
17	Cheveley	81	Knapwell	135	Teversham
28	Childerley	82	Kneesworth	136	Thorney
29	Chippenham	83	Landbeach	137	Thriplow
30	Comberton	84	Landwade	138	Toft
31	Conington	85	Leverington	139	Trumpington
32	Coton	86	Linton	140	Tydd St Giles
33	Cottenham	87	Litlington	141	Upwell
34	Coveney	88	Little Abington	142	Waterbeach
35	Croxton	89	Little Downham	143	Wendy
36	Croydon cum Clopton	90	Little Eversden	144	Wentworth
37	Doddington	91	Little Gransden	145	West Wickham
38	Dry Drayton	92	Little Shelford	146	West Wratting
39	Dullingham	93	Little Thetford	147	Westley Waterless
40	Duxford	94	Little Wilbraham	148	Weston Colville
41	East Hatley	95	Littleport	149	Westwick
42	Elm	96	Lode	150	Whaddon
43	Elsworth	97	Lolworth	151	Whittlesey
44	Eltisley	98	Longstanton All Saints	152	Whittlesford
45	Ely - St Mary	99	Longstanton St Michael	153	Wicken
46	Ely - Holy Trinity	100	Long Stowe	154	Wilburton
47	Fen Ditton	101	Madingley	155	Willingham
48	Fen Drayton	102	Manea	156	Wimblington
49	Fordham	103	March	157	Wimpole
50	Fowlmere	104	Melbourn	158	Wisbech St Mary
51	Foxton	105	Meldreth	159	Wisbech St Peter
52	Fulbourn	106	Mepal	160	Witcham
53	Gamlingay	107	Milton	161	Witchford
54	Girton	108	Newton	162	Woodditton

Notes and Editorial Conventions

Vancouvers survey was published with a page size of $7\frac{3}{4}$ inches by $9\frac{1}{2}$ inches although the text area of the page only occupied $3\frac{1}{2}$ inches by $6\frac{1}{2}$ inches. Gooch's survey was of a much more straight forward format with 1 inch margins, the page size being 5 inches by $8\frac{5}{16}$ inches. In converting the text to a modern page size and type face, the following rules have been applied:

Original spellings and punctuation have been retained. The long 's' used by both Vancouver and Young has been rendered in modern form. The lower case letter 'l', used following an Arabic figure in the original to denote pounds sterling has been rendered using £ in the present conventional manner.

Place-names have been retained in their original form; index entries provide cross-references to the present name.

Other idiosyncratic words or word forms are explained in the glossary.

Where in the original a long blank space denotes a missing data item, the form '[*blank*]' has here been used.

William Gooch's notes have been reproduced in the formats used in the original published text. No editorial foot notes have been added; where necessary explanations have been set out in the introduction.

Page numbers from the original texts of Vancouver and Gooch have been inserted in the left hand margin.

VANCOUVER'S SURVEY
1794

p.7 ## INTRODUCTION

On receiving from Sir John Sinclair, about the latter end of the month of September last, the Request of the Board of Agriculture, to draw up an Account of the present State of the Stock, and Husbandry, of the County of Cambridge; with the means of their Improvement; and from the Board, printed Lists of Queries, in which are included, "Whether proper attention is paid to the draining" of land, particularly the fenny part of it; and if there " are any obstacles to improvements; and in what manner "they can best be removed:" and having so many years ago become acquainted, that a considerable portion of the county of Cambridge, had long laboured under the most pressing inconveniences, from its imperfect drainage: I thought it prudent, as the season of the year was now far advanced, to direct my attention in the first instance, to the present state and condition, together with the means used for the improvement of the low grounds, and fenny parts, of this county.

On the first day of October last I commenced my Survey, and found that a measure of the greatest importance to the fenny part of the county, (but which did not meet the concurrence of all the parties interested,) was then in contemplation, and likely to be brought under the consideration of the then ensuing Parliament. Under this circumstance, and reflecting, on the probable consequences, that might attend any experiment in which such a diversity of interests appeared to be involved: I considered it my
p.8 indispensable duty to the public in this important enquiry, to be minutely attentive, and conform in the strictest manner to the requisitions above mentioned. My particular observations were of course directed to the prominent, and leading features, of the great level of the fens; the means at present employed, not only for their internal district drainage, but that of the external and general one; under the immediate direction of the corporation of the Bedford Level, and how far the proposed measure, of diverting the course of the river Ouze, from its present channel, between Eau-brink, and the Haven of Lynn, would embrace all the objects so fondly anticipated, by the promoters of that measure.

The intersection of this country by the rivers, public lodes, and private drains, render the communication, even in the summer months, between one village and another, extremely difficult; and information respecting a neighbouring township from this extreme want of intercourse, is not to be acquired by any conversation, with the most intelligent persons in the adjoining parish. The variety of interests that are awakened by the means proposed, for the general relief of the fens, the more elevated parts of which, may be considered as islands and want little assistance; the skirty lands, and the passage of the water, to what is injudiciously deemed its natural and proper outfal; together with the injurious effects, apprehended to the navigation, of the several rivers, passing through the level of the fens; all conspired to impress my mind, with the absolute necessity, of a thorough and minute investigation, of this long neglected, though valuable country. For the better investigation whereof I determined to put difficulty out of the question, and that I might perform the task I had engaged in, to the utmost of my abilities; I not only visited every parish in the county, and traced the present, and original watercourses,
p.9 from the foot of the Highland country to their respective outfals, thereby ascertaining the general inclination of the country to seaward, from the antient and voluntary courses of its waters, but anchored in the entrance of the Lynn, and Wisbeach channels, at the low water mark of the ocean; for the purpose of ascertaining the effect, which the sea waters have, on the descent of the land waters; to their only outfal, the low watermark at sea. In prosecuting these enquiries, I have to lament the shortness of the days, in addition to the earnest desire I had, of transmitting this part of my report to the Board, (which was done, at the conclusion of the month of January last,) did not permit me, to establish all the various and necessary facts, and to draw such inferences and conclusions from them, as under less pressing circumstances, with regard to time, I should have thought indispensibly requisite to so material a part of the survey.

The very important information I acquired, of the face of this valuable country; of its structure, and general inclination to seaward; of the original course of its waters; its present mode of draining, and state of husbandry; together with the general opinion I was enabled to collect, by patiently walking over the whole of the Fenny part of the County, and daily conversing with the resident inhabitants, as to the advantages likely to result from any proposed measure of improvement, tempted me, to pursue the same mode of travelling through, and visiting the several districts, and villages, of the upper part of the county, although the inconvenience of riding from place to place, or having the care of an horse, ended with my survey of the Fens.

p.10 As I cannot but be aware that the importance and use, which these surveys, will be of hereafter, must be in proportion to the information they impart, of the detail observed, in the farming, grazing, breeding, and dairy business; of the different counties of the kingdom: I very much regret the time allotted, for the finishing of this enquiry, will not permit my revisiting, those parts of the county, wherein 1 discover, the minutes taken on the spot, to be deficient in the full information I so much wish to communicate, or where, from the absence of the most intelligent persons, I have been able to acquire but little information.

After ascertaining the nature of the soils in the respective parishes, from information; and the exercise of my own observation and reflection in the fields; the district is then described; with all its variety of soil; and the grains, pulse, and grasses, most proper for its cultivation. The present mode of husbandry, and produce per statute acre, taken on an average of five years, then follow; from which (I presume) some judgment may be formed, how far such district is at present properly managed, and what alterations may be prudently encouraged or recommended.

The computed measure in the several open common fields, being extremely various, (seldom exceeding three roods to the acre,) has induced me to reduce the acre, to the legal standard, and in the course of the following observations, whenever I have occasion to speak of an acre, it is to be understood, I mean thereby, one hundred and sixty square poles. The poor's rates are all calculated on a rack rent, at the present value of the farms; and the ratio of five to a family, confirmed by absolute enumeration in many parishes, leaves a far less fraction, than that of any other number.

p.11

PART I.

JOURNAL

ASHLEY including SILVERY.

THE arable land included within these bounds, lies in thirteen open fields; that part of which binding east upon the village, is a dry, thin, stapled, chalky soil; on the north, **a** wet, heavy clay, with a mixture of some gravel, well stapled upon a gravel and chalk; on the west, a tender clay or loam, well stapled upon a clay; on the south, a stiff, heavy, wet clay, upon a gault; to the eastward of which, the soil gradually opens, and forms a good mixture of a fair staple, upon a clay, but which is finally lost in the thin chalky soil first mentioned. The whole contains about two thousand four hundred acres, including one hundred acres of heath sheep walk, and taken together, is rented at seven shillings and six-pence per acre. The enclosures in severalty, which are improved, amount to about sixty acres; and are rented at twenty shillings per acre: those that are in a rough and unimproved state, amount to about ninety acres, and are rented at ten shillings per acre. The stiff heavy lands in the open fields, as also those in the enclosures, lie well for draining: but this material improvement is much neglected.

p.12 The whole of the arable crop and fallow, pay a commutation for the tythes, of two shillings and four-pence per acre. The rotation of crops, first, fallow, dung, and sheep fold; second year, wheat barley, rye, and a few turnips for sheep food; third year, barley, oats, peas, and a small quantity of clover, and trefoil, for sheep food; produce per acre, taken on an average of five years,

Wheat	18 bushels
Barley	20 ditto
Oats	14 ditto
Rye	14 ditto
Peas	20 ditto.

The largest farm in this district is occupied under a lease for twenty-one years, at two hundred and forty pounds per ann. the rest of the farms are held at will. Little or no artificial manure, or foreign composts, are used. The parish contains thirty-six houses, forty families, and, reckoning five to each family, two hundred souls. Poor's rate three shillings and sixpence in the pound. One thousand, three hundred sheep, of the Norfolk breed, amongst which, a growing disease prevails, equally alarming with the rot, though these sheep walks, are happily free from that calamity; the first appearance of which, is indicated by the wool changing to a brown colour; and as the disease advances, drops off at the roots, and leaves the skin quite clean and naked. At this time, the animal appears extremely uneasy, constantly rubbing its head against the hurdles and fences, and scratching its back and sides, with its horns, starting suddenly, running a few steps, then falling down, where it will remain a short time, and then rise, and begin feeding, as if in perfect health. The skin is perfectly free from eruption, or other appearance of disease; nor are there any traces of the disorder discoverable, by examination of the entrails, the body,
p.13 or head of the animal; and as no instance of a cure has occurred, in any of the surrounding parishes; and moreover as this disorder is considered to be infectious, the sheep are usually killed on the appearance of the first symptoms; though some have been known, to have languished under its fatal influence, for ten or twelve weeks together. In the parish of Dallham in Suffolk, which is distant only a few miles from hence, out of a flock of five hundred sheep, the owner sold last year, as many skins at ten-pence each, as amounted to ten pounds; every sheep of which, was either killed in consequence of, or perished by this disease.

It is evident from the great variety of soil in this district, that the several parts of it require a separate and distinct treatment. The thin chalky soil is unquestionably proper for the culture of cinquefoil and trefoil, and though not perhaps certain, good turnip land, worth the annual trial for this crop. The heavy clays to the culture of clean beans, wheat and clover. The tender clay, or loam, to that of barley, wheat, oats, peas and clover; and the mixed soil, (as the water may be more or less at command) to the Norfolk broad cast or the Scotch two furrow turnip husbandry.

The draining of the land, and the culture of these several crops, would be the certain consequences of the common field being laid into severalty; and this arrangement is much wished for by the most intelligent farmers in this parish. The rough pastures are capable of being improved, to an equal value with those at present of the first quality, by previously hollow draining, and opening the soil with the plough; but under the present circumstances of the district, no improvement can be made in its flock or husbandry.

p.14

CHEVELEY.

THE arable land in this parish, lies chiefly in open fields; the soil of which may be divided into three distinct classes: about two-fifths, a stiff heavy clay, of a good staple, upon a gault, and proper for the culture of wheat, beans, black oats, and clover; a like proportion of it, is a mixed soil, of clay, and gravel, of a tolerable staple, upon a gravel, and adapted to the culture of wheat, barley, oats, peas and beans mixed, and clover; the remainder about one-fifth, is of a dry, thin staple, upon a chalk or gravel. The whole contains about three thousand acres, and is rented on an average, at about ten shillings the acre.

There are about two hundred acres of heath sheep-walk, adjoining Ashley, which are valued at half a crown per acre. The enclosures in severalty, (exclusive of the Duke of Rutland's domain, which contains about three hundred acres) include about thirteen hundred acres, a considerable part of which, is rough pasture ground, of a wet, cold, and clayey nature, and which in its present state, is only valued at seven shillings and sixpence the acre; such of the pasture grounds, as are improved, are rented at about eighteen shillings the acre. The enclosures (except some towards Saxham Street, which are rather flat) as well as the open field land, lie well for draining. No artificial, or light manures, are made use of,
p.15 and the usual practice of the country, of two crops and a fallow, obtains in the open field the produce of which, taken on an average of five years, is

Wheat	20 bushels per acre
Barley	20 ditto
Oats	22 ditto
Peas	20 ditto

The largest farm in the parish, is three hundred pounds, per ann. and like all the rest, is held at will. Five hundred Norfolk sheep are here kept, and the Suffolk breed of cows, is generally preferred: amongst this latter stock, the red water, and garget, prevail very much. There are forty-five houses, seventy families, three hundred and fifty souls. The poor's rates are three shillings in the pound, and the tythes are all taken in kind.

The drainage of the stiff, wet, lands in the open field, would be certain, and readily accomplished, were those lands, in severalty; an improvement, which by most of the intelligent people in this parish, is much desired. The rough pasture grounds might be improved, to a rent of fifteen, or twenty shillings the acre.

The destructive practice of paring, and burning, these highland pastures, has unfortunately been adopted in this neighbourhood, and in its consequences, confirmed the dislike, which landlords generally have, to the breaking up, of old pasture ground. Unless the wet, cold, close clays, are hollow drained, and opened with the plough, to the emeliorating influence of the sun, the frost, and the atmosphere; all expeditions of improvement in the herbage, and consequent breed of cattle, must cease; whilst the husbandry in the open field, which requires a system of management, as various as the nature
p.16 of its soils, must also remain at hand, until the intermixed property be laid together, and the right of shackage and sheep-walk be done away.

N.B. About one hundred pounds per ann. in this parish belongs to *Trinity College, Cambridge*.

CATLIDGE

THE soil of the common open fields in this parish, which lie in three shifts, consists of a close, cold, and compact clay, lying upon a very retentive yellow clay, and blueish coloured gault, proper for the culture of wheat, clean beans, black oats, and clover. The whole lies well for draining, but at present, is much neglected; it contains about eighteen hundred acres, and is rented, at eight shillings per acre, to which is to be added, the tythe rent, of three shillings per acre on the crop and fallow. The meadow, or half-yearly land, which produces a very rich and spontaneous herbage, contains about a hundred acres,

and is rented, at twenty shillings the acre. The soil of the enclosures is of a more tractable nature, than that of the open fields, and applicable to the culture of wheat, barley, oats, peas and beans mixed, and clover; these contain about a thousand acres; two hundred acres of which, or thereabouts, are improved pastures, and valued at twenty shillings the acre; whilst those that remain in an unimproved state, are in a great degree covered with rushes, ant-hills, old pollards, black and white thorn bushes, and brambles; and their utmost value does not exceed ten shillings per acre; these enclosures all lie well for
p.17 draining, and generally upon a chalky, and yellowish coloured clay, of an alkaline quality. The largest farm in this parish, is three hundred and eighty pounds per annum. Common farm yard, and stable dung, the only manure in use, and the produce per acre on the usual average, is

Wheat	20 bushels, weighing 62 lb. per bushel.
Barley	30 ditto of the second quality.
Black Oats	24 ditto
Peas and Beans	20 ditto

There are about six hundred Norfolk sheep kept in this parish, which are occasionally subject to the rot. The Suffolk breed of cows, being quite equal to the strength and present herbage of the soil, is preferred. There are seventy-four houses, eighty-four distinct families, and four hundred and twenty souls. The vicarial tythes, are paid by a modus of eighteen pounds per ann. from the parish, to which is yearly added, ten pounds by Lord Guildford. The poor's rates are three shillings in the pound; and the seed time and harvest, later than in the neighbourhood of Newmarket, owing to the neglect of draining.

WOOD-DITTON.

THE land extending towards Newmarket (a part of which town lies within the bounds of this parish) consisting of a thin, dry, white soil, upon a chalk, and a light sandy soil, abounding with flints, upon a gravel, proper for the culture of cinquefoil, and the broad cast turnip husbandry, contains about one
p.18 thousand five hundred acres, and is rented, on an average, at eight shillings per acre. The land lying towards Chevely, Catlidge, and Stackworth, consists of a strong, heavy soil, upon a white and blue clay, or gault, proper for the culture of wheat, beans, black oats, and clover; contains about one thousand six hundred acres, and rented at eleven shillings per acre.

The pastures in severalty, which are improved to a certain degree, contain about four hundred acres, and are rented at sixteen shillings per acre. The coarse, and totally unimproved pastures, amount to about two hundred acres, and are usually valued at about 8s. per acre. About six hundred and fifty acres of heath sheep walk, extending to, and binding upon, the town of Newmarket, valued at five shillings per acre. The pastures, as also the stiff heavy lands in the open fields, lie in general, well for draining; but the soil is of so close and retentive a nature, as to require the drains of the little hollow ditching, (which is done) to be much nearer than they are, or would be necessary, upon a more porous and drawing soil: the whole, however, at a moderate expence, may be considerably improved.

The largest farm is occupied under a lease of six hundred guineas per ann. which, under the common husbandry of two crops and a fallow, produces in common, with the rest of the parish, of

Wheat	18 bushels
Barley	24 ditto
Oats	24 ditto
Peas	16 ditto
Rye	18 ditto

About two thousand one hundred and twenty of the Norfolk sheep, fifty-two houses, sixty families, three hundred souls, poor's rate four shillings.

p.19

STACKWORTH

THE open field, arable land, lying north of this village, adjoining thereto, and bounded by the Devils-ditch on the east, and the lands of Dullingham on the West, consists in part, of a brown loam of a slight staple, lying upon a thin stratum of chalk, under which is a close, compact, and white clay: this part of the field contains about an hundred acres, and is proper for the culture of wheat, barley, oats, peas, and clover. The next, in point of quality, is of a light coloured, chalky, dry nature, thinly stapled, and lying upon a chalk, adapted to wheat, barley, oats, rye, cinquefoil, and turnips, and comprehends about two hundred and fifty acres. That of the third quality, and binding upon the heath, is of a light, sharp, red, sandy nature, of a deep staple, lying also upon a chalk, and applicable to the broad cast turnip husbandry: it contains about six hundred and seventy-two acres, and taken with the rest of the open field arable land, is rented at about seven shillings and sixpence the acre. The heath is valued at two shillings per acre as a sheep-walk, and contains about eight hundred and fifty acres. There are about one thousand acres of enclosures in severalty, of which about one hundred acres are improved pasture lands, and are rented at fifteen shillings the acre; the rough, and unimproved pastures, comprehend about three hundred acres, are valued at ten shillings per acre, and the remainder of the inclosures, which are rented at fourteen shillings per acre, are under the plough.

p.20 The Largest farm in this parish, is under a lease of twenty-one years, rented at two hundred and fifty pounds per ann. the rest of the farms in the parish are held at will. The common farm yard, and stable dung, together with sheep folding, and foreign composts, to the extent, and expence of thirty shillings per acre, are here in general use. The common husbandry of two crops, and a fallow, obtains in this parish, and the average produce

Wheat	22 bushels
Barley	22 ditto
Oats	26 ditto
Rye	18 ditto
Peas and Oats	26 ditto per acre when sown together.

There are twelve hundred sheep kept in this parish, which are supported through the year, by the range upon the heath, the shackage of the common fields, and a small portion of trefoil, turnips, and rye, sown for spring food. A considerable part of this parish, of Wood-Ditton, of Catlidge, of Chevely, and of Ashley, is well adapted for the growth of oak timber. In this parish, there are about three hundred and thirty-five acres of oak woodland, the under-growth of which, consisting of hazel, ash, black and white thorn, sallows and maple, in the moist places, is felled every twelve years, and produces from eight to ten pounds the acre. In this parish, reside sixty families, three hundred souls: poor's rates annually amount to half a crown in the pound, exclusive of a donation of thirty pounds, payable out of an estate in the parish: the tythes are all taken in kind.

The useful practice of hollow draining is here attended to, and much more would be done to the great
p.21 improvement, of the heavy wet lands in the parish, were the intermixed lands in the open fields, laid together and exempt from shackage. It perhaps may be worthy of remark, that the chalky soil, when properly ploughed, and in good heart, produces an excellent sample of wheat; and in a moist, kindly season, a fair quantity.

DULLINGHAM.

THE arable land in this parish, lies in three common field shifts, the soil of which, is to be described under four distinct heads: that of the first quality, a heavy, whitish, clayey soil, of a good staple, lying upon a clay, and proper for the cultivation of wheat, barley, oats, clover, and peas: the second, of a reddish coloured brick earth, of a firm deep staple, upon a stiff brown clay, proper for the culture of wheat, beans and peas mixed, clover, and black oats: the third, a brown mixed soil, of a very good staple, upon a gravel, part of which is moist, and proper for the culture of wheat, with all the former crops, and the Scottish two furrow turnip husbandry: the fourth, is a dry, thin, white, chalky land, adjoining to the heath, and when properly managed, may be adapted to the cultivation of wheat, barley, oats, rye, cinquefoil, trefoil, and turnips. The whole contains about thirteen hundred acres, and, taken on an average, that which is tythe free, is rented at ten shillings; that part which is subject to the payment of tythes, at seven shillings; and about forty acres of enclosed pastures in severality, which lie in, and near the village, are valued at twenty shillings per acre. The inferior pasture land, and that which
p.22 is arable, containing about sixty acres, are valued at about ten shillings per acre. The soil of the enclosures, is a black tender mould, upon a clay, a mixture of which, would much strengthen and improve the surface. In this parish, are three hundred acres of heath, which is valued as a sheep walk,

at three shillings an acre.

The whole of this parish is held at will, and the largest farm is two hundred and fifty pounds per ann. Besides the common farm yard dung, and that from the stable, several light composts are used, to the expence of about thirty-five shillings the acre. The mode of husbandry, two crops and a fallow; and the general produce per acre, is

Wheat	20 bushels
Barley	20 ditto
Oats	20 ditto
Peas and Beans	17 ditto.

There are fourteen hundred sheep kept in this parish, amongst which, in the summer season, a garget, or gang green, appears between the flesh and the skin: this disease has hitherto, been considered incurable, and always proves fatal.

As the sheep walks in this country, are commonly valued at the rate of twenty shillings per score sheep per ann. for fourteen hundred sheep, or seventy score, this would amount to seventy pounds. The shackage of the common fields, with all the clover, trefoil, rye, and turnips, that the flock-masters sow for spring food, cannot be estimated at more than twenty-five pounds a year, which bears no proportion to the injury done by these sheep walks over the open fields, and which the most sensible people, resident in the parish, are extremely anxious should be discontinued. The village contains about
p.23 seventy-eight houses, ninety distinct families, and, by computation, four hundred and ninety-five souls. The poor's rates are three shillings and six-pence in the pound, exclusive of a donation of thirty pounds a year. In this parish, a rental of twenty pounds per ann. belongs to Clare College in Cambridge.

BURROUGH GREEN.

No information could be procured here: the enclosed lands on the way from Dullingham, are wet, rough, and ill managed; near the village, a tender, hazel coloured loam, with a small mixture of sand.

BRINKLEY.

No information. The warm, tender, loamy soil, continues down the field, and across the brook, when the country rises at

CARLTON.

where, likewise, no intelligence could be procured. The surface here, is of a lighter colour than in the preceding villages, and strengthens upon the hill to a whitish compact clay, which prevails through the parish of

WESTON COVILLE.

becoming however still lighter, until it terminates in a thin, dry, chalky soil, binding upon Newmarket Heath.

p.24 It is much to be regretted, that the full and complete information, which the enclosure of this parish about twenty years since demanded, could not be obtained; as its present flourishing appearance, and a short conversation I had with one of the principal farmers, seem evidently to justify the measure; from whom it was clearly to be understood, the population of the parish had not, in consequence of the enclosure, been diminished, and that he was now getting a comfortable living upon the same lands, at the rent of half a guinea per acre, which, in an uninclosed state, the former occupier starved upon at half a crown per acre.

General Hall, of West Wratting, to whom I feel myself much indebted, for his polite attention, confirmed me in the opinion I had formed of this improvement; and observed, that although the estates, in consequence of the enclosure, had been considerably augmented in their value, the parish was nevertheless, at this time, in a very happy state of progressive improvement, and cannot fail in a few years, to be much more productive, not only to the owners and occupiers, but to the publick at large.

p.25 SNAILWELL.

THE arable land in this parish, lies in three open fields, south by east of the village, and towards the turnpike road, leading from Thetford to Newmarket; the soil is of two distinct sorts, that of the first quality, a loamy, or tender clay, of a good staple, lying upon a chalk, proper for the culture of wheat, barley, oats, rye, peas, clover, trefoil, and turnips, and contains about seven hundred acres; the remainder, is of a light, sandy nature, well stapled and proper for the broad cast turnip husbandry, and comprises about three hundred acres, which taken with the lands of the former, or first quality, are rented at nine shillings per acre.

There are besides in this parish, about six hundred acres of sheep-walk, valued at three shillings per acre, and about eighty acres of moor or fen common, valued at seven shillings and six-pence per acre. The enclosures in severalty, contain about one hundred and forty acres, and are rented at twenty-one shillings the acre. There are about twelve hundred sheep of the Norfolk breed, which are kept healthy, by preventing them, from feeding upon the wet, moory, fen common; this would be drained, and improved to a very great advantage, were not the water penned back upon it, by a staunch, forming a fish pond, at Fordham Abbey.

The annual rent of the largest farm in this parish, is three hundred and forty pounds. One tenth part of the first cost, of all the foreign manures used in the parish, amounts to about thirty pounds per ann.
p.26 and is allowed by the worthy minister to the farmers. Two crops and a fallow, is the common mode of husbandry, the produce from which, is

Wheat	22 bushels per acre
Barley	22 ditto
Oats	20 ditto
Rye	20 ditto
Peas	16 ditto

The laying the intermixed lands together in the open fields, is looked up to, as a very desirable improvement; but it should be left to the option of the owners, or occupiers, to enclose, or not. There are in this parish, twenty-one houses, thirty-two families, and, by computation, one hundred and sixty persons. The poor's rates are one shilling and eleven-pence in the pound, and the tythes are taken in kind.

LANDWADE.

NO information could be obtained here; Some coarse pastures, and a deep, rich, white, loamy soil, was observed. The hedge rows, and natural herbage, indicate a good strong soil.

FORDHAM.

The soil of the open arable field, next Chippenham, and adjoining to Snailwell fen, is of a thin, gravelly nature, lying upon a gravel; thence towards Brackland fen, a white, thinly stapled, dry soil,
p.27 upon a firm chalk, or clunch; and thence binding upon Brackland fen, a strong greasy, white, deep, soil, upon a clunch. On the east of the fen, a wet, heavy, cling clay, upon a deep, rich, blue gault, which burns into an excellent white brick, of the value of twenty-seven shillings the thousand, when delivered at the kiln.

On the south of the fen, the country riles into a deep, black sand; thence extending southward, the soil gradually changes to a lighter colour, upon a gravel; thence the staple improves in strength and quality, forming a compact, deep, white, earth, upon a clunch; ascending the hill, the soil becomes lighter, but continuing on the level, towards Isleham, the soil is the same. West of this field, is a common, of a moory nature, of about three hundred acres, lying upon a clay, and gravel, and depastured without stint; this tract of land, drains through Isleham, but is at present in a very bad state, owing to the neglect of the outward leading; and inward partition drains. On the west of this common, is a wet, brown, sandy, soil, which lies well for draining, but in consequence of the intermixture of property, is much neglected: ascending the hill, the soil becomes more dry, and thence, on the east side of Soame Road, it improves in strength, and is of a darker colour. South of this, and binding thereon, is another common, of nearly equal contents with the former; the soil, a moor, lying upon a clay, and well situated for being drained, into the Ely river, but at present, all attempts, for so important an improvement, are much neglected. South of the village, are about two hundred acres, composed of a deep, white loam, lying upon a chalk and clay; these extend to Landwade Hedge; thence, south-east, a dry, poorer, and mixed soil, bounded on the east, by a fen or moor, containing about one hundred acres, which through neglect of draining, are at this time, in a very bad state of cultivation.

p.28 The whole of the arable land, before described, in this parish, is suited to the cultivation of a great variety of crops, which in the event of an enclosure, that is generally and much desired, would be attended to with great advantage. The enclosures in severalty, in, and near the village, partake of nearly the same variety of soil, as the arable; and contain about five hundred acres, which are rented at eighteen shillings per acre. The whole of this parish, contains two thousand, five hundred acres, and taken together, averages nine shillings the acre.

The largest farm is rented at two hundred and fifty pounds per ann. the general produce through the parish, from the usual mode of husbandry, of two crops and a fallow, is

Wheat	18 bushels per acre
Barley	20 ditto
Oats	20 ditto
Rye	18 ditto
Peas	16 ditto

There are eighteen hundred of the Norfolk breed of sheep, amongst which, great losses are often sustained, in consequence of their feeding upon the rotten, boggy sheep-walks, which, however might be much improved, if not totally avoided, by a better drainage of the low lands. This parish, contains about seven hundred souls, and the poor's rates amount to three shillings in the pound.

p.29

KENNET.

THE soil here, in general, is of a light, gravelly, and dry, chalky nature, under which, in many places, is found, a very fair marl, which has been applied in the proportion, of about three thousand bushels per acre, with very good effect upon the gravelly soils, at the expence of about twenty shillings the acre, for filling and spreading, besides that of the carriage, which is in proportion to the distance it is taken from the pit.

The arable land, in general, lies in open field, amounting to about one thousand acres, and is rented at six shillings the acre. The pastures in severalty, contain about thirty acres, and are valued at one pound per acre: the meadows, which are in severalty also, are valued at ten shillings per acre, and amount to about twenty acres. The commons contain about sixty acres, and are valued at seven shillings the acre; and the heath land, which is used as a sheep walk, contains about three hundred and fifty acres, and is valued at two shillings the acre.

The largest farm is about two hundred pounds per ann. and with the rest of the parish, is occupied at will. A considerable part of it, would, no doubt, be highly improved by the marl above mentioned, were not the lands so much intermixed in the open field—the experiment has been successfully made in the enclosures. At present, great exertions are made, at the expence of thirty-five shillings per acre, in
p.30 procuring light composts. The husbandry in the open fields, two crops and a fallow: the produce per acre, withheld. About six hundred ewes of the Norfolk breed, are kept in this parish, which are extremely liable to warp, or slip, their lambs. They are very subject to the garget, or red-water; the symptoms of which are so indiscernible that in two hours after the animal has appeared in perfect health it is found dead. The Welch and Suffolk breeds of cows are preferred; but these breeds, as also of the sheep, might be much improved, by a previous introduction of proper grasses, and otherwise improving the herbage. This parish contains fifteen houses, eighteen families, and ninety persons. The tythes are commuted for, and there is an estate belonging to the dean and chapter of Ely.

CHIPPENHAM.

THE soil of this parish may be described under three distinct heads: - The first quality, a deep white loam, lying upon a chalk; the second, a mixed soil, of a dry, and rather thin staple, upon a chalk and gravel; and the third, a light driving sand, under which, in many places, is found a dry, tender chalk, which has been recently tried as a manure. There are about nine hundred acres comprised under the first quality, which are rented at fourteen shillings the acre; and are proper for the culture of wheat, oats, rye, peas, clover, and the annual trial for turnips. Under the second, are about nine hundred acres, rented at twelve shillings per acre, proper for the culture of cinquefoil, and the broad-cast turnip husbandry. Of the third quality, there are nine hundred acres; rented at eight shillings the acre, proper for the turnip
p.31 husbandry. The pasture grounds (except the park) containing about sixty acres, and rented at twelve the acre, are in a very rough and unimproved state.

There are about two hundred acres of fen-land, which ought to be drained through Fordham; but from the obstructions by mill-dams, &c. in those water-courses, are at present drowned, and in a very deplorable state; they produce little else than sedge, which is cut for thatch, litter, or fuel.

This parish was enclosed about four years ago; is tythe-free, and under leases of twenty-one years, with restraining covenants as to cropping. The population not ascertained, but the poor's rates are tenpence in the pound.

The largest farm at this time in the parish, is rented at two hundred and sixty pounds per ann. The course of husbandry; first year fallow, with dung, sheep-folding, and hand, or top-dressings for turnips; second year, barley, or oats, with clean clover, sixteen pounds to the acre, where the soil is proper for it; where it is of an inferior quality, lie land is laid down with rye-grass, trefoil, and Dutch clover, in proper proportions; third year, clover stubble, sown, or set with wheat. The lighter lands, after lying two years under rye-grass, trefoil, and Dutch clover, are winter fallowed for tartarian oats, or summer tares.

Produce per acre of	Wheat	24 bushels
	Barley	30 ditto
	Oats	36 ditto
	Tartarian ditto	30 ditto per acre.

Some attention is here paid to the forming of dunghills, and the farmers, very judiciously, prefer the
p.32 strongest, and most greasy clay, to form the bottoms of such, as are designed to be spread upon the lighter soils.

The Norfolk sheep are preferred; about one thousand of which are distributed upon the several farms, and are subject to the disease, and accidents, mentioned in the last parish; both of which are attributed to the superior quality, and great quantity of their food: the sudden changing of which, as from turnips to hay, in many instances, has had an extremely good effect. The common breed of cows, are preferred at present, though they are very subject to the garget, but not frequently to slip their calves.

The hamlet of Badlingham, is an appendage to this parish, and consists of one farm only, the arable land of which, amounts to about nine hundred acres; the soil agrees with the several descriptions, given in the survey of Chippenham; besides which, there are about one hundred acres of meadow and pasture land, of a moory nature, affording some turf for fuel, but owing to the present want of draining, which may be referred to the same causes, which operate at Chippenham, these lands are no better, than the fen belonging to that parish.

The common open field husbandry, is practised upon this farm, although it lies compactly together in different pieces, and is tythe free. No manure is made use of, but the common farm yard, and stable dung ; the average produce of which, per acre, is

Wheat	18 bushels
Barley	20 ditto
Rye	16 ditto
Oats	18 ditto

Peas	16 ditto.

p.33 A flock of four hundred sheep is kept on this farm, extremely subject to the disease first noticed at Ashley, the red water, garget, or gangreen, between the flesh and skin the animal - warping their lambs, and dying *dunt,* (as the shepherds term it) that is, dizzy; as a cure for this latter *calamity,* the shepherd will frequently open the sheep's head at the insertion of the horns into the scull, with his knife, and extract one, two, and sometimes more maggots, larger than those commonly generated in tallow. This hamlet contains forty souls, and is assessed to the poor's rates with Chippenham.

ISLEHAM.

THE arable land here, lies in four distinct, open, common fields. On the south side of the village, it may in general be denominated, a whitish, tender clay, or loam, of a fair staple, lying upon a chalk or clunch; it is proper for the culture of wheat, barley, oats, rye, peas, clover, and turnips; contains, about eight hundred and fifty acres, and is rented at fifteen shillings per acre. The pastures in severalty, immediately joining the village, on the north side, contain about two hundred acres, and are rented at twenty shillings the acre. The land skirting upon the fens, consists of about three hundred acres; is rented at eight shillings and six pence per acre. The fen, amounting to fifteen hundred acres, has been greatly injured by the practice of cutting turf, and from the deplorable state of its drainage, but a small portion of it is under cultivation: including the draining tax of eighteen-pence per acre, it does not
p.34 average at this time, more than four shillings and six-pence per acre. There is a small poor's common, of about fifty acres subject to half a draining tax, or nine-pence per acre.

The whole of this parish, is occupied at will, and the largest farm, two hundred and fifty pounds per ann. In addition to the common-farm yard, and stable dung, the following manures are resorted to: soot, fetched twenty miles, first cost, eight-pence per bushel, twenty bushels per acre. Pigeon-dung, twenty bushels per acre, at the like first cost, and procured from any distance within thirty miles. A small fish, caught in great numbers, called stickle backs, and purchased at seven-pence half-penny per bushel, in the village, are made use of at the rate of twenty bushel per acre. Rabbits down, and the trimmings of their skins, consisting of their legs, ears, scalps, *&c.* purchased of the furriers, at four-pence half-penny per bushel, and fetched from Norwich, are applied at the rate of thirty bushels per acre. First year, fallow, dung, sheep-folding, and light manures; for the second year wheat; winter fallow, wheat-stubble, a light hand dressing in the spring; for the third year, crop of barley; barley stubble sown the fourth year, with peas, oats and lentils - produce of these, on the usual average

Wheat	24 bushels the acre
Barley	32 ditto
Peas, Oats } and Lentils }	24 ditto

The harvest here, begins about the twenty-fifth of July, which in general is ten days earlier, than at Soame, owing to the warm nature of the soil, which is kept constantly full of natural or artificial manure. About eight hundred of the Norfolk breed of sheep, are kept in this parish, which answer very
p.35 well, and as they are carefully prevented front *depasturing* upon the fens, and low grounds, are preserved in good health, sound, and free from the rot, and subject only in a small degree, to the diseases of the neighbouring villages. Crossing the breed with the Craven bull, has much improved the beauty of the calves, which are generally suckled for the London markets. There are about two hundred families, and by computation, one thousand inhabitants: the poor's rates are about two shillings and six-pence in the pound.

The unevenness in the beds of the rivers Lark and Cam, are much complained of, in resisting the descent of the water. At Prick Willow, six miles below, the water has been found to be no more than eighteen inches deep, when it has been four feet deep, and full between the banks running through this parish. The working of the bear, has been of much service, but the gravels and hards, forming the obstructions in the beds of these rivers, are only to be removed by hand, which done, the drainage of the fen land in this parish, would be greatly improved.

BURWELL.

ON the west, and south-west of the village, and adjoining thereto, is a deep, rich, white loam, lying upon a chalk, proper for the culture of wheat, barley, oats, peas, and clover; thence extending southwardly, the staple becomes more shallow, and ends in a thin, gravelly soil, upon a gravel, and proper for the broad cast-turnip husbandry. On the north of the village, a dark coloured, strong, brown
p.36 mould, of an excellent staple, upon a clunch, and proper for the culture of wheat, barley, beans, and clover. The whole contains about two thousand acres, which, with about two hundred acres of enclosed pastures in severalty, are rented at seven shillings and six-pence per acre.

The fen contains about two thousand acres, a considerable part of which has been greatly injured by the digging of turf; it is constantly inundated, and valued at one shilling per acre. In this most deplorable situation it is considered by the principal farmers, to be far more productive, than if it were better drained, because the water encourages the growth of reed and sedge, which is cut by the poor people, and sent by water to the upper country, for the purpose of drying malt. Any attempt in contemplation for the better drainage of this fen, is considered as hostile to the true interests of these deluded people. The system of husbandry in the highland part of the parish, is two crops and a fallow; the produce per acre on an average of five years is

Wheat	22 bushels
Barley	20 ditto
Rye	18 ditto
Peas	14 ditto
Oats	20 ditto

Common farm yard and stable dung, with a little oil cake dust, are the only manures in use. This parish is famous for producing fine seed wheat, which is procured by a slight threshing, when the top of the crop only, the prime and bed of the grain, comes out. This is carried early to market, and sells from a shilling to fifteen-pence per bushel, higher than the current feed grain, of the day. The straw is threshed over again in the course of the winter, and by tailing it close, makes a fair merchantable, sample.

p.37 There are about seventeen hundred sheep, chiefly of the Norfolk breed, kept in this parish, and are tolerably healthy. It contains about one hundred houses, two hundred families, by computation one thousand persons. The poor's rates two shillings and nine-pence in the pound.

The enclosure of this parish would, it is here thought, be very desirable; and until such an event takes place, no improvement can be made in the herbage, nor of course in the breed of cattle.

SWAFFHAMS

No information obtained in either of these parishes, though the soil, and circumstances attending them, may probably be pretty well understood, by reference to Burwell, and the parish of

BOTTISHAM.

where the soil is various; on the east of the village, a white, tender clay, or loam, of a fair staple, and proper for the culture of wheat, peas, clover and barley; thence eastwardly, and towards the heath, the staple becomes more thin, and is lost in a dry chalk, and reddish coloured gravel, proper in part for the culture of cinquefoil, and the broad cast turnip husbandry. On the north, a gravelly soil, of a middling
p.38 staple, upon a gravel and sand, and applicable to the culture of wheat, barley, turnips, trefoil, rye, and peas. On the south, a moist, gravelly soil, lying near the springs, upon a chalky marl, proper for the culture of wheat, barley, oats, clover, and the two furrow Scotch turnip husbandry. The whole contains about sixteen hundred acres, and is rented at nine shillings and six-pence per acre.

The improved pastures in severalty, bear a very small proportion to those, which remain in an unimproved state; the former are worth twenty shillings, whilst the rent of the latter, is about twelve shillings per acre; they skirt upon the fen, which at present is in a deplorable situation, and subject to frequent inundations, by the overflowings of the Highland waters, and the river Cam, whose banks are most shame-fully neglected, and are as much too low, as the bed of the river is too high.

The largest farm in this parish, is held under a lease of eighteen years, at the rent of three hundred and fifty pounds per ann. The open field husbandry, with the common farm yard, and liable dung manure, forms the established practice of this village. Lentils mixed with oats or barley, are generally sown in the neighbourhood, as rack-meat for horses; they should always be mown when the oats or barley are in full sap, and when well saved, are an inviting food, though of a hot, and feverish nature; the proportion sown, are two bushels of lentils, mixed with one bushel of oats or barley.

Produce per acre

Wheat	20 bushels
Rye	22 ditto
Oats	18 ditto
Peas	18 ditto

There are about eighteen hundred of the Norfolk breed of Sheep, kept sound in this parish, by carefully attending to the spots, on which they depasture. The farmers here are of the opinion, that no
p.39 new breeds of flock, would answer better than those they now have, even if the parish were enclosed, an alteration, which is neither wished for nor proposed. This parish contains about one hundred and six houses, and by computation, six hundred persons, arising; from one hundred and twenty families; and the poor's rates are four shillings in the pound.

The house of industry in this parish, appears to be of little use; probably arising from the want of proper management.

WILBRAHAM—Magna

[The farmers being all absent when I called at this* Wilbraham, *the reverend* Mr. HICKS *obligingly favoured me by letter with this account]

HERE the soil varies considerably; the arable is all of a light nature; has one general substratum of chalk, and is at eight shillings per acre; the improved enclosures in severalty at twenty shillings per acre. There are about three hundred acres of common; which is depastured by cows, and a large tract of heath, which is appropriated to a sheep-walk, where the Norfolk breed is preferred. The cow cattle very indifferent, small, and ill shaped; seldom yielding more, when fed upon the common, and in full milk, than three quarts at a meal. The low and fenny grounds in this parish of considerable extent, but labour under the same disadvantages and difficulties, with those noticed in the parish of Bottisham, and with those, are incapable of being drained by present means adopted for that purpose. A considerable
p.40 objection arises to the enclosing of this parish, from the supposed impracticability of raising live fences upon the thin, dry land, towards the heath; the intermixed. property is however, greatly desired to be laid together, and the right of sheep-walk suppressed. Cinquefoil might then be cultivated to advantage on the thinnest land; and were the low and fenny grounds, drained and brought into a profitable state of improvement, the then rich pasture, and thin dry soil, would mutually come in aid of each other. The farms here are all held at will: the rent of one only, exceeds one hundred pounds per ann. The common practice of husbandry is two crops and a fallow, assisted occasionally with light composts.

The produce per acre of

Wheat is	16 bushels
Barley	18 ditto
Rye	18 ditto

There are sixty distinct families, and by computation three hundred souls. The poor's rates amount to three shillings in the pound.

WILBRAHAM—Parva.

ON the north and east, and to the westward of the village, the arable land is of a red, sandy, nature, lying upon a gravel, and proper for the Norfolk turnip husbandry. On the south-east, a whitish, tender clay, or loam, of a good staple, upon a chalk, and proper for the culture of wheat, barley, peas, oats, and clover; on the south, and westwardly, a deep brown mould, upon a gravel, applicable to the culture of wheat, barley, oats, rye, clover, peas, and turnips; the whole contains [*blank*] acres, and is rented at ten shillings per acre.

p.41 The improved pastures in severalty, contain about seventy acres, and are rented at twenty shillings per acre. The greater part of the common, which comprises about five hundred acres, produces little else, than sedge, and rushes, which are mown for litter. It has been proposed to effect drainage of this common, by means of a tunnel, placed under the bed of Quy water, but which was objected by the inhabitants of Taversham. This tract of land, would be easily improved to the value of fifteen shillings per acre, could the command of the water be procured, but in its present state, it must continue to labor, under the like general calamity of the fens in this neighbourhood. There are besides in this parish, about one hundred and forty acres of heath sheep-walk, well skinned or turfed over, which are valued at five shillings per acre.

The largest farm is rented at one hundred and thirty pounds per ann. The common open field husbandry, with little attention to the procuring an encrease of manure, produces per acre

Wheat	18 bushels
Barley	20 ditto
Rye	16 ditto
Peas	16 ditto
Oats	20 ditto
Tares	14 ditto

The stock in general is equal in quality to the herbage of the parish, which, however, might be much improved by previously draining the low lands, and enclosing the high lands; both of which are most ardently desired. There are thirty houses, thirty five families, and by computation, one hundred and seventy-five souls: where the poor's rates are three shillings and sixpence in the pound.

p.42

STOW cum QUY.

On the south of the village, is a tender, easy working loam, of a good staple, lying upon a gravel, proper for the culture of wheat, barley, rye, turnips, trefoil, and peas; on the north, intermixed, in about equal quantities, a strong cold clay, a light loam, and a fen, or rather a morass. The first is applicable to the culture of wheat, beans, black-oats and clover; the second to those crops mentioned as proper for the south side; and was the morass well drained, and put under a good system of fen husbandry, it would be rendered very valuable.

The miserable condition of the low grounds, in this neighbourhood, is chiefly to be ascribed to the neglect of the conservators, in not scouring out the leading drains into the Cam, and keeping the banks of that river, and Bottisham lode, in repair; were these works properly attended to, a considerable relief would be obtained, to all the low grounds in this parish, and the neighbourhood. Some hollow draining has been done, and has hitherto answered extremely well. The lands skirting upon the fen, are a dark coloured close clay, upon which the under drains, were laid off, one pole apart, eighteen inches deep, and an inch and a half wide at the bottom; part of these drains were filled with stones, the whole cost of which was four-pence per rod; the other part filled with a straw rope, the whole cost of which, one penny three farthings per rod. At this time, they both draw and work equally well: the lands thus hollow drained, are now richly worth a guinea, which, previous to this improvement, were not worth eight
p.43 shillings the acre. Much more of this under draining would performed, were it not for the wretched state of the general drainage of the low lands, which absolutely forbids further attempts.

The arable land above described, lies in three open common fields, and amounts to about one thousand acres; which are rented at half a guinea per acre. Two crops and a fallow, assisted occasionally with pigeons dung, and cake dust, is the common course of husbandry; from which a produce of

Wheat	18 bushels
Barley	20 ditto
Rye	22 ditto
Oats	22 ditto
Peas	14 ditto per acre is obtained.

The largest farm, is about two hundred pounds per ann. under a lease of twenty-one years. There are thirty-six houses, thirty-nine families, and exactly two hundred and ten inhabitants. The poor's rates are three shillings in the pound.

HORNINGSEY.

THE soil here in the open fields is very much intermixed, being a thin gravel, and a loam, or tender clay, of a good staple; taken together, the land may be properly employed in the culture of wheat, barley, oats, rye, peas, clover, trefoil, and turnips; and including the arable land of Clay-hithe, which amounts to five hundred acres, is rented at twelve shillings and six-pence per acre. The prime of the
p.44 enclosed pastures, containing about two hundred acres, are richly worth a guinea per acre; those of the second quality, skirting upon the fen; include about one hundred acres, and are rented at twelve shillings per acre: exclusive of these, there are about one hundred and fifty acres of common, appropriated to the poor of Horningsey, Quy, and Ditton, which have been much injured, by the digging of turf, and owes its present deplorable condition, as do the other low lands, to the height of the bed of the river Cam, and the shameful neglect of the banks of the inside water courses, in common with the adjoining parishes.

Some hollow draining has been lately done, in the wet parts of the open fields, between the lands; made eighteen inches deep below the bottom of the furrow, and two inches wide at the bottom; they are filled with bushes and sedge, and seem to answer extremely well: the labour and materials for this work, cost two-pence half-penny per rod.

The largest farm in this parish, is two hundred pounds per ann. and held under a lease of twenty-one years. Two crops and a fallow, is the common mode of husbandry: no manure but the farm yard and stable dung, is here in use: the general produce per acre,

Wheat	18 bushels
Rye	24 ditto
Barley	22 ditto
Peas	20 ditto
Oats	22 ditto

A remarkably fine growth of volunteer ash, has lately been cut down; elm likewise flourishes; but there are not any oaks, either planted, or spontaneous. No enclosing nor even laying together the
p.45 intermixed property in the open is desired.

There are thirty-eight houses, forty-five families; by computation, two hundred and twenty-five souls, and the rates are two shillings in the pound.

FENNY-DITTON.

THE soil here in the open fields, may be described, a white, strong, loam, or clay, of a good staple, lying upon a chalk quarry, or clunch, and is proper for the culture of wheat, barley, oats, peas, beans, and clover; and a strong, gravelly, mould, of a good substance, upon a reddish coloured clay, or brick-earth, applicable to the culture of wheat, barley, peas, rye, clover, trefoil, and the two-furrow turnip work: The whole contains about five hundred acres, is rented at twelve shillings and six-pence per acre.

There are about two hundred and fifty acres of enclosed arable, and pasture land, in severalty, which are rented at twenty-five shillings the acre, a kindly soil for the cultivation of ash, and elm; a few oaks,

scattered about, appear likewise in a thriving state. The remainder of the enclosures, amounting to about one hundred acres, being subject to occasional innundations, from the river Cam, are not valued at more than eighteen shillings per acre. Formerly about two hundred acres of fen common were enclosed, but the very bad state of the general drainage since, has defeated the good effects, expected from this measure; the soil of these enclosed lands, is an absolute *sea-silt,* mixed with small *marine*
p.46 *shells,* and vegetable matter, or turf-moor: within this enclosure, a considerable improvement has lately been made, by laying on, about fifteen hundred bushels per acre, of the white, chalky, clay, from the highland.

The largest farm in this parish, is occupied under a lease of twenty-one years, at the rent of three hundred and eighty pounds per ann. Common open field husbandry, farm yard, and stable dung, mixed with mould, together with forty bushels per acre of pigeon dung, are the manures in general use; the produce per acre withheld.

It has been frequently remarked, that the application of raw stable dung, before it is completely rotten, has produced in this neighbourhood, the disease in wheat, called the smut. There are sixty-eight houses, seventy-five families, and by computation, three hundred and seventy-five persons and the poor's rates are two shillings in the pound.

TAVERSHAM

That part of the arable land, adjoining the village, is a tough, wet, clay, lying upon a gault, and which, when made dry, by properly hollow draining, may be well employed in the culture of wheat, clean beans, black oats and clover; beyond this, and extending westwardly, is found a strong, brown, mould, lying upon a reddish coloured, brick earth, proper for the culture of wheat, barley, oats, peas, and clover; thence south-westwardly, a white, chalky soil, and north westwardly, a sandy loam, proper for
p.47 the culture of barley, rye, oats, peas, trefoil, and turnips, The whole contains six hundred acres, and is rented at ten shillings per acre.

The pastures in severalty, which lie in and near the village, contain about sixty acres, and are rented at twenty shillings per acre. There are about one hundred acres of common which at present, are of little value, but which might be greatly improved, by opening a large drain at the lower end, and drawing off, the waters of the common, into Quy water course.

The largest farm in this parish, is held under a lease of twenty-one years, and is rented at one hundred and fifty pounds per ann. The mode of husbandry, is two crops and a fallow, and the manures in use, are the common farm yard and stable dung, with sheep folding.

The general produce from

Wheat is	18 bushels
Rye	18 ditto
Barley	18 ditto
Peas	18 ditto
Oats	22 ditto per acre.

The idea of enclosing, is not at all relished in this parish, the inhabitants being averse to innovation, and for the most well satisfied with the present management. There are twenty-two houses, twenty-five families, and by computation, one hundred and twenty-five souls; and the poor's rates are four shillings in the pound.

p.48
FULBURN

[Having called several times at this village without effect, I was, at length favoured with this account by letter from R. Greaves Townly, Esq.]

THE soil in general is of a thin, light, chalky, and gravelly nature; some part of which is a strong, deep staple, and is good wheat land, containing [*blank*] acres. The enclosures in severalty, containing [*blank*] acres, are rented at [*blank*] per acre. (The timber, hedgerows, and natural herbage, seem to indicate a warm, and kindly soil.) A few of these enclosures, are capable of being overflowed, which in a dry season, has been found to answer very well.

A common of about four hundred acres is appropriated to the feeding of cows, from April to the 26th day of November, from which time, to the ensuing 13th day of February, it is allotted to the feeding of sheep. The upper part of this common, towards Wilbraham, is of a light, and sandy nature, with sufficient substance to pay well for enclosing; this improvement has not yet been proposed, although there can be little doubt of its beneficial consequences, particularly as the open fields lie in general, in pieces of three roods, half acres, roods and half roods, and three quarters of a rood; the expence, and great inconvenience of which, is inconceivable: temporary exchanges are frequently made amongst the
p.49 occupiers, but as these agreements are of necessity loose, and uncertain, little advantage arises from them; and as much of the land is in mortmain no permanent exchanges can be made without the authority of parliament.

The largest farm in this parish, is rented at one hundred and fifty pounds per ann. which, with all the others, is held at will. Common open field husbandry, with natural and artificial composts, produce per acre [*blank*].

The cow cattle are small, but equal to the present herbage in the parish; in which are kept about two thousand eight hundred sheep, amongst which I was not able to learn that any particular disease prevails. There are one hundred and sixty-six houses, and distinct families, amounting to to six hundred and sixty souls, and the poor's rates [*blank*].

CHERRYHINTON.

No information, after three times calling upon the principal farmers, could be obtained here: the face of the country appears to differ but little from the general description of Fulburn and that of

BARNWELL.

The soil of which, in the open common fields, may be described in general, a gravelly loam, a fair staple, being upon a gravel. Of this nature, there are about one hundred acres, rented at thirteen shillings per acre; the part of the open field which lies next to Cherry-Hinton Moor and along Brick
p.50 kiln furlong, is of a close clingy nature upon clay; this may very well be employed in the culture of beans, wheat, clover, and barley; the former in the culture of wheat, rye, barley, peas, oats, clover, trefoil, and turnips.

The enclosed pastures in severalty, contain about thirty acres, and are rented at twenty-five shillings per acre. Coldham Common, containing [*blank*] acres, and lying upon, a bed of rich marl, is now fed by sheep, cows, and horses; would pay extremely well for the expence of enclosing, particularly as it is so situated, that it could be overflowed at pleasure, by the paper-mill stream. The open fields also, would be highly improved should an enclosure take place, at any rate, it would be extremely advantageous to have the, property which is at present much intermixed, thrown together; and as the same kind of marl as is found under Coldham Common, abounds from Barnwell Grove to Chesterton, there can be no doubt of the improvement which this parish is highly capable of. There is a moor of considerable extent lying between the highlands of Cherryton and Barnwell on the north-east, and Trompington and Cambridge on the south-west; which at this time is greatly annoyed by the stream which passes through the west end of Cherryton. This moor is evidently sacrificed to the constant height of the water in this brook, by which it is reduced to the state of an absolute morass, though capable of being highly improved. The rent of the largest farm in this parish is four hundred per ann. occupied under a lease of twenty-one years. The common field practice of two crops and a fallow, assisted by a considerable quantity of dung, procured in return for straw used in Cambridge, with great quantities of brick, and old house rubbish obtained from thence, produces

Wheat	22 bushels per acre
Barley	30 ditto
Rye	26 ditto

Oats	30	ditto

p.51 There are fifty-seven distinct families, and, by computation one hundred and eighty-five inhabitants; and the poor's rate is three shillings in the pound.

TROMPINGTON

This parish is bounded on the west by the river Cam, adjoining which there are about one hundred acres of half yearly meadow and, of a black moory nature; and though subject to frequent overflowings from the river, are rented at twenty shillings per acre. On the north of the village is an open and common field; about thirty-five acres of which binding upon the bounds of Cambridge, consist of a black friable mould of a deep staple, lying upon, and mixed with some gravel; these are proper for the culture of rye, barley, peas, turnips and trefoil. The middle of the field is a strong loamy, well stapled soil, containing about one hundred and fifty acres, proper for the culture of wheat, barley, oats, peas and beans mixed, and clover; and that part of this soil adjoining the village, is a red gravelly soil, of a good depth and proper for the culture of barley, rye, oats, peas, trefoil, and turnips.

On the east of the village, and extending to the moor, are one hundred and twenty acres, the soil of which is perfectly similar to the last mentioned; beyond the moor, and more towards Cherryhinton, are one hundred and eighty acres of a strong, brown earth, of a good staple, lying upon a clay, and proper for the culture of wheat, barley, peas, beans, black oats and clover. South of the village, and adjoining thereto, are about one hundred acres, of a light gravelly nature, proper for turnip husbandry; thence
p.52 southwardly, the soil improves in its texture, and forms a tender clay, or loam, of a good staple, upon a chalk; thence skirting upon the river, the soil becomes more tough and clingy, and is found to lie upon a gault. The three fields contain about twelve hundred acres, and taken together, are rented at about eleven shillings the acre.

The enclosures in severalty, lying in, and adjoining to the village, are of a hot, gravelly nature, containing about sixty acres, rented at twenty-five shillings the acre. The common, or moor, which amounts to [*blank*] acres, is of a fenny nature, from four to nine inches deep, lying upon a gravel, is divided into three parts; and lies in shifts with the three arable fields.

The largest farm is held at will, together with the rest of the parish, and rented at two hundred and fifty pounds per ann. The common open field husbandry, with the farm yard, and stable dung; assisted with oil dust, malt dust, pigeons dung, and what can be procured from Cambridge, at an average expence in foreign manures, of thirty-five shillings per acre, produce

Wheat	24	bushels per acre
Barley	28	ditto
Rye	24	ditto
Peas (in general)	16	ditto
Oats	30	ditto

The common Cambridgeshire sheep are supposed to answer the best, though they have lately experienced a most grievous calamity. The number kept in this parish, is about nineteen hundred and fifty; nine hundred of which perished last year, by the rot, and at this time, though the prospect is much
p.53 brightened, yet great apprehensions are entertained for the safety of the remainder of the old stock, which are daily dying. No enclosure is at present in agitation, though the want of such an improvement, is much lamented by the most thinking farmers, who are extremely desirous, that at least, the intermixed property should be together. There are about eighty houses, one hundred families, and by computation, five hundred souls; and the poor's rates are four shillings in the pound.

STAPLEFORD.

ON the east of the village, and adjoining thereto, the open field arable land, is a thinly stapled, red soil, lying upon a gravel, and proper for the culture of barley, rye, oats, peas, clover, trefoil, and turnips. North-west of the village, and immediately adjoining thereto, a deep, strong, good, wheat soil, upon a chalk; thence in the same direction, the strength and staple of the soil decreases, and ends in a thin dry chalk, or hurrock, proper for the culture of barley, rye, peas, oats, trefoil and cinquefoil. South-east of the village, the soil is similar to that described on the east, but stronger and better stapled, and may be well employed in the culture of wheat, barley, oats, rye, peas, clover, trefoil, and turnips. North and north-east, of the village, a thin, dry, chalky soil, similar to that on the north-west. The whole of which contains about nine hundred acres, and is rented at ten shillings the acre.

The enclosed pastures in severalty, which lie in, and near the village, amount to about one hundred acres, and are rented at twenty-two shillings and six-pence per acre. The half-yearly meadow land,
p.54 amounting to about one hundred acres, and lying south-west of the village, is rented at seventeen shillings and six-pence per acre. There are about forty acres of common, depastured at pleasure, and without stint. North-east of the village, and towards Gogmagog Hills, are about five hundred acres of heath sheep walk, valued at half a crown per acre.

The largest farm is occupied under a lease of fifteen years, at the annual rent of two hundred and eighty pounds. The common husbandry and manure, assisted with a small quantity of oil dust and pigeons dung, produces per acre

20 bushels of	Wheat
22 ditto	Rye
24 ditto	Barley
26 ditto	Oats
16 ditto	Peas

There are about six hundred of a mixture of the Norfolk and Cambridgeshire sheep kept in this parish, subject to no particular disease. The enclosing of this parish, is not looked up to as a probable improvement, nor is such a measure at all wished for. There are forty-five houses, sixty families, and by computation, three hundred inhabitants; and the poor's rates are half a crown in the pound.

BABRAHAM.

THE enclosures in this parish, are a light, gentle, soil, of a tolerable staple, and lying chiefly upon a gravel. A mixture of the broad and narrow leafed plantain, a bent, or wire grass, with a small portion of
p.55 the perennial red and white clover appear to be the natural herbage; about one *hundred and sixty-five* acres of this land is water-meadow, and are valued at twenty-six shillings the acre: the remainder of the enclosures are let at thirteen shillings per acre. The grass or hay produced from the water-meadows, is chiefly inferior to that (weight for weight) which grows voluntarily, upon the unwatered ground. The soil in the open fields is of a thin dry nature, lying upon a chalk, and gravel proper for the culture of barley, rye, peas, trefoil, cinquefoil, and turnips. There are about thirteen hundred and fifty acres in the open fields, which are rented at six shillings the acre; there are besides about two hundred and twenty acres of heath sheep walk, valued at half a crown per acre. All this parish is occupied under leases for twenty-one years, and the largest farm is rented at about four hundred pounds per ann. The common husbandry obtains in the open fields, but in the enclosures the following management is observed - Winter fallowing, dung, sheep-folding, and preparation for turnips; second year, barley with clover or trefoil; third year, wheat, or peas, drilled or sown broad caste, upon the clover or trefoil lay. This system is occasionally varied, for the introduction of the common, open field winter fallow barley husbandry; the latter of which is a winter fallow, and manure for the first barley with seed, second year, lay; third year, wheat drilled, dibbled or broad cast: fourth year, wheat stubble, winter fallowed, and prepared for turnips: the produce per acre from this management

Wheat	24 bushels
Barley	36 ditto
Oats	36 ditto
Rye	24 ditto
Peas	20 ditto

p.56 About one thousand sheep of the Norfolk breed are kept in this parish; the Gloucester brown, and the Suffolk poll'd cows answer; but, they are however subject to a disease called the joint garget, the first symptom of which is a partial relaxation of the nerves and tendons; this soon becomes general, and the whole frame of the animal is so far deranged, as to render it, as incapable, as it seems indifferent, about seeking its food; when in motion the bones are heard to rattle; a fever and great costiveness prevail the whole time the animal lingers, which generally does not exceed two months, and then dies. This disease appears to be but little understood by the cow doctors. The laying of the intermixed land together, doing away the sheep-walks in this parish, and the right of shackage in the common fields, are improvements much desired. There are thirty-two houses, thirty-six families, and, by computation, one hundred and eighty souls. The poor's rates are seventeen-pence in the pound, exclusive of a donation of ninety-seven pounds per ann. appropriated to the use of the poor, under the restrictions of the donor. This parish is tythe-free.

LITTLE ABBINGDON

THE soil on the east side of Bournbridge, in that which is called Hildersham Field, consists of a tough clay, upon a reddish coloured brick earth, proper for the culture of wheat, beans, black oats, and clover; this field contains about three hundred acres, and is valued at ten shillings per acre. Thence extending towards the heath, the staple is lost, in a thin dry chalk, and gravelly soil; of this there are about two hundred acres, valued at three shillings per acre.

p.57 The soil of the arable land, lying north-eastwardly of Bourn-bridge is of a nature similar to the last described; this amounts to about five hundred acres, and being in better condition, from lying nearer to the dung-heap, is valued at five shillings per acre. The remainder, containing about five hundred acres, extending to the heath, and similar to which adjoins the heath, before described, is rented at three shillings per acre.

There are about sixty acres of half yearly meadow land, which though subject to occasional overflowings, is valued twenty shillings the acre: after this meadow land has been flooded, great care is taken to prevent sheep from feeding upon it, as in that state of wetness, it has been frequently known to have produced the rot. The common field husbandry, with the manures, produced in the parish, and aided by malt-chives, pigeons dung, and oil cake dust, produce per acre,

Wheat	16 bushels
Barley	20 ditto
Rye	20 ditto
Peas	20 ditto

Very great advantages would accrue to this parish, from an enclosure; the wet, heavy land, in Hildersham field, would be hollow drained, and highly improved; the dry, chalky soils, would be appropriated to the culture of cinquefoil, and other proper crops; the whole face of the country would assume a more fruitful appearance, and in fact, would soon become so: the arrangements for this improvement, are greatly desired, for by enclosing, or at any rate, laying the intermixed property, in severalty, and together, the convenience and value of the parish, must be greatly augmented.

p.58 The Norfolk breed of sheep, to the number of [*blank*] is preferred; the Gloucester brown, and Suffolk poll'd cows, answer very well. Many of the cottages are very bad, doubly and trebly tenanted: there are ninety persons in this parish; the poor's rates are two shillings in the pound and the great tythes are taken in kind.

HILDERSHAM.

THE soil in this parish, towards Great Abington, is of a light, gravelly nature, lying upon a gravel; but towards Balsham, is found upon a chalk; it is proper for the culture of cinquefoil, and the turnip husbandry. About one third of the arable, and that part, which lies towards Linton, is of a stiff, clayey nature, and proper for the culture of wheat, beans, black oats, and clover: towards Hildersham Wood, the soil improves in its strength, and staple, and produces good wheat, and beans, to which might be added, black oats and clover; the whole contains about nine hundred acres, and is rented at nine shillings per acre. The enclosures in severalty, which lie in, and near the village, and binding upon Hildersham Wood, contain about one hundred and sixty acres, and are rented at fifteen shillings the acre. Common open field husbandry, without foreign manures.

Produce per acre

Wheat	16 bushels
Barley	20 ditto
Rye and Beans	16 ditto

An enclosure here, is much desired, but a difficulty is much apprehended, in raising fences upon
p.59 the dry, thin, chalky land. There are in this parish, twenty-five houses, thirty-two families, and one hundred and sixty persons, and poor's rates, are three shillings and six-pence in the pound. There are five hundred and forty sheep of the Norfolk breed, preserved healthy, by the cultivation of a quantity of rye, turnips, clover, trefoil, and rye grass.

LINTON & BARTLOW.

No information upon the survey obtained here; but the following was afterwards very obligingly communicated from - Keene, Esq, the Rev. Fisher, of Linton, and the Rev. - Hall, of Bartlow, by letter from the last mentioned Gentleman.

The soil in these parishes, consists of chalk, gravel, and clay. The rent of the open common fields, varies from three shillings and six-pence to ten shillings per acre; that of the half yearly meadow land, from fifteen shillings to twenty shillings; the enclosed pastures, from twenty to forty shillings, and the enclosed arable in severalty, from seven to twenty shillings per acre. The tenures of these farms, are from seven to twenty-one years, and the amount of their annual rents, from thirty to three hundred pounds. The rotation of crops, is, first fallow, dung, sheep-folding, malt-chives, and cinder dust; together with oil cake dust; at the rate of three guineas per acre, for the second years, wheat, or barley; third year, or after crop, oats or peas: the next year, where the land will admit of it, the oat stubble is winter fallowed, manured, and prepared for turnips, which is succeeded by barley. Tares, clover,
p.60 cinquefoil, rye grass, and trefoil, are occasionally cultivated, and found to answer. This management produces from twelve to twenty bushels of wheat per acre, and from twelve to twenty-four bushels of barley.

At Linton, there are about three hundred sheep of the Norfolk breed, free from the rot and it is doubtful if any other sort would so well suit this country. The cows not bred upon the soil, are frequently subject to a disorder, called the red water, more commonly in a dry, than in a wet summer: many, remedies have been applied, with a great variety of success.

There are about three hundred acres of woods in these two parishes, the undergrowth of which is felled in ten or twelve years. Seed wheat, is sometimes sown in August, but the principal crop, not until the latter end of September. Barley and oats, in March or April. Harvest is in general began in the neighbourhood, about the tenth of August. There have been no enclosures made in these parishes, and so long as the property remains so widely, and variously dispersed in the common fields, no material improvement can be made in the stock and husbandry of this country. The malting trade, has much increased in these parishes of late years, and is now considerable; but there is no other article of manufacture, or commerce, peculiar to this part of the country.

The number of distinct families in Linton, two hundred and fifty; there are twelve hundred and fifty souls. The poor's rates, *(communibus annis,)* three shillings and six-pence in the pound. In Bartlow, including a hamlet in the county of Essex, there are forty-eight houses, sixty distinct families, and three
p.61 hundred persons. The poor's rates here are three shillings; but in the hamlet, which is always assessed they are five shillings in the pound.

The price of labour, with the allowance of small beer, one shilling per day; without it, fourteen-pence. When task work is performed, or the labourers work by the great, they will earn from seven to nine shillings per week. The hours of work, are from seven to five in the winter; in the summer, from six to six, except in harvest, or when working by the great.

The price of all kinds of provisions has encreased within these last two years, and seems not likely at present to be reduced; at present, that of mutton is five-pence, pork an halfpenny more, veal six-pence, cheese the same, and butter ten-pence the pound; the price of flour is regulated by that of wheat.

SHUDY CAMPS.

THE soil of the enclosed arable is a deep, strong, heavy brown loam, lying upon a blue and whitish coloured clay, proper for the culture of wheat, barley, beans, peas, clover, and black oats; of which there are about three hundred acres, rented at sixteen shillings per acre: the soil of the enclosed pastures is very similar to that of the arable land, affording a rich tender herbage; in these are included about seven hundred acres, rented at a guinea per acre; besides which there are about six hundred acres of open field land, the soil of which is a stiff clay, and is gradually lost in a light dry, thin, soil, upon a chalk and gravel; rented at ten shillings per acre. In this field, all the intermediate crops may be cultivated between
p.62 clean beans and rye, both inclusive. The open field, as well as the enclosures, lie flat; no high back'd lands; they are all hollow drained, and in that respect managed in a very husband like manner. The largest farm is one hundred and thirty-five pounds per ann. which, with the rest of the parish, is held at will. The common practice of two crops and a fallow obtains, as well in the enclosures as in the open fields; produce per acre,

In the enclosures.		In the open field.
22 bushels of	Wheat .	18 bushels
26 ditto	Barley	20 ditto
22 ditto	Oats	18 ditto
18 ditto	Peas	16 ditto
18 ditto	Beans	

There are about four hundred and sixty sheep of the Norfolk breed, which are thought to answer very well; a cross between the Welch and Derbyshire cow is preferred.

There are forty-five houses, eighty families, and, by computation, four hundred and forty inhabitants; the tythes (except of two farms) are all taken in kind.

CASTLE CAMPS.

THE enclosures in severalty, consist of a wet, but tender clay, lying upon a strong blue, and yellow clay, or loam; that part which has been properly hollow drained, and otherwise improved, produces a rich, fine, and luxuriant herbage, valued at thirty shillings per acre; the whole of a similar nature, and lies equally well for draining, and to admit of the same improvement. The unimproved pastures, which
p.63 are coarse, abounding with ants-hills, rushes, whins, and bushes, are valued at twelve shillings the acre. The open arable field contains about three hundred acres; is of a nature similar to that of Shudy Camps; and is rented at about nine shillings the acre.

The largest farm in this parish, is two hundred and fifty pounds per ann. Two crops, and a fallow, was formerly the common practice, but of late years, it has been found that one crop and a fallow answers best. The produce per acre of

Wheat is	22 bushels
Barley	20 ditto
Oats	20 ditto
Peas and Beans	14 ditto

There are about 500 sheep of the Norfolk breed, kept in this parish, and the Derbyshire and Welsh cows, are most generally approved. It contains one hundred and seventy distinct families, two or three of which, are crouded in one house; there are by computation, eight hundred and fifty persons, and the poor's rates are four shillings in the pound. A striking instance of the ill effects of paring and burning of land of a fair staple, is seen in this parish; the whole field is now ruined completely, and is reduced to the state of an absolute *caput mortum.*

HORSE-HEATH.

No information. The country from Shudy Camps; hither and around this village, appears to contain,

a great quantity of rich pasture land: the herbage on which, is now *(being the fast day*)* putting forth,
p.64 and is in most places, commonly good. Many of the farm houses, and offices, appear in a very ruinous condition; the hall in particular, a very elegant and modern building, is now levelling with the ground.

WEST-WICKHAM.

NO information. - On ascending the hill, after passing the tan-yard, on the way from Horseheath hither, the country opens, the soil becomes more light, and loamy, and seems well adapted to the culture of barley, and the turnip husbandry.

BALSHAM.

The open field arable land in this parish, is chiefly a dry, thin, light soil, lying upon a chalk, and gravel, proper for the culture of barley, rye, oats, trefoil, cinquefoil, clover, and turnips, and containing about fifteen hundred acres, is rented at seven shillings and sixpence per acre. The enclosures in severalty, contain about one hundred acres, and are rented at a guinea: the meadow or half yearly land, containing about fifty acres, is valued at ten shillings, and about twelve hundred acres of heath, sheep-walk, are valued at half a crown per acre.

The largest farm in this parish, is rented at three hundred pounds per ann. under a lease of twelve years, from the Charter house. The common field husbandry, without any assistance, from foreign, or artificial manures, produces

Wheat	18 bushels per acre
Barley	18 ditto
Oats	14 ditto
Rye	14 ditto

p.65 There are about eighteen hundred sheep, of the Norfolk breed kept here, and which are supported very well, by their ranging over the heath, and the trefoil, clover, rye, and turnips that are sown for them in the common field. The Welsh and Suffolk breed of cows, are much preferred. The laying of the intermixed property in the open fields together, and the suppressing the rights of sheep walks and shackage, is the only foundation upon which any improvement can be made, in the present stock and husbandry of the parish; in which are about one hundred families, and by computation, five hundred souls. The poor's rates are four shillings in the pound, and the tythes are all taken in kind.

SHELFORDS

No information, upon twice calling, much promised.

SAWSTON.

THE arable land lies in three open fields, northwardly of the village; the soil of which is of a good staple, but of a light and gentle nature, and lying generally upon a chalk and gravel: it is proper for the culture of turnips, barley, rye, oats, trefoil, and cinquefoil. These fields contain twelve hundred acres, and are rented at eight shillings per acre. There are also about one hundred acres of half meadow land, rented at fourteen shillings per acre; three hundred acres of common, the soil of which is of a moory nature, and is much injured, from the pressure of water in the mill dams, which produces a very serious evil to the cows that depasture upon it; as many of them lately been carried off by an absolute rot, which
p.66 is communicated by the foulness of the herbage. This common has likewise produced the rot in sheep; but they are now carefully kept from feeding there. All the low grounds, in this parish, are greatly inconvenienced from the same cause.

The largest farm here, is rented at two hundred pounds per ann. which, with the rest of the parish, under the common field husbandry of two crops and a fallow, assisted with foreign manures, at an expense of thirty shillings per acre, produces,

* 27th February 1794.

18 bushels of Wheat	
22 ditto	Barley
22 ditto	Oats
14 ditto	Peas per acre.

There are about four hundred and sixty sheep, which, by proper attention, are preserved in tolerable health. There are eighty houses, one hundred families, and by computation, five hundred inhabitants; and the poor's rates are four shillings in the pound.

The laying of the intermixed property in this parish together, and in severalty, is greatly desired.

PAMPISFORD.

THE arable land here, lies in three open fields, is of a. light, thin, staple, upon a chalk, and gravel, proper for the culture of barley, rye, oats, peas, cinquefoil, trefoil, and turnips; containing about seven hundred acres, and rented at eight shillings per acre. The soil of the two enter commons, Hay, and Branditch Fields, is of a more gravelly nature, and more particularly adapted to the culture of turnips; is valued and rented with the other open field land.

p.67 The Inclosures in severalty, contain about fifty acres, and are greatly reduced in their value, by the expence and difficulty of preserving fences: formerly these lands were rented at twenty shillings the acre; at present their value is much decreased. The moor, or common, contains about one and fifty acres, and is depastured by cows and horses in the summer, and sheep in winter, which here amount to about four hundred: The common is capable of being completely drained, and highly improved, though at present, it extremely obnoxious to the rot in cows, which frequently happens, as also to those hares which are supposed to feed upon it; neither the stomachs, or intestines of either of animals, have as yet been sufficiently inspected, to any conjecture as to the seat of the disease.

The meadow land contains about twenty acres, enter-common with Whittlesford, from the end of hay harvest to Lady Day, *with a bite on Easter Sunday;* this bite formerly destroyed the whole crop of hay; for although the Whittlesford cattle were only allowed from six o'clock in morning of Easter Sunday, till the end of the morning church service, still the multitudes that were driven on this common, during that time, either eat up, or destroyed prospects of a crop of hay: at present, as Easter falls much earlier, this custom is not so injurious.

The common field husbandry, assisted with occasional top dressings, at an expence of thirty shillings per acre.

Wheat	18	bushels per acre
Barley	22	ditto
Oats	20	ditto
Peas	14	ditto

The largest farm in this parish, is two hundred pounds per ann. An enclosure is much desired,
p.68 although great apprehensions are entertained as to the practicability of railing and supporting live fences. The tythes in this parish, are all taken in kind. There are twenty-five families, one hundred and twenty-five souls, and the poor's rates, which a few years since were ample at six-pence in the pound, now amount to three shillings.

HINGSTON

South of the village, and adjoining the enclosures, the soil of the open field, is of a good depth, and substance, lying upon a gravelly clay; thence towards Saffron-Waldon, the soil gradually loses its staple, becomes dry, and hungry, and is found to lie very near the chalk and gravel. North of the village, and adjoining thereto, the soil is of a very fair staple; thence extending northwardly, and towards Sawston, the soil becomes lighter, and rests upon a dry gravel. There are about fifteen hundred acres, of these descriptions, which are rented at seven shillings per acre; proper for the barley, and turnip husbandry. The enclosed pastures, contain about fifty acres, and are valued at eighteen shillings the acre; besides which, there are forty acres of meadow, or half yearly land, of a moory nature, binding upon the river Grant, valued at ten shillings the acre.

The largest farm in this parish, is rented at about two hundred and eighty pounds per ann. Four hundred and fifty sheep, of the common Cambridgeshire breed, (which in a certain degree, are subject to the rot, but not to such an alarming extent, as will be noticed in the further course of this survey,) are
p.69 kept in this parish, where the common field husbandry, with an expense of forty shillings per acre, in foreign composts, produces

18 bushels of Wheat per acre	
26 ditto	Rye
36 ditto	Barley
12 ditto	Peas

An enclosure is much wished for. In this parish there are thirty-six houses, forty-two families, and by computation, one hundred and ten souls; the tythes are taken in kind, and the poor's rates amount to two shillings and six pence in the pound.

ICKLETON.

THE arable land in this parish, lies in five distinct open common fields, the soil of which, adjoining the enclosures in severalty, consists of a reddish coloured earth, of a fair staple, lying upon a gravel, and proper for the culture of rye, clover, and turnips: thence extending westwardly and ascending the hill, a vein of cold, close clayey land, rather flat, but capable of an high improvement by under or hollow draining: beyond this, in the same direction, the wet, heavy land, is gradually lost in a thin, dry, white soil, upon a chalk or hurrock; the clayey land might be advantageously employed in the culture of wheat, beans, black oats, and clover; the chalky land to what is mentioned in the first class, together with cinquefoil and trefoil. The whole of these fields, contain about two thousand acres, and taken together, are rented at seven shillings and six pence per acre.

p.70 The enclosures in severalty, containing about fifty acres, are rented at twelve shillings; thirty acres of half yearly meadow land, valued at the same price; and a moory common, of about forty acres, valued at about four shillings per acre. There are about fourteen hundred sheep, of the Norfolk breed, kept healthy in this parish, where the largest farm, is held under a lease for twenty-one years, at the annual rent of one hundred and seventy pounds. The common field husbandry, aided by an expence of thirty-eight shillings per acre, in artificial composts, produces

17 bushels of Wheat	
22 ditto	Barley
22 ditto	Oats and Rye each per acre.

There can be no improvement made in the stock of this parish, until the intermixed land, which now lies scattered through the open fields, is laid together. There are seventy-five houses, eighty-four distinct families, and by computation, four hundred and twenty souls; and the poor's rates are four shillings in the pound.

FOULMIRE

The field lying northwestwardly of the village, and towards Sheperheath, is a tender brown clay, of a good staple, upon a soft, wet, reddish coloured brick earth, except the part binding upon Foxton, which is of a thinner staple, and lies upon a gravel. Southward of this field, the soil next the moor, is of a clayey nature, and well stapled; thence the staple decreases, and towards Heyden in Essex, it terminates in a thin, dry gravel: these several parts may be advantageously employed in the culture of
p.71 wheat, barley, oats, rye, peas, trefoil, clover and turnips. They amount to about twelve hundred acres, and are rented at eighteen shillings the acre.

The enclosed pastures contain about sixty acres, and are rented at eighteen shillings; and about two hundred acres of heath sheep walk, valued at two shillings and sixpence per acre. Besides which, there is a common belonging to this parish of a moory nature, containing about two hundred acres; but is at present of little value, owing to the bad state of its drainage. The common husbandry, with an occasional expence of thirty-five shillings per acre, laid out on composts, produces

20 bushels of	Wheat.
26 ditto	Barley
26 ditto	Oats
16 ditto	Peas per acre.

About five hundred and fifty sheep of the common sort, kept tolerably healthy, by means of the artificial grasses. The largest farm is occupied at the annual rent of two hundred pounds.

Paring and burning upland, is here much approved. The spinning woollen, or worsted yarn, for the Norwich north country markets, has a good effect, in giving employment to the women and children in this neighbourhood. In this parish are seventy houses, the like number of, families, and by computation, three hundred and fifty souls, and the poor's rates are three shillings in the pound. The tythes of this, and the neighbouring parish of Triplow, are in kind, by a gentleman, who, much to his honor, allows the farmers one tenth part of the first cost, of all the artificial manure, or foreign composts, which they purchase. Very great advantages are expected, would result to the owners and occupiers of this parish from enclosure.

p.72

TRIPLOW

THE arable land in this parish, may come under one general description, that of a warm, gentle soil, of a fair staple, and proper for the broad cast turnip husbandry. The whole lies in three open common fields, which contain nineteen hundred and forty acres, and are rented at six shillings the acre. About thirty acres of the enclosed pasture lands, are rented at twenty-one shillings, and an equal number of acres in an unimproved state, are valued only at ten shillings per acre. The common, lying east of the village, and containing one hundred and forty acres, is a loose, spungy, black soil, abounding in springs, and is at present of little value, though capable of being much improved. The common husbandry, with an occasional expence, to the amount of fifty shillings per acre, laid out in foreign compost, produces

Wheat	24 bushels per acre
Barley	24 ditto
Rye	24 ditto
Oats	24 ditto
Peas	16 ditto

Eleven hundred and sixty sheep, are kept in this parish, where the largest farm is occupied under a lease of twelve years, at one hundred and sixty pounds per ann. No improvement can be made in the breed of sheep, or cow cattle; until the intermixed property is laid together, or the parish enclosed. There are fifty-eight houses, sixty-four families, and by computation, three hundred and twenty inhabitants, whose poor's rates, are three shillings in the pound.

p.73

DUXFORD.

THE soil adjoining the enclosures, on the S. W. side of the village, is a gravelly loam, well stapled, and proper for the turnip husbandry; continuing on this course, the strength and depth of the soil decreases, and terminates in a thin, dry, white soil, upon a chalk, or hurrock. Westwardly of this, soil again improves in strength, and staple; and on the top of the hill, forms a strong, brown, wet earth, upon a clay, in which there is a mixture of some large stones and gravel; this again gradually fades away, till on the extreme western boundary of the field, it ends in a thin, white soil, uppon a hurrock.

The soil of the middle field, agrees with the above description, except that it does not contain any wet, heavy land.

The soil of the moor field, adjoining north-westwardly, upon the enclosures, is of a deep, and kindly nature, beyond which, the staple fleetens, and is lost, in a hot, dry, burning gravel which continues to the end of the field, and lies at the distance of, at least three miles from the village: the whole of these

fields, contain about eighteen hundred acres, and are rented on an average, at six shillings and sixpence acre. The enclosures in severalty, which lie in, and near the village, contain about fifty acres, and are not valued at more than twelve shillings and sixpence; about forty acres of half yearly meadow land, are rented at fifteen shillings, and the common, which is wholly fed by horses and cows, without stint, contains about forty acres, which would be richly worth, twenty shillings per acre, was it not so
p.74 constantly in a state of inundation, from the Granta River, which reduces its present value, to five shillings the acre. The moor, which amounts to about twenty acres, has been much improved, by draining, of late years, yet it is still an unwholesome pasture for sheep, and cow cattle, and in its present state, esteemed of little value.

The largest farm in this parish, is occupied under a lease for twenty-one years, at the annual rent of one hundred and thirty pounds. The common field husbandry obtains, which aided by an expence of forty shillings per acre, in foreign manures, produces

Wheat	18 bushels per acre
Barley	24 ditto
Rye	16 ditto
Oats	18 ditto
Peas	16 ditto

There are twelve hundred sheep, of the common breed, kept in this parish; exclusive of the right of sheep-walk, two days in the week, possessed by Christal Farm, in the county of Essex. No improvement is possible to be made in the stock or husbandry, without previously laying the intermixed lands together, in the open fields, and suppressing the rights of sheep-walk, and shackage; these are objects greatly desired by the most intelligent farmers, belonging to this parish, which contains sixty-two houses, eighty-seven families, and by computation, four hundred and thirty-five souls; the poor's rates are four shillings in the pound, and the tythes are commuted at half a crown per acre crop, and fallow.

p.75

WEDFORD, or WHITTLESFORD

THE arable land, lies in three open common fields, the soil of which, is of a light, gravelly nature, well stapled, upon a gravel, and reddish coloured brick earth, and well adapted to the barley, and broad-cast turnip husbandry. The fields contain about one thousand acres, and are rented at eight shillings the acre. The enclosures in severalty, contain about seventy acres, and are rented at fifteen shillings, and there are about fifty acres of half yearly meadow land, at ten shillings per acre.

The largest farm in this parish, is occupied under a twenty-one years lease, at two hundred pounds per ann. which under the common practice of two crops, and a fallow, assisted with an occasional expence of thirty-six shillings per acre, in foreign composts, produces

Wheat	18 bushels per acre
Barley	24 ditto
Oats	20 ditto
Peas	16 ditto

There are about eight hundred and forty sheep, of the common breed, kept in this parish; amongst which, the red water greatly prevails, about the age of nine or ten months; the general remedy, is an immediate change of food, particularly from grass to turnips. The rot, has likewise been prevelant in this parish, but has not been so fatal as heretofore owing to the quantity of artificial food provided by the stock master. Upon the thinnest land here, cinquefoil has cultivated to great advantage; five bushels
p.76 of seed is sown per acre; it lies six years, and in that time, gets three hand-dressings of cinder ashes, at the rate of fifty bushels per acre, which cost upon the land, three-pence per bushel; this crop is annually mown, and taking the average of the six crops, produces twenty-five hundred weight of green hay per acre. The same practice obtains, with a similar result therefrom, in the neighbouring parish of Duxford. The laying of the intermixed land together, is thought might answer very well. There are fifty-five houses, seventy-five families, and by computation, three hundred and seventy-five souls. The poor's rates are four shillings in the pound, and the tythes are taken in kind.

NEWTON

NO information here, though much promised.

HAWKSTON

NO information here, after twice calling.

HARSTON

NO information here. The nature of the several soils, in this and the preceding parishes, may be fairly ascertained, by reference to Duxford and Whittlesford.

FOXTON

NO information. The herbage in the enclosures here, indicate a warm, and gentle soil, but the land
p.77 appears to be greatly annoyed, by pollard trees, which give the appearance of an old delapidated forest. Some of the buildings also appear in a delapidated state. On the north side of the village, very good turnip land; on the south a tender, well stapled white loam, lying upon a chalk; thence ascending the hill, the soil loses its strength, and staple, but descending towards Foulmire and Triplow, the staple encreases, and the chalky land is lost, in a brown, gravelly loam, lying upon a gravel. Cinquefoil is cultivated by Mr. Hurrell, whose sheep appear to be of a superior quality, though of the Cambridgeshire breed. His lambs are early, very thriving and some of them fat.

SHEPERHEATH

THE soil on the east of the village, and extending towards Triplow and Foulmire, is a light earth, lying upon a chalk, and gravel; a small portion in this direction, and immediately adjoining the enclosures in severalty, is a deep, rich, black loam, upon a chalk. The whole of this field, is proper for the barley, and turnip husbandry, and containing about one hundred and eighty acres, is rented at seven shillings the acre. The land lying west of the village, consists of a tender gravelly clay, of a good staple, upon a clay, mixed with gravel, is proper for the culture of wheat, barley, oats, clover, and turnips, upon two furrow work; and contains about one hundred and eighty acres, rented at nine shillings the acre. On the north of the village, and towards Foxton, the soil is of a gravelly nature, a small part of which lies upon a clay. The field called home-lands, worked in this shift, and lying in a direction towards
p.78 Melbourne, in a white tender clay, or loam, of a good staple, upon a chalk, and is excellent wheat land. These fields together, contain about one hundred and eighty acres, and are rented on an average, at nine shillings the acre. The enclosures in severalty, are of a fair staple, upon a clay, and gravel, containing about one hundred acres; and rented at twenty shillings the acre. The common field, which lies in a direction towards Foulmire mill, is of a dry gravel, and moory nature; it comprises about one hundred acres, and is depastured without stint, by cows, sheep and horses.

The largest farm is held at will, under the annual rent of two hundred and seventy pounds, and pursuing the common field husbandry, with an occasional expence of fifty shillings per acre, in artificial manure, produces

22 bushels of	Wheat per acre
26 ditto	Barley
22 ditto	Oats
14 ditto	Peas

The laying of the intermixed land together, is much desired, as an opportunity would thereby be had to hollow drain, a considerable part of it, which at this time, is greatly incommoded by water. A cross with the Derbyshire cow, is preferred. About three hundred of the common Cambridgeshire sheep, are kept in this parish, which contains thirty-six houses, thirty-eight families, and by computation, one hundred and ninety souls, and the poor's rates are two shillings in the pound.

p.79

MELDRITH

No information. But observed on the north of the village and towards the hamlet of Walton, some very good turnip land; the soil about the village, and towards Melbourne a strong black earth, producing a rich herbage; it lies rather flat, though the greater part of it, is dry, and appears to be tolerably well-managed.

MELBOURNE

No information. This village is large, and the land about it, appears of a generous, kindly nature; adjoining the enclosures, on the south side, is a tender, well stapled, strong white loam, lying upon a chalk; this falls off towards Foulmire, and ends in a cold, wet, hungry soil, binding upon the moor, and which seems greatly to require the helping hand of skill and industry.

BASSINGBOURN,
Including the Hamlet of KNEESWORTH.

NORTH-WEST, west, and south-west of the village, is a strong, brown, clayey soil, of a good staple, and proper for the culture of wheat, barley, oats, beans and peas, and clover; north-east, east, and south-east of the village, is a deep, loamy soil, lying upon a gravel, proper for the culture of wheat, barley,
p.80 oats, rye, peas, beans, clover, and turnips. Thence in the same direction, beyond the line of Robinhood's Tree, and extending towards Royston, and Litlington, a thin, dry, white soil, upon a chalk, or hurrock, proper for the culture of rye, barley, trefoil, cinquefoil, and the annual trial for turnips. The whole amounts to about two thousand one hundred and forty acres, and is rented on an average, at nine shillings the acre.

The enclosed pastures in severalty, which lie in, and near the village, and hamlet of Kneesworth, are an open, brown, gravelly soil, of a good staple, are taken with the arable land, and rented at the same price. The common contains about one hundred acres, is a clayey soil, depastured without stint by cows, sheep, and horses.

The largest farm is occupied under a lease of fifteen years, at two hundred pounds per ann. and adhering, with the rest of the parish, to the old common field husbandry, without any expence in artificial manure, produces

20 bushels of -	Wheat
26 ditto	Barley
26 ditto	Oats
20 ditto	Rye
16 ditto	Beans and Peas per acre.

There is no preference given to any particular breed of stock, but both sheep, and cow cattle, would be greatly improved, by an enclosure of the parish, which amongst the more intelligent farmers here, is greatly desired. Eleven hundred and forty sheep are kept here, amongst which, the rot, in the year 1792, prevailed, but to no very alarming an extent. There are [*blank*] houses, [*blank*] distinct families, and [*blank*] souls, and the poor's rates four shillings in the pound.

p.81

LITLINGTON.

THE land lying northward of this parish, and adjoining thereto, is a gravelly soil, of a tolerable staple; but thence extending westwardly, and towards Royston, a thin, dry, white soil, presents itself upon a chalk, or hurrock, proper for the culture of barley, rye, trefoil, cinquefoil, and turnips. This field contains about two hundred and fifty acres, and is rented at five shillings and sixpence per acre. The other two fields, answer the same description, which contain about five hundred acres, rented at the same price, and may be appropriated in the same manner. The enclosures in severalty, contain about forty acres, and are rented at eight shillings the acre. There is besides in this parish, a common of fifty acres, subject to frequent overflowings from the Abington millstream; in its present condition, it is esteemed of little value, and is depastured at will, and without stint, by horses, and cows.

The largest farm here, is occupied at will, at the annual rent of one hundred and twenty pounds; the open field assisted at times with a little oil cake dust, produces per acre

Wheat	12 bushels
Barley	14 ditto
Rye	12 ditto
Oats	12 ditto

No expectation that an enclosure would answer from the certain difficulty of raising live fences, upon the chalk, in the upper furlongs. About six hundred of the common Cambridgeshire sheep, are kept
p.82 tolerably healthy. Forty- six houses, fifty distinct families, two hundred and fifty souls by computation, and the poor's rates, three shillings and sixpence in the pound.

ABBINGTON, (*enclosed.*)

This parish has been enclosed about twenty-two years, and although great expence has since been incurred, on the score of fencing; yet on the present day, the business is in general done, at much less expence, than before the enclosure. The soil is of a white, clayey nature, of a good staple, upon a woodland, or yellowish coloured clay, and lies with a good inclination for draining. These lands are proper for the culture of wheat, barley, oats, peas, beans, and clover, which containing about seven hundred acres of arable, and one hundred and fifty acres of pasture, are taken together, and rented on an average, at sixteen shillings the acre.

Hollow draining is here but little attended to, though the land is of such a nature, as to require it very generally, and the reason given for this neglect: is, that the farms are all held at the will of the proprietor. The common husbandry of two crops, and a fallow, without any foreign aid, in the articles of manure, produces

Wheat	18 bushels per acre
Oats	20 ditto
Barley	24 ditto
Peas and Beans	14 ditto

There are about five hundred sheep, of the common breed, which have hitherto escaped, tolerably
p.83 well, from the rot, kept in this parish, which contains twenty-five houses, twenty-nine families, and one hundred and forty-five souls; the poor's rates are two shillings and eight-pence in the pound; the tythes of the parish, are commuted at ninety guineas per ann.

GUILDEN-MORDEN, Including the Hamlet of ODISSEY

EAST of the village, and adjoining the enclosures, are about sixty acres of strong, wet, clayey land, lying upon a gault, proper for the culture of permanent pasture, and of wheat, beans, peas, clover, and black oats; on the north, a brown, strong mould, of a fair staple, upon a brick earth, in which there is a mixture of loose gravel; this may be very well employed in the culture of wheat, barley, oats, peas, clover, and turnips, upon two furrow work. West of this, is a well stapled black mould, upon a chalky marl, but of a soft, and soapy nature, and proper for the culture of most of the common grains, pulse, and grasses, saving white peas, rye, and cinquefoil: the whole amounts to about two hundred acres. On the west of the village, the lower part of the field answers to the gaulty land first described, and contains about two hundred and fifty acres. Southwardly, and adjoining the village, a black earth, of a good staple, upon a gravel; thence south-wardly a brown mould, of a fair staple, upon a hurrock: thence extending to, and binding upon the enclosures of Odissey, a dry, thin, white soil, upon a chalk. The whole containing about two hundred and fifty acres, is proper for the culture of barley, turnips, and the artificial grasses, and with the common fields before described, is rented at eight shillings the acre.

p.84 The Hamlet of Odissey, contains about two hundred and fifty acres, is an enclosure in severalty, and tythe-free. It is in general, a thin, chalky soil, on which cinquefoil is cultivated to great advantage. The enclosures in severalty, which lie in, and near the village, contain about one hundred acres, and are rented at one pound per acre. The meadow, or lammas-ground, is of a low moory nature, and much annoyed by the pressure of water from Hook's mill-stream, by which it is bounded; it contains about forty acres, and is valued at six shillings the acre. The low common is situated by the side of, and subject to much inconvenience from the said mill-stream: the soil is of a cold, gaulty, and gravelly nature. Another common, called the marsh, of about equal extent, is depastured with the low common, from May till November with cows, and from the end of harvest till Lady-day with sheep. These two commons, contain each about eighty acres.

The largest farm in this parish, is held under a lease of twenty-one years, at the annual rent of three hundred pounds. The common field husbandry obtains, which, assisted with oil-cake dust, malt dust, pigeons dung, and old woollen rags, at five shillings and three-pence per hundred weight, ten hundred weight per acre, amounting to two guineas and a half expence per acre, produces

22 bushels of Wheat
28 ditto Barley
26 ditto Oats
18 ditto Peas and Beans per acre.

There are about one thousand sheep kept in this parish, of the west country breed; the wethers of which, when fattened to the bone, at three years old, will weigh about eighteen pounds per quarter, and
p.85 have about four pounds of wool to each fleece, which is of the third quality for cloathing. These sheep were greatly preserved from the rot in the year 1792, by the relief given to the wet, and low lands, from open, and hollow draining. The Leicestershire and Derbyshire cow cattle are thought preferable to any other.

Were the commons in severalty, and the property in the open fields, laid together, and in large pieces, great improvements would be made on the stock and husbandry of this parish; which contains sixty-six houses, seventy-six families, and by computation, three hundred and eighty souls; and the poor's rates are half a crown in the pound.

STEEPLE-MORDEN.

North of the village, taking the church for the centre, is a stiff clayey soil, lying very flat, upon a bed of blue clay, or gault; about a third of this field inclines to a gravel, but still lying very flat, and difficult to drain: it contains about four hundred acres, and is rented at eight shillings per acre: this field is proper for the culture of wheat, barley, oats, peas and beans mixed, and clover. South of the village, the soil is of a thin, dry nature, upon a chalk and gravel, applicable to the culture of barley, oats, rye, peas, tares, cinquefoil, trefoil, and turnips: it amounts to about fifteen hundred acres, and is rented at five shillings per acre. The ploughed land, immediately adjoining Odyssey, and included in the above, is generally valued at one shilling per acre. The heath binding thereon, which lies as a sheep walk, contains about three hundred acres, but to which no specific value is annexed. The enclosures in severalty, parts of
p.86 which are under the plough, are of a good staple, upon a blue and yellowish coloured clay, and veins of gravel; they contain about three hundred acres, and average a rent of fifteen shillings the acre.

The largest farm in this parish is held at will, at the annual rent of one hundred and twenty pounds. A small quantity of oil cake, and malt dust, is occasionally used, which assists the common husbandry in the open fields, to produce

16 bushels of Wheat per acre
22 ditto Barley
20 ditto Rye
18 ditto Peas and Beans
24 ditto Oats

The rotation of crops in the enclosures, are occasionally varied; produce

22 bushels of Wheat per acre

28 ditto	Barley
22 ditto	Peas and Beans
32 ditto	Oats

There are about twelve hundred sheep, of the west country and common Cambridgeshire breed, preserved in good health and condition, by the pains that are taken in the cultivation of artificial food, in the upper parts of the parish, and in the drainage of the lower. The same cow cattle preferred as at Gilden-Morden. The very judicious method of hollow draining, and using therein straw only, is practiced with success, by a very intelligent and industrious farmer, a Mr. Strickland, of this parish; which contains eighty families, four hundred souls, and the poor's rates are two shillings and six-pence in the pound.

p.87

SHINGAY, (*enclosed*)

THE soil in general, may be described, a strong, brown, earth, lying upon a gravel, and a stiff, wet clay, of a thin staple, upon a gault; the whole lies rather indifferently for draining, contains about six hundred and fifty acres; about fifty acres of which, are arable, and averages with the pasture ground, about eighteen shillings per acre; this valley, through which the river Cam flows to Walton, is chiefly laid out into dairy farms, and hence it has its name, *i.e.* the Dairies. A very serious calamity prevails amongst the cows, that are here depastured, that of slipping their calves; this accident generally happens when the cow has gone twenty-one weeks, or rather better than half her time, with her *second calf;* which at the time of exclusion is found to be much smaller than might reasonably be expected, and in general appears to have been dead for some length of time. In this parish, within these five years in a dairy of twenty-three cows, a loss of ninety calves has been sustained. There are about four hundred and fifty breeding sheep depastured with the milch cows in this parish; which contains six families and sixty-six persons; and the poor's rates are sixpence in the pound.

TADLOW, (*enclosed*)

East of the church, and upon the hill, the soil is a wet, strong, loam, of a fair staple, lying upon a yellow clay; it lies well for draining, and in a drained state might be advantageously employed, in the
p.88 culture of wheat, barley, oats, peas, beans, and clover. It contains about five hundred acres, the higher parts of which are rented at eleven, the lower at fifteen shillings per acre. On the north, the soil is very similar to the first described, of which there are about four hundred acres; rented as before and may be employed to advantage in the like manner. On the south the land is of a superior quality, and on which there is a large proportion of swarthe, which is valued at eighteen shillings per acre, and is generally depastured by cows. The arable is valued at fifteen shillings per acre, which is about the average of the whole parish; where all the farms are occupied at will, owing to the uncertainty of title to the estate, which is in dispute between the present possessor, and the trustees for Downing College.

The largest farm is rented at about three hundred pounds per ann. and following the common husbandry of two crops and a fallow, produces per acre

22 bushels of	Wheat
32 ditto	Barley
22 ditto	Oats
15 ditto	Peas and Beans

There are about one thousand and sixty sheep of the Cambridgeshire breed, kept in this parish, amongst which, the rot of the year 1792, produced great mortality; the whole flock of one farm, was carried off, and the greater parts of the others, perished by this disease; which is to be attributed to the bad drainage of the land, an evil which the farmers, are now endeavouring to avert in future by hollow draining. There are here thirteen houses, nineteen families, and by computation, ninety-five souls, and the poor's rates are one shilling and sixpence in the pound.

p.89

HATLEY ST. GEORGE (enclosed.)

The following information was procured, by - Quintin, Esq. a Gentleman to whom I feel much indebted for his politeness and hospitality.

On the east of the village (taking the church for the centre) the soil is of a thin, cold, clayey nature, lying upon a gault, proper for the culture of wheat, black oats, peas, and clover; of this there are about one hundred acres, which, taken with the pasture ground in the same direction, amounting to about fifty acres, is rented at fifteen shillings the acre. On the south, a well stapled, black mould, upon a clay, proper for the culture of wheat, barley, oats, peas, beans, clover, and turnips, upon two furrow work; this amounts to about one hundred and fifty acres, and taken with the swarthe or grass land, in the same direction, is rented as before mentioned. On the west, the soil is similar to that described on the east of the village, comprising about two hundred acres, which are rented at twelve shillings and nine-pence the acre. About one hundred acres, lying north of the village, may come under the same description, and are rented at six-pence per acre less. Thence extending north-eastwardly, the soil improves into a deep, strong, black mould, affording a very rich and luxuriant herbage; of this there are about the like number of acres, which are rented at eighteen shillings the acre.

The farms here, are generally occupied under leases of three, six, nine, or twelve years; the largest
p.90 does not exceed one hundred and seventy pounds per ann. and under the common routine of husbandry, of two crops and a fallow, (as the leases import) produces with the rest of the parish

17 bushels of	Wheat per acre
22 ditto	Barley
22 ditto	Oats
17 ditto	Peas and Beans

About nine hundred sheep, of the common breed, are kept here; of which number, one third perished by the rot of 1792. This calamitous circumstance, is generally ascribed to the wetness of the land, some of which lies very flat, though the greater part of it inclines well for draining; which improvement would take place very generally, were the farmers encouraged, by the benefits that would by this means result, and protected, under leases for twenty-one years.

There appears to be a thriving growth of oak in this neighbourhood; the undergrowth is cut every twelve years, and nets to the proprietor about nine pounds the acre. The bark is estimated at about twenty-five per cent, upon the value of the timber.

In this parish are twenty-five families, and one hundred inhabitants, exclusive of Mr. Quintin's Establishment, which consists of fifteen persons. The poor's rates are twenty-pence in the pound, and the whole parish is tythe free. Although this country is in general healthy, the scarcity of springs throughout the whole of it, is a circumstance much, to be regretted.

p.91

CROWDON

No information. The soil here appears to be of a strong, brown, loamy nature, affording very fine pasturage for milch cows, and store cattle; though apparently inferior to

WYNDEE

The land in general through which parish, consists chiefly of rich pastures, employed in the feeding of ewes and lambs with milch cows. The soil is a deep brown loam, lying upon a gault and gravel, affording a most excellent herbage, and comprising about six hundred acres; are rented at twenty shillings per acre. The meadow, which binds upon the brook that divides this parish from Crowdon, is much injured, by the frequent overflowings of that stream: this diminishes its value, which otherwise would be very considerable.

The Derby and Leicestershire breeds of cow cattle are most approved; but here the same calamity as was before noticed at Shingay, appears to exist in a high degree. In a dairy of twenty cows, ten of them slipped their calves two years since. These accidents seem to prevail generally through this valley, to a greater or less extent, than in this parish, and all seem to be under the same circumstances with those at Shingay. About six hundred and fifty of the west country sheep are fed here, amongst which, the rot is only observed with those, that are brought in thus afflicted. There are twenty families, and according to computation, one hundred souls in this parish, where the poor's rates are fifteen-pence in the pound.

p.92

ORWELL WHADDON.

No information. The land about this latter village (the houses are much scattered) consists of a strong, dark, friable mould, which in a direction towards Wimpole Park Gate, gradually changes to a reddish colour, and seems well adapted to the barley and turnip husbandry. Many of the sheep in these fields, have the melancholy and fatal symptoms of the rot.

ARRINGTON.

The soil, east and south of the village, is of a cold and clayey nature, lying upon a strong, close, and compact gault. West of the village, the soil runs of a fair staple, upon a chalk and hurrock; and northwardly it is of a fair staple, upon a hurrock, and yellow clay; the whole includes about one thousand acres, and taking the arable and pasture together, is rented at twelve shillings per acre; a considerable quantity of well mixed land was observed towards Kneesworth, bearing upon some parts a very fair crop of turnips, and a large tract of land in that direction appeared to be well adapted to that husbandry upon two furrow work. The largest farm here is occupied under a lease of nine years, at three hundred pounds per ann. which under the practice of two crops and a fallow, produces with the aid of some artificial manure,

17 bushels of Wheat per acre
22 ditto Barley
22 ditto Oats
12 ditto Peas and Beans

p.93 About five hundred sheep, of the common breed, are kept here, some of which have perished by the rot of 1792. It is expected that the improving state of drainage, together with the additional quantity of artificial food, that is now, and will hereafter be provided, will on a future day, be the means of averting this dreadful calamity. There are twenty-one families, and the like number of houses; one hundred and five inhabitants, and the poor's rates are six pence in the pound.

WIMPLE

THE following observations, were made by Mr. Robert Harvey, and communicated by letter from Lord Hardwicke.

The soil is observed to be a light coloured mould, free from stones, about the depth of four inches, lying upon a strong, clay or gault. It is in general very wet, but capable of being highly improved, by ditching and hollow draining: it appears to lie in about equal quantities, of pasture and plough land. The old swarthe, produces a very indifferent herbage, but may be much improved, by breaking up and cultivating artificial grasses, together with proper management afterwards. The cow cattle and sheep, are of common breeds, but may be improved.

The farms in general are small, and under the present husbandry, of two crops and fallow, assisted by an additional expense of forty shillings per acre, in foreign compost, produce at present

20 bushels of Wheat
24 ditto Barley
18 ditto Oats
10 ditto Peas and Beans

p.94 At this time no turnips are sown, and but little clover, though both would answer extremely well, under the tilthe, barley, and turnip husbandry. The whole of this parish is enclosed, and the enclosure seems to have encreased its population. Hollow draining, and ditching, were much neglected, until the accession of the present Earl of Hardwick to his estate. In the winters of 1792, and 1793, five thousand and six hundred poles of hollow ditching, and four hundred and forty poles of open ditches, six feet wide, and four feet deep, were executed, all which, appear to answer so well, that the farmers in general, throughout the neighbourhood, are following the example. The rot in sheep, has prevailed here, to a very alarming extent, and is ascribed to a coarse sort of bad grass, which grows upon ill drained land, the red water likewise prevails, and is attributed to the same cause: in a certain degree, change of food, appears to be a remedy for this latter disease.

Hollow draining is here very much improved, and would be more generally in practice, were the leases for twenty-one years. The paring, and burning the thin stapled lands, in this neighbourhood, is very justly reprobated, by the most candid, and intelligent farmers here; where it has been done, but not approved of, in the staple land. Including the Earl of Hardwicke's establishment, there are thirty-six houses, forty-seven families, and two hundred and fifty-six inhabitants, and the poor's rates, are twenty-pence in the pound.

In addition to the foregoing, it is necessary to state the following curious fact. Wimple park, contains about four hundred acres, and is at present, depastured by deer, sheep, and cow cattle; amongst the
p.95 former, a disease does, and has prevailed for some years past, which in some: degree, may be compared, from its resemblance with the extraordinary one, observed amongst the sheep, in the neighbourhood of Ashley. The first symptom of the disorder, observable in the deer, is similar to that amongst the sheep; which in an apparent uneasiness in the head, and the rubbing of its horns against the trees, this action however is common to deer, at particular seasons, in all countries, whether in a perfectly wild, or more domesticated state; but the most extraordinary effect of this disease is, that the animal appears to labour under a sort of madness, in pursuing the herd, which now flee before him, and endeavour to forsake him; trying to bite, or otherwise annoy them, with all his strength and power, which from being exhausted, he becomes sequestered from the rest of the herd, and in that deplorable state of the disease, breaks his antlers against the trees, gnaws large collops of flesh, from off his sides, and hind quarters, appears convulsed for a short time, and soon expires.

The greater part of the stock of deer, which were very numerous in this park, have been carried off by this dreadful disorder, in the course of the last three years. In the months of July, August, and September, and when in full pasture, they are more subject to its fatal influence, than at other times, though it prevails to a certain degree throughout the year.

BARRINGTON.

The arable land lying north-east of this village, consists of a hurrocky, dry soil, proper for the culture
p.96 of cinquefoil; north-west is a strong, brown earth, of a good staple, upon a retentive clay, or reddish coloured brick earth; proper for the culture of wheat, barley, clover, peas and beans mixed, and oats. The lower part of this field is a well stapled clay or loam, lying upon a bed of chalky marl, of a soft and soapy nature, proper for the culture of every species of grain, pulse, and grasses. The whole contains about six hundred acres, and is rented together, at eight shillings per acre. The middle field, agrees with the above in soil and value, and contains about five hundred acres. The west field comes under the like description. and contains about five hundred acres. is valued as before, and may be employed in the same manner. The enclosed pastures in severalty, lie in, and near the village; the soil of which agrees with the lower part of the field first described; these contain about one hundred and sixty-three acres, and are rented at one pound per acre. There are besides, thirty acres of moor, or common, depastured by sheep and cows.

The largest farm is occupied at will, at the annual rent of one hundred and thirty pounds, which, with the rest of the parish, under the common field husbandry, assisted occasionally with light composts, produces

20 bushels of	Wheat per acre
20 ditto	Barley
18 ditto	Oats
12 ditto	Peas and Beans

Four hundred and twenty sheep of the common breed are here kept, one half of which perished last year by the rot; but the prospect at present is much more agreeable. The South down, and Romneymarsh breeds, have been tried, and promise very well. The Suffolk breed of cows is preferred.

p.97 Little attention is paid to hollow ditching, though much would be done, were the open fields enclosed; the laying of the intermixed property together, is particularly desired. This parish contains ninety families, and by computation, four hundred and fifty souls; and the poor's rates are two shillings in the pound.

It may not be amiss to observe, that Mr. Benditche: has documents by him, which shew that a considerable part of his estates in this parish, and at Foxton, were let a century ago, at an actually higher rent than is given at this time. This cannot be ascribed to old grants, and tenures, because the estates were held chiefly by tenants at will; but it strongly proves, that so far from the agriculture in this neighbourhood having been progressively improving, for the last hundred years, it has been greatly on the decline, and the country of course, taking the value of money, &c. &c. into the account, must at present be far less productive, than at that period.

HARLETON & HASLINGFIELD

NO information. But of both these parishes, a very fair judgment, as to the nature of the soil, may be formed by reference to

EVERSDEN

The soil of which, in the low common field, may be described under three distinct heads, (viz.) that binding upon the brook, is a well stapled loamy gravel, proper for the culture of wheat, barley, oats, rye,
p.98 peas, clover, and turnips; adjoining this, and approaching the village, the soil is of a thin, cold, clayey nature, lying upon a gault, and demanding a very different husbandry to the last described. The remainder of this field, extending towards Kingston, is of a thin, dry staple, upon a chalk, but which may, with proper management, be advantageously employed in the culture of wheat, barley, oats, peas, rye, clover, cinquefoil, trefoil, and turnips. The whole field contains about three hundred acres, and is rented at nine shillings the acre.

The soil west of the village, (taking the church for the centre) is a thin, cold, brown clay, in which there is a mixture of small chalk stones: this land is greatly injured from the badness of the drainage, and thereby rendered inferior to the other fields. The drainage here might be made very compleat, in which case the land would be profitably employed, in the culture of wheat, barley, peas and beans mixed, oats, and clover: it contains about three hundred acres, and is rented as before mentioned.

The lower part of the church field, on the east of the village, consists of a strong, deep, white earth, of a marly and mellow nature, upon a chalk: this land properly drained, might be employed in the culture of every species of pulse and grain, to which might be added, clover, trefoil, and turnips. Beyond this, extending towards Orwell, the deep, white loam is lost in a cold, brown, tough, thin clay, upon a gault. This field also contains about three hundred acres, and is valued as before.

The improved pastures in severalty, contain about forty acres, and are rented at twenty shillings per acre. An equal number of acres of the second quality, in a very rough and unimproved state, are valued at ten shillings per acre.

p.99 Under the present circumstances of the parish, no other than the old common field husbandry can be practiced, which, assisted at times by light hand dressings, produces

16 bushels of	Wheat
24 ditto	Barley
18 ditto	Oats
10 ditto	Peas and Beans per acre.

Some of the hurrock, which is of a soft and soapy nature, has been tried upon the cold, close clay, at the rate of fifteen hundred bushels per acre, and found to answer very well. Lime has also been used with good effect.

The obstinacy of some of the farmers in this parish, has defeated the very laudable and spirited exertions, of a very industrious and intelligent young man, by stopping the passage of the water in the leading drains, into which his hollow drains in the open field discharged their water. His drains in consequence have blown up, and a considerable expence has been incurred to produce only a mortifying disappointment. They have also served him with notice to refrain at his peril, from the cultivation of turnips in the open field.

The cows here are very liable to slip their calves; a loss of twenty has been sustained in a dairy of fifteen cows, within these three years. Were the lands laid in severalty, and enclosed, or fenced in, at the option of the owner, or tenant, a very great benefit would arise to the country in general. About two hundred of the common sheep are kept, and no preference given to any breed of cows. There are twenty-six families, and by computation, one hundred and thirty souls; and the poor's rates are two
p.100 shillings in the pound.

COMBERTON.

No information, though much promised. The general character of its soil may be well conceived by reference to

BARTON.

WHERE the soil, binding east upon the village, is a well stapled loamy gravel, upon a gravel, and proper for the culture of wheat, barley, and the two furrow turnip work; this amounts to about one hundred and fifty acres, and is rented at nine shillings the acre. Thence extending east-wardly, and ascending the hill, a tough, cold thin clay, upon a gault, proper for the culture of wheat, peas, beans and black oats; of this there are a like number of acres of the same value. North of the village, and adjoining the enclosures, is a white tender clay, or loam, of a good staple, upon a clay and gravel, proper for the culture of wheat, barley, oats, rye, and clover: Thence, extending northwardly, the staple shallows into a thin, cold clay, upon a gault, and applicable to the culture of wheat, beans, black oats, and clover. The whole of this field contains about three hundred acres, and is rented as before. West of the village are about one hundred acres, of warm gravelly land, proper for the barley, rye, and turnip husbandry. Thence extending south, and westwardly, is a thin, tough, cold clay, upon a gault; and proper for the culture of wheat, beans, clover, and black oats; of this there are about two hundred acres bearing the same value. Whitwell Farm answers this last description in soil and value. The enclosures in severalty
p.101 contain about one hundred and twenty acres, and are rented at one pound six shillings the acre. The largest farm is held at will, at the annual rent of two hundred pounds, and the only variation from the common field husbandry, is, that clover is sometimes sown in the place of oats. As much dung as possible is procured from Cambridge, which brought in aid of the produce of the farm, it yields

20 bushels of	Wheat
22 ditto	Barley
24 ditto	Rye
22 ditto	Oats
14 ditto	Peas

The enclosing, or at least laying the intermixed property in the fields together, is much wished for. There are eight hundred of the common sheep kept here; and no sort of preference with regard to cow cattle. There are thirty-one houses, forty-two families, two hundred and ten persons by computation, and the poor's rates are four shillings in the pound.

GRANTCHESTER.

THE village is bounded on the east by half-yearly meadows, which extend to the River Cam; are similar to the Trompington meadows before described; contain about fifty acres, and are rented at twenty shillings per acre. South of the village, there are about one hundred acres of deep, black, friable mould, lying upon a clay, proper for the culture of wheat, barley, oats, peas, and turnips, upon two furrow work. Extending westwardly from hence, there are about sixty acres of thin, cold, wet, clay land, upon a gault; thence, and composing the middle of the field, are about one hundred and forty acres of
p.102 a well mixed soil, upon a clay and gravel, and proper for the cultivation of the crops first mentioned. North-west of the village, and adjoining the enclosures, are about one hundred acres, of a deep gravelly loam, upon a clay. Thence in the same direction, ascending the hill, are two hundred acres of cold,

clayey land, upon a gault. North-east of the village, and adjoining the meadows, are about one hundred acres of deep, rich loam, lying upon a clay: binding thereon, and extending north from the village, are about two hundred acres, of a cold, clayey nature, upon a gault. North-west from Grantchester, are about one hundred acres more, in this shift, of a well stapled mixed soil, upon a clay and gravel. The whole amounts to about one thousand acres, and rented on an average, at nine shillings and six-pence per acre.

The enclosed pastures in severalty, contain about one hundred acres, and are rented at twenty-six shillings per acre. The largest farm is occupied under a lease for twenty one years, at the annual rent of three hundred pounds. Clover sown sixteen pounds to the acre of the best clean seed; in the second, or breach crop field, in place of oats, is the only deviation from the old practice of husbandry, which with as much manure as can possibly be procured from Cambridge, gives a produce on the general average of

Wheat	24 bushels per acre
Barley	30 ditto
Oats	22 ditto
Peas	18 ditto
Beans	18 ditto

There is no enclosure at present in contemplation, but it is much wished, that the intermixed land, in the several furlongs, should be laid in severalty, and together. About seven hundred of the common
p.103 breed of sheep, are kept in this parish; the cow cattle are similar to those in the neighbouring villages. There are forty-one houses, fifty-three distinct families, and by computation, two hundred and sixty-five inhabitants, and the poor's rates are three shillings in the pound.

COTON.

To the east of the village, and a butting on the bounds of Cambridge, a strong brown soil, of a fair staple, lying rather flat, upon a clay, and difficult to be drained; of this, there are about one hundred and seventy acres, rented at ten shillings per acre. West of the village, there are about thirty acres of mixed soil, worked in the same shift, of a good staple, upon a gravel; upon this latter, turnips may be cultivated to advantage; on the former, wheat, barley, oats peas, beans, and clover. South of the village, and extending along the side of the hill, towards Barton, is a thin, white soil, upon a clay; upon the top of the hill, is a strong, brown, heavy earth, upon a reddish coloured clay, or brick earth: the lower part of this field consists of a dark brown mould, of a good staple, upon a clay, and contains about two hundred acres, rented as before mentioned. There are about one hundred and twenty acres of enter-common, with Grantchester, of a mixed soil, and valued with the other arable land. North of the village, is a loamy, well stapled soil, lying upon a gravel, and proper for the culture of wheat, barley, oats, rye, peas, clover, and turnips; this comprises about two hundred acres, and is rented at the same price with the foregoing. The enclosures in severalty, contain about fifty-five acres, and are rented at twenty-five shillings the acre.

p.104 The largest farm in this parish, is rented at one hundred and sixty pounds per ann, which under the common mode of husbandry, assisted by a great quantity of dung, purchased at Cambridge, at half a crown per load of three horses, with the rest of the parish, produces

22 bushels of	Wheat
24 ditto	Barley
24 ditto	Oats
20 ditto	Peas and Beans per acre.

There are about six hundred sheep of the common breed, kept in this parish, one sixth part of which, in the course of last year, perished by the rot. There are twenty-seven houses, thirty distinct families, and one hundred and fifty souls, and the poor's rates are two shillings in the pound.

MADINGLEY.

For the particular information procured in this parish, I am wholly indebted to Sir John Hind Cotton, whose readiness to afford the fullest, and most complete information to the Board, was only to be equalled by his very cordial and polite reception, and the unbounded hospitality I was honored with.

The arable land in this parish may be described a light coloured cold clay, of a thin staple, upon a gault, of an extremely close and retentive nature; in the hollows and lower parts of the fields, the soil is found to improve in staple, and becomes of a more tender and manageable nature; it is proper for the culture of wheat, barley, oats, peas, beans, and clover; contains about one thousand and thirty acres, and
p.105 is rented at six shillings per acre. To this another rent may be added of four-pence per acre, per head, for sheepwalk, and two-pence per acre, for cow cattle, equal in the whole, to six shillings and six-pence per acre. The improved pastures in severalty, contain about fifty acres, rented at one pound per acre; those in a rough and unimproved state, are not valued at more than half that sum. There are about thirty-five acres of cow common, at present very ill drained, and chiefly covered with ant-hills, and thorns, valued at five shillings per acre, but were they in severalty, they would readily be improved, to three times their present value.

The farms in this parish, are all held at will, the largest of which, is rented at one hundred and twenty-two pounds per ann. The common husbandry of two crops and a fallow, assisted by a small quantity of pigeons dung, produces

15 bushels of	Wheat per acre
20 ditto	Barley
20 ditto	Oats
8 ditto	Peas and Beans

The whole of the lands in the open fields, lie in large pieces; as such, no enclosure is meditated or desired. Gripping is much practised, but very little hollow draining, on account of the great closeness of the land, which prevents the drains from drawing, (particularly in Sir John Cotton's domain) and the looseness of the soil in other places; though on a more particular examination, I was not able to establish the force of this latter objection. Including Sir John Cotton's establishment, there are twenty-seven distinct families, and one hundred and fifty souls. About seven hundred sheep of the common
p.106 breed, are kept in this parish, two hundred of which, perished in the year 1792, by the fatal disease of the rot, which has been frequently observed to have been brought on, by their depasturing upon the low lands, skirting upon the fens. The poor's rates are twenty-two pence in the pound.

DRY-DRAYTON.

On the east of the village, is a thin, cold clay, upon a gault, proper for the culture of wheat, beans, peas, black-oats, and clover; of this there are about six hundred acres, which lie rather too flat, and but indifferently well for draining. North of the village is a brown, tender clay, of a good staple, mixed with gravel, lying upon a reddish coloured clay, or brick earth, well for draining, comprising about six hundred acres, proper for the culture of wheat, barley, oats, peas, clover, and turnips, upon two-furrow work. South of the village, the soil is very similar to that, described on the east, but in which is found a troublesome rag stone. This field contains also about six hundred acres, and though greatly inferior, to the last described, is taken with the other two on an average of six shillings and eight pence per acre. One hundred acres of rough sheep-walk, which might be greatly improved by draining, and opening the soil with the plough. About forty acres of the most improved pastures, which lie in, and near the village, are rented at twenty shillings per acre; the remainder, consisting of about sixty acres, are valued at fifteen shillings per acre.

p.107 The farms in this parish are all held at will, the largest of which, is rented at one hundred and ten pounds per ann. The common field husbandry, which is the practice here, produces

16 bushels of	Wheat per acre
20 ditto	Barley

20 ditto	Oats
20 ditto	Peas

About one thousand sheep, of the common breed, are kept in this parish, one half of which fell a sacrifice to the rot in the course of last year, imputed to the bad state of drainage in the open fields. Some hollow draining is done between the lands, and were the parish enclosed, which is much desired, that practise would become general, and great improvements would result from it. There are fifty families in this parish, and by computation, two hundred and fifty souls; and the poor's rates are four shillings in the pound.

LOLWORTH.

THE arable land in this parish, lies in three open common fields. The soil of which may be described, a tender clay, of a good staple, lying upon a gault, and reddish coloured, brick earth, proper for the culture of wheat, barley, peas, beans, oats, and clover: the whole of which contains about six hundred and fifty acres, and is rented at ten shillings per acre. About fifty acres of cow common, abutting upon Swasey and Long-Stanton, are valued with the fields.

The enclosures in severalty, contain about ninety acres, and are rented at twenty shillings the acre. The largest farm in this parish, is occupied under a lease of twenty-one years, at the annual rent of one hundred and seventy pounds.

p.108 The common husbandry, of two crops and a fallow, aided by considerable quantities of mould, mixed with farm-yard, and stable dung, with light composts of pigeons dung, oilcake, and cinder dust, produces

Wheat	20 bushels per acre
Oats	24 ditto
Barley	24 ditto
Peas and Beans	20 ditto

Clean beans are often sown, and sheep fed, which is found to answer very well. About six hundred of the common sheep are here kept, amongst which there has not been the least appearance of the rot; this is attributed to the good state of the drainage in the open fields, where much gripping and hollow draining has been done, and where, should an enclosure take place, it is thought, that in ten years, the land would be improved to the value of twenty shillings the acre. There are ten families, and fifty-eight persons, by absolute enumeration, in this parish; and the poor's rates are two shillings and three-pence in the pound.

BOXWORTH.

HAVING surveyed this parish some years ago, the following was then the state of it, and since that time, no material alteration appears to have been made.

The whole of this parish lies within a ring-fence, and containing two thousand one hundred acres; is the sole property of one Gentlemen. There are nine hundred acres of arable in three open fields, rented at eight shillings the acre. The soil in general may be described a brown, strong earth, of a fair staple,
p.109 lying upon a soft yellow; and a strong blue and reddish coloured clay or brick earth. The field binding upon Lolworth, is of a more tender and manageable nature, than the other fields; which abut upon Conington, Knapwell, and Childersley. The whole lies in large pieces, very conveniently for draining, and in a properly improved state; might be well employed in the culture of wheat, barley, oats, peas, beans, clover, and cole-seed for winter food. There are about two hundred acres of improved pasture ground, valued at twenty shillings, and the like quantity of inferior pastures, valued at ten shillings per acre: besides which, there are one hundred and twenty acres of elm wood land, which flourishes in this soil particularly well. The remainder amounts to about seven hundred acres, and consists of very coarse, rough, pasture grounds and commons, which at present cannot be valued at more than five shillings per acre, though they might be improved in the course of a few years, to the net value of fifteen shillings per acre, by hollow draining, stubbing and levelling the ants-hills, at an expence from fifty to

sixty shillings per acre, which would render them completely fit for the plough, under which they might be kept for about three crops, and then laid down for permanent pasture with great advantage.

The only deviation from the common husbandry, of two crops and a fallow, is that of taking a crop of clover sometimes, in the second, or breach field, in the place of oats. The number of sheep is estimated at fifteen hundred, amongst which the rot has prevailed to a very great extent, chiefly imputable to the very bad state of the drainage. The produce, population, and poor's rates, from the absence of the farmers, were not ascertained.

The farm houses and cottages, form a most beautiful village, well situated, and in excellent repair:
p.110 were the land in the same highly improved state as the village, there would be no doubt of its being by far the most valuable and desirable estate, for its extent, (except Shudy Camps) of any parish in the highland part of the county. The tythes are commuted at three shillings and nine-pence per acre, crop and fallow.

CONINGTON

BEING trifled with here, and deceived, was prevented from receiving any information.

GRAVELY

OMITTED through mistake, I being informed that this parish was in the county of Huntingdon.

PAPWORTH EVERARD.

NO information.

ELSWORTH.

NO information.

These four parishes may be described to be a cold, clayey soil, lying upon a stiff blue, and a wet, yellow clay; the natural chill of which is much encreased, from the present bad state of its drainage; and to which, (from the conversation I held, with many of the shepherds, in crossing the fields,) is to be ascribed the rot in the sheep. The country in general, wants springs and good water, although it lies well for draining. Its present value to landlord and tenant, may be estimated by that of

ELTSLEY

THE arable land in which parish, is a tender, cold, loose clay, lying very flat, and difficult to drain,
p.111 upon a wet, yellow clay, or woodland earth; it amounts to about nine hundred acres, and is rented at six shillings and eight-pence per acre. The soil of the enclosures, resembles that of the open fields, producing a coarse, sharp, sour grass, applicable to the feeding of milch cows, and store cattle only. About fifty acres however, of these enclosures, being in a more completely drained, and improved state, put forth a tender and more generous herbage, and may be fairly valued at twenty shillings the acre. The remainder of the enclosures, which are partly under the plough, and in coarse pastures, are valued together, at about twelve shillings the acre.

The largest farm, is held at will, under a rent of one hundred and fifty pounds per ann. which, with the rest of the farms in the parish, under the common husbandry, assisted occasionally with fifty bushels per acre, of pigeons dung, produces

18 bushels of Wheat
22 ditto Barley
20 ditto Oats
10 ditto Peas and Beans per acre.

There are about twelve hundred sheep, of the common Cambridgeshire breed kept here, seven hundred of which, perished by the rot, in the course of last year; the present prospect is something mended, though as the sheep still continue to die, it is greatly apprehended, that most of the diseased sheep, will be carried off in the course of the spring. It has been observed, that in the first stage of this disease, the liver has not been infected with the snails, or plaice; it has preserved a vivid sound appearance, but when touched, was found tender, and rotten, and in every respect like cold, and coagulated blood. This stage of the disease, or rather the disease itself, is called the blood rot.

p.112 The common cow cattle are considered quite good enough for the present herbage, though that would be very much improved by an enclosure, which is much wished for; the partition drains whereof, in the open field, would greatly facilitate the drainage, and in its consequences, would produce a very general and important benefit to the country. In this parish are forty houses, sixty distinct families, by computation, three hundred and thirty inhabitants; and the poor's rates are five shillings in the pound.

CROXTON.

THE arable land in this parish lies in three open fields, which contain about one thousand acres; its soil is similar to the adjoining parish of Eltsley, but lies much better for draining: it is also rented at six shillings and eight-pence per acre, and the management and produce nearly the same. The improved pastures in severalty, amount to about one hundred acres, and are rented at one pound; the remainder which lie in a rough, and neglected state, contain about three hundred acres, and are not valued at the utmost, at more than ten shillings per acre. About fourteen hundred sheep of the common breed are here kept, one thousand of which, were carried off by the rot in the course of the last year. To prevent so dreadful a calamity, and to improve the stock in general, and the husbandry of the parish, an inclosure is desired. Forty houses, forty-eight families, two hundred and forty souls; poor's rates three shillings in the pound.

p.113

CAXTON.

The soil of the common field, lying east of the village; is a cold, brown earth, upon a reddish coloured clay, or brick earth; proper for the culture of wheat, barley, oats, peas, beans, and clover: of this there are about three hundred and thirty acres, rented at eight shillings the acre. The field south of the village, corresponds with the former, in description, extent, and quality. West of the village, are about eighty acres of enclosed, and open, half-yearly meadow land, which are rented at seven shillings and six-pence per acre. About fifty acres of enclosed pastures in severalty, which have been drained, and otherwise improved, are valued at thirty shillings per acre ; the remainder, which amounts to about eighty acres, and which are also equally capable of the same improvement, are not valued at more than ten shillings per acre.

The largest farm is held at will, at the annual rent of one hundred and twenty pounds; which occasionally assisted with a small quantity of pigeons dung, produces in common with the rest of the parish,

20 bushels of	Wheat
28 ditto	Barley
22 ditto	Oats
14 ditto	Peas and Beans per acre.

The common Cambridgeshire sheep are kept in this parish; the three year old wethers, when fattened to the bone, will weigh about fourteen pounds to the quarter, and taking the flock through, the average
p.114 of the fleeces from off the ewes and wethers, will be about ten fleeces to the tod; the number to which this parish is stinted, are nine hundred and thirty-eight; six hundred of which perished in the course of last year by the rot. A very small and inferior breed of cow cattle are kept here, and which must still be continued, until the parish may be enclosed; from which improvement, great benefits are expected to be derived. The open field, meadow, and pasture lands, are much in need of hollow draining; by means of which they would be greatly improved. In this parish there are forty houses, fifty families, and two hundred and fifty persons. The poor's rates are half a crown in the pound.

GRANSDEN - Parva

No information.

GAMLINGAY

THE soil of this parish, on the east of the village, and adjoining the meadows, is a loamy sand, proper for the culture of barley, turnips, rye, and clover; of this there are about sixty acres, which are rented at eight shillings per acre. The remainder of this field, amounting to about three hundred and forty acres, extending to, and binding upon Mr. Quintin's wood, is a thin, cold, hungry clay, lying upon a gault, proper for the culture of wheat, beans, peas, clover, and black oats. South of the village, and also adjoining the meadows, there are about eighty acres of a deep, loamy, sandy nature; thence towards Potton wood, are about four hundred and seventy acres, of a similar cold, and clayey nature, with that before described. North of the village, and immediately adjoining thereto, the sandy land prevails, to
p.115 the extent of about sixty acres; thence towards Warsley, are about four hundred and ninety acres, of a cold, clayey, soil. The meadow, or half-yearly land, is of a moory nature, contains about eighty acres, and is on an average, rented with the open field arable, at eight shillings the acre.

The largest farm is held at will, at the annual rent of one hundred and fifty pounds. The common husbandry, with turnips, or rye, on the sandy lands, in the place of a thorough summer fallow, assisted occasionally with hand-dressings, to the amount of forty shillings per acre, produces

16 bushels of	Wheat
24 ditto	Barley
22 ditto	Oats
12 ditto	Peas and Beans per acre.

There are about twelve hundred of the common Cambridgeshire sheep kept in this parish, three hundred and forty of which, perished in the course of last year, by the rot, and the mortality at this time still continues. This dreadful disease is here imputed to the bad state of the drainage, in the open fields, which in the event of their being enclosed, as is much desired, would be hollow drained, and improved to very great advantage ; and until the herbage is made better by inclosure, no improvement can possibly be made in the stock and husbandry of this parish; which contains four hundred and five cottagers, in the whole, seven hundred souls. The poor's rates are three shillings, with an annual donation for the support of ten widows, out of the estate of the Earl of Macclesfield.

N. B. Chiefly college lands.

p.116

LONG STOW - BOURNE

No information in either of these parishes. - The latter of which, seems to contain a large village, and a considerable quantity of rich pasture ground, worth from twenty to twenty-five shillings per acre. The arable land appears of a more gentle, and tractable nature, than in the neighbouring fields of Caxton, and Caldicot. The most interesting details in these parishes, are the calamities arising from the rot in the sheep, three fourths of which, are affected by the shepherds, to have been carried off, by this dreadful disease, in the course of the last eighteen months, and those remaining of the old flock, are daily dying. The soil of Bourne, may be very well conceived, by attention to the description of the parish of

KINGSTON

which consists chiefly of a tender clay, upon a brick earth; lying in general with a good descent for draining; is proper for the culture of wheat, barley, beans, peas, black oats, and clover. Some of the furlongs adjoining the village, in the direction towards Wood farm, produce a thick and spontaneous trefoil. In these furlongs there is a mixture of gravel, which if properly drained, might be very advantageously employed in the Scotch two-furrow turnip husbandry. The whole open field, contains about nine hundred acres of arable, and is rented at eight shillings per acre. Much hollow draining has

been done at the Wood farm, by a very industrious and intelligent farmer: the drains of which, when
p.117 made only eighteen inches deep, (without the assistance of the plough) cost for labour two-pence halfpenny per rod. The practice of paring and burning the old pasture grounds, has unfortunately obtained footing in this neighbourhood; the crops produced from this pernicious practice, were at first remarkably good, but are now evidently fallen off, and what the final result may be, is uncertain, though it is a practice, generally advocated, by those farmers, who are tenants at will. In this parish is found some very good woodland, in which the elm, ash, and oak, seem to flourish; the undergrowth is cut once in fourteen years.

The largest farm is occupied at will, at the annual rent of one hundred and ten pounds, and under the common mode of husbandry, aided by oil cake dust, and pigeons dung, produces, with the rest of the parishes,

17 bushels of	Wheat per acre
24 ditto	Barley
20 ditto.	Oats
16 ditto	Peas and Beans

There are about four hundred and fifty of the common breed of sheep, kept here, amongst which, the rot has prevailed, but not to so alarming a degree, as at Bourne, and Long-stow; it is attributed to the bad drainage of the open fields, where the laying of the intermixed property together, is considered as a great and necessary improvement. In this parish, which contains twenty-four houses, thirty-two families, and one hundred and sixty inhabitants; the poor's rates amount to one shilling and nine-pence in the pound.

p.118

COLDICOT

No information. - But the nature of the soil, may be pretty well understood, by reference to the foregoing parish, and the description of

TOFT.

Which was very obligingly communicated by letter from the Rev.-TRANT; the substance of which is as follows: The surface of the soil, in this parish, is covered with a very thin bed of vegetable earth, immediately under which, lies a stiff, strong gault, with a few veins of gravel in different parts. The grains cultivated upon which, are wheat, barley, oats and peas; the land will neither produce clover, nor turnips. The parish lies in three open fields, with a few enclosures in severalty, near the village. The common sheep and milch cows are preferred, and cannot be changed, it is thought, for the better. A little oil cake dust, and pigeons dung, are used with the common husbandry, in addition to the farm yard stable dung and sheep folding. Hollow draining, with wood and straw, is found to be the most beneficial mode of improving the soil, in this neighbourhood; but owing to the expence of it, amounting to twenty-eight shillings per acre, very few of the farmers can afford to practice it; and those who have it more in their power, being tenants at will, and labouring under the influence of old habits and prejudices, are not fond of doing it, or of varying much, from the established mode of farming. In this parish, there are thirty-seven families, one hundred and seventy-three souls, and the poor's rates are one shilling and six-pence in the pound.

p.119

HARDWICKE

THE soil in general, may be described as a cold, close clay, lying upon a yellow, and white clay, and reddish brick earth; there are about ten acres of a dark, brown, strong mould, rising from blackish coloured clay, which are esteemed the most valuable part of the parish; the fields lie well for draining, but are at this time extremely wet, and constantly chilled, with two much water, though in a drained and improved state; would be proper for the culture of wheat, barley, oats, peas, beans, clover, and coleseed, for winter, and spring food; they contain about nine hundred acres, and. are rented on an average, at five shillings and four-pence per acre. The enclosures in severalty, contain about seventy acres, and are rented at sixteen shillings per acre, though they afford in general, a very coarse and indifferent herbage from a soil, very similar to that of the open fields.

The largest farm is occupied at will, at the annual rent of seventy pounds. The common husbandry assisted with pigeon dung, oil cake dust, and dung brought from Cambridge, produces

16 bushels of Wheat per acre
18 ditto Barley
17 ditto Oats
8 ditto Peas and Beans

A little hollow draining has been done, in the open field, where it would be continued on a larger scale, were the intermixed property laid together. Six hundred of the common breed of sheep are here
p.120 kept, one third of which, perished lately, by the fatal disease of the rot, which still continues - among them, and is ascribed to the wetness of the land. There are thirty houses, thirty-three families, and one hundred and sixty-five souls in this parish, where the poor's rates amounts to three shillings in the pound.

KNAPWELL (*enclosed*)

No information, though much promised. The soil is similar to that of Hardwicke. The whole parish was enclosed about fifteen years ago, and at this time, appears to be in a profitable state of cultivation. Farm houses and offices, have been judiciously erected; the crab and hawthorn hedges have flourished, and now form not only beautiful, but effectual fences. From the facility of getting quit of the water, by means of the internal, and ring ditch fences, the least: shadow of the sheep rot, has not made its appearance within these bounds, although the adjoining parishes, have all been greatly afflicted with this dreadful calamity, one only excepted, which is likewise enclosed, and from which, a fair estimate of the improvements in this parish, may be made, by a comparison with it and Hardwicke; being that of the parish of

CHILDERSLEY

The soil of which, is a brown, clayey earth, lying upon a white and blue clay, and reddish coloured brick earth, proper for the culture of wheat, barley, oats, peas, beans, and clover; of this there are about seven hundred acres of arable, and three hundred acres of pasture ground, which on an average, are
p.121 rented at thirteen shillings per acre. The whole of the pasture ground, from the natural chill of the sub-stratum, and the great length of time in which it has lain, in a closely compressed state, at present affords but a very coarse, sharp, sour, and indifferent herbage; every acre of which, by previously hollow draining, and opening with the plough, and then after a few crops properly taken, laying it down again with grass seeds, might be improved to the value of twenty-five shillings per acre. In the course of this year, about six hundred acres out of the thousand, which are comprehended within the bounds of this parish, will be completely hollow drained, at an expence of twenty shillings the acre. The high backs of the lands, are by means of proper ploughings, gradually lowering, and no difference is to be felt in walking over the fields, or to be seen in the last years stubble, or present growing crops, between the tops of the lands, and the furrows; a distinction which must strike the traveller with melancholy, as he traverses the open common fields, of this and some of the neighbouring counties. The whole of this parish is under lease for twenty-one years.

The common farm yard, and stable dung, mixed with considerable quantities of mould, which the industry of the farmer is still gathering from old banks, and the borders of the fields, under the following management: (viz.) First, fallow; second year, barley, with clover; third, wheat, dibbled in, or sown above furrow upon the clover lay, (with such other variety, as the good sense and experience of the farmer naturally dictates,) produces at present

24 bushels of Wheat
36 ditto Barley
36 ditto Oats
20 ditto Peas and Beans per acre.

p.122 The fallow is frequently sown with cole seed, for the feeding of sheep in the winter, and succeeded in the spring with oats or barley. The small Highland scots for the coarse pastures, and straw yard, are found to answer very well; there are here some very good cows of the Leicester, and Derbyshire breeds; the Berkshire breed of sheep is most approved, of which there are about six hundred kept in this parish, and amongst which, not the least symptoms of the rot, or other disease, so as to be of an alarming nature, has yet appeared. There are no rates for the poor in this parish worth noticing, which contains only three houses, and thirty inhabitants.

GIRTON.

The land lying in the open field east of the village, is of a gravelly nature, and proper for the barley and turnip husbandry; on the west, and adjoining the enclosures in severalty, is a black, deep mould upon a gravel; thence west-wardly, a reddish coloured loam, upon a tender clay, which ends in a strong clay, upon a gault.

The largest farm is held at will, at the annual rent of two hundred pounds per ann. which under the common husbandry, assisted by some hand dressings, and dung procured from Cambridge, produces

18 bushels of Wheat per acre
10 ditto Rye
22 ditto Barley
20 ditto Oats
16 ditto Peas and Beans

The arable land amounts to about twelve hundred acres, and is rented with the pastures, which
p.123 contain about two hundred acres, at twelve shillings per acre. There are four hundred sheep kept here, the right of walk, for which is rented at this time at one hundred and ten pounds. The sheepmaster has a privilege of folding his flock forty nights in the year on his own land; the remainder of the folding season, is divided amongst the rest of the parish. The expence of hurdles, and the shepherd, falls on the sheep-master, who has the privilege of mowing as much grass, from the baulks, and spots of meadow, in the open fields, as generally carry his flock through the winter.

HOGGINTON

The only difference in the soil of this parish, and that of Girton, is that the land here is better treated; the arable land is rented at about eight shillings and six-pence; the pasture at twenty shillings the acre.

The largest farm is held under a college lease of [*blank*] years, at two hundred pound per ann. and pursuing the common husbandry without any aid from foreign manures, produces on an average of five years

16 bushels of Wheat
24 ditto Barley .
18 ditto Oats
20 ditto Rye
16 ditto Peas and Beans per acre.

Much of the open field land, is well calculated for the turnip husbandry, and great advantage would accrue from the cultivation of that crop, after an enclosure, which is greatly desired. The rot prevailed to an alarming extent amongst the sheep of this parish, (which are of the common Cambridgeshire sort)
p.124 last year, but its fatal effects are at present much abated. The common home breeds of cows, seem to answer best. There are fifty-five families, and exactly two hundred and sixty-four souls.

LONG STANTON

I am much indebted to Thomas Hatton, Esq. for the following observations, which were communicated at his desire, by a very intelligent tenant of Lady Hatton's.

East of the village is a deep, black mould, with some gravel, proper for the turnip husbandry; south west, and adjoining the enclosures, a strong, brown, well stapled soil, lying upon a clay, and proper for the culture of wheat, beans, barley, and clover; the whole contains [*blank*] acres, and is rented at nine shillings per acre. The enclosures in severalty, which lie in, and near the village, contain [*blank*] acres, and are well worth twenty shillings per acre: there are besides about one hundred and fifty acres of cow common, which are capable of great improvement, by proper draining, &c. &c.

The largest farm is rented at one hundred and sixty-five pounds per ann. which produces with the rest of the parish

18 bushels of	Wheat per acre
24 ditto	Barley
24 ditto	Rye
16 ditto	Peas and Beans

As turnips and clover are found to answer extremely well, they would be generally cultivated, were the open fields enclosed, and laid into severalty, in which case also, much of the heavy land in the *p.125* parish, would be hollow drained, it having answered a valuable purpose, where it has been tried. The common breed of sheep are kept in this parish, amongst which, the rot unhappily prevailed last year, to the loss of more than half their number; this fatal calamity is here likewise attributed to the bad drainage of the heavy lands. Amongst the cow cattle, the home breeds are preferred, which in the spring of the year, are subject to stale blood, from their feeding upon the browse, or black and white thorn-bushes. The elm and oak timbers flourish extremely well here, and in the event of an enclosure, would be generally cultivated. The consolidated parishes of Long Stanton, contain forty houses, forty-eight distinct families, two hundred and forty inhabitants, and the poor's rates are two shillings and six-pence in the pound.

FENNY-DRAYTON—SWASEY—OVER—WILLINGHAM—RUMPTON.

Having began the survey at Girton, and taking these five villages in the way, before the objects of it were generally known in the county, I became here a suspected person, and could obtain no information whatever.

This district of country, contains a great portion of very good arable and rich pasture grounds, together with extensive and valuable commons. The large herds of cattle, which depasture on these commons, and the fodder, straw, and litter, which is produced and gathered from the fens, accumulate such prodigious quantities of manure, as to preserve the arable land in good heart, and condition, *p.126* without the dung from the dove-cotes, which is generally sold to the farmers in the higher country. By conversing with several ploughman and labourers I met by the way, found the average produce to be

24 bushels of	Wheat
24 ditto	Barley
22 ditto	Peas and Beans per acre.

The draining of the fens and low grounds, and enclosing the commons, and open fields, would render this district of country, inestimably valuable.

COTTENHAM.

The soil immediately adjoining the town, is a reddish coloured, deep, sandy loam, abounding with springs, and proper for the culture of wheat, peas, and barley; below this, and extending northwardly towards the fens, is a strong, well-stapled, black loamy mould, proper for the culture of wheat, peas, beans, and barley. The whole lies in five distinct open common fields, containing about fifteen hundred acres, which are rented at an average at about sixteen shillings per acre.

The enclosures in severalty contain [*blank*] acres, and are rented at about twenty-five shillings per acre. About eighteen hundred acres of common are divided into one hundred and seventy common

rights, of seven cows, and fifteen sheep each. A part of these commons are generally depastured from the first of May until Candlemas; part is mown, producing very good upland hay; and the lower parts fen-fodder. The rent of the greatest occupier in this parish does not exceed one hundred pounds per ann.
p.127 The rotation of crops is first fallow, with sheep-folding; second year, wheat; the wheat stubble winter-fallowed and highly manured for the third year's crop of barley; fourth year, peas and beans ; fifth year, barley; produce

18 bushels of	Wheat
30 ditto	Barley
20 ditto	Peas and Beans

No turnips, clover, tares, or other green crops are cultivated, though it is evident from the soil that they might be brought to very great perfection. About two thousand five hundred sheep of the common breed are kept in this parish, three fourths of which were unfortunately lost by the rot, in the course of the last season; the major part of the remaining old stock, have a dismal appearance, and are still dying with the disease.

The cheese so famous through England, by the name of this parish, is made here, and in the neighbouring villages; the superiority of which, is not to be ascribed to any particular mode in the management of the dairies, but solely to the nature of the herbage on the commons. The suckling of calves for the London market, is carried on here to great advantage; it commences at Michaelmas, and is continued to Lady Day. The common allowance is the milk of two cows to a calf, which is considered as the winter profit, and answers very well. There are one hundred and seventy-five houses, and as many families, by computation, the number of persons amount to eight hundred and seventy- five.

p.128

WATER-BEACH with DENNY-ABBEY.

Of which latter place, Mess. Hemingtons, sen. and jun. are from their free and candid communication, justly entitled to my best acknowledgments.

On the west of this parish, and extending towards Landbeach, is a well stapled gravelly soil, proper for the culture of rye, barley, turnips, and clover; on the side binding upon the River Cam, a deep, brown loam, without gravel, lying upon a clay, and proper for the culture of wheat, beans, barley, and clover: these contain [*Blank*] acres, and are rented at sixteen shillings per acre. About an equal quantity of enclosures in severality, are rented at [*Blank*] per acre. One thousand eight hundred and fifty-two and a quarter acres of commons, divided into one hundred and nineteen and a half common rights, at fifteen and a half acres each, or eight cows and four horses, or twelve cows and eight sheep to each common right: about five hundred acres of these commons, are at present out of the reach of the winter floods; the remainder, which are subject to be drowned, can in no way be improved, until that evil be removed, and the commons laid into severalty.

To assist in some degree the drainage of the adjacent fen common, the Chillerin, and the north fen, which latter is in severalty, a sluice should be erected at Harrimire head, to issue the waters of the fen into the river Cam, when the level is drowned, or when the water, which is frequently the case, rides higher in the level, than in the river just below. With regard to the scouring out of the bed of the old
p.129 ouze, or west river, little advantage can be expected to result from that measure, except that, of a better supply of water, during the dry season of summer, to the adjoining country, as the waters descending by the present channel of the Cam, from a higher level, would on a certainty, (were the bed of the west river cleaned out) revert, or flow through it towards Hermitage. Had not the river Cam been diverted from its ancient and original course, from above Clay-hithe, leaving the hurds of Denny-Abbey upon the east, and voluntarily discharging its waters into the ouze, below Cottenham common, the present evils in the navigation below Clayhithe, would not have existed, nor would the country, which is now a melancholy sacrifice to the diversion of that river, have been endangered.

The common husbandry of two crops and a fallow prevails in this parish, and after the spring crops are sown, the dung is removed from the yards to some convenient, intermediate spot, where after a time, if found necessary, it is turned over, and by the end of October, and after the stubbles are haulmed, twenty loads thereof (thirty-six bushels to the load) are carried upon the stubbles, and ploughed in by the following spring; the vegetable nourishment contained in this dung, combines completely with the soil, and abundantly feeds the crop of barley then growing upon the land. There are about one thousand sheep, superior to the common Cambridgeshire; the three years old wethers of which, when fattened to the bone, will average about eighteen pounds per quarter. Some Yorkshire, and Irish steers are here grazed, the largest of which, however, are seldom finished without the assistance of oil cakes.

In preparing the rennet for the purpose of making cheese, which is here brought to very great
p.130 perfection, nothing more is necessary than salting down the bags, in which state they remain for twelve months; about six of these bags will make two gallons of brine, strong enough to suspend a new laid egg, which being put into a jar, is fit for use in about a month, when a gill of it to every four gallons of new milk, or warmed as from the cow is sufficient; the milk should all be of the same age, or meal, and much depends upon breaking the curd with the hands; for unless that is done very completely, the wey cannot be expressed; any of which remaining in the cheese, communicates a harsh fiery taste, produces blue mould, and leaves the cheese full of holes, or cells, like a honey-comb. In short, the dairymaids attention should never be called off, or diverted from the very essential part of the process of breaking the curd.

There are eighty-six houses, one hundred and six families, five hundred and thirty souls. Baptisms for last seven years one hundred and thirty, burials sixty-three, encrease of inhabitants sixty-seven.

LAND-BEACH.

The soil south east of the village is a gravelly loam, proper for the culture of wheat, barley, oats, rye, peas, clover, and turnips. North-east, and extending towards the fens, is a strong well stapled clay, lying upon a gault, and proper for the culture of wheat, beans, black oats, and clover; of these there are about eight hundred acres, which are rented at twelve shillings per acre. The enclosures in severalty contain about one hundred and fifty acres, and are rented at twenty shillings per acre. The commons contain
p.131 about one thousand acres, all of which, except about sixty acres, are high and dry. The soil of the lower parts is a compound of strong earth and vegetable matter; of the higher parts, a loamy clay, lying upon a gault. The largest farm is held under a lease for fifteen years at one hundred and sixty pounds per ann. The common husbandry of two crops and a fallow is here the usual practice. An enclosure is greatly desired, under the encouragement of which, very considerable improvements in the stock and husbandry of this parish would immediately take place; in which there are forty houses, fifty families, and two hundred and fifty souls.

The produce per acre is

26 bushels of	Wheat
28 ditto	Barley
18 ditto	Peas and Beans.

MILTON.

To Samuel Knight, Esq. I feel myself much indebted for his polite attention, and the following observations, (viz.)

The arable land in this parish, consists of a rich brown mould, of a good staple, lying upon a gravel, and a strong deep loam, upon a clay, proper for the culture of wheat, barley, rye, turnips, peas, and clover: it contains about eleven hundred and twenty acres, and is rented at twelve shillings and six-pence per acre. The enclosed pastures in severalty, contain about two hundred acres, and are rented at twenty-one shillings per acre. There are besides about three hundred acres of improvable common, binding upon the River Cam; at present greatly injured by the occasional overflowings of that river, and the defective state of its banks.

p.132 The largest farm is under a lease of twenty-one years, rented at two hundred pound per ann. which produces with the rest of the parish under the common husbandry,

20 bushels of Wheat per acre

24 ditto Barley
2o ditto Oats
18 ditto Peas and Beans

The common sheep are kept here, the breed of which, would in the event of an enclosure, be greatly improved. The natural herbage is white clover, burnet, yellow nonsuch, or trefoil. The ash and elm flourish extremely well, but their culture under the present circumstances of the parish, is much neglected. Oak also might be cultivated to advantage. There are forty-one houses, fifty-five families and exactly two hundred and fifty-six souls. The hamlet of Westrick which comes nearly under the above description, contains five families, and twenty-eight inhabitants.

IMPINGTON.

THE soil of the open fields, containing about one thousand acres, and which are rented at seven shillings and six pence per acre, is a deep, sandy loam, lying upon a gault, which in a properly drained state, might be advantageously employed, in the culture of wheat, barley, rye, clover, and turnips; these fields lie extremely flat, near the springs, and subject to the soak of the fens, which rises thus high when the fens are under water. The drainage however might be greatly helped, were the Huton people who have a great quantity of land, lying within the bounds of this parish, to co-operate in cleansing the
p.133 principal drains which are here, greatly grown up, and remain in a shamefully and neglected condition. About forty acres of common, which lie in a hollow, and receive the waters of the surrounding fields, have been formerly known to give the rot to the sheep. The enclosures in severalty, amount to about one hundred and thirty acres, and are rented at twenty shillings per acre. Were the property in the open fields, which now lies dispersed and intermixed in small parcels, laid together, a better drainage, and consequent improvements would ensue; at present, it is a matter of doubt, whether the present stock, is not too good for the present herbage, which of course must be very bad.

The largest farm is occupied under a lease for twenty years, at three hundred pounds per ann. which by the common mode of husbandry, in common with the rest of the parish, produces

18 bushels of Wheat per acre
20 ditto Barley
20 ditto Oats
16 ditto Peas

There are twenty houses, twenty-three families, and one hundred and fifteen souls.

CHESTERTON

THE land north east of the village, is a gravelly loam, of a fair staple, lying upon a gravel, proper for the culture of wheat, barley, peas, rye, clover and turnips: on the west, is a strong cling clay, difficult to manage either wet or dry; is of a tolerable staple, upon a gault, proper for the culture of wheat, beans,
p.134 black oats and clover. The whole lies in three open common fields, which contain about eighteen hundred acres, rented at eleven shillings per acre. The enclosed pastures in severalty contain [*blank*] acres, and are rented at twenty-two shillings and sixpence per acre. About one hundred acres of well-stapled good common land, that would be highly improved by a general enclosure of the parish, which is greatly desired. The largest farm is occupied under a lease for twenty-one years, at the annual rent of four hundred pounds. The common husbandry, assisted with forty bushels of soot, the like quantity of pigeon dung, at the same price, (viz. eight-pence per bushel first cost) and fourteen bushels of oil cake dust, at two shillings and six-pence per bushel, per acre, produces

24 bushels of Wheat
28 ditto Barley
26 ditto Rye
20 ditto Peas and Beans per acre.

There are one hundred and sixteen houses, one hundred and twenty-five families, and six hundred and twenty-five inhabitants.

WICKIN

THE arable land consists of a deep brown mould, upon a dry bed of ragstone; of this there are about two hundred and eighty acres, which are rented at sixteen shillings per acre. The enclosed pastures contain about one hundred and fifty acres, and are rented at twenty shillings per acre, About two hundred and twenty acres of enclosed arable land and pasture, skirting upon the fens, are rented at ten shillings per acre; a fen common, at present appropriated to the digging of turf, and cutting sedge, *p.135* rushes, &c. contains about one hundred acres. One hundred and fifty acres of Laas fenland, is annually mown for fodder, and when the fen is not drowned, is rented at five shillings per acre. High fen farm contains about three hundred and fifty acres, which are rented at six shillings per acre; this has long been in a state of uncertain cultivation, from the frequent drownings of the fens. At Spiney Abbey there are forty acres of enclosed pastures, rented at twenty shillings; thirty acres of skirty land, at ten shillings, and one hundred and fifty acres of fen, at six shillings per acre.

The largest farm in this parish, is held under a lease for twenty-one years, at four hundred and forty pounds per ann. which with the rest of the parish, subject to a rotation of three crops, and a fallow, produces

24 bushels of	Wheat per acre
28 ditto	Barley
22 ditto	Peas and Beans

Oats and coleseed are seldom cultivated. There are three engine mills occasionally employed in this parish, but are far unequal to its drainage; the river Cam is here the only outfalling drain, and should staunches be erected at Upware, the water must be held back, and in addition to the present calamitous condition of the country, the whole level would be constantly under water. There are in this parish, eighty-seven houses, about one hundred and eight distinct families, and five hundred and forty souls.

SOHAM with BARRAWAY

On the east of the town is found a black sandy moor, lying upon a gravel; on the west, a deep, rich, *p.136* black mould, lying upon a blue clay or gault. The greater part of this land lies in pastures of the second quality, and containing two thousand five hundred acres, is rented at twenty-five shillings per acre. South of the village are about five hundred acres of the first-rate pastures, which are rented at thirty shillings per acre; thence, extending southwardly, are about nine hundred acres of open field arable land, consisting of a rich deep, black mould, lying upon a clunch, proper for the culture of every species of grain, pulse, grasses, and garden stuff, which are rented at twenty-one shillings per acre. North of the village there are about three thousand acres of rich pastures, rented at twenty-five shillings per acre; thence extending northwardly, is an open arable field, of a deep rich and loamy nature, lying upon a tough clay, or gault. This field contains about three hundred acres, and is proper for the culture of wheat, beans, and peas, and is rented at twenty-one shillings per acre. The lands skirting upon the fens, contain about one thousand acres, and are rented at fifteen shillings per acre. The fen amounts to about eight thousand acres, and in its present condition, is not valued at more than four shillings per acre. The bad state of this fen is not attributed to any want of internal works, or powers for lifting the water, but to the constant pressure and soakage of the Highland waters, through the loose and neglected banks of the rivers Cam and Lark. The most inferior fens, and low grounds, in this parish, effectually drained, and properly cultivated, would on a certainty be improved to the annual value of twenty or twenty-one shillings per acre.

There are here about two hundred acres of rich pasture ground, belonging to the poor, and affording the possessors of a common right, the pasturage of three cows or two horses, no one eligible to hold *p.137* any of these rights, who possesses or occupies four pounds per ann. There are besides one hundred and fifty acres of horse common, depastured under a decree from the Court of Exchequer; both these tracts are richly worth, and are valued at twenty-five shillings per acre.

Soham-mere, which was formerly a lake, is now drained, and brought into a profitable state of cultivation. The soil is a mixture of vegetable matter and brown clay; it contains about fourteen hundred acres, and is rented on an average, at fourteen shillings per acre. No enclosure of the open field has been proposed, nor is wished for, though the laying of the intermixed property together is much desired.

The largest farm, which is under a lease of twenty-one years, does not exceed the annual rent of two hundred and fifty pounds. The rotation of crop, is first, fallow, with a thin coat of dung; second year, wheat; third, beans; fourth, wheat, and the fifth, wheat stubble is winter fallowed, and dunged for barley; another course is, fallow, wheat, barley, and the fourth year beans and peas; these with several other changes, but all taking three crops before a fallow, produce

26 bushels of	Wheat per acre
24 ditto	Barley
32 ditto	Beans
20 ditto	Peas

The soil is kindly for the growth of ash and elm; a few straggling oaks appear very thriving; the hawthorn hedges grow remarkably strong and luxuriant. The population of the parish, and its appendages, is estimated at three thousand souls, and the poor's rates are one shilling and eight-pence in the pound.

p.138

CITY of ELY

THE town is bounded on the east by the fens, low grounds, and river Ouze. - Crossing the river, and extending thence about a mile eastwardly, the hamlets of Stuntney, Nornery, Thorney, and Quaney, rise from the level of the fens, and form an island, in which there is about an equal mixture of arable and pasture land of the first quality; and of a similar value with that hereafter described, lying west of the city. The skirty lands may be valued at about ten shillings, and the fens, which are two frequently inundated, at three shillings per acre. The town is bounded on the north, by very rich pasture lands, variable in their soil, and lying upon a gravel, clay, and gault; in this direction, we find the beautiful villa of New-Barns, and extending thence northwardly, the hamlet of Churcham. The pastures of the first quality, in this quarter, may contain about twelve hundred acres, and are rented at twenty-eight shillings per acre. The lands skirting upon the fens, may be appropriated as before, but the fens below, and bearing eastwardly are miserable indeed.

The arable land in this quarter, exclusive of many acres of very rich garden and nursery ground, is divided into two open fields, the soil of which, consists of a well mixed soft, sandy loam, lying upon a clay, and a strong tough cling clay, upon a gault. West of the city, and binding upon the enclosures, another open field, consisting of a sandy loam, upon a clay, and a tough clay, upon a gault; extending thence southwardly, are two more open fields, and some enclosures; the soil of which, consists partly
p.139 of a wet, heavy clay, and a light dry gravel. The whole lies in five distinct shifts, and contain about twenty-one hundred acres; is applicable to the culture of a great variety of crops, and in its present state, is rented on an average of fifteen shillings per acre. South of the city, there are about seven hundred acres of enclosed pastures, of a variable nature and quality, but averaging with each other, the annual rent of twenty shillings per acre.

The fen contains about six thousand acres, including the skirty lands, which together are valued at three shillings per acre. To this may be added about five hundred acres of common, appropriated to the purpose of digging turf, and mowing sedge, and fen fodder. The farms are generally held at will, the largest of which, amounts to about five hundred pounds per ann. The course of crops, is first, fallow, with dung, and sheep-folding; second year, wheat; the wheat stubble is winter fallowed, with sheep-folding; for the third year, barley; fourth year, beans, and peas; then winter fallow again with dung, and sheep-folding; for the fifth year, barley ; summer fallow in course for wheat, &c. this mode produces

22 bushels of	Wheat
24 ditto	Barley
20 ditto	Peas and Beans per acre.

It is to be remarked here, that the barley is of superior quality, weighing in general about fifty-six pounds to the the Winchester bushel; the wheat seldom exceeds sixty pounds. Were the property in the

open fields laid together, a very considerable improvement would take place in hollow draining the stiff, heavy, wet lands; turnips and other green crops would be cultivated to advantage, upon the
p.140 gravelly and light loamy soils. The deplorable state of the fens is attributed to the want of a better outfal through the Haven of Lynn.

A great quantity of coarse pottery is manufactured here, with the same clay that is made use of in making the celebrated Ely white bricks. There are in this city [*blank*] houses, [*blank*] distinct families, and [*blank*] souls. The poor's rates are about four shillings in the pound. There are not more than four hundred sheep of an inferior mixture kept in this district; and the strength of the soil, and the excellence of the herbage, are a very severe reproach to the resident farmers, for their present inferior breed of cow cattle.

LITTLE PORT with APSHALL.

East of the village, and immediately adjoining it, are about fifty acres of strong, rich, deep, black land, proper for the culture of hemp and potatoes, which are readily rented at forty-five shillings per acre. Thence extending south eastwardly, are about one hundred acres of a warm, sandy loam, of a good staple, lying upon a clay and sand; westwardly of the village, are three other fields, containing about one hundred acres each, the soil of which, consists of a black and brown mould, of an irregular depth, lying upon a clay, and sand. The whole is proper for the culture of every species of grain, pulse, and green crops, and is rented at an average, at fourteen shillings per acre.

The enclosed pastures of the best quality, lie in and near the village; these contain about one hundred
p.141 acres, and are rented at twenty-five shillings per acre. The quantity of fen in this parish, amounts to six thousand two hundred and thirty-five acres, which being rendered extremely precarious, from the very bad state of the drainage, under its present cultivation, is not rented at more than six shillings per acre, but were it improved to the full extent, would be amply worth double its present rent. The dried and best part of it, is appropriated to the culture of wheat, oats, turnips, cole seed, and bare cole, all of which, in a favourable season, are found to answer extremely well.

The hamlet of Apshall comes under the same description as Little Port, containing similar proportional parts of high grounds, and fens. The produce in the common open fields is

28 bushels of	Wheat per acre
26 ditto	Beans
32 ditto	Barley

In the fens when they are not drowned, and that the crops hit, the produce per acre is

32 bushels of Wheat, weighing fifty-five pounds per bushel
42 ditto Oats, weighing thirty-two pounds per bushel

Cole seed, and other green crops, to the value of thirty-five shillings per acre. The fen wheat is thicker skinned, and of an inferior quality to the Highland wheat, but makes a good change as to feed in that country. There are about one thousand sheep kept in this parish, of the common breed, amongst which, I did not learn any particular disease prevailed. There are [*blank*] houses [*blank*] families in this parish, and the poor's rates are two shillings and three-pence in the pound.

Mr. Tattershall's fen farm, which is a part of burnt fen, binding west: upon the present course of the river Ouze, contains about nine hundred and fifty acres, and is under the following management: first,
p.142 It is pared and burned, which with all expences included, the cole seed, bare cole, or turnips, are sown for fifteen shillings per acre; these crops are fed off in the winter with sheep, followed by a crop of oats, or barley, the stubbles of which, are winter fallowed; sown again, with oats, or barley, and laid down with four bushels of good hay seeds, or clover, and rye grass per acre; the latter, with four pounds of clean clover, and two bushels of clean rye grass, is preferred. Under this course, one hundred and ten acres of this farm is annually broken up, and the same quantity laid down, with a design of having two hundred and twenty acres constantly under corn. The whole of this farm would readily let for ten shillings and six-pence per acre, the produce of which, is thirty bushels of wheat; barley, which is only

fit for change of feed, or swines food, thirty-six bushels, and oats forty bushels per acre; the green crops are worth about thirty shillings per acre.

DOWNHAM

On the east of the village, are about one hundred and twenty acres, which are rented at sixteen shillings per acre, of a heavy, strong loam, of a deep staple, lying upon a clay, proper for the culture of wheat, beans, barley, and clover. West of the village, are about two hundred acres, which are rented at fifteen shillings per acre, of a heavy, close, wet, cling, and tough clay, upon a gault; which in a properly drained state, is fit for wheat, beans, clover, and black oats. About ninety acres south of the village, and adjoining the enclosures, is a warm, deep, friable mould, upon a reddish coloured clay, or brick earth, proper for the culture of wheat, beans, peas, hemp, clover, barley, and turnips, and are rented at eighteen shillings per acre: thence extending southwardly, the warm brown mould is lost, in a tough, hungry,
p.143 thin, cold clay, upon a gault; of this there are about fifty acres, which are rented at fifteen shillings per acre; add to which, there is another field answering to the last description, and bearing about the south-east from the village, containing the same number of acres.

The enclosed pastures of the first quality, comprehend about four hundred and eighty acres, and are valued at twenty-five shillings per acre. The lands skirting upon the fens amount to about one thousand acres, and are valued at twelve shillings per acre on and average. The fen includes five thousand seven hundred and forty-four acres, two thousand acres of which, have been much injured by the cutting of turf, and are not valued at more than one shilling per acre. The remainder of it, is appropriated to the growth of fen fodder, except a small part under the common fen husbandry, which is estimated at six shillings per acre; and five acres in a very uncertain state, from the frequent overflowings of the fen, lying north of the old Bedford river, and adjoining Manea, are rented at five shillings per acre. There are besides about one thousand acres. Lying in the Hundred Foot Wash Way, which are rented at eight shillings per acre.

The largest farm here is occupied under a lease of sixteen years, at three hundred pounds per ann. the course of husbandry in the open fields, is three crops and a fallow, producing

24 bushels of	Wheat per acre
24 ditto	Barley
20 ditto	Peas and Beans

The land in the open fields, are much injured by the neglect of draining, which cannot be obviated until the intermixed property be laid together, an arrangement greatly desired by the most sensible and
p.144 intelligent farmers. The miserable state of the fens, is imputed to the inattention of the commissioners, in not keeping the engine mills in proper repair, and the leading drains, and there outfall properly cleaned and scoured out. The practice of paring and burning the fen land, under proper restrictions and limitations, is the best mode of brining such land into a proper state of cultivation. There are three hundred sheep, of the common breed, preserved by proper care in very good health in this parish, which contains one hundred and seventy families, eight hundred and fifty inhabitants, and the poor's rates are two shillings and three pence in the pound.

COVENEY

No information. An island rising from the level of the fens, containing much rich pasture ground; the village is well peopled; the houses and other buildings in good repair, and for its more particular description, the reader may be very well referred to that of the preceding parish.

WITHAM

No information. Very similar to the forgoing.

MAYPOLE

The arable land in this parish lying in an open common field, south-east of the village, contains about one hundred acres, and is rented at nine shillings per acre; it consists of a strong, close clay, of a fair staple, lying upon a gault, and is proper for the culture of wheat, peas, beans, barley, and clover. There are about two hundred acres of highland pastures in severalty, rented at fifteen shillings per acre, and *p.145* about forty acres of land lying in the wash between the Old and New Bedford Rivers, rented at ten shillings per acre. The Highland and Wash Common contains about one hundred and fifty acres, and a Fen Common, containing about one hundred and thirteen acres, had formerly by digging of turf, been much injured, but is now completely reclaimed, and under a fine crop of coleseed, the winter food of which has been eagerly purchased at forty-five shillings per acre. Previous to this fen being drained, and the turf bars levelled, it was not valued at more than one shilling per acre. The other fen common, is a mow fen, and depastured only from Lammas to Christmas. The fen land in severalty amounts to about six hundred and eighty acres, and is rented at ten shillings per acre:

The largest farm does not exceed one hundred pounds per ann. which with the rest of the parish, under a system of three crops and a fallow, produces

22 bushels of	Wheat
26 ditto	Barley
16 ditto	Peas and Beans per acre.

An enclosure of the openfields and commons is much desired. There are in this parish fifty families, two hundred and fifty souls, and the poor's rates are two shillings and three-pence in the pound.

SUTTON

THE arable high land lies in four distinct open fields, north eastwardly of the village, the soil of *p.146* which, is a brown earth, of a good staple, upon a reddish clay, or brick earth; a tough, thin clay, upon a gault; and a small part of a mixed nature upon a gravel; the whole of these contain about seven hundred acres, which are rented at ten shillings and six-pence per acre, and their respective parts might be usefully employed in the culture of wheat, barley, beans, peas, clover, and turnips, upon two furrow work. The improved pastures lying in and near the village, contain about fifty acres, and are rented at twenty shillings per acre; those of the second quality, some of which are rough, and abounding with ant's-hills, contain about one hundred and fifty acres, and are rented at twelve shillings per acre. The lands skirting upon the fens, amount to about fifty acres, and are estimated at fourteen shillings per acre. The fen of the first quality amounts to about two thousand acres, rented at ten shillings; and there are about eleven hundred of the second, or inferior quality, which are rented at five shillings per acre. This fen drains partly into the old Ouze, and Hundred Foot rivers, and partly into the old Bedford river, the latter of which is best drained.

The largest farm is held at will, at the annual rent of two hundred and eighty pounds, and under the common husbandry of three crops and a fallow, produces

20 bushels of	Wheat per acre
26 ditto	Barley
16 ditto	Peas and Beans

The fen management is much the same in this parish as at Little-port, the practice being to pare and burn for cole seed, which is fed off by sheep; then oats, or oats and barley, are sown for two years; the latter grain is unfit for malting, and only used for swines food, or change of feed in the Highland country. With the last crop of oats, or barley, are sown two bushel of rye grass, with ten pounds of red *p.147* clover per acre. The red clover is not generally approved of, from the encouragement it is supposed to give to the growth of turn-hoof, or ground ivy, as the roots of this species of ground ivy, are found to be destructive to horses. The fen produce is

22 bushels of	Wheat per acre
24 ditto	Barley

40 ditto	Oats

The laying of the intermixed property together in the open fields, is an arrangement greatly desired. This parish contains one hundred and forty houses, one hundred and sixty families, eight hundred souls, and the poor's rates are two shillings in the pound.

HADDENHAM, with the Divisions of HADDEN-HAM-END, LINDON-END, HILL-ROW and ALDRETH-END

The soil of about five hundred acres, which are rented at nine shillings per acre, at Haddenham-end, near the village, is a cold, tough, thin clay, lying upon a gault, proper for the culture of wheat, beans, clover, and black oats; this division is under a routine of two crops and a fallow. Lindon-end is in four distinct open fields, the upper part of which, consists of a warm, sandy loam, upon a clay; but descending towards the fen, the sandy loam is gradually lost, in a cold, wet, thin clay, lying upon a
p.148 gault; this division contains about four hundred acres, and is rented at ten shillings and six-pence per acre. The Hill-row division lies in four shifts, and consists of a firm, brown mould, well stapled, upon a gault, and reddish coloured brick earth; this contains about four hundred acres, and is rented at ten shillings per acre. The Aldreth-end corresponds in part with the adjoining lands, in the Hill-row and Lindon divisions, and may in like manner, be advantageously employed in the culture of various crops, including those of rye, clover, and turnips; it contains about four hundred acres, which are rented at ten shillings and six-pence per acre. The improved pastures in the several divisions of this district, comprehend various soils, corresponding with those described in the open fields; they amount together, to about two hundred acres, and are rented at eighteen shillings per acre. The inferior pastures, or those skirting upon the fen, contain about two hundred and eighty acres, and are rented at ten shillings per acre. The fen land amounts to about two thousand acres, and in its present state, is valued at seven shillings per acre.

The largest farm is held at will, at the annual rent of four hundred pound, the produce of which, averages with the rest of the parish

22 bushels of	Wheat per acre
24 ditto	Barley
20 ditto	Peas and Beans

No inclosure is talked of, but the laying of the intermixed property together, in the open fields, is greatly desired, as thereby an opportunity would be afforded to drain, and relieve the open fields, which at present are greatly annoyed by too much water. It is supposed that the drainage of the fens might be considerably improved, by cleansing out the old Ouze, or west river, from Hermitage to its junction with the Cam. There are about one thousand sheep kept and preserved tolerably healthy in this parish, which contains two hundred distinct families, one thousand inhabitants, and the poor's rates amount to
p.149 three shillings in the pound.

WILBURTON

East of the village are about one hundred and fifty acres, which are rented at ten shillings per acre; a gentle, warm, and sandy loam, of a good staple, and proper for the culture of wheat, barley, rye, clover, and turnips. North of the village, are one hundred and fifty acres of a strong, deep clay, lying upon a gault, and rented at ten shillings per acre. South of the village are two other fields, of nearly the same size and quality, and rented likewise at the same price. The improved pastures which lie in and near the village, contain about one hundred acres, and are rented at twenty shillings per acre. The fen at present, though at a very considerable expence, is tolerably well drained; it contains about eleven hundred acres, and is rented at ten shillings per acre.

The largest farm is occupied under a lease of twenty years, at two hundred and fifty pounds per ann. The common rotation of three crops and a fallow, obtains through this parish, which produces, on an average of five years

26 bushels of	Wheat
30 ditto	Barley
30 ditto	Peas and Beans per acre

About nine hundred of the common sheep are kept here, the breed of which, has been much improved lately by a cross with Hertfordshire rams. The bulls of Derby and Leicestershire, and the horses of Nottinghamshire, are greatly preferred. Hogs of a large size have been fed here, up to five and a half
p.150 hundred weight, or forty-four stones, at the age of twenty months. There are forty-two houses in this parish, fifty distinct families, two hundred and fifty inhabitants, and the poor's rates are two shillings and six-pence in the pound.

STRETHAM with THETFORD

East of the village are about one hundred acres of enclosed pastures, the soil of which, consists of a strong, deep, black mould, lying upon a gault, and rented at twenty shillings the acre. The village on the south is bounded by the fen. West and adjoining the town, are two open common fields, the soil of which, gradually resembles that of the pastures first described; they contain about four hundred acres, and are rented at ten shillings per acre. There are about fifty acres of enclosed pasture in the hamlet of Thetford, which are of the same quality and value with those first described. The skirty land, common included, amounts to about two hundred acres, and are rented at ten shillings per acre; and there are about six hundred acres of fen land valued at four shillings per acre.

The fen is of a remarkably good quality, very similar to that of Wilburton, but is reduced to a small value, from the present very defective state of the drainage. The open field land, is kept very well drained, by a wise regulation in this parish, of appointing field-reeves, who have the authority to order any drains to be opened that may require it, at the expence of those to whom such drains properly belong; such an arrangement at Eversden, would have saved Mr. Finch a most cruel mortification. Ash and elm flourish here extremely well, and were the intermixed property laid together, this timber would be very generally cultivated.

p.151 Under the present circumstances of this district, and from a rotation of three crops before a fallow, the general produce upon the Highland is

24 bushels of Wheat weighing sixty pounds pcr bushel
28 ditto Barley weighing fifty-six pounds per bushel
20 ditto Peas and Beans per acre.

There are one hundred and twenty-two houses, one hundred and fifty families, and seven hundred and fifty inhabitants in this parish, where the poor's rates amount to two shillings in the pound.

WENTWORTH

NO information.

WICKFORD

NO information, after several times calling.

CHATTERIS

THERE are about one hundred and fifty acres east of the village, which are rented at twenty shillings per acre; the soil a deep, brown, compact, clayey loam, lying upon a gault, proper for the culture of wheat, barley, beans, and clover. South of, and adjoining the town, is a common field, containing about two hundred acres, and rented at twenty shillings per acre, the soil of which, consists of a strong, brown clay, of a good staple, lying upon a red clay; the lower parts of this field are much injured by lying near the springs, but is nevertheless proper for the culture of wheat, beans, black oats, and clover. North-
p.152 west of the village, the soil is of an open, warm, and gravelly nature, lying upon a clay mixed with gravel, proper for the culture of wheat, barley, clover, and turnips; of this, there are one hundred and fifty acres, rented at sixteen shillings per acre.

The enclosed pastures partake of the same variety of soil with that of the open fields, they contain about two hundred acres, and are rented at twenty-five shillings per acre; there are about three hundred acres of highland common, which in severalty would be richly worth the same rent as the enclosed pastures.

The fen-land common contains about three thousand five hundred acres, which in severalty would readily let for fifteen shillings per acre; there are about one thousand five hundred acres of this last-mentioned common, now under cultivation by the authority of parliament, and the remainder, will, at the option of the proprietors of common rights, come in regular rotation for breaking up; five hundred acres of this fen common are at present under tillage, and two hundred acres still under pasture, but subject to the regulations of the same act. There are about seven thousand acres of fen land in severalty, and under cultivation, valued, free of the draining tax, at ten shillings per acre.

From long experience, it has been found, that the fen land answers much the best, when it is properly laid down with the following grass feeds, mixed, (viz.) three pounds of red clover, three pounds of Dutch white clover, or honey suckling, three pounds of trefoil, or black nonsuch, three pounds of narrow leaved plantain, or ribbed grass, and one bushel of clean rye grass per acre; two bushels of
p.153 highland hay feeds, are generally preferred to the bushel of rye grass, when conveniently to be had. The produce in the fen in general, about forty-five bushels of oats, and the coleseed for sheep feed valued at thirty-eight shillings per acre. On the highlands

26 bushels of	Wheat per acre
30 ditto	Barley
24 ditto	Peas and Beans.

A provision was made in the act before mentioned, for cleansing and scouring the highland drains; in consequence of which, the open fields are very well drained; and under cover of the same authority, the fen lands and low grounds, are so well drained, as to render them, tolerably certain summer grounds. The population is estimated at one thousand eight hundred souls, but there are many double families in the same house; the poors rates are one shilling and six pence in the pound: there are about eight thousand sheep of the common breed, which by proper attention are preferred here, in tolerable good health: there are no sheep walks belonging to this parish: the cow cattle in general, are pretty good, and equal to the strength and herbage of the pastures.

MANEA

Omitted through necessity. - It is a small island, rather less than Coveney; rising in like manner from the level of the fens.

DODDINGTON and its Appendages.

No information upon twice calling.

The village of Doddington, is surrounded with pasture, and some arable land, in open fields towards
p.154 Merch. The soil in general is of a more light and gentle nature than that of Chatteris; an enclosure of part of the open field, seems to have been made formerly, and where the arable has been laid down, a very rich and tender herbage has been produced, covering the whole surface with a complete carpeting of white clover, burnet, narrow leaf plaintain fescue or dog's tail, and several other herbs and grades, which indicate a rich and genial soil. The elevated parts of the several islands, rising out of the same level and annexed to this parish, may be considered under the same general description.

MERCH

No information could be procured here, without paying for it. Merch is a market town, an hamlet of Doddington; the river Nene passes through it, by means of which, a considerable trade is carried on; an enclosure has lately taken place; but as all information was with-held, it is impossible to state to the Board, what have been the effects of it.

ELM

East of the village, taking the church for the centre, the Highland may be described, a silty, tender loam, lying upon a loam and proper for the culture of hemp, flax, wheat, oats, beans, clover, and turnips after flax; it contains about one thousand acres, and is rented at twenty shillings per acre. South-west and north of the village, is a clayey loam, mixed with a small portion of infinitely fine sea sand or silt,

and vegetable matter, of a manageable nature, well stapled, and lying upon a clay, proper for the culture of hemp, flax, cole seed, wheat, oats, clover, cabbage, colewort, and carrots; of this there are about
p.155 twenty-two hundred acres, which are also rented at twenty shillings per acre. The fen land in this parish amounts to about seven thousand acres; the soil or surface of which, is composed of black, putrid, vegetable matter, lying upon a substratum at different depths of turf moor, and *bears muck*, which finally rests upon a clay, the natural and antient surface of the country; this fenland is proper for the culture of cole seed, oats, wheat, clover, and rye grass, and is rented at fifteen shillings the acre. The grades cultivated for permanent pasture upon the Highland, (which through the whole of this level is a superinundation of the sea) are twelve pounds Dutch white clover, and four bushels of the cleaned and best hay feed that can be procured. In the fen two and a half bushels of rye grass, and six pounds of red clover per acre.

The sheep are generally of the Lincolnshire breed, though they are occasionally crossed with the Leicestershire; the three years old wethers of which, when fattened to the bone, will weigh upon an average about twenty-six pounds per quarter, and eleven pounds per fleece. The general proportion of stock allowed for the Highland pastures during six summer months, are twenty-two sheep, and one steer, or bullock for every five acres; and three sheep for every two acres, during the winter months; in which time they will improve in value, but in general not in grazing or growing fat.

The husbandry of the Highland arable is usually, first year, flax, or oats, the flax ground sown with turnips, or cole seed, and fed off with sheep; second year, oats; third year, wheat; fourth year, cole seed, beans, hemp, or oats.

p.156 The produce per acre as follows, (viz.)

Wheat	20 bushels of per acre
Oats	50 ditto
Cole Seed	18 ditto
Beans	16 ditto
Merchantable	}
Hemp	}650 pounds
Ditto Flax	700 ditto worth 6d. per pound, is produced in a kindly season,

from one well cultivated acre. The weeding this last crop is exceedingly expensive, often amounting to a guinea per acre. The fen husbandry is first, paring and burning, sowing with cole seed, and feeding off with sheep, if not overstocked; and the plants are strong; it sometimes afterwards stands for a crop, and then it is succeeded by wheat the third year, or (instead of oats, the second year, and wheat the third year,) oats, when it is laid down for three or six years, with the proportions of feeds before mentioned. The produce per acre

20 bushels	of Cole Seed
20 ditto	Wheat
52 ditto	Oats

The drainage of the fens, is at present attended with very considerable expence, and still rendered very uncertain, from the obstructions in the Nene river, above Guyhirne, and the upper end of Kenderly's cut; the remedy for which, is pointed out in the section of this report, which treats on the internal works, and district drainage of the fens.

The largest farm is held under a lease, at seven hundred pounds per ann. though the rest of the farms in general are held at will; the poor's rates are four shillings in the pound; the population was not
p.157 ascertained. The sheep in this parish, have been subject to a very extraordinary disease, by feeding upon newly laid down land, which by the farmers, is considered to arise from their eating an herb, or grass, by them called cockspire (cocksfoot) which is said to produce a relaxation of the shoulder; this calamity is most to be apprehended, in moist forward seasons: the light long legged horned sheep of Norfolk and Suffolk, have been equally liable to it, with the heavy Lincoln and Leicestershire breeds, as are young neat cattle, from one to three years old; but since the removing of them to the high land on the first appearance of the disease, is found soon to effect a cure, a careful farmer will not allow his stock to remain more than a month, or six weeks, according to the moistness and forwardness of the season in the spring of the year, which by duly attending to, this evil is in a great degree prevented.

The following information was procured on repeating my visit at Doddington. This parish, with its dependancies, comprehends highland and fen country to the amount of thirty thousand acres. The soil of the Highland may be described in general, to be a gravelly loam, of a warm and kindly nature, lying upon a clay or gravel. The fen, a light moor, of various depths, and of the same structure with the level in general. The skirty land is rented at ten shillings, and the fen land at eight shillings per acre. The Highland pastures of the first quality at thirty shillings, the second at eighteen shillings, and the Highland arable at twenty-five shillings per acre.

The largest farm is occupied under a lease for twenty-one years, at the annual rent of five hundred
p.158 pounds; there are some smaller farms under leases for seven years, but the tenants in general are at will. The course of husbandry in the open Highland field, first, fallow; second, wheat; third, beans, and fourth year, wheat again; the produce per acre was withheld. In the fen, the first year after paring and burning, it is sown with cole seed, which is fed off with sheep; the second and third years, sown with oats, the fourth barley-big, and wheat; the produce was here also with-held. After these four crops, the land is generally laid down, with clover, rye grass, and a few hay feeds.

The cross between the Lincoln and Leicestershire breeds of sheep is most approved, the three years old wethers, weighing on an average when fat, twenty-two pounds per quarter. The short horned Yorkshire bullocks are found to answer best, though they are seldom fattened to the bone without the aid of oil cake. The fen at a great expence is tolerably well drained; the draining tax amounting from two shillings to six shillings per acre annually. Population not ascertained. The poor's rates one shilling and six-pence in the pound.

UPWELL

The highland, consists of a strong silty loam, of a good staple, proper for the culture of wheat, hemp, flax, and potatoes, and permanent pastures; this amounts to about two thousand acres, and is rented at twenty-five shillings per acre. The soil, or surface of the fen, is a silt mixed with vegetable matter, or fen mould, lying upon a turf moor, under which, in many places, is found a bear's muck; though the
p.159 soil, or super-stratum, is sometimes found upon a clay, proper for the culture of wheat, barley-big, oats, coleseed, and were the fen in a proper drained state, it might be advantageously employed in the culture of artificial grades; it contains about fifteen thousand acres, which are valued at six shillings per acre; but under a proper drainage, would readily rent at fourteen shillings per acre.

The largest farm is held at will, at a rent of three hundred pounds per ann. The practice of husbandry on the highland, is first flax, second wheat, third hemp, fourth wheat, and the fifth year it is well dunged for flax again, and the same rotation of crops. The produce per acre

Flax.	50 stone
Hemp	40 ditto
Wheat	40 bushels

In the fen, the practice is, first to pare and burn, after which, coleseed is sown, and fed off with sheep; the second year oats, third wheat, and fourth year oats, or barley-big, when it is laid with rye grass and hayseeds; when the coleseed is intended to stand for a crop, it is sown later than when it is proposed to be fed off. The produce per acre is

28 bushels of	Wheat
45 ditto	Oats
32 ditto	Barley-big

The wheat in general, weighs sixty-three pounds per bushel, but has a coarse thick skin, and runs much to bran in grinding. The weight of the barley-big is about forty-two pounds to the bushel.

The Lincolnshire breed of sheep, is most approved; the Wethers, when fattened to the bone, at three years old, will average about twenty-four pounds per quarter; it is generally thought, that a cross with
p.160 the Leicestershire, may improve the carcase, and bring it sooner to market, but will not add to the value of the wool; the weight of the fleece is rather in favor of the two years old wethers, weighing about ten and a half pounds. The defective drainage of the fens, is imputed to the want of a better outfal, for the

fen waters through the Haven of Lynn to the sea. This parish contains about four thousand inhabitants, and the poor's rates are one shilling and six-pence in the pound.

OUTWELL

The Highland in this parish, answers to the same description of that given of Upwell; it amounts to about seven hundred acres, and is rented at twenty-five shillings per acre. The nature of the fen land also is similar to the adjoining fens of the preceding parish; of this there are about six hundred acres, and in their present inundated condition, are not estimated higher than two shillings and six-pence per acre.

The largest farm does not exceed two hundred pounds per ann. which with the rest of the parish, is under the following routine of management; first year, flax; second wheat, which is sometimes omitted, for fear of the wire worm; third, hemp; fourth, wheat, and fifth year dunged for flax; produce per acre.

Flax	40 stone
Hemp	40 ditto
Wheat	32 bushels

p.161 The hemp generally sells for four shillings per stone. The lands skirting upon the fens, which do not exceed sixty acres, are under the common fen husbandry, with the same produce as at Upwell, The deplorable state of this fen, is imputed to the cause assigned at Upwell; there are one hundred and fifty houses, one hundred and fifty-eight distinct families, seven hundred and ninety inhabitants in this parish, where the poor's rates are one shilling and three-pence in the pound.

LEVERINGTON

THE upland of this parish, is a deep, brown, under clay, or loam, lying upon a clay; the marshes are a loamy silt, of a gentle nature, and easily to be managed, lying upon a silt, or sea sand. The fen land is composed of vegetable matter, or loose black mould, upon a turf moor, resting upon a *bears muck,* and a clay. The upland is proper for the culture of wheat, beans, barley, clover, cole seed, and permanent pasture, and is rented at twenty-five shillings per acre. The marshes have been too long injudiciously employed in the cultivation of wheat and oats, and being now much exhausted of their original richness, are not valued at more than sixteen shillings per acre: clover and turnips have been tried with tolerable success upon these lands; but the produce will never be obtained from them, that they would have yielded, had they been suffered to have rested under pasture at an earlier day. The third description is employed under the common fen husbandry, and valued at twelve shillings per acre. The Highland arable is under much the same treatment as at Elm, with a difference only of sowing white mustard. Produce per acre

28 bushels of	Wheat
60 ditto	Oats
20 ditto	Beans
26 ditto	Cole Seed

p.162 The weight of oats on this land, is thirty-five pounds to the bushel; those grown on the fen will not weigh more than thirty pounds. The cole seed when fed off by sheep, is valued at two guineas per acre; the other produce of the fen, is fifty-six bushels of oats, and twenty-four bushels of barley-big, weighing fifty pounds per bushel. There are one hundred and ten houses, one hundred and twenty-five families, six hundred and twenty-five souls, and the poor's rates are not ascertained.

NEWTON

THE inside or Highland agrees in general with the description of that in Leverington; it contains about twelve hundred acres, and is rented, on an average, at twenty-two shillings per acre. The marshes also correspond with those in that parish; they contain about five hundred and sixty acres, and are rented at fifteen shillings per acre. The fen amounts to about nine hundred acres, is rented at twelve shillings per acre, and agrees in description likewise with that in Leverington. About one-third of the Highland

and marshes are under tillage, and about two-thirds of the fen.

The annual rent of the largest farm, is five hundred and fifty pounds per ann. The highland mode of treatment, is first and second year, oats; then the land has a thorough fallow, and is well dunged for wheat, which is the third crop; the wheat stubble is winter fallowed and prepared for fourth year's crop
p.163 of cole seed; this is fed off with sheep until Candlemas, and then left for a crop, or ploughed up and sown with oats, and laid down with grass seeds, produce

		In the Marshes.
56 bushels of	Oats	36 bushels
24 ditto	Wheat	22 ditto
24 ditto	Cole Seed per acre	

under nearly the same practice of husbandry as on the Highland.

The fen husbandry is to pare and burn for cole seed, and the two following crops, and then to lay down the land with rye grass and clover, which produces

22 bushels of	Cole Seed
60 ditto	Oats
22 ditto	Wheat per acre

The fen in this parish is as well drained, as the present outfal will admit of. There are forty houses, forty-five families, and two hundred and twenty-five souls, and the poor's rates are one shilling and six-pence in the pound.

TID ST. GILES

THE Highland lying around and near the village, may be described a strong loam, or clay, of a very good staple, lying upon a gault, and proper for the culture of wheat, oats, beans, and cole seed; contains about one thousand acres, and is rented on an average, at twenty shillings per acre. The soil in the marshes, is an hungry silt, with little or no variation, from the bed upon which it lies, proper in a less exhausted condition to permanent pasture, but has been two long improperly employed in the culture of wheat, barley, and oats; it contains about four hundred acres, and is rented at eight shillings per acre,
p.164 The fen answering the general description of such land, amounts to about two thousand acres, and is rented at ten shillings per acre.

The largest occupier rents about two hundred and fifty pounds per ann. and with the rest of the parishioners, pursues the following mode of husbandry; first, the land is half-fallowed, and dunged for cole seed, which is fed off with sheep, and fallowed the second year with oats, and the third, wheat; after this process is repeated, it is then laid down with red and white clover, and ribbed grass, four pounds each, and one bushel of rye grass per acre, and thus it remains in pasture for six years. The produce under this management is

24 bushels of	Wheat per acre
56 ditto	Oats

The fen practice is to pare and burn, to sow cole seed, which is fed off with sheep, and succeeded by two crops of oats, and then laid for three years, with clover and rye grass. Upon breaking up the skirty or fen lands, which lie near the clay, fallowing instead of paring and burning ought strongly to be recommended; produce in the fen, forty-eight bushels of oats per acre.

The Lincolnshire breed of sheep is generally preferred; the wethers when fattened at three years old, will average at twenty-four pounds the quarter, and the fleece will weigh about ten pounds. The cross between Lincoln and Leicestershire seems best adapted to the soil and herbage of this neighbourhood; in this cross, the carcase and staple of the wool is improved, though the quantity of the latter is evidently lessened. The black cattle for grazing, are generally brought from Lincolnshire and Yorkshire, which being unaccustomed to the pure and lively streams of Derbyshire or Scotland, answer much the best for the thick, and stagnant waters of this country.

p.165 It is much to be lamented that raising of live fences is so much neglected; the high and marsh lands, are well adapted to the cultivation of the hawthorn, and elm; this improvement would considerably add to the beauty of the country, afford shelter to the cattle, which are now fully exposed to all the severity of winter, and promote on the surface an earlier vegetation in the spring. There are seventy houses in this parish, one hundred distinct families, five hundred souls, and the poor's rates are one shilling and six-pence in the pound. In addition to the above information, procured on the survey of the three last parishes, the following observations are subjoined, which were communicated by letter from Mr. Stone, of Leverington, in answer to some queries sent him.

Q. What is the nature of the soil and climate in your neighbourhood?

A. As the term neighbourhood is equivocal, as to its extent, I will consider mine to be the three parishes north of Wisbech - "Leverington, Newton, and Tid St. Giles;" the last of which, is the northern extremity of Cambridgeshire, adjoining to Lincolnshire. These three parishes are upwards of ninety miles north of London; a situation which I suppose sufficiently points out the climate as to temperature. The soil is extremely various, each parish consisting of three districts or divisions of land; *the marshes, the high lands, and the fens.* The river Nene runs nearly due north from Wisbech, on the west side of which, an embankment was made in these parishes from the sea, about one hundred and eighty, or one hundred and ninety years ago, and lies parallel with it, at the average width of about a mile, bounded on the west by the old Roman bank. This portion of land is called *the marshes*, and consists throughout
p.166 of a light soil, composed of a mixture of sand, with clay; the former generally prevailing, and is called by the local term of silt. These marshes are in some places enclosed, in others open, and intermixed in the small lots in which they were originally apportioned, and might receive vast improvements by being laid in severalty. It is clear at the time these marshes were divided, that the principle of the division, was by quantity and not by quality, as the lots, as they were called, are in one parish, two acres, in another, two acres and one rood, and in the third, eight and a half acres; so that the number of rights, and the quantity of land were considered, and to each right the same sized parcel was given. It is evident there was no mode of equalizing the allotments, but by saving the single rights out of the middle quality, and giving to those persons who had more rights than one, as many separate allotments, each laid in a different quality of the land; and hence it is, that if an owner had five or any given number of rights, he had as many allotments scattered over the whole waste. This made a separation by fencing impracticable, but at an expence equal to the value of the land; the soil cut up for the grips, and the materials for the dry fencing set between them considered. The great objects of enclosing at the present era, contiguity and distinctness of property, might possibly be known, but certainly had not reached this neighbourhood at the period above mentioned. Where the enclosed pieces in this tract, are larger than the lots described, they have been made so by purchasing the lands adjoining, till a quantity worth fencing off was obtained.

A small part of the parish of West Walton, in Norfolk, extends into these marshes, and is principally intermixed and open. The enclosed parts of them, all consist of both pasture and arable land, the pasture
p.167 is used for young stock, principally sheep; as the water in general is bad, the [*blank*] being saline, and there being no possibility of taking in fresh water. The herbage is very healthy, and for young sheep, answers very well; but none of it sufficiently good to fat sheep upon, unless improved by clay or lime; the difficulty and expence of obtaining which, are likely to prevent the experiment from being made. The arable parts of the enclosed marshes have generally two crops of corn taken from off them, are then fallowed for turnips, or cole seed, which when fed off with sheep, the common practice, enable the land, to produce two crops of corn more; the first is generally oats, the second wheat, and when the land tires of this round, and becomes foul of weeds, it is seeded down with red clover, and rye grass, (fourteen pound per acre of the first, and a peck an acre of the last) is allowed to lie two years, and is then taken up again: if clear of twitch, is sown with oats, if not, is fallowed from the swerd for cole seed, or turnips. By this routine the enclosed part of the marshes, is occupied to great advantage; whereas the open and intermixed parts are in a most wretched state; two crops and a fallow are perpetually taken; the last crop is seldom good for any thing; the land is over run with weeds; it wants resting in pasture, and enriching and compressing by sheep, eating that pasture, which its open state must forever forbid. If these lands (the open lands) were laid in severalty, and enclosed, they would in general bear a double rent, and the occupiers be better off than at present.

The next portion of these parishes to be considered, is the "high lands," and these lie west of the

marshes, between the Roman bank on the east, and the fens on the west. The soil of the high lands,
p.168 resembles that of the marshes, with a larger proportion of clay, and less sand in them; so that it may be said, they are, generally speaking, of a heavier soil, increasing in their value as they increase in this particular. Of these by much the largest quantity is in pasture, and could these parishes be supplied with fresh water, it is to be presumed, but few of the high lands would be ploughed; but the want of this essential in grazing, is an apology for so large a part, as there is at present, being arable. The management of the high lands that are ploughed, is settled into no system, except that of growing as many crops of corn, in succession from them, as they will produce.

The largest part of these parishes is occupied by the owners, who have become within these few years, the purchasers of the lands they occupy; and notwithstanding this, there is scarcely an instance of a piece of good high pasture land being ploughed, that is not lowered in the value of its fee simple, five years purchase. A regular and rational system of agriculture may be recommended, and partially adopted in such a country, but cannot be made general or enforced.

In Tid St. Giles there is some of the best sheep pasture in the kingdom; the soil is that due mixture, the density and solidity of which, are sufficient to hold the manure arising in vast abundance from the crops of the fen land, whither none ever returns; capable too of resisting the frost, and yet not so strong a clay as to retain the wet, or to burn in a drought extremely; that it is on the best of these lands, an unfading verdure is always to be seen. They would be equally good for oxen, could good fresh water be obtained; of which there is no supply but by rain; and this in a summer like the last, proves very
p.169 insufficient. The want of water in all these parishes is a great hardship. In the parish of Leverington it might be remedied, as to the highlands; and if the present Honourable Board attend so minutely to the interests of agriculture as to regard partial and local evils, I pledge myself to shew not only the possibility, but the facility, of remedying it. I have frequently suggested it to the principals of the parish; but the want of unanimity and joint effort among them, to promote the general good, have left this, as well as many other material matters, disregarded. An alteration of the ancient practice of commoning, or depasturing stock, on the wastes of the parish of Leverington, has been introduced within these few years, and is continued to the prejudice of the poor cottagers, who are thereby deprived of keeping cows for the succour of their families. If the former custom could be restored, a great benefit to the parish would arise from it. I believe the labourers families would be much more comfortable from the article of milk, as well as more healthy, and our population, which is often greatly reduced by the unhealthiness of the climate, being good or bad, as the stagnant waters of our country are made fresh by rain, or putrid by long draught, would be increased; the excessive use of tea among these people would be abated, and of course themselves and children would be more vigorous and healthy. This alteration crept in about eight years ago, on the death of a gentleman, whose probity and activity, rendered him as much as an individual could be, the regulator of the parish, and his humanity, the guardian of the poor's interests in it. It was frequently attempted in his time, but his opposition prevented its taking effect.

The *fens* lying on the west side of these three parishes, and remaining nearly parallel with the high lands, as the high lands do with the marshes, and the marshes with the river Nene, form the whole of
p.170 them. The soil of these (their skirts excepted, which are like the high lands) is a moor, or black soil. The larger part of them has not been drained more than twelve or fourteen years; the outfal of this part is through the high lands and marshes into the river, or rather a continuation of the river just mentioned, by means of water mills that go by wind. It was this continuation of the river Nene in a confined, and which when confined, soon became a deep channel, that rendered the drainage of these fens, and indeed a great part of the high lands in these parishes, practicable. For before this a vast expanse of sands or bay, laid in front of the outfal, through which the waters of the Nene used to serpentize in shallow and shifting channels, or rather streamlets, on which it w'as impossible to navigate but in high tides, or great freshes, and into which it was impossible to drain the adjoining lands. The surface of the bay or sands being so many feet above that of the lands, no interior banks could have been raised sufficiently high, nor no mechanical powers invented to force the waters between them, so as to have rendered the drainage as effectual as it now is, without any increase of banks, or mechanic force, more than is necessary to throw the waters through, the high lands and marshes as before mentioned. The leading of the river Nene in a confined channel through part of this bay nearer to a deep water, was part of the great plan known by all who ever attended to the interests of this vast trail of level country, to an immense part of which, besides the parishes under consideration, this partial execution of this plan, has proved

a work of salvation: It has served to establish a position before much controverted, " that a deep and confined channel, ending in an expanse of deep waters, is the only method of uniting the interests of navigation and drainage."

These fens were recovered at an immense expence at first; those of Tidd and Newton, having
p.171 borrowed upon them near ten thousand pounds, contain between three and four thousand acres, and pay an annual tax of four shillings per acre, for the interest of the sum borrowed, and the support of the works of drainage. And here the eye of justice cannot help glancing at a circumstance so very repugnant to her, that as soon as these fens were recovered and rendered productive, they were immediately subject to, and did render a tenth of their produce in corn, or a composition equal to, and often exceeding it, though the rectors deriving this immense advantage, were no contributers to the expence incurred.

In stating this, I am aware it is only a common evil, but its universality does not lessen it, nor has even one plea from the most ingenious advocate for tythes, ever reached this neighbourhood, in justification, or even palliation, of this suffering. We are told of *communi jure*, but this overturns the cause it is meant to support. It is a fact that the parts of these fens producing corn, have yielded more to the tythes for the first seven years, than to the owners who let their lands to be occupied, and the proportion of such lands for that term was more than two thirds of the whole. The hazard and disrepute of fens when first drained, that have been long drowned, as these were, even kept the rents low for a time, and before the owner can let his lands for their value, they must be established in good credit, both as to soil and security in drainage. The culture of these lands, consisting of moor or black soil, is that of paring and burning, sowing with cole seed, feeding off with sheep, taking two crops of corn, the first, oats, the second, wheat, laying down with the last, continuing pasture two years, and then repeating the same course.

p.172 *Q. What manures are made use of, and whether particular attention is paid to the making of dunghills?*

A. Pigeon dung and soot are sometimes sown upon marsh and high land fallows, whereon turnips or cole seed are sown; and sometimes soot upon wheat at spring, to embitter the surface and upper stratum of the land, to make the wire worms eating the wheat, retreat from it, and where this has been used it has always succeeded; there having been a vast yield after it, when, if it had not been tried, it has been believed the crop would have been entirely destroyed: twenty bushels an acre, is the quantity generally used. Wire worms are the greatest annoyance we experience in our husbandry; they are yellow in their colour, and resemble the centipede, from the number of their feet, but not quite so long in their bodies; the heavy and light soils are equally subject to them.

No particular attention is paid to the making of dunghills, nor do I see that our country furnishes anything likely to give rise to the practice. To clay our light silty lands would be the first, and greatest improvement, and this, I fear, must be ever retarded by the badness of the roads, and the dearness and scarcity of labourers: the manure in our straw yards we are very careful of, and think it much improved by caking our beasts upon it with linseed cakes.

Q. What are the usual sorts of ploughs, carts, and other implements of husbandry?

A. These are certainly best described by drawings of them; the levelness of our country may be
p.173 supposed to make only the most simple necessary. The common cart with shafts, waggons with poles, drawn by horses abreast, though shaft waggons are becoming more general; ploughs with one hale, or single handed, varying in their size as the soil renders necessary, and these are distinguished by whole Dutch three-quarter, and half Dutch ploughs; very few implements of experimental husbandry have been introduced; the drill machine has been a little used; a piece of wheat was sown with it last year in this parish; every other land was drilled, and the intervening ones sown broadcast; the latter appeared to have the preference at harvest; the experiment was made on land where nothing was to be feared but too luxuriant a crop, and had the summer been as wet as it was dry, the whole would certainly have been laid; there must have been abundance of straw, and the corn as in the year 1792, on similar lands, very thin and bad: when I say the broadcast was the best crop, I mean the straw was the brightest, and the freest from leaf, and did not seem so high as the straw on the drilled lands. Every farmer will

therefore conclude, the grain was the best, and that there was the most of it. Indeed one would suppose, this experiment was made with a view to shew the drill husbandry to disadvantage; for if I understand its intention, it is of most use on exhausted ploughed lands, where fresh rigour is required to be given to the crop by a fresh moulding, and on such land I have no doubt it would have had the preference.

Q. What is the size and nature of the inclosures?

A. By inclosures I understand the wastes, for which acts of parliament have been obtained for authority to inclose and divide them. These in this country have consisted of interior, commons and wastes of the different parishes, whereon right, of commoning was vested in the inhabitants of the
p.174 ancient messuages, &c. also of salt marshes, whereon the like right has been exercised. Three enclosures within ten miles of us, Sutton, Gedney, and Tidd St. Mary's, of the former description have taken place, in the course of the last four, or five years; the first, of about thirty-three hundred acres; the second, about one thousand acres; and the last, about six hundred acres; and two of the latter description, much nearer us. Walpole and Terrington salt marshes; the first, consisting of about sixteen hundred acres, and the last, about one thousand acres. To furnish an idea of the quality of these lands, I will state what I suppose the average rent of them;

Of Sutton, not less than	30s. per acre	These were interior commons and waste lands of these parishes.
Of Gedney, about	20s. per acre	
Of Tidd St. Mary's not less than	30s. per acre	
Of Walpole and Terrington, about	25s. per acre	The salt marshes of these parishes

N. B. In these values, the extra rents of lands let for woad and flax, are not considered, but of the lands only let for the common purposes of occupation.

The hazardous situation of the salt marshes, can alone account for the rent of them being inferior to that of interior commons and waters, as their quality for growing corn is much superior: both these salt marshes, produce the best and biggest crops I ever saw; no part of the crops upon them was destroyed by wire worms, or any other reptile, and their having been so continually and immediately overflowed by salt water, previous to being embanked, may be considered the cause of this. The crops on the interior common and washes, suffered extremely by these at first, and still continue to suffer every year, in a greater or less degree.

p.175 *Q. Whether inclosures have increased or decreased population?*

A. Inclosures appear to increase population; in those made above, cottages are built, which are filled with families: a great proof of their effect in this way is, that the labour in those parishes is double what it was, and it is done with more ease than before. The additional employment seems to attract more than additional assistance, some, part of which, becomes stationary, and thus the population is encreased.

Q. What is the rate of wages and price of labour, by the day or the piece, and what are the hours at which labour commences and ceases at the different seasons?

A. From Martinmas to Lady-day, fifteen-pence per day, from Lady-day to Midsummer, eighteen-pence per day, from Midsummer to beginning of corn harvest, two shillings and two shillings and six-pence per day, during harvest, from three shillings to five shillings per day, and sometimes six, seven, eight and nine shillings per day, from the end of harvest to Martinmas, eighteen-pence per day. The hours from Martinmas to Lady-day, from seven to five, from Lady-day to Martinmas, from six to six.

N. B. The want of more hours of work in the summer months, greatly retards the business of the country, and occasions great dissoluteness among the labourers: the day that is not ended in labour, generally is in drunkenness.

By the piece, mowing of grass, from two shillings to two shillings and six-pence per acre, reaping, from seven to fourteen shillings per acre, threshing, oats from five to six shillings per last, (or twenty-
p.176 one coom Winchester) wheat one shilling per coom Winchester, and barley eight-pence and nine-pence per coom. The labour in those parishes is very ill done. There are very few resident labourers that is to say, householders, now in them. These were taken off in the late sickly autumns, and the number of labourer's widows, and families relieved by these parishes, is an incontestible proof of this. Our labourers are generally aukward and unskilled in the processes of agriculture, such as ploughing, sowing, reaping, mowing, stacking, &c. and this happens from having few but the outcasts of other countries among us. That they are immoral and unmanageable in a greater degree than in upland countries, is also certain. The extraordinary number of alehouses conduces to these evils, and since the spirit of revolt from order and duty, so much inculcated by certain publications, has prevailed, the difficulty of conducting the business of this country, has become fatiguing and dispiriting in the extreme. The expence keeps pace with the difficulty, and in proportion as the wages are high, the conduct of the labourers is insolent and unfaithful. This unseemliness of manners, grew to its present height in the unhappy summer of 1792, when all the subordinate ranks were ready to invert the settled system of the community, and reduce the order of things to chaos and confusion. How long this daemon will continue its baneful influence, and whether it will at last prevail, the event of the present conflict between vice, irreligion, anarchy, and bloodshed, on the one part, and virtue, religion, morality, and good government, on the other, only can determine. It was in this unfortunate summer that the carpenters, the bricklayers, blacksmiths, &c. combined, and advanced their wages and work in this country; this was very unnecessarily done, and it would be a right step, was every parish to hold a vestry
p.177 meeting, and enter into resolutions to return with these people to their former terms: It was no necessity, but a spirit of exaction that dictated it.

Q. Whether proper attention is paid to the draining of land, particularly the fenny part of it, and what sorts of drains are commonly made use of?

A. There is no land but what is drained in these three parishes; a field in Leverington, of about two hundred acres, only excepted, called Gorefield; if the owners of this were to solicit the Court of Sewers, to admit them to the common drainage of the parish, there is little doubt but they would be admitted on terms proportioned to the relief given; this I suppose the commoners have power to do. The residue of these parishes are drained by water engines that go by wind, the marshes excepted, which drain naturally. The drains are from twelve to sixteen feet wide at top, cut as deep towards the outfal (through the marshes) as the quickness of the soil will allow, the sides so sloped as to make the bottom about half the width of the top. On the depth of these drains towards the outfal, depends their depth as far inland as the first mill to which a level bottom is necessary, and so from the first to the second mill, &c.

Q. Whether paring and burning is practised, and how it is managed and found to answer?

A. On the fen lands this is gencral. The toughness of the fen swerd is such, that it will not fall to decay, nor be got in pieces unless burnt. Cole seed on fen land will not feed sheep, unless the land producing it is burnt to prepare it for the coleseed. An excess of this practice often consumes a great
p.178 deal of the soil, and when the land is laid down, a barreness where this has taken place is very apparent. Goose-grass (or clivers) is the general symptom of this impoverishment. Breast ploughing is certainly the best method, it may be done thinner, and more uniformly than by the plough drawn by horses, though the latter is the practice of this country. And indeed I do not think the damage done by burning, arises from the burning of the swerd, or the quantity pared off, so that it exceeds not one inch and a half or two inches, but from the fire getting hold of the land from allowing the heaps to lie unspread too long, and not watching the fire carefully, and putting it out immediately after spreading, before it gets such hold of the land as to make it difficult to be extinguished; the fire then hits, as it is called, and this is very prejudicial.

Q. What is the price of provisions, and whether the price is likely to be steady, to rise or to fall?

A. Beef from one to five shillings per stone, (fourteen pounds to the stone) varying according to the more plentifully or scarce seasons of the year. Mutton from four-pence to five-pence per lb. varying in like manner. Pork generally high, seldom less than four-pence per pound; this owing to the small quantity of grain proper for pig-feed grown hereabouts. None of our soils suit peas, and barley-big is generally used for this purpose, of which but little is grown. Wheat generally below the average of the kingdom. These form the state of Wisbeach market. I see no probability of a fluctuation in these articles of provision. Our population altering but very little, there being no manufactures in this country; the prosperity or depression of trade affects us not as to home consumption. Potatoes are grown in great plenty, and contribute greatly to the sustenance of the poor.

p.179 *Q. What is the state of the roads, both public and parochial, whether they are in good order, and whether any improvements in regard to making roads have been discovered?*

A. By public roads, as distinguished from parochial, I suppose are meant turnpikes; these are made of the best silt that can be got, which when pulverized, is nearly all sand. Our parochial roads, where silt can be got, are made in like manner. We carry this some miles for this purpose, but the inner roads of these parishes are and ever must be, bad in winter.

Q. What is the state of farm houses and offices, whether in general they are well situated, and properly constructed?

A. The farm houses in this country are generally esteemed good. The farm yards and offices ill constructed, and from the high price of materials and workmanship, these will probably continue so. Situation for convenience of occupation is little thought of, the property being so dispersed; there are but few farms that have much land contiguous to the houses.

Q. What is the nature of the leases commonly granted, and what are found to be the most advantageous covenants between the landlord and tenant?

A. From this state of the neighbourhood described in the general observations I have attempted, there
p.180 are of course but few leases; but it has been found, when leases have been granted, or agreements for farms made, that the covenants and conditions the best calculated to preserve the fee simple of the land letten undiminished, are the following: To restrain the sowing of hemp, flax, woad, madder, and mustard-seed; and though the police gives rewards for growing the two first, yet it is the interest of the owner of the land, to insist penalties on the sowing them, as no manure arises from them. The restraining cole seed from standing for a crop, is founded on the like objection. Where the first five of these are grown, the land ought to be expressly let for the purpose, and an extra rent set upon it; because it must necessarily be the worse for what it produces, which is never the case with a farm properly let, and skilfully managed. Every farm should render the occupier a handsome interest for his capital employed upon it, in stock, crop, and labour, and improve in its condition. And here is seen the difference between a good and bad tenant, which needs no illustration, either to condemn the one, or render the other approved in the eyes of his landlord; the former will always improve the land he occupies, and his own property together; the latter generally reduces both. The general covenants of use for any farm in this neighbourhood, besides the foregoing, are to forbid the ploughing of the high lands in general, if water can be got to render them fit for grazing. Of the portion of fen land belonging to any farm, not more than one-third of the land permitted to be ploughed, should be in corn in every year, and the same as to the marshes, and from neither more than two successive crops should be taken. To restrain the laying manure on the ploughed lands is very expedient. I have seen instances where leases have been silent as to directing the routine of the crops, and the lands on which the manure should be
p.181 laid, of bad tenants manuring the ploughed lands, and cropping them without intermission during the terms of their leases. By this abuse the ploughed land, at the expiration, was extremely foul, and wanted fallowing and laying down, and the grass land not improved as it would have been with proper manuring. Fewer crops of corn and timely fallowing are therefore insured by forbidding the ploughed lands to be manured. Moreover the best species of pasture in every grazing farm, ought to be restrained from being mowed.

Q. Whether the people seem to have a turn for improvement, and how such a Spirit can be best excited?

A. In grazing considerable emulation exists; in farming very little; the cause of this perhaps is owing to the labour, so scarce and high in this country, necessary to the one more than the other. Labour must be on a better footing before any spirit of excellence in farming can be roused.

Q. What improvements can be suggested either in regard to the stock, or the husbandry of the country?

A. Before the husbandry of the country can be improved, labour must be had on better terms; this accomplished, no doubt but some experiments would follow; for instance, I have no doubt but we could grow very excellent wheat on our feeds of two years lay, taken up in October, and dibble upon them in the Norfolk method; but such an attempt would frighten all our poor women and children; each would want a manager, and before works of this sort can be introduced, a great change among these
p.182 people must take place; perhaps the introduction of the work would best effect this, but we have nobody enterprizing enough to attempt it; some pieces have been done near us, but by strangers.

This question as to stock, opens a very spacious field, and as much difference of opinion has arisen on it, and been agitated with much virulence, every one is careful how he engages in it. I think the arcana of animal nature are so far discovered, as to have established principles by which that sort of stock is ascertainable, that changes a given quantity of vegetable food into more animal weight than any other sort, and that animal that pays most for what it eats, seems to me to be preferable. I know this doctrine is resisted by those who are so prejudiced as to be reconciled to give food to stock, without improving them. The backwardness of the *science of cattle* cannot perhaps be better demonstrated, than by observing there is no name for it. Farming and grazing are talked of, as the distinct branches of rural business; but agriculture, compounded as it certainly is of *agri cultura*, must be considered descriptive of, and applicable to, the former only. And by grazing can be only meant that process by which the stock is fattened; and here I have reason to believe, "the eye of the master maketh the ox fat." But the art of breeding and chusing such as will fatten quickest, and to the greatest perfection, with which care has been taken, so to breed them as to be fullest of flesh, and thickest covered both with flesh and fat in the best parts of them, that have the most *eatable*, and the least *offal* parts in them, is among the nondescripts of the present age, and generally speaking, it is as little understood as described. The Honourable Board lately, instituted, will find in their enquiries, that the stock kept in the greatest part of this kingdom, is of such a kind, as a greater loss attends the keeping of than can be imagined, unless
p.183 examined into; for instance, the sheep in general are grazed a year longer than they need be, if bred as they ought. The individuals concerned, and the community at large, suffer from this defect; for wheresoever this is the case, the man who breeds and feeds his own sheep, will always send one-third less stock to market, than he otherwise would do. A sale of stock is at hand, of a gentleman, retiring from business, and will be in the ensuing week, two hundred breeding ewes will be disposed; it is said these will make an immense sum, two thousand pounds is talked of, but if they make one thousand pounds, five pound a piece, will any of the antediluvian breeders and graziers say, that this is phrenzy, when probably they will be divided into lots of five each, and that no one person will purchase two lots. Among so many purchasers as here will be, surely prejudice itself (which now upon this score is laughed at, and is often distinguished by the term of ignorance) will allow there may be some judgment. When this sale is over, I have no doubt but catalogues of prices and purchasers will be issued, as was the case of the late Mr. Fowler's neat stock in Oxfordshire; after his sale, catalogues were circulated, and the preface to them has a great deal of sound remark and good sense in it, and though a trifle, deserves a place among the collections of this noble society. The principles of breeding stock here attended to, must be supposed to have their origin somewhere, and here the ingenious Mr. Bakewell must be mentioned, who with a small property in the outset of life, attended to this mystery, and has clearly enlightened it. The triumph of prejudice and error over him in his clouded situation, during the fatal American war, was universal and no less illiberal. But he has risen the greater from his fall. His disciples increase every day, yet he must ever be regarded as the head of the sect.

p.184 *Q. Are there no obstacles to improvement, and how would these be best remedied?*

A. The bad roads are certainly obstacles; these prevent us from claying our light silty lands, for in winter, in the part of these parishes, where clay only can be got, a team cannot be stirred, and these roads can never be made good."

LEVERINGTON—PARSONDROVE

The more elevated parts of the inside highland, consist of a strong loam, upon a silt, and the lower parts of a mild silty loam, lying upon a silt also, taken together, the whole may be advantageously employed in the culture of wheat, beans, oats, hemp, flax, cole seed, and turnips; but it is

unquestionable most proper for the culture of grass and permanent pasture; it contains about nine hundred acres, and is rented at twenty-four shillings per acre, on an average. Another description of inside land, consists of a clay, with a mixture of vegetable matter, or fen mould, of a good depth, lying upon a buttery clay or gault; this contains about nine hundred acres, but in its present state of drainage, is not valued at more than fourteen shillings per acre; is proper for the culture of wheat, oats, and cole seed. The fen land of the first quality, consists of a vegetable matter, or moor, mixed with an hazel-coloured loam, or tender seaclay, of a rich deep stable, upon a silty clay, and proper for the culture of wheat, oats, and cole seed; contains about eight hundred and fifty acres, and is readily rented at twenty shillings per acre. The fen of the second quality, consists of moor, or fen mould casually mixed with
p.185 clay, from off the road hams, or small hills, which are intermixed through this level, and rising from the bed of the fen; of this there are about five hundred acres, but from the uncertainty of its drainage, is not valued at more than fourteen shillings per acre.

The largest farm is occupied under a lease for fourteen years, at four hundred pounds per ann and with the rest of the parish, is under the following management: Upon the highland, first, oats upon the flag; second year, oats; third, wheat; the wheat stubble is fallowed, and dunged for the fourth years crop of cole seed, which is fed off, and the same rotation of three crops, and a fallow is again repeated. The produce

64 bushels of	Oats per acre on first rate
28 ditto	Wheat ditto
40 ditto	Oats per acre on second rate high-land
20 ditto	Wheat ditto

The practice upon the fen of the first quality, is first to pare and burn, sow cole seed, and feed that crop off with sheep, which hitherto has proved the most effectual remedy for the mischevious effects of the wire worm and grub; the second year, oats: third, wheat; fourth, oats; fifth, wheat; the sixth year fallow for cole seed; and it is either then laid down with two bushels of rye grass, and eight pounds of Dutch white clover, or is continued another year with oats, and then laid down, and afterwards the new grass is highly manured. The produce on an average of seven years, is sixty-four bushels of oats, and of wheat twenty-four bushels. The practice upon the fen of the second quality is precisely the same for the two first years; the third crop, oats; fourth, wheat; the fifth year, a fallow for cole seed, which is fed off with sheep, and the sixth year it is laid down with a crop of oats. The produce on an average of six
p.186 years from this management, is forty-eight bushels of oats, and twenty bushels of wheat.

The intermixture of property in the fen, and inside districts is much against an effectual drainage of those lands. An improvement to the drainage of the low lands in the inside might be made, by additional mills, properly placed. The cottages in this parish are rather scarce. The population and poor's rates are comprehended in Wisbich St. Peters.

WISBICH ST. MARYS, including a Part of WISBICH ST. PETERS, and the Hamlets of GUYHIRNE, THOLMAS DROVE, and MORROW

It is much to be regretted, that the information obtained here, is by no means so full or satisfactory as could be wished, being unfortunately suspected to be in the interests of the rector, I was not only received coolly, but treated with great jealousy and distrust. Such information as I was able to obtain, and such observations as I was enabled to make, are as follow: The inside high land of the first quality, lying between the Murrow banks and Wisbich St. Peters, and binding north westwardly upon Leverington Parson Drove, is an open, loamy soil, very similar in its nature, to that described in the preceding parish; it amounts to about three thousand acres, and is rented at twenty shillings per acre. The low land within the same district, consists of a fen mould, mixed with and lying upon a clay; is at present adapted to the culture of wheat, oats, barley-big, and cole seed, but from the uncertainty of its
p.187 drainage, is not valued at more than twelve shillings per acre. The course of husbandry much the same as in Leverington Parson Drove. The produce with-held.

The fen land of the first quality greatly resembles that of the same quality in the preceding parish; it comprehends [*blank*] acres, and is rented at fifteen shillings per acre. That of the second description, is chiefly composed of vegetable matter, or fen mould, with little or no mixture of silt, lying upon a turf moor; of this there are [*blank*] acres, which are rented at nine shillings per acre.

N. B. This fen is not so well drained as the fen of Parson Drove.

THORNEY

THE high-land consists of an ash-coloured, tender clay, of a good staple, lying upon a gault and gravel, and proper for the culture of permanent pasture, or grazing ground; it contains about six hundred acres, and is rented at twenty-five shillings per acre.

The fen of the first quality, is composed of completely putrified vegetable matter, with the natural clay, upon which it rests, forming together, a deep, strong, black earth, proper for grazing ground, in which it is at present chiefly and judiciously employed; of this there are about three thousand acres, which on an average are rented at eighteen shillings per acre. That of the second quality is a fen mould, or moor, from fourteen to twenty-four inches deep, lying upon a gault and gravel, and proper for the culture of wheat, oats, cole feed, and temporary pasture; it contains about six thousand acres, and is
p.188 rented at sixteen shillings per acre. The third class of fen land, consists of fen mould, upon a turf moor, under which it bears much of various depths, which finally rests upon a clay; this class of fen is proper for the culture of oats, cole seed, and temporary pasture; it amounts to about eight thousand acres, and is rented on an average at eleven shillings per acre.

The whole parish is the property of his Grace the Duke of Bedford, and notwithstanding that the farms are all held at will, from twenty-five to four hundred pound per ann. a spirit of improvement pervades the minds of every tenant, beyond what is to be met with in any other part of the county, and which can only be attributed to the very proper confidence, which the tenants repose in the justice and generosity of their noble landlord, and to the good sense and superior abilities, which mark the conduct of the gentleman in every particular, who has directly the management of this valuable property. The course of husbandry upon the fen of the second quality, is alone sufficient to illustrate this observation, and to justify the opinion.

The practice here, is first, pare and burn, but with great care, and under proper limitations; sow cole seed, and feed it off with sheep; second year, sow oats; third, oats or wheat, when the land is laid down for not less than six years with proper quantities of rye grass, white clover, and hay feeds. The first year of the new grass it is stocked very hard with sheep, which curbs the partial luxuriancy of the feeds, and makes them unite and mat at the bottom, forming a tender and inviting herbage; for the remainder of the period it is destined to remain at rest. The produce per acre

48 bushels of	Oats weighing 33 lbs per bushel
24 ditto	Wheat ditto 56 lbs ditto

p.189 The same rotation of crops is observed upon the fen land of the third quality, from which an equal bulk in grain is usually produced, though of less weight, and evidently of an inferior quality. The breeding of sheep has in a great measure been relinquished in this parish, on account of a weakness that prevails among the lambs; it affects the whole frame of the animal, and seems to be an extension of a disease, similar to that, well known in many counties, by the name of the rickets. The rickets however, is a disease originating in the animal, whereas this disease appears to have its origin, from the nature of the soil or herbage which the animal when young feeds upon; it is observed to prevail most generally upon new or lately laid down land, and it is the opinion of many farmers, that the rye grass contributes to this effect. A malady amongst: the young stock, not unlike this at Thorney, has been noticed at Elm; where it is ascribed to the cockspire or cocksfoot grass: the same cause may probably contribute to produce a similar effect in both places.

The Lincoln and Leicestershire breeds of sheep are most approved; those at three years old, returned from grass or cole seed, usually weigh about twenty-two pounds per quarter, and their fleeces about eight pounds each. The mixed breed or cross between the sheep of these two counties, is held here in high estimation. The Fifeshire and Irish cattle are found to answer best for grazing; although the short horned Yorkshire breed, being more conveniently procured, are more generally in use; these latter however are but rarely fattened to the bone, without the assistance of oil cakes. The annual draining tax for the internal drainage, of this parish, is about one shilling per acre, where there are about two hundred and fifty families, one thousand two hundred and fifty inhabitants, and the poor's rates are one shilling in the pound.

p.190

WHITTLESEA

THE field lying north eastwardly of the village, and adjoining thereto, (called Barsonby Field) consists of a brown friable mould, of a good staple, lying upon a clay, and gravel, proper for the culture of wheat, barley, peas, clover, and turnips, and with the meadow land annexed to it, contains about four hundred acres, which taken together, are rented at sixteen shillings per acre. The second, or Lattice High Field; binding southwardly upon the foregoing, and adjoining the village upon the south-east, consists of a mixed brown earth, and gravelly, loam, of a tolerable staple, lying upon a clay and gravel, may be employed to advantage in the same manner with the last described; it contains about four hundred acres, and is rented at fourteen shillings per acre. The Churchfield adjoining the village, answers to this last description, and is applicable to the culture of the same crops; it contains about four hundred and fifty acres, and is rented at fourteen shillings per acre. The fourth field adjoining the above, and binding westwardly upon the village, answers to the description of the first field, and contains about three hundred acres. The King's delph-land extending southwardly from Whittlesea dyke, is found to be a fen mould, incorporated with clay; proceeding thence south eastwardly, the clay is gradually lost in an unmixed mass of fen mould, upon a turf moor, and bears muck; this is appropriated to the culture of wheat, oats, barley, cole seed, and clover, and contains about twelve hundred acres, which are rented at sixteen shillings per acre.

p.191 The pastures in severalty, called black-birch reach grounds, bind south eastwardly, upon the N.W. side of the King's delph lands; they contain about twelve hundred acres, and are rented at eighteen shillings per acre. The soil of the fen, consists of putrid, vegetable matter, upon a turf moor, under which is bears muck of different depths; it amounts to about seventeen thousand acres; and in its present deplorable state of drainage, is not estimated at more than five shillings per acre. The washlands amount to about three thousand acres, lying between the north and south banks of Moreton's Leam; but being subject to frequent overflowings, even in the summer season, from the highland freshes, is not valued at more than three shillings per acre.

The farms are chiefly held at will, and an internal round of cropping in the four common fields here prevails; first year, beans; second, wheat; third and fourth years, barley, this practice answers to the four shifts; dung is occasionally made use off on the bean stubble, for wheat, and also on the wheat and barley stubbles for the succeeding crops, Produce per acre

18 bushels of	Beans
22 ditto	Wheat
24 ditto	Barley

The miserable condition of these fens, in consequence of the deplorable state of the drainage, preclude any comparison at present with those of Thorney. The number of cottages are very unequal to the families, as five distinct families have been found residing in the same house; the population here is not
p.192 ascertained, and the poor's rates in this parish, are about two shillings in the pound; these have been much reduced within these few years by farming out the poor, under which system they are at present well fed, and properly attended to.

Vancouver's - Summary Table

In his report between Parts I and II Vancouver set out two tables the first and larger, a fold-out table of very small print has in the following pages been separated into a number of easily readable tables.

Names of the Parishes	Their Contents in Acres, distinguishing each									
	Enclosed Arable.	Rent.	Open Field Arable.	Rent.	Superior and Partially improved Pasture.	Rent.	Unimproved or inferior Pasture.	Rent.	Wood Land.	Rent.
Ashley including Silvery	-	-	2300	7.6	60	20.0	90	10.0	-	-
Cheveley	-	-	3000	10.0	300	18.0	1000	7.6	-	-
Catlidge	-	-	1800	8.0	200	20	800	10.0	-	-
Wood-Ditton	-	-	{ 1500 { 1600	8.0 11.0	400	16.0	200	8.0	-	-
Stachworth	600	14.0	1022	7.6	100	15.0	300	10.0	335	15.0
Dullingham	-	-	1300	7.0	40	20.0	60	12.0	-	-
Snailwell	-	-	1000	9.0	140	21.0	-	-	-	-
Fordham	-	-	2500	9.0	500	18.0	-	-	-	-
Kennett	-	-	1000	6.0	30	20.0	-	-	-	-
Chippenham	2700	11.4	-	-	-	-	6	10.0	-	-
Hamlet of Badlingham	-	-	900	-	-	-	-	-	-	-
Isleham	-	-	850	15.0	200	20.0	300	8.6	-	-
Burwell	-	-	2000	7.6	-	-	200	7.6	-	-
Bottisham	-	-	1600	9.6	-	20.0	-	12.0	-	-
Wilbraham (Magna)	-	-	-	8.0	-	-	-	-	-	-
Wilbraham (Parva)	-	-	-	10.0	70	20.0	-	-	-	-
Stow cum Quy	-	-	1000	10.6	-	-	-	-	-	-
Horningsey	-	-	500	12.6	200	21.0	100	12.0	-	-
Fenney - Ditton	-	-	500	12.0	350	23.0	-	-	-	-
Taversham	-	-	600	10.0	60	20.0	-	-	-	-
Fulburn	-	-	-	-	-	-	-	-	-	-
Barnwell	-	-	1000	13.0	30	25.0	-	-	-	-
Trompington	-	-	1200	11.0	60	25.0	-	-	-	-
Stapleford	-	-	900	10.0	100	22.6	-	-	-	-
Babraham	-	13.0	1350	6.0	165	26.0	-	-	-	-
Little Abington	-	-	1500	6.0	-	-	-	-	-	-
Hildersham	100	15.0	900	9.0	-	-	-	-	-	-
Linton and Bartlow	-	13.6	-	6.9	-	-	-	-	-	-
Shudy Camps	100	16.0	600	10.0	700	21.0	-	-	-	-
Castle Camps	-	-	300	9.0	-	30.0	-	12.0	-	-
Balsham	-	-	1500	7.6	-	-	-	-	-	-
Sawston	-	-	1200	8.0	-	-	-	-	-	-
Pamisford	-	-	700	8.0	50	18.0	-	-	-	-
Hingston	-	-	1500	70.0	50	18.0	-	-	-	-
Ickleton	-	-	2000	7.6	50	12.0	-	-	-	-
Foulmire	-	-	1200	9.0	200	18.0	-	-	-	-
Triplow	-	-	1940	6.0	30	20.0	-	-	-	-
Duxford	-	-	1800	6.6	50	12.6	-	-	-	-
Whittlesford	-	-	1000	8.0	70	15.0	-	-	-	-
Shepperheath	-	-	540	9.0	100	20.0	-	-	-	-
Bassingbourn and Kneesworth	-	-	2140	9.0	-	9.0	-	-	-	-
Litlington	-	-	750	5.6	-	-	40	8.0	-	-
Abbington	700	16.0	-	-	150	16.0	-	-	-	-
Guilden Morden and Odissey	-	-	1010	8.0	100	20.0	-	-	-	-
Steeple Morden	-	15.0	1900	5.6	-	15.0	-	-	-	-
Shingay	50	18.0	-	-	600	18.0	-	-	-	-
Tadlow	-	15.0	-	-	-	15.0	-	-	-	-
Hatley St George	250	14.3	-	-	450	14.3	-	-	-	15.0
Wyndee	-	20.0	-	-	600	20.0	-	-	-	-
Arrington	-	12.0	-	-	-	12.0	-	-	-	-
Wimple	-	-	-	-	-	-	-	-	-	-
Barrington	-	-	1687	8.0	100	20.0	-	-	-	-
Eversden	-	-	900	9.0	40	20.0	40	10.0	-	-
Barton	-	-	900	9.0	120	21.0	-	-	-	-
Grantchester	-	-	1000	9.6	100	26.0	-	-	-	-

sort of land, the rent or value

Fen under casual cultivation	Rent.	Drowned and Waste Fen	Rent.	Half Yearly Meadow	Rent.	Highland Common	Value	Fen or Moor Common	Value	Heath Sheep Walk	Value	No. of Sheep
-	-	-	-	-	-	-	-	-	-	100	3.0	1300
-	-	-	-	-	-	-	-	-	-	200	2.6	500
-	-	-	-	-	-	-	-	-	-	-	-	600
-	-	-	-	100 -	20.0 -	-	-	-	-	650	5	2120
-	-	-	-	-	-	-	-	-	-	850	2.0	1200
-	-	-	-	-	-	-	-	-	-	300	3.0	1400
-	-	-	-	-	-	-	-	80	5.0	600	3.0	1200
-	-	-	-	-	-	-	-	700	5.0	-	-	1800
-	-	-	-	-	-	60	7.6	-	-	350	2.0	600
-	-	-	-	-	-	-	-	200	3.0	-	-	1000
-	-	-	-	-	-	-	-	100	-	-	-	400
-	-	1500	4.6	-	-	-	-	50	3.0	-	-	800
-	-	2000	1.0	-	-	-	-	-	-	-	-	1700
-	-	-	-	-	-	-	-	-	-	-	-	1800
-	-	-	-	-	-	300	-	-	-	-	-	-
-	-	-	-	-	-	-	-	500	3.0	140	5.0	-
-	-	-	-	-	-	-	-	-	-	-	-	-
-	-	-	-	-	-	-	-	150	-	-	-	-
200	7.0	-	-	-	-	-	-	-	-	-	-	-
-	-	-	-	-	-	-	-	-	-	-	-	-
-	-	-	-	-	-	200	-	203	-	-	-	2800
-	-	-	-	-	-	-	7.6	-	-	-	-	-
-	-	-	-	100	20.0	-	-	-	-	-	-	1950
-	-	-	-	100	17.6	40	5.0	-	-	500	2.6	600
-	-	-	-	-	-	-	-	-	-	220	2.6	1000
-	-	-	-	-	-	-	-	-	-	-	-	-
-	-	-	-	-	-	-	-	-	-	-	-	540
-	-	-	-	-	-	-	-	-	-	-	-	300
-	-	-	-	-	-	-	-	-	-	-	-	460
-	-	-	-	-	-	-	-	-	-	-	-	500
-	-	-	-	100	20.0	-	-	-	-	1200	2.6	1800
-	-	-	-	100	14.0	-	-	300	-	-	-	460
-	-	-	-	-	-	20	-	150	-	-	-	-
-	-	-	-	40	10.0	-	-	-	-	-	-	460
-	-	-	-	30	12.0	-	-	40	4.0	-	-	1400
-	-	-	-	-	-	-	-	200	2.6	-	-	550
-	-	-	-	-	-	-	-	140	-	-	-	1160
-	-	-	-	40	15.0	40	20.0	20	-	-	-	1200
-	-	-	-	50	10.0	-	-	-	-	-	-	840
-	-	-	-	-	-	-	-	-	-	-	-	300
-	-	-	-	-	-	100	-	-	-	-	-	1140
-	-	-	-	-	-	-	-	50	-	-	-	600
-	-	-	-	-	-	-	-	-	-	-	-	500
-	-	-	-	-	-	-	-	200	6.0	-	-	1000
-	-	-	-	-	-	-	-	-	-	300	1.0	1250
-	-	-	-	-	-	-	-	-	-	-	-	450
-	-	-	-	-	-	-	-	-	-	-	-	1060
-	-	-	-	-	-	-	-	-	-	-	-	900
-	-	-	-	-	-	-	-	-	-	-	-	650
-	-	-	-	-	-	-	-	-	-	-	-	500
-	-	-	-	-	-	-	-	-	-	-	-	-
-	-	-	-	-	-	-	-	-	-	-	-	420
-	-	-	-	-	-	-	-	-	-	-	-	200
-	-	-	-	-	-	-	-	-	-	-	-	800
-	-	-	-	-	-	50	20.0	-	-	-	-	700

Names of the Parishes	Their Contents in Acres, distinguishing each									
	Enclosed Arable.	Rent.	Open Field Arable.	Rent.	Superior and Partially improved Pasture.	Rent.	Unim-proved or inferior Pasture.	Rent.	Wood Land.	Rent.
Coton	-	-	720	10.0	5	25.0	-	-	-	-
Maddingley	-	-	1030	6.6	50	20.0	-	10.0	-	-
Dry Drayton	-	-	1800	6.8	40	20.0	60	15.0	-	-
Lolworth	-	-	650	10.0	90	20.0	-	-	-	-
Boxworth	-	-	900	8.6	200	20.0	900	7.0	120	15.0
Eltisley	-	-	900	6.8	50	20.0	-	12.0	-	-
Croxton	-	-	1000	6.8	100	20.0	300	10.0	-	-
Caxton	-	-	660	8.0	50	30.0	80	10.0	-	-
Gamlingay	-	-	1500	8.0	-	-	-	-	-	-
Kingston	-	-	900	8.0	-	-	-	-	-	15.0
Toft	-	-	-	-	-	-	-	-	-	-
Hardwicke	-	-	900	5.4	70	16.0	-	-	-	-
Childersley	700	13.9	-	-	-	-	300	13.0	-	-
Girton	-	-	1200	12.0	200	12.0	-	-	-	-
Hoggington	-	-	-	8.6	-	20.0	-	-	-	-
Long Stanton	-	-	-	9.0	-	20.0	-	-	-	-
Cottenham	-	-	1500	16.0	-	25.0	-	-	-	-
Waterbeach and Denny Abbey	-	-	-	16.0	-	16.0	-	-	-	-
Landbeach	-	-	800	12	150	20.0	-	-	-	-
Milton with Westwick	-	-	1120	12.6	200	21.0	-	-	-	-
Impington	-	-	1000	7.6	130	20.0	-	-	-	-
Chesterton	-	-	1800	11.0	-	22.6	-	-	-	-
{Wickin	-	-	280	16.0	150	20.0	220	10.0	-	-
{ Spinney Abbey	-	-	-	-	40	20.0	50	10.0	-	-
Soham with Barraway	-	-	1200	21.0	6000	26.8	1000	14.0	-	-
City of Ely	-	-	2100	15.0	1900	25.0	-	-	-	-
Little Port and Apshall	-	-	345	18.9	100	25.0	-	-	-	-
Downham	-	-	680	15.9	480	25.0	-	-	-	-
Maypole	-	-	100	9.0	200	15.0	-	-	-	-
Sutton	-	-	700	10.6	50	20.0	200	12.6	-	-
Haddenham	-	-	1700	9.9	200	18.0	280	10.0	-	-
Wilburton	-	-	900	10.0	150	20.0	-	-	-	-
Stretham with Thetford	-	-	400	10.0	150	20.0	200	10.0	-	-
Chatteris	-	-	450	17.9	200	25.0	-	-	-	-
Doddington	3000	25.0	-	20.0	-	24.6	-	10.0	-	-
Upwell	1000	25.0	-	-	1000	25.0	-	-	-	-
Outwell	350	25.0	-	-	350	25.0	-	-	-	-
Elm	2100	22.6	-	-	2100	22.6	-	-	-	-
Leverington	-	25.0	-	-	-	25.0	-	-	-	-
Newton	600	22.0	-	-	600	22.0	560	15.0	-	-
Tid St Giles	500	20.0	-	-	500	20.0	400	8.0	-	-
Leverington Parsondrove	450	24.0	-	-	450	24.0	900	14.0	-	-
Wisbech St Mary, Hamlets &c.	1500	20.0	-	-	1500	20.0	-	-	-	-
Thorney	-	-	-	-	600	23.0	-	-	-	-
Whittlesey	-	-	2750	15.4	1200	18.0	-	-	-	-
	GENERAL AVERAGE *deduced from the foregoing Abstract, together*									
General Average	-	18.0	-	10.0	-	28.4	-	10.9	-	-
Open Field and Waste Land	-	10.0	-	-	-	-	-	-	-	-
Difference	-	8.0	-	-	-	9.7	-	-	-	-

☞ Besides the above list of Parishes, it appears from the Journal, that there were forty-one other mistake, making in the whole fourty-four Parishes,

sort of land, the rent or value

Fen under casual cultivation	Rent.	Drowned and Waste Fen	Rent.	Half Yearly Meadow	Rent.	Highland Common	Value	Fen or Moor Common	Value	Heath Sheep Walk	Value	No. of Sheep
-	-	-	-	-	-	-	-	-	-	-	-	600
-	-	-	-	-	-	30	50.0	-	-	-	-	200
-	-	-	-	-	10.0	-	-	-	-	-	-	1000
-	-	-	-	-	10.0	40	-	-	-	-	-	600
-	-	-	-	-	-	-	-	-	-	-	-	1500
-	-	-	-	-	10.0	-	-	-	-	-	-	1200
-	-	-	-	-	10.0	-	-	-	-	-	-	1400
-	-	-	-	80	7.6	-	-	-	-	-	-	938
-	-	-	-	80	8.0	-	-	-	-	-	-	1200
-	-	-	-	-	-	-	-	-	-	-	-	450
-	-	-	-	-	-	-	-	-	-	-	-	-
-	-	-	-	-	10.0	-	-	-	-	-	-	600
-	-	-	-	-	-	-	-	-	-	-	-	600
-	-	-	-	-	10.0	-	-	-	-	-	-	-
-	-	-	-	-	10.0	-	-	-	-	-	-	-
-	-	-	-	-	10.0	150	-	-	-	-	-	-
-	-	-	-	-	-	800	-	1000	-	-	-	2500
500	6.6	-	-	-	-	500	-	1352	-	-	-	1000
-	-	-	-	-	-	1000	-	-	-	-	-	-
-	-	-	-	-	-	-	-	300	-	-	-	-
-	-	-	-	-	-	40	-	-	-	-	-	-
-	-	-	-	-	-	100	-	-	-	-	-	-
350	6.0	-	-	150	5.0	-	-	-	-	-	-	-
150	6.0	-	-	-	-	-	-	-	-	-	-	-
1400	14.0	8000	4.8	-	-	350	25.0	-	-	-	-	-
-	-	6000	3.0	-	-	-	-	500	-	-	-	-
6235	6.0	-	-	-	-	-	-	-	-	-	-	-
5214	6.4	2000	1.0	-	-	-	-	-	-	-	-	300
720	10.0	-	-	-	-	150	10.0	113	1.0	-	-	-
2000	10.0	1100	5.0	-	-	-	-	-	-	-	-	-
2000	7.0	-	-	-	-	-	-	-	-	-	-	-
1100	10.0	-	-	-	-	-	-	-	-	-	-	900
-	-	600	400	-	-	-	-	-	-	-	-	-
{ 4200	15.0 }		-	-	-	-	-	300	25.0	-	-	8000
{7000	10.0 }											
-	8.0	-	-	-	-	-	-	-	-	-	-	-
15000	6.0	600	2.6	-	-	-	-	-	-	-	-	-
60	6.0	-	-	-	-	-	-	-	-	-	-	-
7000	15.0	-	-	-	-	-	-	-	-	-	-	-
-	12.0	-	-	-	-	-	-	-	-	-	-	-
900	12.0	-	-	-	-	-	-	-	-	-	-	-
2000	10.0	-	-	-	-	-	-	-	-	-	-	-
1350	17.6	-	-	-	-	-	-	-	-	-	-	-
{	15.0	-	-	-	-	-	-	-	-	-	-	-
{ inferior	9.0	-	-	-	-	-	-	-	-	-	-	-
7000	14.0	-	-	-	-	-	-	-	-	-	-	-
-	-	2000	4.8	-	-	-	-	-	-	-	-	-
with the difference of Rent and Produce between Enclosed and Open Field, and the Improved Waste Lands.												
-	10.0	-	2.10	-	-	-	-	-	-	-	-	1062
-	2.10	-	-	-	-	-	-	-	-	-	-	-
-	7.11	-	-	-	-	-	-	-	-	-	-	-

parishes, in which no Information could be obtained, two were omitted from necessity, and one by
exclusive of those of the City of Ely and Town of Cambridge.

Names of the Parishes	Highland Produce in Bushels per Acre									Population	Poor's Rates	Fen Produce per Acre				
	Wheat	Rye	Barley	Oats	Peas	Beans	Pease & Beans	Flax	Hemp	No. of Souls	per £.	Wheat	Barley	Oats	Coleseed	Coleseed fed off green
Ashley including Silvery	18	14	20	14	20	-	-	-	-	200	3.6	-	-	-	-	-
Cheveley	20	-	20	22	20	-	-	-	-	383	3.0	-	-	-	-	-
Catlidge	20	-	30	24	-	20	-	-	-	462	3.0	-	-	-	-	-
Wood-Ditton	18	18	24	24	16	-	-	-	-	300	4.0	-	-	-	-	-
Stachworth	22	18	22	26	-	-	-	-	-	330	2.6	-	-	-	-	-
Dullingham	20	-	20	20	-	-	-	-	-	493	3.0	-	-	-	-	-
Snailwell	22	20	22	20	16	-	-	-	-	160	1.11	-	-	-	-	-
Fordham	18	18	20	20	16	-	-	-	-	500	3.0	-	-	-	-	-
Kennett	-	-	-	-	-	-	-	-	-	99	-	-	-	-	-	-
Chippenham	24	-	30	36	-	-	-	-	-	-	0.10	-	-	-	-	-
Hamlet of Badlingham	18	16	20	18	16	-	-	-	-	40	0.10	-	-	-	-	-
Isleham	24	-	32	24	24	-	-	-	-	1000	2.6	-	-	-	-	-
Burwell	22	18	20	14	14	-	-	-	-	1000	2.9	-	-	-	-	-
Bottisham	20	22	22	18	18	-	-	-	-	600	4.0	-	-	-	-	-
Wilbrham (Magna)	16	18	18	-	-	-	-	-	-	300	3.0	-	-	-	-	-
Wilbrham (Parva)	18	16	20	20	16	-	-	-	-	175	3.6	-	-	-	-	-
Stow cum Quy	18	22	20	22	14	-	-	-	-	-	-	-	-	-	-	-
Horningsey	18	24	22	22	22	-	-	-	-	225	2.0	-	-	-	-	-
Fenney - Ditton	-	-	-	-	-	-	-	-	-	375	2.0	-	-	-	-	-
Taversham	18	18	18	22	18	-	-	-	-	125	4.0	-	-	-	-	-
Fulburn	-	-	-	-	-	-	-	-	-	640	-	-	-	-	-	-
Barnwell	22	26	30	30	-	-	-	-	-	285	3.0	-	-	-	-	-
Trompington	24	24	28	30	16	-	-	-	-	500	4.0	-	-	-	-	-
Stapleford	20	22	24	26	16	-	-	-	-	300	2.6	-	-	-	-	-
Babraham	20	24	36	36	20	-	-	-	-	180	1.5	-	-	-	-	-
Little Abington	16	20	20	-	20	-	-	-	-	90	2.0	-	-	-	-	-
Hildersham	20	20	20	-	-	16	-	-	-	160	3.6	-	-	-	-	-
Linton and Bartlow	16	-	16	-	-	-	-	-	-	1550	3.6	-	-	-	-	-
Shudy Camps {	22	-	26	22	-	18	{Inclosures			400	2.3	-	-	-	-	-
	18	-	20	18	16	-	open field}					-	-	-	-	-
Castle Camps	22	-	20	20	14	-	-	-	-	850	4.0	-	-	-	-	-
Balsham	18	14	18	14	-	-	-	-	-	500	4.0	-	-	-	-	-
Sawston	18	-	22	22	14	-	-	-	-	500	4.0	-	-	-	-	-
Pamisford	18	-	22	28	14	-				125	3.0				-	-
Hingston	18	18	22	-	12	-	-	-	-	210	2.6	-	-	-	-	-
Ickleton	17	22	22	22	-	-	-	-	-	420	4.0	-	-	-	-	-
Foulmire	20	-	26	26	-	16	-	-	-	-	3.0	-	-	-	-	-
Triplow	24	24	-	24	-	-	-	-	-	320	3.0	-	-	-	-	-
Duxford	18	16	24	18	16	-	-	-	-	435	4.0	-	-	-	-	-
Whittlesford	18	-	24	20	16	-	-	-	-	350	4.0	-	-	-	-	-
Shepperheath	22	-	26	22	14	-	-	-	-	190	2.0	-	-	-	-	-
Bassingbourn and Kneesworth	20	20	26	26	-	-	16	-	-	-	4.0	-	-	-	-	-
Litlington	12	12	14	12	-	-	-	-	-	250	3.6	-	-	-	-	-
Abbington	18	-	21	20	-	-	14	-	-	145	2.8	-	-	-	-	-
Guilden Morden and Odissey	22	-	28	26	-	-	18	-	-	380	2.6	-	-	-	-	-
Steeple Morden	16	20	22	24	-	-	18	}		400	2.6	-	-	-	-	-
	22	-	28	32	-	22	inclosures }					-	-	-	-	-
Shingay	-	-	-	-	-	-	-	-	-	66	0.6	-	-	-	-	-
Tadlow	22	-	32	22	-	-	15	-	-	95	1.6	-	-	-	-	-
Hatley St George	17	-	22	22	-	-	17	-	-	115	1.8	-	-	-	-	-
Wyndee	-	-	-	-	-	-	-	-	-	100	1.3	-	-	-	-	-
Arrington	17	-	22	22	-	-	12	-	-	105	0.6	-	-	-	-	-
Wimple	20	-	24	18	-	-	16	-	-	256	1.8	-	-	-	-	-
Barrington	20	-	20	18	-	-	10	-	-	450	2.0	-	-	-	-	-
Eversden	16	-	24	18	-	-	10	-	-	130	2.0	-	-	-	-	-
Barton	20	24	22	22	14	-	-	-	-	210	4.0	-	-	-	-	-
Grantchester	24	-	30	22	-	-	18	-	-	265	-	-	-	-	-	-

Names of the Parishes	Highland Produce in Bushels per Acre									Population	Poor's Rates	Fen Produce per Acre				
	Wheat	Rye	Barley	Oats	Peas	Beans	Pease & Beans	Flax	Hemp	No. of Souls	per £.	Wheat	Barley	Oats	Coleseed	Coleseed fed off green
Coton	22	-	24	24	-	-	20	-	-	150	2.0	-	-	-	-	-
Maddingley	15	-	20	20	-	-	8	-	-	150	1.10	-	-	-	-	-
Dry Drayton	16	-	20	20	20	-	-	-	-	250	4.0	-	-	-	-	-
Lolworth	20	-	24	24	-	-	20	-	-	50	2.3	-	-	-	-	-
Boxworth	-	-	-	-	-	-	-	-	-	-	-	-	-	-	-	-
Eltisley	18	-	22	20	-	-	10	-	-	300	5.0	-	-	-	-	-
Croxton	18	-	22	20	-	-	10	-	-	240	3.0	-	-	-	-	-
Caxton	20	-	28	22	-	-	14	-	-	250	2.6	-	-	-	-	-
Gamlingay	16	-	24	22	-	12	-	-	-	700	3.0	-	-	-	-	-
Kingston	17	-	24	20	-	-	16	-	-	160	1.9	-	-	-	-	-
Toft	-	-	-	-	-	-	-	-	-	173	1.6	-	-	-	-	-
Hardwicke	16	-	18	18	-	-	8	-	-	165	3.0	-	-	-	-	-
Childersley	24	-	36	36	-	-	20	-	-	30	Nil	-	-	-	-	-
Girton	18	18	22	20	-	-	16	-	-	-	-	-	-	-	-	-
Hoggington	16	24	14	18	-	-	16	-	-	264	-	-	-	-	-	-
Long Stanton	18	-	24	24	-	-	16	-	-	240	2.6	-	-	-	-	-
Cottenham	28	-	30	-	-	-	20	-	-	875	-	-	-	-	-	-
Waterbeach and Denny Abbey	28	-	30	-	-	-	20	-	-	530	-	-	-	-	-	-
Landbeach	26	-	28	-	-	-	18	-	-	250	-	-	-	-	-	-
Milton with Westwick	20	-	24	20	-	-	18	-	-	284	-	-	-	-	-	-
Impington	18	-	20	20	16	-	-	-	-	115	-	-	-	-	-	-
Chesterton	24	26	28	24	-	-	20	-	-	625	-	-	-	-	-	-
{Wickin	24	-	28	-	-	-	22	-	-	540	-	-	-	-	-	-
{ Spinney Abbey	-	-	-	-	-	-	-	-	-							
Soham with Barraway	26	-	24	-	20	32	-	-	-	3000	1.8	-	-	-	-	-
City of Ely	22	-	24	-	-	-	20	-	-	-	4.0	-	-	-	-	-
Little Port and Apshall	24	-	24	-	-	26	-	-	-	-	2.3	32	36	42	-	35
Downham	24	-	24	-	-	-	20	-	-	-	850	2.3	-	-	-	-
Maypole	-	22	-	26	-	-	16	-	-	-	250	2.3	-	-	-	45
Sutton	22	-	24	-	-	-	20	-	-	1000	3.0	-	-	-	-	-
Haddenham	26	-	30	-	-	-	30	-	-	250	2.6	-	-	-	-	-
Wilburton	24	-	28	-	-	-	20	-	-	150	2.0	-	-	-	-	-
Stretham with Thetford	26	-	30	-	-	-	24	-	-	1800	1.9	-	-	45	-	36
Chatteris	-	-	-	-	-	-	-	-	-	-	1,6	-	-	-	-	-
Doddington	40	-	-	-	-	-	-	50	40	2000	1.6	2.8	28	32	45	-
Upwell	32	-	-	-	-	-	-	40	40	790	1.3	-	28	32	45	-
Outwell	20	-	-	50	-	-	16	50	46	-	0.4	20	-	52	20	-
Elm	28	-	-	60	-	-	20	-	-	625	-	-	24	56	26	42
Leverington	24	-	-	56	-	-	-	-	}	225	1.1	22	-	60	23	-
Newton	22	-	-	36	In the marshes }											
Tid St Giles	24	-	-	56	-	-	-	-	-	500	1.6	-	-	48	-	-
Leverington Parsondrove {	28	-	-	64	-	-	-	-	}	-	-{	24	-	64	-	-
	20	-	-	40	-	Inferior land }						20	-	48	Inferior fen	
Wisbech St Mary, Hamlets &c.	-	-	-	-	-	-	-	-	-	-	-	-	-	-	-	-
Thorney	-	-	-	-	-	-	-	-	-	1250	1.0	24	-	24	48	40
Whittlesey	-	-	24	-	-	18	-	-	-	-	2.0	-	-	-	-	-
General Average	23.3	20.2	36.1	26.2	18.3	17	16.1	46.9	48.6	428	2.6½					
Open Field and Waste Land	20.2	19.3	21.0	25.1	16.2	20	17									
Difference	3.1	0.3	15.1	1.1	2.1											

A COMPARATIVE VIEW of the present Average and the eventually improved Rental, or Value, of the County of CAMBRIDGE, distinguishing each Description of Land, and the probable improvement thereon, together with the annual Amount of the Difference in Favor of Improvement.

	Number of Acres	Perfect Rental, or Value per acre			Total Amount of the present Rental, or Value			Improved Rent or Value per acre			Total Amount of Improved Rent or Value			Total Amount of difference of Rent in Favor of Improvement		
		£.	s.	d.	£.	s.	d.	£.	s.	d.	£.	s.	d.	£.	s.	d.
Enclosed Arable	15000	0	18	0	13500	0	0	0	18	0	13500	0	0			
Open Field Arable	132000	0	10	0	66000	0	0	0	18	0	118800	0	0	52800	0	0
Improved Pasture	52000	1	0	4	60666	10	4	1	0	4	60666	10	4			
Inferior Pasture	19800	0	10	9	10642	10	0	1	0	4	20130	0	0	9487	0	0
Wood Land	1000	0	15	0	750	0	0	0	15	0	750	0	0			
Improved Fen	50000	0	15	0	37500	0	0	0	15	0	37500	0	0			
Waste and Unimproved Fen	150000	0	4	0	30000	0	0	0	14	0	105000	0	0	75000	0	0
Half Yearly Meadow Land	2000	0	12	6	1250	0	0	1	1	0	2100	0	0	850	0	0
Highland Common	7500	0	10	0	3750	0	0	1	1	0	7875	0	0	4125	0	0
Fen or Moor Common	8000	0	3	0	1200	0	0	0	13	0	5200	0	0	4000	0	0
Heath Sheep Walk	6000	0	2	6	750	0	0	0	2	6	750	0	0			
	443300				226009	0	4				372271	10	4	146262	10	0

The Improved Rent may be multiplied by 3, in order to give the value of the Improved Produce, which consequently cannot be calculated at less than £438,787. 10s. Per annum

p.195

PART II

ARABLE

The preceding Journal, Abstract, and General Average, show so clearly the nature of the soil, and its value, to the proprietors, the occupiers, and the public at large, that little further should seem necessary, to call attention towards the adopting of such general measures, as are evidently justified in the few instances of exertion that have occurred in the survey of this county. The laying of the intermixed property together, and in severalty, which is now dispersed in the common open fields; and enclosing, where such a measure shall be found advisable, appear to be indispensibly necessary, as previous steps, to the general improvement of the highland part of the county; but as these objects involve a great diversity of interests, and as it is material that the Board should understand the general disposition as fully as possible, I have made it my particular care, to mix, and converse with the yeomanry of the county, and in their sedate, and sober moments, to possess myself fully of their experience, and local knowledge, and finally, to ascertain the general sentiment, as to this important innovation upon the establishment of ages. A few have given an unqualified dissent, but they were stock-masters; others have concurred under certain limitations, but the mass of the farmers are decidedly for the measure in question. The general average of the rent of the enclosed arable, compared with that of the open
p.196 common field arable, in the whole county, exceeds the latter in the proportion of eight shillings per acre, and the average produce of the former, exceeds that of the latter, as under

	Bushels	Pecks
Wheat	3	1
Rye	0	3
Barley	15	1
Oats	1	1
Peas	2	1

But if a single instance be adverted to, and a comparison made between the parishes of Childersley, which is enclosed, and Hardwicke, which remains in open common field, and which parishes, appear by the journal, to consist of a perfectly similar soil, and are divided only by a hedge row; the excess of the produce in favour of the enclosed, will appear infinitely more abundant, viz.

Childersley enclosed		Hardwicke open	Excess of produce
24 bushels of Wheat		16 bushels	8 bushels
36 ditto	Barley	18 ditto	18 ditto
36 ditto	Oats	18 ditto	18 ditto
20 ditto	Peas and Beans	8 ditto	12 ditto

Now if the good effects of enclosing were even to stop here, surely sufficient benefit is apparent to justify the general principle; but when to that is added the exemption from a disease, the dreadful consequences of which, have desolated the sheep walks in most of the neighbouring parishes, whilst in Childersley and Knapwell (both of which are enclosed) not the least shadow of the disease, has made its appearance; it is surely reasonable to conclude that it is highly expedient; relying fully on the wisdom of parliament, for all the arrangements which necessarily apply to the complete adjustment of so complicated a business.

p.197

ENCLOSURE.

A few observations in addition to what has been just said upon this subject, will be sufficient to convey my decided opinion in favour of this measure. It is universally acknowledged by all writers on political oeconomy, that the population of a country, must ever depend upon the means which it possesses, and the proper application of those means, for subsisting its inhabitants. Britain at this time unquestionably possesses the unemployed means of subsisting in addition to her present numbers, one third more of inhabitants; that such an augmentation must be deemed politically right, there can be no question; because the internal strength, and productive labour of the nation, would be encreased. By inviting to early marriage the peasantry of the country, who under their present want of confidence, that their

industry will enable them to support an infant offspring, are not allured to the gratification of an early and generous passion, which lawfully indulged, is doubtless of the highest political as well as moral consequence. Hence the rapid encrease of the inhabitants of North America, where by propagation only, exclusive of the accession of foreigners, their numbers are estimated to double in twenty-eight years. That the objects for the employment of the poor, could be multiplied, there can be no doubt, when we look at the additional quantity of labour, the country will demand from a general enclosure. The fencing, draining, claying, marling, ploughing, sowing, reaping, mowing, threshing, that will then be necessary to attend to, over and above what the business of the country at this time produces, are
p.198 objects, which, from their employment of the poor, cannot fail creating in the most essential degree, the greatest moral and political advantages; whilst the idle objection, that in the event of a general enclosure, there would be more land thrown into pasture than there ought to be, is too weak and frivolous to deserve attention.

TENURES.

THERE is no greater error in the whole oeconomy of country business, than that which the gentlemen of Cambridgeshire, are too apt to fall into, respecting the tenures they grant to their estates. Few are inclined to give their tenants such assurances of the certain and quiet enjoyment of their improvements, as reason dictates and justice demands. Had the same jealousy prevailed in Norfolk, on the early improvement of that county, in vain would the landlords, in conjunction with their tenants, have expended such large sums in claying, marling, and otherwise improving their estates; if the tenant had not been assured of an eventual benefit, and reward for his expence and labour, under the protection and encouragement of a lease for twenty-one years. The general state of the husbandry in the county of Cambridge, demands the like assistance from the proprietor as to the means, and the same indulgence in point of possession, as a reward for the industry and labour of the tenant, who will otherwise be little inclined to bury his property in the earth, or improve the surface by the sweat of his brow. In all cases however, the most strict and rigid observance ought to be exacted, as to the performance of the stipulated covenants, but the confidence of a lease, is indispensible to the advancement of agriculture in every county; and where it is found so backward as in the county of Cambridge, it is highly
p.199 expedient, that the term should not be of a shorter duration, than that of twenty-one years; though in the highly improved counties, such an extension of time, may not be found so essentially necessary.

GRASS.

THE proportional difference in the value of the superior, and partial improved pasture, and the totally unimproved and inferior, is sufficient to induce some alteration in the present management of the latter described lands. The general average does not illustrate this difference in so full, and ample a manner as necessary; nor could that have been done without forming an intermediate class, which certainly would have been attended to, had the necessity of it, occurred upon the commencement of the survey. The principal divisions of the pasture grounds which are noticed, are first, those which produce a rich tender grass and herbage, from a loose black soil, proper for feeding or grazing cattle, and worth from twenty-five to thirty shillings per acre. The second, a more coarse, but luxuriant grass and herbage, produced upon a close, moist soil, proper for the depasturage of milch cows, and store cattle, worth from fifteen to twenty shillings per acre. The third class produces very coarse, sharp, sour grass and herbage, vegetating very late in the spring from wet, cold, and compact clays, worth from five to ten shillings per acre: this last division owes its inferiority, to the wet, cold, and compressed state, in which it has lain for ages, and is only to be relieved by hollow draining, breaking up with the plough, and exposing the soil to the meliorating influence of all those external powers; the benign effects of which, long experience has clearly proved to communicate fertility.

p.200 The two first classes are to be held sacred from the plough, though the latter of them may be improved by hollow draining, manuring, and scarifying the surface, with a coarse bush-harrow. By previously hollow draining and breaking up with the plough, in two or three years, every remnant of the former surface, of the last or third class, together with the roots of all the weeds, and beggary it produced, will be completely putrified. The soil thus opened, becomes pulverized, mellow, open, free, and ready for the reception of the following proportions of grass feeds, proper for permanent pasture, viz.

6 lbs. of perennial red clover, called cow grass (*trifolium alphistre*)

4 lbs. of Dutch white clover, called honey suckle (*trifolium repins*)
3 lbs. of narrow leafed plantain, or ribwort
4 lbs. of yellow trefoil, called black nonsuch
3 lbs. of burnet, and
1 bushel of rye grass per acre

In place of the latter article, two bushels of clean light hayfeeds, which when properly lifted, and well cleaned, ought to weigh twenty pounds to the bushel, or four gallons of timothy (cat's-tail) and four gallons of fescue (dog's-tail) may be recommended in preference to the rye grass. The crops which should not exceed three, and which may be taken from the old pasture ground before it is again laid down, will amply repay every expence that may arise in the hollow draining, stubbing, levelling the ant-hills, and purchase of grass feeds; when this description of land will be thus improved from five shillings, or seven shillings and six-pence, to fifteen shillings of twenty shillings per acre. Were the climate of the south east of the island, less favourable to the culture of grasses than it is, necessity
p.201 would have driven the farmers to the same practice, which the want of so good a climate has long ago induced in Scotland. The plough is there brought forth, and used with great propriety, as a sweetener of the soil, and the new pasture lay, is generally estimated at three times the value of the old; such would be the necessary consequence of the same management in other parts of the island, where under similar circumstances it may prudently be recommended. The absence of the sun's rays, and the consequent chill from that deficiency, together with the effect of the springs, lying in general so very near the surface, compels the husbandman in Scotland, to resort more frequently to the agency of the plough, than under a more genial climate and favoured soil, would be necessary. About once in twenty or twenty-five years, the old pastures which lie upon close, and compact clays (as are described under the third class,) may require opening with the plough, in the south east part of the island; and be highly benefited by the management above recommended.

PARING and BURNING

THIS practice is admissible to a certain extent upon land, composed entirely of vegetable matter, where the water is at command, and where lowering the surface is not likely to be attended with material inconvenience. Paring and burning is here the only effectual means of quickly bringing land of this description, into a profitable state of cultivation: In such land, wherever there is a considerable depth of vegetable matter, after a few years rest, the surface becomes uneven, resembling a field covered with innumerable ant-hills; and the tops of these inequalities, producing little herbage, and that of an inferior
p.202 quality, are only to be improved by a judicious application of the plough, and burning about one third part of the thinnest of the flag, that can possibly be pared. Even here this practice ought only to be permitted under certain restrictions, and performed with great care; but to extend the same, to the thinly stapled high lands in the county, thereby dissipating the vegetable mould, and leaving a surface of cold, sour clay, harsh gravel, or other inert matter, is so highly destructive to the country where it prevails, that in the King's, the Queen's, and other counties in Ireland, where paring and burning the thin high lands have been unfortunately practiced, extensive and naturally fruitful tracts, have been reduced to the lowest, and most exhausted state of barrenness and poverty; and as the like effects, must on a certainty under similar circumstances, follow the same practice in this kingdom; it is not easy to comprehend the reasoning of those persons, whose judgment leads to the general recommendation of so pernicious a system.

FEN

UPON this subject, the want of opportunity to revisit the great level of the fens, and the parishes bordering upon them, is a circumstance much to be lamented, as the quantity of fen land that is in an improved and profitable state, and that which is drowned and of little value, would thereby have been more correctly ascertained. Reference, however, may be had to Chatteris, Elm, Leverington Parson-drove, Wisbich St. Mary's, and Thorney, for a comparative view of what the lost country of the fens is capable of, in point of improvement, by recovering the natural outfal of the middle, and south level waters. The fenny land in the above parishes, under improved cultivation, amounts to about fifty
p.203 thousand acres, and yields a produce far beyond the richest high lands in the county; averaging a rent of more than fifteen shillings per acre: Whereas the waste, the drowned, and partially improved fens, amounting on a moderate computation, to one hundred and fifty thousand acres, cannot be fairly

averaged at more than four shillings per acre. Hence in this county only, an encreased rent of ten shillings per acre, amounting to seventy-five thousand pounds annually, may be reasonably expected from a complete, and effectual drainage of the fens, and restoring to the country, a tract of far more fruitful, and productive land than is to be met with of the like extent, in any part of the Island.

FEN or MOOR COMMON

IN the highland part of the county, there are about eight thousand five hundred acres of this description, which at present, contribute little to the support of the stock, though greatly to the disease of the rot in the sheep and cows: These commons generally lie well for draining, and are otherwise capable of very great improvement; but until a Court of Sewers shall be established, with powers to oblige the mills upon the several streams which pass through these moors, to be pitched lower; so that the mill dams shall not hold the water up to its present height, and override the surface of the commons as they now do; no remedy can be applied to this very serious evil, which must necessarily be removed, before any improvement can be undertaken.

p.204

HALF YEARLY MEADOW LAND.

THESE lands lying dispersed through the hollows of the open fields, and receiving the richest juices of the surrounding lands, even in their present neglected state, are rented on an average, at twelve shillings and six-pence per acre only; but would by proper draining, and being put into severalty, readily be improved to thirty shillings per acre, as the crop which is now only mown twice in three years, would then be annually secured.

HIGHLAND COMMON.

THERE are about seven thousand five hundred acres of this land in the county, which in severalty, would be readily improved, to the annual rent of a guinea per acre. In its present state, it cannot possibly be valued at more than half that price; though no alteration in the present mode of depasturing, can apparently be made, to encrease the present estimated value.

HEATH SHEEP WALK.

THIS land appears to be chiefly appropriated to the original design of nature; the surface or skin, forming a tender and wholesome food for the sheep, which are generally depastured thereon. The staple of the land is in general so very dry, and thin, that once broken, it will be ages before it can acquire an equally valuable turf or covering with that it now produces. The substratum is generally a chalk, though in some places, there is found a deep, rank sand, abounding with flints, and where the surface is broken,
p.205 the sand in the dry season of summer, is very liable to be driven by the wind, to the inconvenience not only of the adjoining lands, but of those at some distance. Were these plains in severalty, and were it practicable to raise live fences upon them, trefoil, cinquefoil, and rye grass, would be found the most profitable grasses to cultivate: The less however that this kind of land is disturbed, the better.

SHEEP.

IT appears from the general average, that, one thousand and sixty-two sheep is the proportion per parish in the sixty-two parishes, in which the number kept was ascertained. This ratio multiplied by one hundred and forty-four, the number of parishes in which sheep are kept in this county, is equal to one hundred and fifty-two thousand nine hundred and twenty-eight sheep, for an extent of highland country of about two hundred and forty-three thousand and three hundred acres, which is not quite one and a half acres per sheep. This general stock may be divided into three distinct breeds, though there are many intermediate shades amongst them. The Norfolk, the West Country, and the Cambridgeshire, are the principal ones. The three years old wethers of the former when fattened will average about sixteen pounds per quarter, and about two and three quarter pounds per fleece; and the West Country breed will average about eighteen pounds per quarter, and four pounds per fleece. These two sorts are generally found between the Cam and Mildenhall rivers, extending along the plains of Newmarket Heath, towards Linton, Foulmire, and Royston, binding upon the counties of Suffolk, Essex, and part of Hertfordshire, and to the head of the valley distinguished by the name of the Dairies—Crossing this p.206 Valley, and extending thence westwardly towards Caxton, and northwardly towards the fens, binding east on the river Cam, and south and westwardly upon Bedford and Huntingdonshires, the common Cambridgeshire breed prevails; the three years old wethers, of which sort, when fattened to the bone, will average about fourteen pounds per quarter, and two and a quarter pounds to the fleece.

Proceeding into the Isle, a medley of the Norfolk, Cambridgeshire, Berkshire, Hertfordshire, Southdown, West Country, Lincoln, and Leicestershire breeds are found, but on approaching the country about Wisbich, extending thence northwardly towards Holland in Lincolnshire, an inferior breed of the Lincolnshire sheep generally prevails: the three years old wethers of this description, averaging, when fattened, about twenty-four pounds per quarter, and twelve pounds per fleece. In this neighbourhood, a cross between the Leicester and Lincoln breeds has been tried lately, and is much approved.

This part of the country is very happy exempt from the ravages of the rot; the cause of which, so far as the enquiries and observations made in the course of the survey will lead to a conjecture, seems to arise from an extremely wet season in summer. Extremely wet winters do not produce this disease. The moors, low grounds, and wastes, in the common open fields, upon which the sheep are by necessity obliged to feed, as well in wet, as in dry summers, frequently in wet seasons, become overflowed with the highland waters, which leave prodigious quantities of filth and fullage upon the grass and herbage, in which is most probably involved the germin, or egg of those snails or insects, which being conveyed
p.207 with the food into the stomach of the sheep, and there meeting with a proper nidus become vivified, and invited by the gall, their proper aliment, pass through the bile ducts into the liver, where, in a certain stage of the disease, they encrease to the frightful size and number which destroy the animal.

Another species of rot, was noticed on the survey, which does not appear to be ascribeable to the like cause. This is called by the farmers, the blood rot. The liver appears to the eye in these cases to be perfectly sound, and as free from disease, as in the most healthy animal; it is however covered with an extremely thin transparent membrane, as tender as a spider's web, but which the smallest pressure imaginable, immediately ruptures, when the whole liver resembles a mass of coagulated blood, without any cohesion whatsoever; the liver and intestines, at this time, are free from any appearance of insects, alive or dead; nor was it understood from the farmers, that the liver in the state before mentioned, was offensive to the smell; though certain it is, that in its progress to that condition, it must have been rendered gradually inert, and corrupt, as it became disorganized.

COWS.

The various mixtures of this cattle that are found in this county, are not easily enumerated: the Suffolk polled, the Craven, the short-horned Yorkshire, the Derby, the Welch, the Leicester, the Fifeshire, Gloucester-brown, and the common Cambridgeshire, are the breeds of cow cattle most generally preferred; nor is it conceived possible to mould this variety into any one uniform sort until
p.208 the open field lands, are laid into severalty, and the coarse and low lands drained and improved, so, that by subsequent cultivation, it shall be ascertained, what are the species of cattle most proper for the then improved grasses and herbage, in the several districts of the county.

From Isleham to Newmarket, Linton, Caxton, and northwardly to the fens, these breeds prevail either distinctly, or casually compounded; in which latter case, the animal, generally speaking, is badly formed, small, and when in full milk, seldom affords more than four quarts at a time. In the neighbourhood of Ely, where the herbage is infinitely superior to that in the higher parts of the county, it is a matter of concern to observe that so little attention is paid to the improvement of the common breed of cow cattle. In the neighbourhood of Wisbich, a very sensible alteration in this particular, for the better, is with pleasure observed.

To the considerations of the general inferiority of the cows in the upper part of the county, are to be added some important evils, which are perhaps, scarcely to be paralleled in any other county in the kingdom; (viz) the frequency of slipping calf, and the perishing by the rot; a few conjectures may be hazarded upon the cause of the former, whilst the cause of the latter, evidently speaks for itself; arising from the foulness of the herbage in the low grounds, on which the cows depasture.

It is a truth generally acknowledged, and very well established, throughout the whole of animated nature, or at least, so far as hath come within the view of writers upon comparative anatomy, that all animals, in a state of gestation, require for the preservation of their own health, and the sustenance of the foetus, the most uniform circulation of the blood, and other fluids; to preserve which, in some
p.209 constitutions, apparently very unequal to such exhaustions, frequent and repeated bleedings, when in that state, are indispensibly necessary: this material point in the oeconomy of bleeding cows, is observed to be much neglected through the whole valley of the dairies, nor is it generally practised on the margin of the fens, or in other parts of the country, where the accident of abortion is likewise very common. The business of milking cows, and the extended scale of necessaries, comforts, and luxuries, which are derived by the human race from the juices of that animal, are all to be considered as artificial, and as a direct inversion of the laws of nature.

The cow in a wild state, and under the control of her natural instincts only, at a certain age, like all other female animals, weans her young; but in a domesticated state, the keeping of her low, and drawing from her twice a day all the richest of her fluids, and that at a period of her pregnancy, when the foetus she is carrying, is so far advanced and grown, as to require every particle of nourishment that the system of its mother can assimilate and convey, is surely such a dereliction of the laws of nature, as to require in the event of necessity, the most generous and fostering care of the person who thus drains, and exhausts the animal of its essential juices, and deprives it of the only possible means of subsisting the embryo in its womb. When this exhaustion is carried beyond a certain point, and the necessary nutritious secretions are withheld, the principle of life must be extinguished, and abortion must consequently ensue.

Cows, like every other animal bearing young, are subject to miscarriage, by fright, or by external injury; but in the instances before us, taken from the journal, it does not appear possible to ascribe so
p.210 general a calamity, to such partial and accidental causes, though it may be attributed in a degree to mismanagement, and a combination of those causes, before attempted to be explained; or may arise from some noxious herb, which the animal in the greediness of hunger involuntarily swallows.

It is however, sufficient that the evil exists, to engage the wisdom of the Board in devising a remedy. That cows are timid, and subject to fear, in common with other animals, there can be no doubt; for one spoonful of blood will set hundreds of them in an uproar: but as they are not frequently exposed to alarms of this nature, few accidents inconsequence thereof are likely to happen.

Mares also in a state of gestation, are particularly obnoxious to fear, induced from blood, or recently slaughtered carcases; and hence the hunters in the interior of America, will encounter any fatigue, rather than expose their mares, to the accident of slipping their foals, and endangering their lives, by loading them with a carcase, of venison, or a load of buffalo, or bear's-meat, to carry, though but for a very, short distance to the camp, or village; well knowing that such accidents are thus produced; and in that country are deemed inevitable.

WOODLAND.

FEW woods, it may be presumed, afford less matter for observation in the kingdom, than the woodlands of Cambridgeshire, which are thinly dispersed; and this nakedness must remain, so long as the county continues in an uninclosed state. The journal sets forth in, many places a kindly soil for the culture of oak, ash, and elm, and on the chalky lands for that of beach; all of which in the event of a
p.211 general enclosure, might, be cultivated to advantage. The under growth of the few detached woods in the county, pays at the rate of about fifteen shillings per acre per ann. and when there is a fell of oak timber, (which rarely happens) the bark is usually rated at twenty-five per cent, on the value of the timber.

POPULATION.

THE proportion of four hundred and twenty-eight souls per parish, in the eighty-nine parishes, whence such information could be obtained, applied to one hundred and forty-four parishes, gives the number which the county contains, to be sixty-one thousand six hundred and thirty-two. To this aggregate should be added nine thousand eight hundred and sixty-eight in the Town and University of Cambridge;

three thousand seven hundred and seventy-nine in the City of Ely; about five thousand in Wisbich, and for the sake of round numbers, about two thousand seven hundred and twenty-one in; the hamlet of Merch; making the whole population of the county to amount to eighty-three thousand inhabitants. This however falls greatly short of former calculations, which have stated the population at one hundred and forty thousand. How such an estimate was formed, is not easily to be comprehended, as it is proved from the following extracts, procured from the registers, that the number of inhabitants in those parishes, have of late years been considerably encreased. In the last thirteen years there appears to be an encrease in the City of Ely of one hundred and forty-seven persons, and in the parish of Waterbeach, which now contains about five hundred and thirty souls, there has been an encrease within these laft
p.212 seven. years of sixty-seven inhabitants, equal to an encrease of one-eighth of the whole number: and within the last twenty years, the parishes of Wimple, Whadden, Arrington, and Kingston, all of which are very small, have encreased in number one hundred and twenty souls (exclusively of any addition that may have been made by artificers and strangers) from all which considerations, it is more than probable that the former estimate was infinitely over-rated; and that fixing the population on the present day, at eighty-three thousand souls, would be found nearly correct, though this question still remains to be ascertained from absolutc enumeration.

PROVISIONS.

THE general average price from repeated statements in different parts of the county, appears on the several articles to be as under, viz.

All these necessaries of life have increased to their present value, within the last few years; and it is with concern to be apprehended, there is not at this time, the most remote prospect of a reduction in any of the prices, which certainly do not bear a proportion to the

VALUE of LABOUR.

THE general average of men-servants wages through the county, is ten pounds per ann. maid-servants four pounds ten shillings; that of boys forty-five shillings, and girls, washing included, thirty-eight
p.213 shillings a year. During eight months of the year, the wages to the day labourer is seven shillings per week; after which, for the next two months, it is increased to nine shillings; and the remaining two months, during the time of hay and corn harvest, he receives two shillings and six-pence per day, or fifteen shillings per week; amounting in the whole to twenty-two pounds four shillings, if the labourer is blessed with constant health and employment during the whole year. To this may be added the casual earnings of his wife and children, which if estimated at three pounds sixteen shillings, will make the total amount of the earnings of a poor family, twenty-six pounds per ann. How far this is equal to the demand for the common and absolute necessaries of life, the Board (there can be no doubt) will in due time take into consideration. Upon all occasions however it is greatly to be wished, that as much of the country business as possible, should be done by the great, or task work, which thus performed, is ever more to the satisfaction of the master, than by the day; whilst: the labourer, considers his time when thus engaged, as his own; and feels an independency in his exertions, that lightens his fatigue, and distinguishes the industrious workman, from the idle and less deserving.

In the county of Northumberland, the honesty, and exertions of the threshers of the crop, are wisely secured, by making them independent of their masters. A regular account of the number of sheaves which are deposited in the time of harvest, in the barn, or comprising the stack, is accurately taken; when these are to be threshed, the farmer attends the thresher, and sees him thresh, dress, and measure the produce from a certain number; from this result, the contents of the barn, or stack are ascertained,
p.214 and according to the sort of grain, a certain proportion is allowed to the thresher for his labour; the keys of the barn are then given to him, and the instances are very rare, where the master has occasion to complain, or that the thresher fails in rendering the stipulated proportion to his employer. Were this excellent method in general practice over the island, much of the grain which is now turned out with the straw would be preserved; the anxious attendance of the farmer to his barn doors would be spared, and the industrious man, would ensure a reward for his extraordinary exertions.

HORSES.

NOTHING in the husbandry of Cambridgeshire is more replete with error, and abuse, or more capable of reform, under the present circumstances of the county, than the feeding, and working management of farm horses. The only true judgment to be formed of this oeconomy, is by a comparison between this and that of other counties. In Norfolk the plough-teams consist of five horses, which are under the care of one man, who feeds, and cleans them all; and occasionally works two pair of them, the odd horse being generally employed at harrow, and at job work. These horses are generally taken into the stable about the beginning of November, and receive four bushels of corn per team per week, till about Candlemas, when their allowance is encreased to a bushel per week per horse. From November until Candlemas they are racked up, with, pea, or well saved clover barley straw; when the spring work begins to press, the rack meat is changed for clover, rye grass, and trefoil hay. The road teams, which are of a larger and heavier breed, and which are employed in long journies, in carrying out the crop,
p.215 consists likewise of five horses, under the care of a single person also; and these are allowed six bushels of corn per team per week, and upon occasions of very extraordinary exertions, an extra feed of corn per horse is given them; and through the winter, they are constantly racked up with clover, and rye grass hay. The mode of working these horses is thus: The men who look after them, are seldom in bed after three o'clock in the morning, particularly in the spring season in the dead of the winter they rise about four, (and as candles are always allowed for the purpose) they clean, and feed (with sifted chaff, in which they put a small portion of oats) their horses, till breakfast time, which is, sooner or later, according to the length of the days, usually reaching their ploughs (with one pair) by the time they can conveniently see to work; they plough till noon (twelve o'clock) when they drop their traces, and shuffle home as quick as they can to dinner. Should it not immediately be ready on their arrival, they collar, and prepare the horses which were left at home in the morning, and immediately after dinner, proceed with each another pair and plough till night. This practice continues through all the dead time of winter, and until such time as the days are of sufficient length to permit their working seven hours at a journey. As the spring advances, the ploughs are shifted, i.e. the servant who has the care of the team, rises at three, attends his horses, and after his breakfast, gets to plough about five; at eleven o'clock he is relieved by a labourer, who goes out to him with a pair of the horses, left at home in the morning, and who ploughs till three in the afternoon. During this interval, the servant refreshes himself, and the pair of horses, and returns with them to the labourer, whom, with his horses, he relieves, continuing to plough so long as he can see. When the business becomes still more urgent, particularly
p.216 during the season for sowing barley, from the middle of April until old May-day, they make four journies with two pair of horses; and the wheels of the ploughs are constantly kept going, from four o'clock, or earlier in the morning, until eight at night; a quarter of a peck of oats, as an additional bait, being allowed each horse for the double journey. The seed furrows are never carried larger than four to a yard, and it rarely happens that the traces are dropped, after a four hours journey, without completely finishing seven-eighths of an acre. Thus is this business usually conducted in that county, which is now to be compared with the general management in the feeding and working of farm horses in the upper parts of Cambridgeshire.

The scarcity of pasture ground, the want of proper attention in the farmers to the raising of green food for soiling their horses in summer, and the great neglect in the culture of artificial grasses, all conduce to an expence in supporting the farm horses in the upper parts of this country, that is absolutely enormous. They are kept in the stable throughout the year, each horse is fed with a peck of corn per day, with as much chaff, chopped straw, and hay, as they can eat, and work but one journey in the day; which seldom exceeds seven hours, but never eight; except in the neighbourhood of Leverington Parson-drove, and Thorney, where two journies a day are not unusual, ploughing from seven to twelve, and from two in the afternoon until night; or when the day will admit of it, till seven in the evening, doing about an acre each journey.

IMPLEMENTS of HUSBANDRY

IN the fens, the common fen plough, with a running coulter, which with the share, is constantly filed
p.217 and kept particularly sharp, is in constant use. By carrying only two furrows and an half to the yard, about an acre and an half is usually ploughed in a journey of seven hours. To these ploughs is frequently annexed an appendage, which in the fen country is called a boy, the business of which, is to lap in the rushes, reeds, and other early produce of the fens, on which the plough-share lays the earth, and thus

completely buries under the soil. It is usual to work three horses abreast in these ploughs, and it is truly astonishing to observe with what dexterity, and adroitness the ploughs and horses are managed. The half and three quarter Dutch ploughs, together with the common swing and foot ploughs, are in the highland part of the county in general use.

The dagger, whole and half winged shares, are variously employed, but one general plough, with three occasional different shares, might be introduced with great advantage. The principle to be recommended, should be a compound of the Norfolk and Hampshire wheel plough, with a short well turned iron plate, inclining gradually to the point of the share. There are no lands in the kingdom, which require more attention in ploughing than the stiff ones in this county. To plough with a regular uniform pitch, and to cut the bottom of the furrows clean, and even from side to side, is a great desideratum, in good husbandry, but that is not possible to be attended to correctly with the common foot plough, which is usually resorted to, for breaking up the fallows of Cambridgeshire. The foot at the end of the beam, in these ploughs, which drags upon the ground, and is contrived as a regulator to the pitch of the plough, is at so great a distance from the point of friction, as to occasion the share, in strong and hard ground, to be constantly and alternately dipping, and rising upwards, rooting too deep, or skimming too shallow.
p.218 A fixed permanent rest for the beam, as in the wheel plough, would obviate this objection, and save the ploughman the necessity of setting his plough too deep, which he is continually obliged to counteract, by pressing upon the handle or plough tail, and consequently unnecessarily augmenting the draft and weight upon his horses, by the increased friction that is thus induced. The harrows, carts, waggons, and all other implements of husbandry, are after the common sort, and not worth the time of a particular description.

Mr. Shepherd, steward to Mr. Tharpe of Chippenham, has invented, and now uses harrows of a particular and uncommon construction. A drawing of these harrows with their exact proportions, would have been very acceptable. The single harrow appears to consist of five beams, with six teeth in each; the beams are not laid parallel with each other, but fanning, and forming the tail of the harrow about six inches wider than the head; the beams are all curved, forming a convex upon the top, and when connected together, a concave space of about an inch and a half perpendicular, under the middle of the harrow, over and above what would necessarily obtain, were the beams straight, and parallel to the surface; the teeth are all curved, feather or basil edged, and are set springing with their sharp edges and points forward; and their length in the front of the harrow, is about six and a half inches, which gradually, increases, till on the tail of the harrow they are eight inches, long. Harrows thus constructed, have a wonderful effect, in drawing into the ground, rather than scratching upon the surface, and in dividing the clods, by cutting through, rather than by rubbing, or grinding them against each other; and
p.219 by gathering the twitch grass, in the increased space, formed by the concavity of its beams, it is rendered an excellent cleansing harrow, and does much credit to the ingenuity of the inventor.

HEMP.

THE culture of this important plant begins deservedly to be regarded in a far more favourable light in the present day than formerly. In those countries where it is generally cultivated, it is considered as an extremely exhausting, and impoverishing crop, but in parts of this county, where the occasional culture of hemp, forms a part of a system of perpetual cropping without rest or fallow, it is not only viewed as an ameliorating crop, but experience proves that upon those lands it is the best possible preparation for a crop of wheat. Flax is cultivated by way of a change upon the same lands.

The fertilizing qualities of hemp upon the soil, may possibly be referred to the same cause, which so powerfully operates upon sowing grey peas on land in Ireland, when it is so far exhausted, as not to yield the quantity of feed in return of oats, or any other grain. But as the pea-crop seldom fails, the land is thereby brought into so high a state of preparation, as to insure an abundant crop of wheat, without manure or fallow. Lands which thus become productive, probably contain a great quantity of vegetable matter, in an imperfect state of rottenness, and unfit for the food of plants. The combination of heat and moisture can only affect its perfect dissolution, and to the umbrageous influence of hemp and peas, which prevents exhalation and keeps the surface during the heat of summer, constantly moist, may be ascribed the good effects arising from these crops.

p.220 The average produce of hemp from the break is about forty-eight and a half stone and of flax about forty-six and a half stone per acre. As these crops have been returned by various persons, in different stages of manufacturing, sufficient information could not be obtained as to the culture, and previous process for the manufacturer. The practice of water-rotting is generally prefer'd to that of dew-rotting, or simple exposure to the open air. In America, where hemp and flax are cultivated, upon an extensive scale, but where the heat of the climate at the season of exposure is more favourable to putrefaction, than in this country, dew-rotting is generally preferred, because its effects are observed to be more uniform, and the hemp and flax can be more particularly attended to, and the moment for binding and housing, (upon which the value of the crops greatly depend) is to be discovered and embraced with the fullest certainty.

ROADS.

THE public roads in general through the county, are tolerably good; the private roads are very indifferent; and it is not very probable that they will be much improved under the present regulation of the surveyors of the highways. The materials for mending them in many places are extremely scarce, and lying at a considerable distance, are not to be obtained, without more particular attention is paid to the statute duty of each parish, and the present laws for keeping them in repair.

p.221

RECAPITULATION

FROM the preceding statements, and from a due consideration of the information acquired on the survey and contained in the journal, it appears clearly evident that the complete and effectual drainage of one hundred and fifty thousand acres of fen land in this county, would produce an additional revenue to the proprietors only, an augmented rent of..	75,000	0	0
That the laying into severalty, or generally enclosing one hundred and thirty-two thousand acres, of open common field arable land, would yield an additional rent of..	52,800	0	0
That a general improvement of the coarse and rough pastures, amounting to about nineteen thousand eight hundred acres, would produce an increased rent of	9,487	10	0
That the enclosing in severalty seven thousand five hundred acres of highland common, would produce in addition to its present estimated value, an increased income of	4,125	0	0
That the draining, properly improving, and enclosing eight thousand acres of fen or moor common, would necessarily produce an increased rent upon its present value of	4,000	0	0
That laying into severalty, draining, and improving two thousand acres of half yearly meadow land, would produce an encreased rent of	850	0	0
Total improvement of which the county is capable, according to the foregoing statements, is..	146,262	10	0
Stating the increased produce, at thrice the increased rent, hence per annum to the public	438.787	10	0
Which at thirty years purchase, would increase the value of the national capital to the amount of	13,163,625	0	0

APPENDIX

TO

Mr. VANCOUVER's

AGRICULTURAL ACCOUNT

OF

CAMBRIDGESHIRE.

TO THE READER.

Mr. VANCOUVER, having annexed, to the preceding observations, the following Appendix, upon a question of the utmost consequence to the agriculture of a very extensive district, it was thought advisable to print it, for the consideration of the Members of the Board, as too much light cannot be thrown on so important a subject. It is not proposed, however, to circulate this Appendix with the Report, though a perusal of it will be given upon special application being made for that purpose, by any of the parties interested in the contest, particularly to such as may be desirous of bringing about an accommodation, a circumstance that would be highly acceptable to the Board, and, it is believed, to the Public in general.

EDITORIAL NOTE-

The appendix, separately printed and sold, was apparently, at the uestreq of some purchasers, bound into a single volume with the Cambridgeshire survey. A page of errata was inserted at the end, as part of the publication, in this volume here copied. This page is not reproduced, all the reuired amendments having been incorporated silently into the present text.

APPENDIX

OBSERVATIONS

On the proposed Eau Brink Cut for the further draining of the Fens.

PART I.

OF THE FENS.

SECTION I.

Of their Nature and Origin.

So much has already been written on the subject of' the fens, that when I first engaged in the present undertaking, I greatly despaired of being able to add any thing of moment to a subject so far exhausted. It is not however without some hopes of being useful that I at present venture a few conjectures on the subject, trusting to the indulgence of the Board of Agriculture, and my subsequent reader, for such inaccuracies as the very short time that has been allowed me to examine the country, and form an opinion upon it, in some measure intitles me to look for. I am nevertheless, much concerned that an opportunity has not been offered me of pursuing my inquiries on this occasion with that minuteness and attention, with which the operations of nature ought ever to be regarded, particularly where I have chosen nature principally for a guide.

As my leisure has not afforded me an opportunity of reading upon the subject, of course my facts, both historical and otherwise (touching the original and present state of the fens) are drawn solely from actual observation, and from conversations with the most intelligent inhabitants I have met with by the way in that hitherto ill-fated country. From their data alone, my conclusions will be drawn.

p.4 Whoever will make it his business to examine attentively the surface and structure of these fens, will find that the general bed of the Bedford level, or the ancient and natural surface of the country upon which the great body of the fens now rests, and which bed consists chiefly of a strong retentive gault or clay, was once, and (for aught we know to the contrary) is at this time, sufficiently elevated above the level of the sea to drain itself. At the same time that I assume this opinion as a point of unquestionable certainty, it is necessary to bear in our remembrance; that not only the valley in which the level of the fens now lies, was then covered with wood, but that the higher parts of the country, particularly the counties of Huntingdon, Bedford, Buckingham, and Northampton, were one continued forest also: I am particularly desirous of impressing this idea, as being of consequence in leading to a more perfect knowledge of the primary cause and origin of that vast mass of vegetable matter which now composes the body of the fens, and I shall therefore illustrate it by a reference to the case of Ireland.

When in former ages the country of Ireland was divided into principalities, colonized from different nations, and subdivided again into various tribes, a constant and cruel warfare appears to have been waged among them. At that time the whole country was covered with wood, and as advantages were obtained by one chieftain over another, or as their views of annoyance were likely to be answered by the measure, they set on fire (as has been done recently against the royalists in France) their adversaries' forests, thus destroying their strong holds, and despoiling them of their hunting grounds. The consequences were such, that many of the trees only partly consumed by the fire, were thrown down by the succeeding winds, into and across the rivulets, by which the drainage of the country was naturally performed. An obstruction to the usual discharge of the waters was thus produced, and a large pond, or lake of water, soon spread itself over the whole level, which heretofore drained voluntarily through those channels which were thus choaked up. A prodigious quantity of putrid, and putrifying vegetable matter in the stagnant waters gave immediate encouragement to the growth of vegetables of the aquatic tribe, which annually growing and annually proceeding to decay, proved a constant and regular cause of the accession of vegetable matter, and finally became a morass: from which stage (by gradual means) it has increased to its present bulk, forming what in Ireland is called a bog: which like a spunge filled with water, swells in many places above the level of the country by which it is surrounded.

My first step towards the improvement of a large tract of bog in the King's County in Ireland was to form and recover an outfal drain, 12 feet wide and about a quarter of a mile long, at the foot of the bog which was designed to be drained. The bottom of this drain was formed of a compact retentive clay or gault; above which, in many places, there was a depth of twelve and fifteen feet of turf moor; under which, and on the bed or resting place of the bog, there were distinctly to be seen ridges and furrows, the indisputable remains of an antient cultivation. In other places, on the bed of the bog were found considerable quantities of oak, yew, and pine, all of which appeared to have been more or less exposed to the action of fire; the more valuable pieces of this timber were easily discovered by probing with a
p.5 spit and then raised out of the bog; an oak which I remember particularly measured fifty-five feet in length, and twenty-two inches through at the butt end. Such of the yew, as was not cut, or wind-shaken, was cut into planks and made into beautiful furniture, and for the remainder, as well as for the oak and pine, I found a ready demand for forming flood gates, for building and for farming use. Upon the gault or clay at the bottom of the outfal drains we found the dash, and lid, of an hand churn, and a large crane necked brass spur, with a rowel a full inch in diameter.

The outfal drain being compleated and proper sluices erected to give a command of the water; the next step was to cut foot drains, or drains one foot wide and one spit deep, at right angles to, and parallel with the outfal drain; thereby dividing the whole surface of the bog into squares of four plantation acres each. The following year these drains were deepened and enlarged to three feet wide, and two and a half feet deep. The result was, that within two years from the time the outfal drain was began, the whole mass of bog from actual and accurate observation, subsided and shrunk downwards, four feet in perpendicular height; and from being in a state, in which with much difficulty, I could step from one hassock to another, without slipping off, and sinking up to my middle, it became so far consolidated and compact, that the store cattle in the spring following, roamed over and browsed upon it with ease and perfect security.

The *Mosses of Scotland* seem to be derived from an accidental and similar cause; and the *Swamps of America*, though evidently of a later date, are chiefly to be imputed to an accidental origin. In confirmation of this latter opinion, I must solicit the indulgence of the Board, whilst I relate the amount of my observations as they regard this production of nature in the new and uncultivated country.

Many of the swamps of America (and some of considerable extent) are produced from the ingenious and unparalleled labours of the half reasoning beaver. At the back of the town of Frankford in Kentucky (which is now the seat of the government of that flourishing and happy slate) I was present at the cutting of a beaver dam, the heart of which, consisted of a very large locust tree,* which had been cut, and thrown down by these animals, across one of the principal drains which discharged the waters of that plain, and of the higher lands into the Kentucky river. About two hundred acres of land were immediately recovered; the surface of which was composed of putrid vegetable matter or fen mould, clear from wood, and ready for the plough. It was in the early settlement of that town, and before any idea was entertained of its being made the seat of the present government, that I was called upon, in conjunction with another person, to value this reclaimed land; and although the current price in the
p.6 neighbourhood for the uncleared land of the first rate quality did not exceed one guinea per acre, we readily agreed to a valuation of five pounds per acre for the reclaimed beaver pond. On the rich bottom lands upon the margin of the Ohio river, and all the river bottoms throughout the whole extent of that delightful country, forsaken beaver ponds and those still inhabited by that sagacious animal of several miles in length, and very wide, are gradually assuming the appearance and nature of morass; but which by cutting away the beaver dams, and opening the natural passage for the water, are hourly and easily reclaimed; and prove in a country, like that (where the clearing of heavy timbered land is an expensive,

* The locusts of America, are the acacia of this country. The honey locust derives its name from a rich sweet pulp, that invelops the seed, which is inclosed in pods about nine inches long. The black locust is a beautiful tree, but not so strait and lofty: it encourages every species of vegetation under its shade. The honey locust is armed with strong spikes up the whole of the stem, and to its extreme branches. The black locust has also thorns, but less formidable. The timber of both is extremely hard and durable; but that of the black locust is preferred, whether under cover, in the open air, or for posts in fencing.

tedious, and Herculean labour) an immediate convenience and an acquisition of considerable value to the owners, and occupiers of them. The shades of death (as they are called) on the top of the Alleghany Mountain, the buffalo swamp in the lower part of Pennsylvania, and the dismal swamp in Virginia, all seem to owe their origin to an accidental arrestment of their natural waters, but for which cause alone, their superior elevation would have left them dry ages ago, like the adjacent country.

From this view of the operations of nature in the silent and solitary course, is it not fair to infer, that a small cause compact'd with the magnitude of the effect (assisted by negligence, and confirmed by an operation of the ocean not possible to be controlled) may have produced the alteration of the level of the country now covered by the fens? The appearance of the effects of fire is not so generally seen on the timber that has fallen, or the stumps that are found rooted in the bed of the fens, as under the bogs of Ireland; still a sudden and violent tempest, or some other, incidental cause, might have thrown down so many, trees into the natural water courses, as to obstruct the discharge of the waters, and at the time of great floods; resist the floating off to sea the drift wood and rack, descending in great quantities from an high and woodland country.[+] The obstruction remaining for a few days only, would acquire additional strength from seaward, by the deposition of mud and sediment brought up, by the succeeding tides, and lodged on the seaside of the obstruction thus formed in the principal river. In a few years a bank, of considerable substance would be thus accumulated, and the land waters being thus arrested in their passage downwards, must of necessity be constantly increasing, and in a short time from one extensive lake over the whole level of the country which is now occupied by the fens. At what time; it fell into that state, I believe there is neither tradition or historical record to afford us any probable account, unless we suppose it to have happened in the time of the Danes, by whom this part of England was much infested; but certain it is, that it must have been in that situation for many ages, or the prodigious quantity of vegetable matter, which now composes the body of the fens, could not have been produced, though it has evidently arisen from the same general, cause that has generated the bogs of
p.7 Ireland, the mosses of Scotland, and the swamps of America; (viz.) the annual growth and annual decay of vegetable bodies combined with too much water. In the state either of a lake or morass, the whole level of the fens would most probably have been at this day, but for the timely intervention of human industry. On the other hand, a country would have been raised to the highest level of the sea, on the coasts of the counties of Norfolk, Cambridge, and Lincoln, though the extent of the sea waters, and their effects inland, was then, and must for ever have been prescribed, by the acclivity of the country, and the presence of the land waters upon it. As far as the force and pressure of the sea waters have been made to penetrate inwards, by the power of winds and the strength of extraordinary tides, their effects are distinctly to be seen, by the salt and sea sediment they have left behind them; for as you proceed from the general line of the sea coast, into the bosom of the fens, the effect of the sea water gradually decreases; till at length it finally vanishes, and the surface of the level becomes a pure and un-mixed mass of vegetable matter or fen mould.

The same industry which has been exerted in endeavours to carry the surface waters of the fens to sea, has also been employed, but with more effect, in anticipating the operation which the sea must finally have had in excluding itself from the sea made countries of Marshland, Wisbeach, north and south side, and South Holland in Lincolnshire. These improvements have ever been regarded, as of the first consequence to individuals, and the public at large; and it is only to be lamented in many of them, that the adventurer suffers the new in-take to be too much exhausted by repeated croppings, before it is laid down to rest in pasture and in grazing ground, the state to which it is by nature most properly adapted.

We uniformly find a certain point of elevation, to which the sea raises its sands, before they begin to assume the appearance of salt-marsh. Here the first dawning of vegetation is samphire, and a species of grass, which partakes a good deal of the same nature; and here the more loamy and divisible part of the sea-sediment is deposited, which gives a strength and confidence to the surface, which the larger

\+ I have seen the Ohio River, at the mouth of the Muskingham River, when it is about eight hundred yards wide, rise thirty-two feet perpendicular height in about five days; the top of the fresh ran at the rate of about five miles and a half per hour, and the whole surface of the river, during the greater part of the time, was covered with drift wood from shore to shore. A dam, formed by an arrestment of this driftwood and rack, and corroborated afterwards by the influx of the tides depositing a sediment at the foot of such dam, must throw the whole country above in the state o£ a lake: such arrestments account for the number of mouths the Mississippi has at this time.

and more gravitating particles of sea-sand below, are incapable of affording; and in proportion as this matter is exhausted, and deprived of its virtue by repeated crops, so we approach to an hungry tilt, and the permanent value of the embankment is lessened. There are other points and of the first consequence to be attended to, in undertakings of this nature; particularly not to be too impatient, or too greedy in the embankment proposed. If the sea has not raised the salt marsh to its fruitful level, all expectation of benefit is vain, the soil being immature and not ripened for inclosing; and if again, with a view of grasping a great extent of salt marsh, the bank or sea wall is pushed farther outwards, than where there is a firm and secure foundation for it to stand upon, the bank will blow up, and in both cases great Losses and disappointments will ensue.

It will appear from the Journal, that a considerable part of the inclosed marshes on the sea-side of the old Roman embankment in *Tid St. Giles's*, are valued by a proprietor only at eight shillings the acre,
p.8 which can only be accounted for from the adventurer having been too early with that in-take, or from the improper treatment it has since received; whereas the new embankment on the opposite and east side of Kenderley's cut in the same parish, was greedily fought for, immediately after the bank was raised at thirty shillings the acre.

We shall now proceed to a farther investigation of the nature of the fens; in which I shall endeavour to account for their most singular phenomena.

Heat and moisture are inseparably connected with the process of putrifaction; *and it is impossible that any substance whatever can be brought to operate as a direct manure and food for plants,*[*] *unless it has undergone the putrid ferment, and is rendered completely soluble in water, that being the only vehicle by which nourishment can be conveyed to the roots of vegetables.* We find the surface of the fens, which is occasionally exposed to the influence of the summer heats, consists of completely decompounded and putrified vegetables; and regarding the soil only, it is impossible to trace in it any vestige of the original substances that composed it. The sub-stratum, or turf-moor next below the soil, is also a composition of vegetable bodies, but in a less perfect state of rottenness or decomposition; and in this may very plainly be seen the original form and substance of its component parts. Below this again, and lying on the natural and antient surface of the country, is another stratum of vegetable matter, commonly called bears muck.[+] This stratum retains every appearance of what it originally was, saving its life and colour, being an assemblage of the roots, leaves and stems of an aquatic vegetation; which has undergone but little alteration since the remote period of its first formation; because it has been, beyond the reach of the essential principle of heat to combine with moisture and air in effecting its natural and necessary dissolution.

An opinion prevails very generally through this country, that the turf-moor which is usually cut for firing, has a quality of growing and of reproducing itself in a very short time. This idea originates from a well known fact, that when turf pits are made, they will in a few years afterwards, be capable of affording an equal quantity of a similar substance fit for the purposes of fuel. In opening a turf pit, it is usually found necessary to throw off about eighteen, inches of the superstratum, which is always cast
p.9 into the last made pit, by the side of which the new one is formed. This vegetable soil or fen-mould is then in a proper state for producing a luxuriant vegetation, and in consequence, a prodigious growth of sedges, flags, reeds, and bull-rushes, are immediately produced; the very roots of which contain more vegetable matter and are far more capacious and bulky than some of the plants which proceed from

* The Farmer says, "if I apply my dung in this state, it is eaten by the land in the course of one year." It is granted, that no appearance of the rotten dung will probably remain after that time; but it does not follow that its virtues are exhausted, because it cannot be found in the same form in, which it was spread upon the land. The process of its operation as a manure, is unseen by the human eye, and the existence of it in the soil is only to be estimated from its effects. Upon a stubborn, cold, and compact clay, long dung may operate in fertilizing the soil, by rendering it more admissible to the ameliorating influence of the sun, frost, air, and dews; but it can never operate as a direct manure and food for plants, till it is rendered capable of combining with water. Top dressings which contain a fixed Alkali (which is indispensibly necessary for the union of oil with water), manure, or oileagenous matter, or a compound of them all; must in some measure, though not cognizable to our senses, be obedient to the same laws.

\+ This substance is cut into large sods, about twice the size of a common brick, and forms the red spungy kindling, turf, which is used in large towns for the purpose of lighting fires.

them. The greater part of these roots being generally, and the whole of the plants being constantly, in an annual state of increase and decay, will at once account for that very rapid accretion of vegetable matter which in a certain stage of rottenness constitutes the turf-moor.

SECT. II

Of the General Drainage of the Fens.

As the preceding section contains the amount of my observations and opinion, on the nature and origin of the fens, I shall now direct my attention to the next points which appear to demand our most serious consideration (viz.) the cheapest and most effectual means of forming a good drainage and navigation from the Highland country through the level of the fens to the sea; so as by one and the same means to render commerce more diffusive and beneficial to the country at large, and obtain a more effectual drainage of the fens and low grounds.

As the drainage of the fens and the navigation of the rivers passing through them to the upper country, are inseparably united, and must ever be regarded in a discussion of this nature as one and the same thing; it is necessary to establish some first principle, which of necessity applies equally to both, and from which, as from a point we may take our departure and to which we must return again. The level of the sea I conceive to be this point, since "all rivers" run into the sea, yet the sea is not full; and unto the place from whence the rivers come, thither "they return again."

The waters of the *middle level* at this time diverted from their natural course, by the present forced system of drainage in the river Nene, at Outwell, arrive within ten miles (reckoned on the general course of the old Ouze river) of Gunthrope sluice, through which all the waters of the north level are freely uttered. From Outwell church, the waters of the Nene are driven six miles farther, before they can obtain a very slow and languid descent to seaward, through Salters-lode sluice. The same erroneous system prevails in the whole drainage of the middle, and the greater part of the south levels of the fens;
p.10 and *is the legitimate offspring of the first diversion of Old Ouze from its natural channel and forcing its waters into the Lynn or lesser Ouze through the cut which was formerly made from Littleport Chair to Priests Houses.*

From the Highlands in Suffolk (between the Mildenhall and Brandon Rivers) to the east: of Welney, Outwell, Emneth, and thence to the sea; a positive dividing ground exists, formed by the hand of nature, strongly marked and distinctly to be seen between the waters of the Lynn and of the Wisbeach Ouze. The hanging level or natural inclination of the country on the north side of this dividing ground, draw the waters off to sea through the lesser Ouze to the outfal of Lynn; and on the south side of it draws them off to the sea through the greater Ouze to the outfal of Wisbeach. *To the cutting through this divided ground* (before mentioned) *in order to force the water of the greater into the lesser Ouze, are all the evils of the south and middle levels of the fens, and of the country below, solely and originally to be ascribed.* At this time the bed of the Ouze where Denver sluices now stand, was at least thirteen feet below the general surface of the surrounding country; and then it was, that by the free action and re-action of the tides, the water flowed five hours in the haven of Lynn, ascended into the Stoke and Brandon Rivers, and into other streams which nature had wisely appropriated to be discharged through that outfal; forming the bed of the Ouze to one gradually inclined plane, *from the junction of the principal branches of the river in the low country, to the level of the ocean very near or in the harbour of Lynn.* Then it was, that the province of Marshland was recovered from the sea; and all the county which by nature belonged to the drainage of the Lynn ouze, was effectually drained, and made into good winter grounds.

The counter-acting this disposition of nature, *by forcing a greater quantity of water into the river than it could discharge into the sea during the time of ebb*; necessarily occasioned the high land and foreign waters to over-ride all those, which during the time of ebb, would naturally have drained into the Lynn river, and gave the waters of Buckingham and Bedford an exit into the sea, in preference to those which lay inundating the country, within a few miles of their natural outfal.— In this condition at present, are all the lower parts of the country bordering upon the Lynn Ouze; and the country above Denver sluices, Downham, Marshland, and Bardolph fens, exhibits the most important of many other melancholy examples and evidences of it. In the higher parts of the country, the consequences of this measure seems

to have been severely experienced, on the lands exposed to the unembanked waters of the old Ouze, between Hermitage and Harrimere. The old Bedford river was then cut, from Erith to Salters Lode, as a slaker to the Ouze, to relieve the country through which the Ouze flowed, from Erith to Ely. The Ouze water, thus divided, a great part of them descended through the old Bedford river in a straight line of twenty miles into the Lynn Ouze. But as that work was judged insufficient and defective, the new Bedford, or one hundred foot river, was determined upon; and sluices were erected at Hermitage to drive all the waters of old Ouze from Erith, (through the one hundred foot) into the Lynn Ouze; but that river not having sufficient capacity to utter them to the sea, they reverted up the Ouze, the Stokes, and Brandon rivers, drowning the whole of that country, and finally urging the necessity of erecting Denver
p.11 sluices as the only apparent cure for the evils with which the country was then oppressed, and seemed farther threatened with. In the execution of this business, with a view of bringing the bottom of the Ouze on a level with that of the one hundred foot river, (which was cut only five feet deep) it was judged expedient to raise a dam eight feet high across the bed of the Ouze, upon the top of which, the sole or base of the Denver sluices was laid. This measure has not only defeated the purpose it was designed to promote, but has been the unfortunate cause of a body of sand and sea sediment being deposited in the bed of the Lynn Ouze, at least eight feet deep at Denver sluices; and only terminating in its injurious conferences at the mouth of the Lynn Channel (or low water mark at sea.) This shews to every calm and candid mind, the necessity of duly considering the probable effects of counter-acting the laws of nature, in cases where nature appears experimentally to have had success on her side. By great and continued exertion the strength and ingenuity of man may in some instances delay the evil which otherwise would immediately accrue from a counter-action of those laws, but his energy is not only feeble, but soon expires; whereas that of nature is potent, and if relieved only from the operation of incidental obstacles, as it is unalterable in its essence, so it must be uniform in its effects from the beginning of time, till time shall be no more.

From a due consideration of the obstacles which will appear at this time to exist in what has long been considered the principal outfalling drain to the middle and south levels of the fens, it is surely reasonable to direct our attention to the general inclination of the country with respect to the sea, and to what has all along been pointed out by nature as the main outlet thither, for the waters of the middle and south levels, and see if some means cannot yet be devised for recovering the general course of the antient and voluntary passage of the waters through their natural channel of Wisbeach to the sea. To begin this enquiry we must take our departure from the low water mark at sea; and trace the effect of the tidal waters as they regard the discharge of the land waters, through the channels of Lynn and Wisbeach. On this occasion, I have been as accurate as the time and means in my power would enable me to be, but still I must lament the necessity I have been under of resorting to the materials of art rather than adhering closely to those of nature to establish my facts upon.

The flowing of the tide above the haven of Lynn, at stated distances to Denver sluice at the times I was moored at the entrance of the Lynn and Wisbeach channels, would be more satisfactory and conclusive to my mind, than any scientific authority, however high, and deferredly to be depended upon. Such data however as I have been able to collect from the flowing of the tides, will be found in the following tide tables.

TABLE of the flowing of the tide on the 19th day of November, 1793, in the Harbour of Lynn, and at the mouth of the Lynn Channel, two miles below the Terror Sands, at the White or Flag Buoy, distant about fourteen miles on a strait line below the Harbour of Lynn.

At the Mouth of the Lynn Channel.							In the Harbour of Lynn				
Tide		Depth of water in which are included		Rise			Time		Rise		
Hours	Min.	Feet	Inches	Feet	Inches		Hours	Mins.	Feet	Inches	
At 2		19	6{	In which we anchored in dead low water							
3		22	4	1	10						
3	30	25	2	5	8						
4		28		8	6						
4	30	31		11	6						
5		33	8	13	2	Young flood at Lynn	At 5		Dead low water, or the first flow of the		
5	30	36	3	16	9		5	30	6	6	tide
6		38		18	6		6		3	5	
6	30	39	6	20			6	30	2	3	
7		40		20	6		7		1	5	
7	23	40	6	21			7	32		11	
7	40	41		21	6	Ebb begins	7	40			Ebb began.
In 5	40	2 flow of		21	6		In 2	32	14	8	Flow.

N.B. The above observations at the flag buoy in the chops of Lynn Channel, were made by Mr. Lionel Self, Mr. Middleton, (master Pilot) and the Author; and those in the Harbour of Lynn, by Mr. Thomas Brame, and Mr. William Dunham; a gentle breeze blowing from the south east the whole time.

To explain in some measure the phenomenon that appears from the within tide tables, of the ebb in the Harbour of Lynn, being noticed at the same point of time, it was felt in the mouth of the Lynn Channel, fourteen miles on a straight line nearer to the Sea, we must recur to the set of the tides in the Bay which is formed by the coasts of Lincolnshire and Norfolk. The flood tide makes in Brancaster Bay, on the coast of Norfolk about two hours sooner, and off Hunston one hour sooner than at the Flag or White Buoy, which is placed in the entrance of the Lynn Channel, and of course returns in the same proportion of time before it is high water in the mouth of the Channel. During the last hour's flood at the Flag Buoy, the tide off Hunston sets eastwardly, and towards the Sea between the sunk sand and shore; in consequence of which, the water along shore in the Old Eastern Channel, between Hunston and Nottingham point, is affected; and Ebb in the Harbour of Lynn in felt sooner, than would be expected from the Harbour of Lynn, being fourteen miles farther from the Ocean, than the Mouth of the Channel. At the time these observations were made, the Terror Sands which are about two miles above the Flag Buoy, had not at low water more than four feet depth upon them.

TABLE of the flowing of one and the same tide on the 3d day of December, 1793, in the town of Wisbeach; also at Gunthorpe Sluice, about six miles below the town; also on the north side of the Bar Buoy, about eighteen miles below the town, being in the entrance of Wisbeach Channel; and also, in the Harbour of Lynn.

On the North Side of the Bar Buoy							At Gunthorpe Sluice					In the Town of Wisbeach						In the Harbour of Lynn				
Time		Depth of water		Rise			Time		Rise			Time		Rise				Time		Rise		
Hours	Minutes	Feet	Inches	Feet	Inches		Hours	Minutes	Feet	Inches		Hours	Minutes	Feet	Inches	10ths		Hours	Minutes	Feet	Inches	
At 1	20	12	{In which we anchored at dead low water																			
2		13	9	1	9																	
2	30	16	6	4	6																	
3		19	4	7	4																	
3	30	22	3	10	3																	
4		24	6	12	6													At 4	12	{Dead low water, or the first flow of the tide		
4	30	27	6	15	6																	
5		31		19														4	42	3	8	
5	25	32		20		Flood at	5	25	The first flow of the tide									5	12	3	10	
6		33		21			5	55	4	2								5	42	2	6	
6	20	33	3	21	3	High water	6	25	6		High water	At 6	20	The first flow of the tide				6	12	1	3	
6	30	33	3	21	3							6	50	1	0	3						
6	40	32	6	Sensible ebb								7	20	2	6	3		6	30		9	High water
							6	55	7			7	50	3	5	3						
In 5				21	3	Rise or flow of the water	In 1	35	7	Rise or flow of water		8		3	6	3	Rise or flow of water	In 2	38	14	Rise or flow of water	
N.B. The above observations were made by the Author, assisted by SAM. GARDINER, THO. GARDINER and SAM. BOUCH. - A gentle breeze South by West the whole time.							N.B. The above observations were made by THO. PEARS who lives at and has care of the sluice. There were 2 feet, 7 inches of water, at the time of young flood, over the threshold of the sluice.					N.B. The above observations were made by Mr. JOHN TURPIN of Wisbeach.						N.B. The above observations were made by Mr. THO. BREAME of Lynn				

p.14 From the preceding tables the following summary may be drawn:

When the tide at the mouth of the Lynn channel has flowed three hours, and has there risen thirteen feet two inches, it is young flood in the harbour of Lynn. But as it flows in the mouth of the Lynn channel, two hours and twenty minutes longer, the whole flow or rife of the water there is twenty-one feet fix inches, in five hours and twenty minutes of time; while the whole flow of the water in the harbour of Lynn in two hours and thirty-two minutes, is fourteen feet six inches; and (adjusting the difference between the watches) at forty minutes past seven, ebb has made, and is first noticed as well in the harbour of Lynn, as in the mouth of the channel. The inference is plain, allowing a small effect for the operation of the tide in the eastern channel (as before explained.) There is an absolute acclivity of seven feet perpendicular height, between the low water mark in the entrance of Lynn Channel, and the low water mark in the harbour of Lynn; to overcome which acclivity and the obstructions upon it, in three hours of time, a force of moving water from the ocean of thirteen feet two inches perpendicular pressure is required.

Secondly—When the flood tide has been made four hours and five minutes at the mouth of the *Wisbeach channel,* it has there risen twenty feet, and at this time it is young flood at Gunthrope sluice. It flows in the mouth of the Wisbeach channel fifty-five minutes longer, making in the whole time five hours, and the whole flow or rise of the water, is twenty-one feet three inches. The time from first flood at *Gunthrope sluice,* to high water there, is one hour and 35 minutes; in which time the tide flows or rises seven feet in perpendicular height: from whence it is plain that there is an acclivity of fourteen feet three inches, from the level of the sea at low water, to the low water at Gunthrope sluice. Again, when the water has flowed five hours in the mouth of the Wisbeach channel, and has there risen twenty-one feet three inches, the first flood is perceived in the town of Wisbeach. At this time it is high water at sea; though from the momentum of the tide, the water is continued flowing in the town for one hour and forty minutes longer, and there rises three feet six inches three tenths. From hence it is also plain that there is an acclivity of seventeen feet eight inches seven tenths between the low water at sea, and the low water mark in the port of Wisbeach; to overcome which acclivity, and the obstructions upon it in five hours of time, a pressure of water from the ocean of twenty-one feet three inches perpendicular height is required. It is also to be remarked, that when the water has flowed in the entrance of the Wisbeach channel two hours and fifty-two minutes, and risen thirteen feet nine inches, it is young flood in the harbour of Lynn, it continues to flow two hours and eight minutes longer in the mouth of the Wisbeach channel, where the whole flow or rise of the water is twenty-one feet three inches. In the harbour of Lynn the same tide flows two hours and thirty-eight minutes and there rises fourteen feet. From hence it follows that there is a declivity of three inches more between the harbour of Lynn and the mouth of the Wisbeach channel, than between the same harbour and the mouth of the Lynn channel; or in other words, that the low water in the mouth of the Wisbeach channel is three inches lower than that in the mouth of the channel of Lynn, or so much nearer to the low water mark at sea.

p.15 From this view of the Lynn and Wisbeach rivers the following opinions are fairly to be drawn: First, that the low water in the harbour of Lynn, is ten feet nearer to the low water mark at sea, than the low water in the port of Wisbeach. And secondly, allowing a fall of six feet four inches in the distance of near sixteen miles from Denver sluice to the harbour of Lynn, that there exists at the former place the same obstruction to the descent of all the middle and the south level waters, as the waters of the north level uttered through Gunthrope sluice have to encounter and completely overcome, (viz.) about 14 feet perpendicular height above the level of low water at sea. This difference however must be observed, that whereas Gunthrope sluice is situated within twelve miles of the absolute and lowest level of the sea (and within a much shorter distance of where there is a constant and eternal depth of from seven to ten fathom at low water,) Denver sluice is not within thirty miles of this lowest level, and to which point the land waters must descend, before it can with reason be said that we have got completely rid of them.

This being the present state of the Lynn and Wisbeach rivers, as they relate to navigation and the discharge of the land waters to the sea; the next objects which command our attention, are the cheapest, the quickest, and most effectual means of removing the obstructions at present existing in their respective channels; and bringing deep water, or the level of the sea, as near as the laws of nature will admit of, to the seats of the present marine navigations; to the end, that by their improvement the drainage of the country may be rendered more immediate and compleat, and a more permanently valuable property be restored to individuals and secured to the nation. In the furtherance of this object, and as it particularly regards navigation and the drainage of the country through the haven of Lynn, a plan has been submitted to the consideration of Parliament as an effectual and complete remedy for all the evils so justly to be deplored, in the middle and south levels of the fens, and the country below bordering upon the Lynn Ouze. A part of the preamble of the bill sets forth; That by altering the course of the river Ouze from a place called Eau-brink (below St. German's bridge) to the port of Lynn, an improvement to the outfal of the river will be made, and a better drainage produced both to the adjacent country, and also to the middle and south levels of the fens. On this proposition I will be as candid and as clear as possible; and that we may the better understand the basis and foundation upon which the super-structure must be raised; I shall here subjoin, a journal of several sets of borings which I ordered and saw made in the direction of the proposed cut, also under the walls, and in the town of Lynn.

Journal of a set of borings made in the direction of a cut proposed to be made from the upper end of the haven of Lynn, across the marshes to strike the Ouze river again, at a place called Eau-brink.

No. I. Being in the middle of the proposed cut at its entrance into the haven of Lynn, and at the common high water mark.

p.16 At the surface, an infinitely fine sea sand or silt, mixed with ouze or sea clay; at two feet a more compact and firmer substance, but still mixed, with silt; at three feet, the same substance continued, but touching upon a black dry sea mud with a small mixture of silt.

N. B. The surface and substrata thus far, when wet having a greasy appearance, and feelings to the touch; the only sure way to discover the presence of the silt or fine sea sand is to put a small portion into the mouth when it will be immediately detected.

At four feet, the same kind of mud, but rather softer continued, and here too was found water; at five feet, a grey ouze with a small mixture of fine silt; at six feet, nearly the same; at eight feet, a black soft sea mud (through which the boring rods with the strength of a single person, can with ease be pushed a foot and eighteen inches at a time; at ten feet, a very soft black mud, extremely offensive to the smell, and containing a portion of very fine silt; at twelve feet the same; at fourteen feet, little or no difference; at fifteen feet, vegetable matter or moor appeared, the depth of which is uncertain.

No. II. Being on the north side of the north sea bank in the land of which is a ploughed field.

The surface, an hazel coloured greasy soil, with a mixture of silt; at two feet, a brown compact loam, with a mixture of silt; at three feet, a dry firm and compact loam, with a mixture of silt; at four feet, a wet soft loam with silt; at six feet, a black soft sea mud (which was equally penetrated by the boring rods, as the black sea mud at eight feet in the first boring;) at eight feet the same; at nine feet, a putrid vegetable matter or moor, very dry and offering some resistance to the bite of the augur; at ten feet, the same; at eleven feet, the same, with a strongly marked appearance of rotten wood; at thirteen feet, vegetable matter but less firm; at fifteen feet, moor, with rotten wood.

No. III. Being on the south side of the north sea bank in Mr. Carey's land.

The surface, an hazel coloured loam, or gentle clay, with a mixture of vegetable matter and silt; at two feet, a strong dry loam with silt; at four feet, a similar substance, but soft and wet; at six feet a dry vegetable matter, or moor; at eight feet, the same; at ten feet, a soft buttery clay of a bluish colour (which I expected to have found the natural and original surface of the country;) at twelve feet, much the same as the above, but rather softer. By digging eighteen inches, we reached a depth of sixteen feet and a half from the surface of this level, where I was disappointed in finding a white sea sand, or coarse quick silt.

No. IV. Being about eighty yards distant, and below the river bank at Eau-brink, on a low part of the common, about the middle of the proposed cut, and by the south side of Sampson's wheat field, marked thus. ✠

p.17 The surface an hazel coloured loam or sea clay, with a mixture of fine silt and vegetable matter; at two feet, a dry tender loam, containing some hard crombs, (which easily dissolve in water) and silt; at four feet, a sheer dry silt, without any mixture of unctious matter, ouze, or sea clay; at five feet the same, but loose, owing to admixture of water; at six feet the same; at eight feet the same, and very easily penetrated; at ten feet the same, but blackish coloured; and making still less resistance to the weight and working of the boring rods; at twelve feet the same, but with a more active silt; at fourteen feet, a very coarse silt, or sea sand.

No. V. Being between the present harbour and under the walls of Lynn, a little below the Ball fleet, at a place called Millers Entry.

The surface, silt, with a mixture of ouze or brown mud; at two feet, silt and rubbish; at four feet, black firm silt, with some rubbish; at seven feet and a half, a closely compressed black sea mud with some silt, but little or no rubbish; at ten feet the same; at twelve feet, sheer firm silt, but of a lighter colour; at fourteen feet, coarser sheer silt, and of a still lighter colour; at seventeen feet, cockle shells, burnt bones, brick rubbish, black gravel, and silt; at eighteen feet, black coloured firm silt; at nineteen feet, a brown coarse silt with a vein of very coarse sand; at twenty feet sand or very coarse silt and no perceivable mixture of clay or ouze.

No. VI. Being, in Mrs. Partridge's back-yard, and at a short distance from the Haven of Lynn.

The first, nine feet through made ground, then reached silt and water; at twelve feet the same; at sixteen feet and a half a sheer silt, which being very quick and active, was washed by the water into the augur-hole, so that after several attempts, it was found impossible to penetrate farther.

I have been careful to preserve samples of all the most striking variety of strata in the several sets of borings, to justify the description that I have given of them. They exhibit at one view, the structure of the country through which the cut is proposed to be made; and at the same time shew that the site or foundation of the town of Lynn, is composed of the same adventitious matter, excepting the rubbish (though in a more compressed state from the incumbent weight and traffick of the town) with that which forms the country of Marshland, and which is plainly to be traced through the whole level, from the foot of the high-land country to the fens and to the sea. To those who are acquainted with the means of prescribing a path to the raging tides, saying thus far shalt thou go, and no further, or directing the descent of refluent waters through quicksand and morass, I must leave the practicability of constructing such banks to the proposed cut as will effectually secure the surrounding country. Were we acquainted with the depth of the cut intended to be made, and had we an opportunity of comparing it with the level of the country and with the section of strata, through which the cut must go; some clue might be firmed
p.18 towards a tolerable judgment; but pressed as I am at this time with the other objects of the survey, it would be imprudent to give an opinion which I cannot be prepared to support. In this situation, I must leave this part of the question as to the construction of the cut; but I shall say a few words upon the supposition of this work being executed.

It is universally agreed by all writers on mechanics, that bodies in motion operate with their fullest force, when they strike another at right angles; and that their power diminishes in proportion to the obliquity of their stroke. This being the case, and seeing that the town of Lynn is situated on a bed of sand, and of compressed sea mud; I have no hesitation in pronouncing the inevitable destruction of it and of its present harbour, were the proposed cut to strike its walls nearly or in the same direction with that of the present river above the town; but as this direction cannot obtain from the proposed cut, no danger is to be apprehended on that score. Why in fact it does not operate to that destructive end at present, is owing, I conceive, to the meandering circuitious course, which the tidal and fresh waters now make among the loose sands, in the extensive bason above the town; where, after the first quarters ebb, the sands above the town begin to top and shew themselves. At this time, the ebb begins to act with a powerful and inconvenient force, and a sharp recoil in the returning waters is produced; carrying the channel from a little above Purfleet, directly across the Haven to the west side, that is towards Old Lynn.

This being premised, we come next to a consideration of some of the probable consequences of the proposed cut, supposing, (as before) the banks strong and permanently made.

The present harbour of Lynn forms the segment of a circle of about twenty degrees, in the hollow of which and extending along the walls of the upper part of the town the ships ride and lie at low water, and receive and discharge their cargoes; and from its contiguity to the wharfs and granaries, the greatest part of the shipping business of this port is done here. Lying thus in the hollow of an arch, the vessels are defended against the force of the flood tides, by the lower part of the town acting as a pier, which

shoots the *flood tide*, in a straight line through the Haven into the bason above; at which time so powerful is its operations, that an eddy is always produced in the harbour, and at times, a counter-stream (called the *trains*) of such vehemence, as to endanger the mooring of the vessels *down stream*, whilst the water is swelling or flowing in the harbour, at the rate of twelve and fourteen feet in the hour, directing its stream upwards. Now if from the removal of the present channel into a line with the proposed cut, the present harbour should be silted up, and the shelter which is now afforded to the shipping by the town from the north and easterly winds, should to a certain degree be lost; the shipping would then ride or lie in the middle of the Haven, fully exposed on the one hand to the fury of the flood tide, combined with that of the northerly and westerly winds, and on the other, to the undiverted force of the ebb land waters, strengthened by a southerly wind, and descending in a torrent down the proposed cut, into, and through the Haven of Lynn. What effect this might have in addition to the increased distance to which the harbour may then be removed from the wharfs and granaries; must be left to those who are acquainted with the shipping and lighterage business of the port.— In other respects I can have no hesitation in
p.19 forming an opinion: for should the water be led down the channel which now forms the harbour of Lynn, considering the increased violence with which they must act from their precipitant descent, unless capacious locks are made for the reception of shipping and small craft, (for which however the port affords great conveniency) little business can be expected to be done during the last three quarters ebb. Considering also the impelling and sapping powers of such waters upon a foundation so extremely moveable as that of the town of Lynn, although those waters may act upon it nearly in a tangent (and of course approach the direction of all others the least liable to produce injury) yet, unless great care be had, and considerable works erected, to preserve the present foreland and foot of the town, between its walls and harbour, the most serious evils to the west side of the town may justly be apprehended.

In the distance of five miles and five furlongs, what is comprehended in the present bend of the river from Eau-brink to the Haven of Lynn, there now exists a fall (according to Mr. Watte's scale of levels) of four feet ten inches and four-tenths, (equal to ten inches in a mile;) and which in a confined channel would produce a torrent; but which in the present wide and extended bay, where the waters ramble over, and among a large expanse of loose sands, their gravitating powers being thus diminished, the existing fall is reduced to a dam, against the waters descending from the upper country.

It is generally allowed that three inches fall in a mile in a confined channel, is sufficient to produce a smart current; now allowing a fall of something less than four inches in a mile for the current through the proposed cut, the water on the opening of the cut may be presumed to subside four feet at Eau-brink; between which place, and Denver sluices, in the distance of ten miles there is said to be a fall of one foot five inches and two-tenths (allowing nearly the same fall for the current of the water, between Eau brink and Denver sluices as is allowed through the proposed cut) provided the bed of the river presents no obstruction from four feet under the present low water mark at Eau brink to two feet, one inch two-tenths, under the present low water mark at Denver sluice. So much therefore, viz. two feet one inch two-tenths would the water be lowered also at Denver sluices on the opening of the proposed cut. This line of subsided water extended from the Haven of Lynn, through all the streams at this time discharging into the Lynn Ouze, will, according to the present fall of water in those several streams, terminate in a point or nothing; beyond which several points of termination, the good effects or operation of the proposed cut, can in the first instance have no influence whatever.

Upon these principles it should seem, that the momentum of the first quarters flood through the proposed cut, will be greater than the first quarters flood now is through the Haven of Lynn; inasmuch as in the Haven of Lynn it has to encounter with an acclivity of eight inches per mile; whereas, in the proposed cut, it will only meet with half that obstruction. Also, as the water down the proposed cut, will be led nearly in a strait line into the Harbour of Lynn, its present recoils would be lost; it would act with its full weight, and propel itself to the sea ward, over and through the loose sands in the bay below the town of Lynn, with its utmost force. It would also appear from the same reasoning, that the current of the water
p.20 in its direction, must tend to straiten the present channel, and remove some of the most formidable obstructions in it; and finally find its nearest way to sea, and in its consequences, bring deep-water (or the level of the ocean) nearer to the Port of Lynn than it is at present.

The result, however, from the whole of these considerations, ought to be regarded more, as the probable consequences, than the certain effects of the proposed measure. The lowering the water from the upper end of the Haven of Lynn to the ascending line of subsided water in all the streams, discharging into the Lynn Ouze above Eau-brink, *must* produce these advantages. In proportion as the water is thus lowered in all these rivers, lodes, and leading drains, the engines at present established, will have a less head to work against; and as the soakage through the spungy fen banks will be considerably reduced, their effect in lifting the water out of their respective districts, will be more immediate and certain. By lowering the water in the drains, their capacity may be enlarged, and by fresh digging, their bottoms will approach nearer to the bed of the fens, where either the gault, or gravel, will furnish a greater, more constant, and more wholesome supply of water during the dry season of summer, than at present; and the partition drains will form a more effectual and permanent fence.

The relief which the outfal through the Channel of Wisbeach, holds out at this time to the middle level of the fens, and how that advantage may be prudently improved, come next under confederation.

It appears from the preceding tide tables, that in the distance of twelve miles, from the Bar Buoy at the entrance of the Wisbeach Channel to Gunthorpe Sluice, there now exists an acclivity of about fourteen feet; but as there is a constant depth of from seven to ten fathoms at low water between the Bar Buoy and Eye, so on a more minute inquiry, the obstruction will be found to lie within the distance of eight or nine miles from Gunthorpe Sluice, rather than twelve, as set forth in the Journal of observations.

I am here at a loss for an accurate data which I wished to have derived from the flowing of the tides, above the Haven of Lynn to Denver Sluices, at the time I was moored in the entrance of the Lynn and Wisbeach Channels; for certain I am, (although I am not prepared to prove it,) that when the tide flows seven feet high at Gunthorpe Sluice, it does not flow, or make the same depth of water, at Denver Sluices. This assertion being granted, by inference it follows, that the low water mark at Denver Sluice is higher than the low water mark at Gunthorpe Sluice: a fall of considerable moment, and which ought to be accurately ascertained, in order to give it its full weight and consideration.

The waters of the North Level, at this time descend from Gunthorpe Sluice into the sea with considerable rapidity; whilst in the most calamitous times, those of the middle and south levels of the fens, are frequently locked up at Denver Sluices and Salter's Lode, for several days together, by the
p.21 power of the tides and superior pressure of high-land waters. The proposed cut from Eau brink to the Haven of Lynn, presents to us a probability of lowering water twenty-five inches at Denver Sluices, and an hope that in time the advantages resulting from that measure, may be greatly improved. The recovery of the original and natural outlet for the discharge of the high-land and fen waters to the sea, through the channel of Wisbeach, encourages a well grounded expectation, that the whole country now occupied by the fens, may yet be recovered to its pristine state; and rendered equally fruitful and desirable to inhabit, as any of the most captivating vallies in the three Kingdoms.

The very important benefits which have hitherto resulted to the navigation of the Port of Wisbeach, and the drainage of the north level of the fens, from the contraction of the Nine waters below the rivers end to the washway, by Kenderly's Cut; justifies a conclusion, that by the farther contraction of the descending waters over the washway, that the navigation and drainage through the Wisbeach River, will be farther improved. To effect this contraction of the refluent waters, two modes are presented to our view: The one sudden, but expensive; the other slow and cheap; but equally certain of the desired. effect. The former is, to continue Kenderly's Cut through the embanked-marshes on the shore of Lincolnshire, below the banks end to deep water at the Eye. The latter, (which is the slow and patient method of the Dutch and Flemmings,) consists in pursuing from the mouth of Kenderly's Cut, the general course of the present channel over the washway; and placing on each side of it logs, to which should be attached fascines and hurdles, to procure an arrestment of the silt and sediment suspended in the waters of every tide. This latter work, carefully attended to, and assisted when necessary from time to time, would in a few years form such a strength of foundation, as to refill the utmost efforts of the winds and tides; and since after the first quarters ebb, (for it is designed that the fascine work should be covered at high water,) the returning waters would now be confined to one certain channel, they would not wander over the washway as they do at present; but act in this prescribed channel with their utmost force. The sands and marshes would fill with sediment, and soon grow up to the highest level of the sea; they would rise higher and higher with each succeeding tide, whilst, from the moveable nature of the bed of the channel, *that,* would be scoured and made deeper and deeper, till at length it would be brought to the level of the low water at the Eye below; or probably to the lowest level of the sea. Then, if the salt marsh shall have been embanked or enclosed from, the sea too soon, its surface will be so much improved by the richer and finer parts of the sea sediment, that its fertility would be immense, and during the neap tides, the high water in the channel thus formed, would generally ride below soil; and thus a country of prodigious extent, and inestimable value; would be rescued from the ocean, and added to the national stock.

What effect this deepening of the river below, must have upon navigation, and the discharge of the land waters from above, it is easy to conceive; for under all the evils which this outfal: at present labours, it still retains a power of affording relief to the middle level of the fens, of, from twelve to eighteen inches,
p.22 of water; when that devoted country is labouring under the most deplorable of evils, and can obtain no succour or relief whatever, through the outfal of Lynn. And this strongly enforces the necessity of taking up the Outwell Canal Scheme, upon a broad and extended bottom, combining *navigation with drainage*; which (as I before observed) in a discussion of this nature, should ever be regarded as one and the same thing.

SECT. III.

Of the Internal Works and District Drainage of the Fens.

WHEN the dictates of nature are pursued, as in the instance of recovering the proper outfal of the waters of the north level of the fens through the channel of Wisbeach, the good effects of the measure speak loudly for themselves. Additional works, are, however yet necessary to completion of that excellent drainage; and so far as it is possible to effect them through the influence and exertion of the gentlemen who have the care of the principal estates on the north and south sides of Moreton's leam, so far I am persuaded, that their unwearied diligence and good sense will not suffer them to remain neglect'd.

The obstructions, which for ages have existed in the town of Wisbeach, to the discharge the water of the Nene and great Ouze below to the sea, were a principal cause of the decay and final loss of that outfal; and are at this time a very great hindrance to the drainage of Waldersey, Wisbeach north and south side, and to the present navigation of the Wisbeach river, removing of the obstructions from above Guyhirn down *through Wisbeach*, and continuing the course of the river below the town as strait as conveniently possible, to the upper end of Kenderly's Cut, must have a very important effect, upon the internal drainage of the fens; as some of the present meanderings of the Wisbeach river would be cut off, and the general bed brought to a more evenly inclined plane from Peterborough to the eye at sea.

Another work of considerable moment proper in this quarter, is, the forming of an inside wash-bank, not exceeding three feet in height, at a proper distance from, and parallel to the navigable river from Guyhirn to Peterborough. The effects of this in the first instance, would be, That the spring tides would be restrained from spreading, as they now do, the lower part of the wash-way; and the small freshes from the high-land country, would be caught above, and confined in their descent to the channel of the present river; thereby scouring it more effectually, and at the same time preventing the deposition of sediment, from the land and sea, overflowings of the wash-way, and the consequent reduction of its capacity as a reservoir.

p.23

Other consequences would result from this measure, such as the protection and encouragement it would give to the growth of reeds and bull-rushes; between the navigation and wash-bank, which at the time of high winds, would break and smooth the swell of the water, acting upon, and against the north bank of Moreton's Leame; and prevent the destructive operation which the winds have on the banks of all wash-ways, when full of water. The rendering the lands in the wash-way, constant and good summer grounds, must also prove a considerable benefit. But in the execution of this work, regard ought strictly to be had to the preservation of the navigation from Whittlesea to the present navigation of Moreton's Leame, through a drain called Delph Dyke; that being the nearest and best communication between the town of Whittlesea and the port of Wisbeach, The navigation from Guyhirn through the counter drain, up to Whittlesea field, should also be preserved for the purpose of conveying proper materials for the repair of the north and south banks of Moreton's Leame.

Underwood's drain, which heretofore conveyed the waters of Ugg Mere, Ramsey Middle Moor, Fassett Fen, and Whittlesea Lamas Grounds, and was of considerable relief to the country surrounding Whittlesea Mere, by conveying these waters to Whittlesea Dyke and Bevil's Leame; is now in a great measure lost as a drain, and is useless in many places even as a mere fence, between the drove way and the abutting lands. This is chiefly to be attributed to the diversion of the Whittlesea Mere, and land waters at the angle corner through the Whittlesea Dyke, from their strait course in the judicious continuation of Bevil's Leame to Moreton's Leame; when the water is constantly dam'd up, and deprived of its natural descent to seaward, through the outfal of Wisbeach. By this means, the water is forced into a circuitous course, through Whittlesea Dyke into the Old Nene above; and through the twenty foot drain below, along Waldersey Old Bank, striking the Old Nene, a little above the upper end of the (old grown up) Elm Leame. Thence it is driven through the Nine and Popham's Eau to Nordelph corner, where uniting again, it is forced to Salter's Lode Sluice, and there it waits an uncertain, short, and languid discharge into the Lynn Ouze.

From this forced system of drainage (which from the journal will appear to cost the owners and occupiers of the middle level from two shillings to six shillings annually per acre) we find this melancholy result; That after the waters have been thus lifted and driven to Saller's Lode, they are often overridden by those of the one hundred foot, Old Bedford, and Ouze rivers, and frequently obtain no utterance whatever into the Lynn Ouze for several days together. The only relief to which the country can at that time look up, is small indeed; and is merely that of admitting the waters into the embanked washway of the Tong's drain; through which, (according to the present system of draining) for obvious reasons, all the waters of the Nene ought long ago to have been discharged into, the Lynn Ouze. The distresses of the country at these times, are beyond all description or belief. The inhabitants are watching night and day upon the banks cradging.(or raising) their tops, and in hourly expectation of the
p.24 banks giving way and drowning the whole of their devoted country; and too often when the wind blows hard from the south west, their melancholy presages are verified. The waters being already lifted to the height the powers can force them to, are thus prevented from reverting again towards Whittlesea (which in calm times they do) to the temporary relief of the fens, but to the utter destruction of all the skirting lands which border on upon the Highland country.

The upland waters of Berry, Biggin, Wood Walton, Sautre, Conington, Glatton, and a part of Holm; which formerly flowed into Ugg, and Ramsey Meres, and thence were conveyed a branch of the Nene river, past Binwick to the Wisbeach outfal, have been diverted from voluntary course by the forty foot river or Vermuden's drain, into which they are lifted, forced through Welches dam, into the Old Bedford river. Upon this latter river, between Erith and Salter's Lode, there are nine powerful engines at this time employed in lifting the waters out of their respective districts; its doors or flood gates have now (20th Nov 1793) five feet depth of silt and sediment lodged against them; and should the high land continue to fill the wash or reservoir as full as it is at present, the presumption is, that the discharge of that water from the mouth of the one hundred foot level above into the Ouze, continue to keep them shut for some time longer. These engines have now an head of fourteen inches to work against above the thresholds of their water ways, and the utmost that the and most powerful of them can do with effect, is to work against the level of the axis of water wheel, and as these mills are generally pitched against a four feet head. If the wind is sufficient to enable them to work against this head, the river will then be full to the top of banks.

As the discharge of this water into the Ouze, is rendered impossible from the superior of the silt and water pressing against the doors of the Old Bedford River; these engines continue lifting, till the water in the Old Bedford over-rides that in the forty feet river: The doors at Welche's Dam, will then, of course be shut; and the waters that are thus lifted the into Old Bedford and forty feet rivers, from the spunginess of their banks will be constantly soaking through them, and spreading again into and through the same districts, out of which they have before been raised; this was a consequence most severely experienced during greater part of last winter, and an evil which seriously threatens the country at this time. The whole middle level, so far as the influence of this pernicious and extensive system of draining extends, and it is wide indeed, exhibits a melancholy proof of the truth of this assertion.

Can there be any thing in nature more preposterous than forcing the waters of Wittlesea, Ugg, Benwick, and Ramsey Meres, along the circuituous course they are now obliged to make to Salter's Lode; there to remain locked up on an higher level, than when they might by a short passage, have had a rapid and tumbling fall into the sea from Gunthorpe Sluice.

p.25 A tunnel has been laid under the bed of the Old Bedford River (by an ingenious enterprising Gentleman) to drain a part of the embanked washway lying between the Old Bedford and one hundred foot rivers. The water rises through this tunnel in the counter-stream, on the north-west side of the Old Bedford, and thence spreads into the river between the Old Bedford Well Creek. A very powerful engine erected lately (by the same gentleman, between Nordelph Corner and Salter's Lode, lifts the water from this level into Well Creek, proving thereby, the present system of draining by the Old Bedford river, is not only ineffectual but radically wrong.

It appears from an examination of the one hundred foot river, that for about a mile and a quarter above Denver sluice, the wash bank on the Well side of the river, is raised to nearly an equal height, with the prime bank on the east side. A bank of the same height then stretches across the wash way, to the east bank of the Old Bedford river; thus excluding from the lower part of the wash, the wash waters from that bank to the Ouze river. On the south side of this bank is a drain called Wellmore Lake, at the confluence of which with the one hundred foot river there was heretofore a sluice, which is now gone to decay. This sluice answered a valuable purpose in regulating the discharge of the wash waters, at particular times into the one hundred foot river; but in the place of the sluice a rude and barbarous contrivance at this time is resorted to, by forming a dam over the mouth of Wellmere lake drain, which remains for the purpose of preventing the regular overflowing of the lower part of the wash, with the tidal water, as also the descent of the land waters on the ebb tide into the one hundred foot river. This dam is annually made, and annually cut through, when the water within the wash accumulates to a certain height, above the water in the one hundred foot river. The dam being thus thrown down, gives ready access to the tidal waters, over the whole surface of the lower part of the wash, there by increasing its height by the sediment it leaves, and consequently reducing its capacity as a reservoir. At the time I made this survey, there was a head of about fifteen inches in the wash way pressing upon the dam, above the low water in the one hundred foot river; and as the whole wash was then flooded above Mepel, little benefit could have accrued to the owners of that property long before that time.

The remedy I conceive to be as follows: Pointing doors, or flood gates, should be re-erected, and made small enough to be constantly kept open winter and summer when the tide returns; and small enough to constantly be kept open winter and summer when tide turns; and by the discharge of the wash and Wellmere lake waters, scour back the sediment that would be lodged in the eye or goole at every tide. If the doors and strings leading to them from the river (which by the bye will be very short) are disproportionably large for the quantity of water they will have to utter, they will of course silt up (as they did formerly, and indeed as most of the doors, through which there is not a navigation, now do) in summer; but in this case, as the strings of the goole will be very short and narrow, the silt may be easily removed whenever the water rises in Wellmere lake drain, sufficiently high to require a discharge into the one hundred foot river. Many more slakers or tunnels should be placed in the wash bank, particularly in the lower part of it, and that bank should be raised about two feet, and carried to a corresponding
p.26 height, above a standard level in the one hundred foot river, from Wellmere lake sluice to Erith. The consequence of this improvement would be nearly similar to those I have anticipated from the inside wash bank, recommended to be erected against Moreton's leame. Great care ought to be in future, that by planting the staves with oziers, the best materials are not lost for repairing prime bank, and also, that the oziers do not produce a current against the counter shore, for with the gangs passing up and down, will wear away the foreland, and weaken the sound: the prime bank, as is plainly the case now, and where it is much to be lamented, above Mepal.

Under the present system of draining, little, in my humble opinion, can be done, to serve the drainage of the country above Denver sluice, except cleansing out St. John Eau, and suffering that drain to act as a slaker to the Ouze, above Denver sluices, when the water rises in that a certain height so as to press with a threatening and destructive head upon the country above, it is, that the inhabitants of that country implore relief, and it is at that time only, that St. J Eau, is required by them to come in aid of the distresses, of which, at this time they so complain, and which a timely and well regulated discharge of the highest waters of the level through St. John's Eau, would completely afford. And this surely might be done without injury to navigation, or the consequences which generally attend the dividing of a stream; for the twelve or eighteen inches of water, which would thus be conveyed through St. John's is the surface water only, and such as would go off in the first quarters ebb, so its scouring would be but little felt between Denver sluices and the mouth of St. John's Eau below.

Thus have I collected together, in the best manner my leisure and ability will admit of, observations on the nature and drainage of the fens, as came within my view, during the short. time I have been engaged in the survey. According to the best of my judgment, the following conclusions are fairly to be drawn from them:

I. That the Eau-brink cut, must have a tendency to improve the navigation of the Lynn and the drainage of the country, which properly belongs to it.

II. That its good effects cannot possibly extend to the complete and effectual relief of the middle and south levels of the fens; and

III. That this relief is only to be obtained by following the laws of nature, and assisting her in the efforts he uniformly makes to relieve herself; and where a complete and effectual drainage of the middle and south levels of the fens, is yet to be obtained through the channel of Wisbeach.

Hoop-Inn, Cambridge.
February 1, 1794

CHARLES VANCOUVER

GENERAL VIEW

OF THE

AGRICULTURE

OF THE

COUNTY OF CAMBRIDGE.

DRAWN UP FOR THE CONSIDERATION OF

THE BOARD OF AGRICULTURE

AND INTERNAL IMPROVEMENT

BY THE REV. W. GOOCH, A.B

1813

PREFACE

So multifarious is the information necessary for obtaining full and correct knowledge of the Agriculture of any district, and persons of sufficient zeal, disinterestedness, and patriotism, for full and unreserved communication are so rarely to be met with, that there is great difficulty in collecting materials for a work of this sort; I mean not however to ascribe the defects of the following pages to this cause, it would be an ill return for the most handsome reception, and the greatest attention in every part of the county. I found few instances of narrow-minded and groundless suspicion. I had no doubt but I had all the information the persons whom I saw had to communicate on the subjects they respectively were acquainted with; the defects, therefore, on those subjects are with myself only; but there are many
p.iv particulars on which only few persons were prepared to give information, owing probably to those subjects not being generally thought worthy attention: a little reflection however, would convince any one they are; the particulars I allude to are objects of attention principally with those who farm, not only for profit but for amusement and for information; the farmer whose only object is the former, goes but little way into these particulars, he is perhaps timorous and diffident of his abilities, he adopts the practice of his neighbours, who are esteemed money-getting men, and takes it for granted he is on safe ground, not recollecting that he whom he takes as his guide may have been deceived by the same ideas, and though on the whole he may farm to profit, he may in particular branches be a loser. I had many instances of this in Cambridgeshire, perhaps none more striking than corn-grazing of bullocks; the accounts I had of losses from that practice are amazing, with barley at 9s. and 10s. per co. price of lean
p.v beasts, 5s. to 6s. per stone, on what they would fat to, and price fat 9s. to 10s. per stone. To the question, " why this practice? " the answer was, " because others (good farmers) did it, and barley was low." " Did your beasts pay you that low price ?" "No, not near it." Why not? " " Because they cost too much keeping." Now this cost might have been very nearly ascertained by previous calculation; but the experience of his money-getting neighbour was relied upon, and hundreds of coombs of barley returned not a farthing; instances of the like nature might be given on other subjects, such as the comparative profit between dairying and grazing, between sheep and bullocks on different systems, &e. &c. but farmers attentive to inquiries of this sort are not numerous in Cambridgeshire, owing perhaps to the want of a Bedford, a Coke. &c. &c. amongst them, and perhaps also to the want of an agricultural society, which, properly conducted, would stimulate to inquiry: for men would feel a pride in being able to communicate, when flattered by applications for information, nay they would be uncomfortable in not being able to give it.

p.vi In drawing up this Report, my aim has been that it should nearly as possible accord with its title, and the plan for its execution given by the Board; I found, however, that some information I had obtained, and the observations suggesting themselves could not with propriety be placed as prescribed by the Board; I have therefore placed such communications under titles suitable to them, in the Chapter of Miscellanies.

Conceiving that a great public benefit may be derived from communicating the practice of individuals of experience, ability, and celebrity, I have noted that of such gentlemen, and feeling it a tribute justly due, (and that reference may be made to them) I have given their names.

In a county so extensive, and possessing land so valuable, and of such various qualities, and occupiers
p.vii of the description I have alluded to, it may be a subject of surprize to the reader, that this work contains accounts of so few experiments, (by experiments I mean any new practice, or any practice not generally known, and the result so satisfactorily ascertained as to determine absolutely their merit or demerit). I assure him it does of all such as I heard, and the reason given for their paucity is, that the state of great part of the county, (open-field) precludes the opportunity of making them, and in most of the districts, where enclosures have taken place, time enough has not yet elapsed to bring the lands into a state for the making any; indeed they are scarcely recovered from the effects of the old impoverishing system; no doubt, however, ere long this county will distinguish itself as others have lately done; it cannot be otherwise, having in it a Hardwicke, an Adeane, a Tharpe, a Mortlock, a Jennyns, &c. &c. the practice of these gentlemen, and of several others enabled by the late enclosures to act upon their own ideas, warrants this prediction; but partiality to the practice of their grand-fathers, is so deeply rooted in the minds of the generality of the farmers of the county, that they will not soon, nor easily be prevailed upon to depart from it; no less convincing argument will avail, than the proof that their new rents cannot be
p.viii paid, but by a more lucrative system; that they cannot, might be easily shewn. Wheat, barley, fallow will

not pay 25s. to 40s. per acre rent with the expenses of 1806, it is to be feared that the *best system* will not do it, in many districts where it is well known these rents exist.

Much of the arable husbandry of this county is so foreign to the present practice in the best cultivated countries, that I frequently could not refrain from making that observation, and expressing my surprise that the example of those countries had in so few instances been followed, but I found (except amongst some individuals) that great doubts were now entertained whether any better plan than their old one can be practised; much as this bigotry is to be lamented, and widely as it is spread, there is great reason to hope that the spirit, skill, and success of those who are happily free from this bane to improvement, will
p.ix root it out. As graziers the Cambridgeshire farmers may justly pride themselves, and if they were to communicate their practice in this branch of Agriculture to their Norfolk neighbours, and receive in return from them a few arable lessons, mutual benefit might be derived.

With these observations I present the following to the Board, assuring its members that however defective it may be, it is the best my abilities and opportunities could produce.

W. G.

Whatfield Parsonage,
Suffolk, 1807.

AGRICULTURAL SURVEY

OF

CAMBRIDGE.

CHAP. I.

GEOGRAPHICAL STATE.

SECT. I.—SITUATION AND EXTENT.

CAMBRIDGESHIRE is situated north of London, (its nearest parish being about forty miles from it,) and its extent from N. to S. 40 miles from E to W. 25 miles: its circumference 130 miles, being bounded on the N. by Lincolnshire and Norfolk, on the S. by Hertfordshire and Essex; on the E. by Suffolk and Norfolk, on the W. by Bedfordshire, Huntingdonshire, and Northamptonshire; it contains 686 square miles, and (as Mr. Vancouver reported to the Board of Agriculture, in 1794) 443,300 acres, which he describes and values thus;

	Acres	Rent		Total Rental		
		s.	d.	£.	s.	d.
Enclosed Arable	15,000	18	0	13,500	0	0
Open field Arable	132,000	10	0	66,000	0	0
Improved Pasture	52,000	20	0	60,666	10	4
Inferior Pasture	19,800	10	0	10,642	10	0
Woodland	1,000	13	0	750	0	0
Improved Fen	50,000	15	0	37,500	0	0
Waste and Unimproved Fen	150,000	4	0	30,000	0	0
Half-Yearly Meadowland	2,000	12	0	1,250	0	0
Highland - Common	5,700	10	0	3,750	0	0
Fen or Moor-Common	8,000	3	0	1,200	0	0
Sheep-Walk Heath	6,000	2	6	570	0	0
	443,300			22,609	0	4

Editors Note:- *The figures above are exactly as set out in Gooch's survey report, there are however issues with his calculations.*

p.2 The open-field arable, waste and unimproved fen, half-yearly meadow, highland-common, fen or moor-common, and sheep-walk heath, are much lessened now (1806), full 43,000 acres of the open-field arable, being now enclosed arable and pasture; and great part (supposed about 20,000 acres) of the waste and unimproved fen, half-yearly meadow, highland- common, fen or moor-common, sheep-walk heath, being now become also enclosed arable and pasture, and the total rental increased, in open field more than double, and on the other lands three times at least (in the opinion of most persons) that of the former rents and value.

SECT. II. - DIVISIONS.

The county contains seventeen hundreds (including the isle of Ely), one city, one sea-port, nine market-towns, one-hundred and fifty-seven parishes and as every one knows, an university.

SECT. III. - CLIMATE.

Cambridgeshire lies between 52° 3' and 52° 40' N.L. And between 0° 25' E and 0° 10' W.L. The following meteorological table I was furnished with from the public library, Cambridge.

Meteorological Journal for the Year 1805.								
1805.			1805.			1805.		
Jany.	Deg	Weather	Feb.	Deg	Weather	Mar.	Deg	Weather
1	31.70	Frosty	1	32	Frosty	1	43.50	Stormy
2	38.50	Rain	2	34	Fine	2	42.50	Cloudy
3	36	Cloudy	3	30.50	Rain	3	46	Fine
4	37	Fine	4	39.50	Do.	4	54	Do.
5	38.50	Do.	5	41.50	Do.	5	52	Do.
6	41	Foggy	6	34	Fine	6	50	Cloudy
7	45	Frosty	7	38	Cloudy	7	45	Do.
8	41	Fine	8	45	Fine	8	44	Fine
9	34	Foggy	9	51	Do.	9	37	Cloudy
10	25.50	Frosty	10	49	Rain	10	38	Do.
11	34	Hazy	11	42.50	Cloudy	11	44	Fine
12	33	Foggy	12	40	Do.	12	62.75	Do.
13	40.50	Do.	13	39	Do.	13	61	Do.
14	40	Fine	14	42	Fine	14	52.50	Cloudy
15	37	Rain	15	39	Cloudy	15	50	Do.
16	44	Cloudy	16	40	Do.	16	54	Fine
17	44	Fine	17	38	Fine	17	57	Do.
18	37.50	Do.	18	37.50	Cloudy	18	46	Rain
19	37	Do.	19	39	Fine	19	51	Fine
20	40	Rain	20	41	Fine	20	47	Rain
21	38.50	Cloudy	21	47	Foggy	21	50	Cloudy
22	35.50	Do.	22	47.50	Fine	22	45	Fine
23	34	Snow	23	48	Do.	23	50	Do.
24	32	Frosty	24	40	Rain	24	49	Do.
25	36	Hazy	25	48.50	Fine	25	47.50	Do.
26	30	Frosty	26	49	Do.	26	49	Do.
27	31	Frosty	27	48	Cloudy	27	45	Cloudy
28	30	Do	28	48	Fine	28	41	Fine
29	35	Fine				29	40	Rain
30	36	Snow				30	53	Do.
31	34	Do.				31	55	Cloudy

Meteorological Journal for the Year 1805.								
1805.			1805.			1805.		
April.	Deg	Weather	May.	Deg	Weather	June.	Deg	Weather
1	55	Cloudy	1	51	Cloudy	1	54	Fine
2	57	Fine	2	49	Fine	2	57	Do.
3	54	Cloudy	3	52	Cloudy	3	62	Do.
4	45	Rain	4	54	Fine	4	53	Cloudy
5	46	Cloudy	5	54	Fine	5	53	Do.
6	45	Do.	6	60	Do.	6	61.50	Do.
7	50	Fine	7	57	Cloudy	7	66	Fine
8	51	Do.	8	46	Rain	8	66	Do.
9	55	Do.	9	49	Stormy	9	70	Cloudy
10	58	Fine	10	53.50	Cloudy	10	64	Rain
11	59	Do.	11	51	Fine	11	65	Cloudy
12	59.50	Do.	12	54	Stormy	12	61	Fine
13	61	Do.	13	56	Cloudy	13	64	Cloudy
14	60.50	Do.	14	55	Do.	14	58	Rain
15	49.50	Cloudy	15	51	Rain	15	58	Cloudy
16	46	Do.	16	59	Fine	16	60	Rain
17	49	Do.	17	58	Cloudy	17	64	Fine
18	53	Fine	18	57	Do.	18	60	Showery
19	55	Do.	19	59	Do.	19	57	Rain
20	59	Do.	20	60	Fine	20	55	Cloudy
21	59.50	Do.	21	62	Cloudy	21	55	Do.
22	55	Do.	22	58	Do.	22	60	Do.
23	50	Cloudy	23	49	Fine	23	64	Fine
24	50	Do.	24	57	Do.	24	70	Do.
25	53	Fine	25	60.50	Do.	25	59	Rain
26	53	Rain	26	61	Do.	26	63	Cloudy
27	50	Cloudy	27	64	Do.	27	64	
28	48	Fine	28	63	Do.	28	67	Fine
29	36.50	Snow	29	66	Do.	29	62	Do.
30	48.50	Fine	30	65	Do.	30	65	Do.
			31	58	Cloudy			

Meteorological Journal for the Year 1805.								
1805.			1805.			1805.		
July.	Deg	Weather	Aug.	Deg	Weather	Sept.	Deg	Weather
1	68	Fine	1	69	Cloudy	1	71	Fine
2	65	Cloudy	2	70	Do.	2	66	Cloudy
3	66	Do.	3	67	Fine	3	66	Do.
4	75	Do.	4	71	Cloudy	4	69	Do.
5	66	Do.	5	70	Fine	5	72	Fine
6	63	Rain	6	70	Do.	6	69	Do.
7	60	Do.	7	68	Do.	7	66	Cloudy
8	60	Do.	8	70	Do.	8	65	Rain
9	65.50	Fine	9	73	Cloudy	9	67	Fine
10	70	Do.	10	73	Do.	10	69	Fine
11	59	Rain	11	73	Fine	11	71	Do.
12	66	Fine	12	76	Do.	12	66	Cloudy
13	66	Do.	13	70	Do.	13	68	Fine
14	66.50	Do.	14	66	Do.	14	69	Do.
15	61.75	Cloudy	15	66	Do.	15	71	Do.
16	64.50	Fine	16	68	Fine	16	73	Do.
17	61	Cloudy	17	68	Do.	17	70	Do.
18	63.50	Fine	18	68	Rain	18	75	Do.
19	65	Do.	19	68	Cloudy	19	70	Cloudy
20	73	Do.	20	64	Do.	20	66	Do.
21	72	Do.	21	62	Do.	21	64	Fine
22	67	Cloudy	22	64	Do.	22	59	Cloudy
23	70	Fine	23	68	Fine	23	60	Fine
24	64	Cloudy	24	71	Do.	24	56	Cloudy
25	65	Fine	25	70	Do.	25	60	Fine
26	70	Do.	26	69	Cloudy	26	60	Rain
27	72	Cloudy	27	70	Fine	27	61	Cloudy
28	68	Do.	28	69	Cloudy	28	62	Fine
29	70	Fine	29	71	Fine	29	61	Do.
30	70	Do.	30	73	Do.	30	60	Cloudy
31	69	Do.	31	71	Cloudy			

Meteorological Journal for the Year 1805.								
1805.			1805.			1805.		
Oct.	Deg	Weather	Nov.	Deg	Weather	Dec.	Deg	Weather
1	58	Cloudy	1	42	Clear	1	45	Cloudy
2	63	Fine	2	46	Fine	2	37	Fine
3	60	Do.	3	45	Do.	3	41	Rain
4	60	Do.	4	46	Do.	4	50	Cloudy
5	62	Fine	5	44	Do.	5	45	Fine
6	58	Cloudy	6	43	Foggy	6	49	Cloudy
7	58	Fine	7	45	Cloudy	7	49	Rain
8	60	Cloudy	8	42	Do.	8	44	Fine
9	58	Do.	9	47	Fine	9	43	Rain
10	52	Fine	10	42	Foggy	10	37	Fine
11	50	Cloudy	11	43	Cloudy	11	36	Do.
12	50	Fine	12	42	Rain	12	35	Snow
13	52	Rain	13	42	Cloudy	13	27	Frosty
14	53	Fine	14	45	Fine	14	34	Snow
15	53	Do.	15	45	Cloudy	15	35	Do.
16	51	Cloudy	16	45	Fine	16	31	Frosty
17	48	Rain	17	42	Do.	17	28	Do.
18	49	Fine	18	39	Do.	18	37	Fine
19	50	Do.	19	40	Do.	19	39	Cloudy
20	50	Do.	20	42	Do.	20	48	Rain
21	52	Cloudy	21	38	Do.	21	50	Do.
22	50	Fine	22	46	Do.	22	42	Fine
23	53	Do.	23	40	Do.	23	43	Do.
24	52	Cloudy	24	44	Cloudy	24	38	Do.
25	57	Do.	25	46	Fine	25	38	Rain
26	52	Do.	26	46	Cloudy	26	46	Do.
27	48	Rain	27	43	Cloudy	27	40	Cloudy
28	45	Fine	28	43	Foggy	28	38	Rain
29	45	Cloudy	29	51	Cloudy	29	49	Fine
30	44	Stormy	30	52	Fine	30	50	Cloudy
31	45	Fine				31	53	Rain

The inhabitants of the Fens are most unhealthy in the season when the Fens are driest, noxious effects being immediately felt, from the soil usually under water, being exposed to the atmosphere. Mr. Scott of Chatteris observes, "the country of late years has been much more healthy than formerly; few natives
p.6 are now troubled with the ague, say for the last ten years, resulting from the greater power and number of mills. "Strangers coming to reside, are still liable to it."

SECT. IV. SOIL.

Mr. Vancouver has so fully and so ably, in the opinion of all whom I consulted, written on this subject, that it would savour of invidious affectation to give any other than his account of the soil of this country. It may indeed be thought by indifferent persons too minute for a work of this sort, but by those in any way interested in the landed property of the county, it will not be objected to on that account. Mr. V.'s route was from Ashley, taking the parishes in the order in which they here follow,

Ashley including Silvery. - "The arable-land included within these bounds lies in thirteen open fields, that part of which binding east upon the village, is a dry, thin stapled Chalky soil; on the north, a wet heavy clay, with a mixture of some gravel, well stapled upon a gravel and chalk; on the west, a tender clay or loam, well stapled upon a clay, on the south, a stiff, heavy, wet clay, upon a gault ; to the eastward of which the soil gradually opens, and forms a good mixture of a fair staple upon a clay, but which is finally lost in the thin chalky soil first mentioned."

Chevely. -"The arable land in this parish lies chiefly in Open fields, the soils of which may be divided into three distinct classes; about two fifths, a stiff heavy clay, of a good staple, upon a gault; a like
p.7 proportion of it, is a mixed soil of clay and gravel, of a tolerable staple, upon a gravel, the remainder, about one-fifth, is of a dry thin staple, upon a chalk or gravel."

Catlidge. -" The soil of the common open fields in this parish consists of a close, cold, and compact clay laying upon a very retentive yellow clay, and blueish coloured gault."

Wood-Ditton. -" The land extending towards Newmarket consists of a thin, dry, white soil, upon a chalk, and a light sandy soil abounding with flints, upon a gravel. The land lying towards Cheveley, Catlidge, and Stetchworth consists of a strong heavy soil, upon a white and blue clay or gault."

Stetchworth.- " The open field arable land lying north of this village adjoining thereto, and bounded by the Devil's Ditch on the east, and the lands of Dullingham on the west, consists in part of a brown loam of a light staple, lying upon a thin stratum of chalk, under which is a close, compact, and white clay; the next in point of quality, is of a light coloured chalky dry nature, thinly stapled and lying upon a chalk; that of the third quality and binding upon the heath, is of a light, sharp, red, sandy nature, of a deep staple, lying also upon a chalk."

Dullingham. - "The arable land in this parish is to be described under four distinct heads, that of the first quality, a heavy whitish clayey soil of a good staple, laying upon a clay; the second, that of a reddish coloured brick earth, of a firm deep staple, upon a stiff brown clay; the third of a brown mixed soil, of a very good staple upon a gravel, part of which is moist; the fourth is a dry thin, white, chalky land, adjoining the heath. The soil of the enclosures is a black tender mould, upon a clay".

Burrough-Green. - " The enclosed lands in the way from Dullingham are wet and rough, near the village a tender hazel-coloured loam, with a small mixture of sand."

p.8 *Brinkley.* - " The warm, tender, loamy soil, continues down the field, and across the brook."

Carlton. - " The surface here is of a lighter colour, than in the preceding villages, and strengthens upon the hill to a whitish compact clay; which prevails through the parish of

Weston Coville, becoming however still lighter until it terminates in a thin, dry, chalky soil, binding upon Newmarket Heath."

Snailwell. - "The arable-land lies in three open fields; south by east of the village; and towards the turnpike road leading from Thetford to Newmarket, the soil is of two distinct sorts, that of the first quality, a loamy or tender clay, of a good staple, lying upon a chalk, the remainder is of a light sandy nature, well stapled."

Landwade. - " Some coarse pastures, and a deep rich white loamy soil, and indications of a good strong soil."

Fordham. - " The soil of the open arable field, next Chippenham, and adjoining to Snailwell Fen, is of a thin, gravelly nature, lying upon a gravel, thence towards Brackland fen, a white, thinly stapled, dry soil, upon a firm chalk or clunch, and thence binding upon Brackland Fen, a strong, greasy, white, deep soil, upon a clunch. On the east of the fen, a wet, heavy, cling clay, upon a deep, rich, blue gault, which burns into an excellent brick. On the south of the fen, a deep black sand, thence extending southwardly, the soil gradually changes to a lighter colour upon a gravel, thence the staple improves in strength and quality, forming a compact, deep, white earth; upon a clunch, ascending the hill, the soil becomes lighter, but continuing on the level towards Islesham, the soil is the same;
p.9 west of this field, is a common of a moory nature lying upon a clay and gravel. On the west, of this common, is a wet, brown, sandy soil; ascending the hill, the soil becomes more dry, and thence on the east side of the Soam road, it improves in strength, and is of a darker colour; south of this and binding thereon, is another common, the soil a moor, lying upon a clay; south of the village is a deep white loam, lying upon a chalk and clay, extending to Landwade hedge, thence south east, a dry, poorer, and mixed soil. The enclosures in severalty, in and near the village, partake of nearly the same variety of soil as the arable."

Kennett. - "The soil here in general, is of a light, gravelly, and dry chalky nature, under which in many places is found a very fair marl, which has been applied in the proportion of about three thousand bushels per acre with very good effect * upon the gravelly soils."

Chippenham. -" The soil of this parish may be described under three distinct heads. The first quality, a deep white loam lying upon a chalk; the second, a mixed soil of a dry and rather thin staple, upon a chalk and gravel; and the third, a light driving sand, upon which in many places is found a dry tender chalk, which has been recently tried as a manure."+

p.10 *Islesham.* - "The arable land here lies in four distinct open common fields; on the south side of the village, a whitish tender clay, or loam of a fair staple, lying upon a chalk or clunch."

Burwell. - " On the west and south west of the village, and adjoining thereto, is a deep, * rich, white loam, lying upon a chalk; thence extending southwardly the staple becomes more shallow, and ends in a thin gravelly soil, upon a gravel.+ On the north of the village, a dark coloured strong brown mould of an excellent staple upon a clunch."

Swaffham. - "Soil similar to Burwell and Bottisham."

Bottisham. - "On the east of the village, a white tender clay or loam, of a fair staple; eastwardly and towards the heath, the staple becomes more thin, and is lost in a dry chalk, and reddish coloured gravel; on the north, a gravelly soil of a middling staple, upon a gravel and sand; on the south, a moist gravelly soil lying near the springs, upon a chalky marl."

Wilbraham-Magna. -" Soil varies considerably, the arable is all of a light nature, general substratum of chalk."

---

* I was told, with "no effect".

+ Under the fen-peat surface in this parish is a very fine white marl, this Mr. Tharpe has spread on the land and found it a very great improvement, twenty loads to an acre, sufficient. A.Y. Annals. V. 4.

* Not deep. This is the soil usually called in the county "white land."

Wilbraham-Parva. -" On the north and east, and to the westward of the village, the arable land is of a red sandy nature, lying upon a gravel; on the south east, a whitish tender clay or loam of a good staple upon a chalk; on the south and westwardly, a deep brown mould upon a gravel."

Stow cum Quy. - " On the south of the village, is a tender, easy working loam, of a good staple lying upon a gravel; on the north, a strong cold clay, a light loam, and a fen or rather a morass."

Horningsey. - " Soil here is intermixed, being a thin gravel, and a loam or tender clay of a good staple."

Fenny-Ditton. - "A white strong loam or clay of a good staple, lying upon a chalk-quarry, or clunch;
p.11 and a strong gravelly mould of a good substance, upon a reddish-coloured clay or brick-earth."

Taversham. - "Adjoining the village, a tough wet clay, lying upon a gault; westwardly, a strong brown mould, lying upon a reddish coloured brick-earth; south-west wardly, a white chalky soil; north-westwardly, a sandy loam."

Fulburn. - "A thin, light, chalky soil, some part of which is a strong deep staple; there are indications of a warm and kindly soil. The upper part of the common towards Wilbraham, is of a light and sandy nature."

Cherryhinton. - " Soil similar to Fulburn and Barnwell."

Barnwell. -" A gravelly loam of a fair staple lying upon a gravel next to Cherryhinton Moor, and along Brick-kiln Furlong, soil of a close clingy nature upon a clay. Coldham-common is upon a bed of rich marl."

Trumpington. - "Adjoining river Cam. Soil of a black moory nature, on the north of the village a black friable mould, of a deep staple, lying upon and mixed with some gravel. The middle of the field, a strong loamy well stapled soil; adjoining the village a red gravelly soil; on the east of the village a similar soil; beyond the moor towards Cherryhinton, a strong brown earth, of a good staple, lying upon a clay. South of the village and adjoining thereto, soil of a light gravelly nature; southwardly the soil improves in its texture, and forms a tender clay or loam, of a good staple upon a chalk; thence skirting upon the river the soil becomes more tough and clingy, and is found to lie upon a gault. The enclosures lying in and adjoining to the village, are of a hot, gravelly nature. The common or moor is of a fenny nature from four to nine inches deep, lying upon a gravel." *

Stapleford. - "On the east of the village and adjoining thereto, a thinly stapled red soil, lying upon a
p.12 gravel. North-west of the village, and adjoining thereto, a deep, strong, good wheat soil upon a chalk; thence in the same direction the strength and staple of the soil decreases, and ends in a thin dry chalk, or hurrock. South-east of the village, soil similar to that on east, but stronger and better stapled. North and north-east of the village, a thin, dry, chalky soil, similar to that on the north-west."

Babraham. - "The enclosures, a light gentle soil, of a tolerable staple, and lying chiefly upon a gravel. The open fields, soil of a thin dry nature, lying upon a chalk and gravel."

Little Abbington. -"On the east side of Bournbridge, soil a tough clay, upon a reddish coloured brick-earth; thence towards the heath, the staple is lost in a thin dry chalk and gravelly soil; north eastwardly of Bournbridge a similar soil."

Hildersham. -" Towards Great Abbington, soil of a light gravelly nature, lying upon a gravel; towards Balsham, upon a chalk; towards Linton, soil of a stiff clayey nature; towards Hildersham Wood, soil improves in its strength and staple."

Linton and Barlow -"Soil a chalk, gravel and clay."

---

* Trumpington, "soil a light loam." (A. Y. Annals, v. 4.)

Shudy-Camps. - "The enclosed arable, a deep, strong, brown loam, lying upon a blue and whitish-coloured clay; the enclosed pastures, are similar; the open fields, a stiff clay, gradually lost in a light, dry, thin soil, upon a chalk and gravel."

Castle-Camps. - "The enclosures, a wet, but tender clay, lying upon a strong blue and yellow clay or loam; the open arable field similar to Shudy-Camps."

West Wickham. -"Soil more light and loamy."

Balsham. - "The arable land chiefly a dry, thick, light soil, upon a chalk and gravel."

p.13 *Sawston.* - " The arable land northwardly of the village, is of a good staple, but of a light and gentle nature, and lying generally upon a chalk and gravel. The common is of a moory nature."

Pampisford. - "The arable land is of a light thin staple, upon a chalk and gravel. The two enter-commons are of a more gravelly nature."

Hinkeston. - "South of the village and adjoining the enclosures, the soil of the open field is of good depth and substance, lying upon a gravelly clay; thence towards Saffron Walden gradually loses its staple, becomes dry and hungry, and is found to lie very near the chalk and gravel; north of the village, and adjoining thereto, the soil is of a very fair staple, thence extending north-wardly and towards Sawston, the soil becomes lighter, and rests upon a dry gravel."

Ickleton. -"Fields adjoining the enclosures, are a reddish coloured earth, of a fair staple, lying upon a gravel; thence westwardly and ascending the hill, a vein of cold, close clayey land, rather flat; beyond this in the same direction, the wet heavy land is gradually lost in a thin, dry, white soil, upon a chalk or hurrock."

Foulmire. - "Northwardly of the village, and towards Sheperheath, is a tender brown clay of a good staple, upon a soft, wet, reddish-coloured brick-earth, except the part binding upon Foxton, which is of a thinner staple, and lies upon a gravel, Southward, the soil next the moor, is of a clayey nature, and well stapled, thence the staple decreases, and towards Heydon (in Essex) it terminates in a thin, dry gravel."

Triplow. - "A warm, gentle soil, of a fair staple. The common, east of the village, is a loose, spungy, black soil, abounding in springs."

p.14 *Duxford.* - "Adjoining the enclosures on the S. W. side of the village is a gravelly loam well stapled; continuing this course, the soil decreases and terminates in a. thin, dry, white soil, upon a chalk or hurrock;" westwardly of this the soil again improves in strength and staple, and on the top of the hill, forms a strong brown, wet earth, upon a clay, in which there is a mixture of some large stones and gravel, this again gradually fades away, till on the extreme western boundary of the field, it ends in a thin, white soil, upon a hurrock. The soil of the middle field agrees with the above, except that it does not contain any wet heavy land. The moor field adjoining north-westwardly upon the enclosures, is of a deep and kindly nature, beyond which the staple fleetens, and is lost, in a hot, dry, burning gravel, which continues to the end of the field."

Whittlesford or Bedford. -"The arable land is of a light, gravelly nature, well stapled, upon a gravel and reddish-coloured brick-earth."

Newton, Haukston, and Harston. - "Similar to Duxford and Whittlesford."

Foxton. - Indications of "a warm and gentle soil in the enclosures; on the north side of the village, very good turnip land; on the south, a tender, well stapled, white loam, lying upon a chalk; thence ascending the hill, the soil loses its strength and staple, but descending towards Foulmire and Triplow, the staple increases till the chalky land is lost in a brown gravelly loam, lying upon a loam."

Sheperheath. - "East of the village towards Triplow and Foulmire, is a light earth lying upon a chalk and gravel; a small portion in this direction and adjoining the enclosures, is a deep, rich, black loam, upon a chalk. West of the village, a tender gravelly clay, of a good staple, upon a clay, mixed with
p.15 gravel: on the north of the village, and towards Foxton, the soil is of a gravelly nature, a small part lying upon a clay. The field called "Home Lands," towards Melbourne, is a white tender clay or loam of a good staple, upon a chalk. The enclosures are of a fair staple, upon a clay and gravel. The common field towards Foulmire, is of a dry, gravelly, and moory nature."

Meldrith. - "On the north of the village, and towards Watton, very good turnip land; about the village and towards Melbourne, a strong black earth."

Melbourne. - "Land of a generous kindly nature; about the villages, adjoining the enclosures, on the south side, is a tender well stapled, strong, white loam lying upon a chalk; this falls off towards Foulmire, and ends in a cold, wet, hungry soil." *

Bassingbourn, including the Hamlet of Kneesworth. - "Northwest, west, and south west of the village, is a strong, brown, clayey soil, of a good staple. North east, east, and south-east of the village, is a brown, deep, loamy soil, lying upon a gravel; thence in the same direction, beyond the line of Robin Hood's Tree, and extending towards Royston and Litlington, a thin, dry, white soil, upon a chalk or hurrock. The enclosed pastures are an open, brown, gravelly soil, of a good staple.",

Litlington. - " Northward of the parish and adjoining thereto, is a gravelly soil, of a tolerable staple, but thence westwardly and towards Royston, a thin, dry, white soil, upon a chalk or hurrock. The other lands are similar."

Abbington. - "Soil of a white, clayey nature, of a good staple; upon a woodland, or yellowish-coloured clay."

p.16 *Guilden-Morden, including the Hamlet of Odissey*. - "East of the village, and adjoining the enclosures, strong, wet, clayey land, lying upon a gault; on the north, a brown strong mould, of a fair staple, upon a brick-earth, in which there is a mixture of loose gravel; west of this, is a well stapled black mould, upon a chalky marl, but of a soft and soapy nature; on the west of the village, the lower part of the field answers to the gaulty land first described; southwardly and adjoining the village, a black earth of a good staple, upon a gravel; thence southwardly a brown mould, of a fair staple, upon a hurrock; thence extending to and binding upon the enclosures of Odissey, a dry, thin, white soil, upon a chalk; Odissey is a thin, chalky soil. The meadow or lammas-ground, is of a low moory nature. The low common is of a cold, gaulty, gravelly nature."

Steeple Morden. - "North of the village, taking the church for the centre, is a stiff clayey soil, lying very flat upon a bed of blue clay or gault; about a third of this field inclines to a gravel, but still lying very flat and difficult to drain. South of the village, the soil is of a thin, dry nature, upon a chalk and gravel. The enclosures are of a good staple, upon a blue and yellowish coloured clay, and veins of gravel."

Shingay. - "A strong brown earth, lying upon a gravel, and a stiff wet clay, of a thin staple upon a gault."

Tadlow. - "East of the church and upon the hill, the soil is a wet, strong loam, of a fair staple, lying upon a yellow clay; on the north, a similar soil; on the south the land is of a superior quality."

Hatley, St. George. - " On the east of the village, (taking the church for the centre) the soil is of a thin, cold, clayey nature, lying upon a gault; on the south, a well stapled, black mould, upon a clay;
p.17 on the west, soil similar to that on the east of the village as are about one hundred acres on the north of it; thence north-eastwardly the soil improves into a deep strong black mould."

Croydon. - "Soil of a strong, brown, loamy nature."

---

* "About Melbourne, the land is all chalk, the surface being chalky, on a hard rock, that breaks into cubes and oblongs." (A. Y. Annals, v. 4.)

Wyndee. - "Rich pastures, the soil a deep brown loam, lying upon a gault and gravel."

Orwell Whaddon. - "A strong, dark, friable mould, which in a direction towards Wimpole Park Gate gradually changes to a reddish colour."

Arrington. - "The soil east and south of the village is of a cold and clayey nature, lying upon a strong, close, and compact gault; west of the village the soil runs of a fair staple, upon a chalk and hurrock; and northwardly it is of a fair staple upon a hurrock, and yellow clay; towards Kneeswell a well mixed soil land."

Wimpole. - "Soil a light coloured mould free from stones, about the depth of four inches, lying upon a strong clay or gault; it is in general very wet."

Barrington. - " The arable land lying north-east of the village consists of a hurrocky, dry soil; north-west is a strong brown earth, of a good staple upon a retentive clay, or reddish-coloured brick earth; the lower part of the field is a well stapled clay or loam; lying upon a bed of chalky marl, of a soft and soapy nature; the middle field is of a similar soil; as is the west field: the enclosed pastures lie in and near the village, and are of a similar soil to the lower part of the field."

Harlton and Haslingfield. - " Similar soil to" *

Eversden. - " The soil binding upon the brook is a well stapled loamy gravel; adjoining and
p.18 approaching the village, the soil is of a thin, cold, clayey nature, lying upon a gault, the remainder
of this field towards Kingston, is of a thin, dry staple, upon a chalk. The soil west of the village
(taking the church for the centre), is a thin, cold, brown clay, in which there is a mixture of small
chalk stones. The lower part of the church-field, on the east of the village, consists of a strong, deep,
white earth, of a marly and yellow nature upon a chalk; beyond this towards Orwell, the deep, white
loam is lost, in a cold, brown, tough, thin clay, upon a gault."

Comberton. - "Soil similar to Barton."

Barton. - "The soil binding east upon the village, is a well stapled loamy gravel, upon a gravel; thence eastwardly and ascending the hill, tough, cold, thin clay upon a gault; north of the village, and adjoining the enclosures, is a white tender clay or loam of a good staple, upon a clay and gravel; thence northwardly the staple shallows into a thin, cold clay upon a gault: west of the village, about one hundred acres of warm, gravelly land, thence south and westwardly, is a thin, tough, cold clay upon a gault."

Grantchester. - "South of village, deep, black, friable mould, lying upon a clay; westwardly from
hence about sixty acres of thin, cold, wet clay-land upon a gault; thence and composing the middle
of the field about one hundred and forty acres of a well mixed soil upon a clay and gravel; north-west
of the village and adjoining the enclosures, are about one hundred acres of a deep gravelly loam,
upon a clay; thence in the same direction ascending the hill, are two hundred acres of cold, clayey
land, upon a gault; north-east of the village and adjoining the meadows are about one hundred acres
of deep rich loam, lying upon a clay; binding thereon and towards the north from the village, are
p.19 about two hundred acres of a cold, clayey nature, about one hundred acres more of a well stapled
mixed soil upon a clay and gravel."

Coton. - "To the east of the village and abutting on the bounds of Cambridge, a strong, brown soil of a fair staple, lying rather flat, upon a clay: west of the village, is a mixed soil of a good staple upon a gravel. South of the village towards Barton, is a thin, white soil, upon a clay; up the top of the hill is a strong, brown, heavy, earth, upon a reddish-coloured clay, or brick-earth; the lower part of this field consists of a dark brown mould, of a good staple, upon a clay; the enter-common, with

---

* Hauxton Mills ("adjoining these parishes") is the first place where chalk, is to be seen, it lasts from hence, quite across the kingdom." A. Y. Ans. v. 4.

Grantchester, is of a mixed soil. North of the village is a loamy well stapled soil, lying upon a gravel."

p.20 *Madingley.* - "The arable land is of a light coloured cold clay of a thin staple, upon a gault of an extremely close and retentive nature; in the hollows and lower parts of the fields, the soil is found to improve in staple, and becomes of a more tender and manageable nature."

Dry-Drayton. - "On the east of the village, is a thin cold clay upon a gault; north of the village is a brown tender clay of a good staple, mixed with gravel, lying upon a reddish-coloured clay or brick earth. South of the village the soil is very similar to that on the east, but has in it a very troublesome rag-stone."

Lolworth. - "The arable land is a tender clay of a good staple, lying upon a gault, and reddish coloured brick earth."

Boxworth. - "The arable land is a brown strong earth of a fair staple, lying upon a soft, yellow, and a strong blue and reddish coloured clay, or brick earth; the field binding upon Lolworth, is of a more tender and manageable nature."

Connington, Gravely, Papworth-Everard and Elsworth, all "a cold, clayey soil, lying upon a stiff blue, and a wet, yellow clay."

Eltsley. - "The arable land, a tender, cold, loose clay, lying very flat, upon a wet yellow clay, or woodland earth."

Croxton. - "The arable land similar to Eltsley."

Caxton. - "East of the village, a cold, brown earth, Upon a reddish coloured clay or brick-earth: south of the village, a similar soil."

Gamlingay. - "East of the village and adjoining the meadows, is a loamy sand; the remainder of this field, is a thin, cold, hungry, clay, lying upon a gault; south of the village and also adjoining the meadows, a deep, loamy sand, thence towards Potton wood, a similar cold and clayey nature; north of the village and adjoining thereto, the sandy land prevails; thence towards Wersley, a cold clayey soil. The meadow, or half-yearly land, is of a moory nature." *

Kingston. - "A tender clay upon a brick earth."

Toft. - "The surface of the soil is covered with a very thin bed of vegetable earth, immediately under which lies a stiff, strong gault, with a few veins of gravel."

Coldcot. - "Soil similar to Kingston and Toft."

Hardwicke. - "A cold, close clay, lying upon a yellow and white clay, and reddish brick-earth."

Knapwell. - "Soil similar to that of Hardwicke." +

Childersley. - "A brown clayey earth, lying upon a white and blue clay, and reddish-coloured brick-earth."

p.21 *Girton.* - "Soil of a gravelly nature; on the west adjoining the enclosures, a black deep mould upon a gravel; thence westwardly a reddish-coloured loam, upon a tender clay which ends in a strong clay upon a gault."

---

* Long-Stow, stiff, wet, clay, or gault. AY Ans. v. 4.

\+ Clay. A.Y.

§ Cottenham-Fen, "soil a black, turf, or moor, three feet deep." A. Y. Ans. v. 4.

Oakington. - "Soil similar to Girton."

Long-Stanton. - "East of the village a deep, black mould, with some gravel; south-west and adjoining the: enclosures, a strong, brown and well stapled soil, lying upon a clay."

Cottenham - "Adjoining the village, a reddish-coloured deep, sandy loam, abounding with springs; towards the fens is a strong well stapled, black, loamy mould." §

Waterbeach, with Denny Abbey. - On the west and towards Landbeach, is a well-stapled gravelly soil; binding the river Cam, a deep, brown loam, without gravel, lying upon a clay.

Landbeach. - "South east of the village a gravelly loam; north east and towards the fens, is a strong well stapled clay, lying upon a gault. In the lower parts a compound of strong earth and vegetable matter. In the higher parts a loamy clay, lying upon a gault."

Milton. - "The arable land a rich brown mould of a good staple, lying upon a gravel, and a strong deep loam upon a clay." +

Impington. - "A deep sandy loam lying upon a gault."

Chesterton. - " North-east of the village, a gravelly loam of a fair staple, lying upon a gravel; on the west a strong cling clay of a tolerable staple upon a gault."

p.22 *Wickin.* - "The arable land a deep brown mould, upon a dry bed of rag-stone."

Soham with Barraway. - "On the east of the town, a black sandy moor, lying upon a gravel; the remainder a deep, rich, black mould, lying upon a blue clay or gault, and clunch. Pasture extensive and of first quality; a large tract also, of the second quality."

The Mere, formerly a lake, now drained and cultivated, and the soil a mixture of vegetable matter and brown clay, contains about fourteen hundred acres.

City of Ely. - " On the north very rich pastures, variable in their soil, and lying upon a gravel, clay and gault; the arable lands, a well mixed, soft, sandy loam, lying upon a clay, and strong tough cling clay, upon a gault; west of the city, and binding upon the enclosures, a sandy loam upon a clay, and a tough clay, upon agault; thence southwardly, a wet, heavy clay, and a light, dry, gravel."

Little-Port with Apshall. -"East of the village, and ad joining it, a strong, rich, deep, black land; thence southeastwardly, a warm, sandy loam, of a good staple, lying upon a clay and sand; westwardly of the village, a black and brown mould of an irregular depth, lying upon a clay and sand."

Downham. - "On the east of the village, a heavy strong loam, of a deep staple, lying upon a clay; west, a heavy close, wet, cling, and tough clay upon a` gault; south, and joining the enclosures, a warm, deep, friable mould, upon a reddish-coloured clay, or brick-earth, thence south-wardly, the warm, brown mould, is lost, in a tough, hungry, thin, cold clay, upon a gault."

Mepal. - "The arable land, a strong close clay, of a fair staple, lying upon a gault."

p.23 *Sutton.* - "The arable, a brown earth, of a good staple, upon a reddish clay, or brick-earth; a tough, thin clay upon a gault; and a small part of a mixed nature upon a gravel."

Haddenham, with the divisions of Haddenham-End, Linden-End, Hill-row, and Aldreth-End. "Soil, a cold, tough, thin clay, lying upon a gault. Lindon-End, upper part, a warm, sandy loam, upon a clay; towards the fen, the sandy loam is gradually lost, in a cold, thin clay, lying upon a gault. Hill

---

§ "Cottenham open-field, a fine reddish loam on good gravel." A. Y. Ans. v. 4.

\+ Milton, "a very fine loam on gravel, and continues so to Cambridge." A. Y. Ans. v. 4.

row, a firm brown mould, well stapled upon a gault and reddish-coloured brick-earth. The Aldreth End, is similar to Lindon-End'."

Wilburton. - "East of the village, a gentle, warm, and sandy loam, of a good staple; north, a strong, deep clay, lying upon a gault; south, a similar soil."

Stretham with Thetford. - "East of the village, the pastures consist of a strong, deep, black mould, lying upon a gault; the soil of the fields is similar."

Chatteris. -" East of the village, a deep, brown, com pact, clayey loam, lying upon a gault; south, a strong, brown clay, of a good staple, lying upon a red clay; north-west, an open, warm, and gravelly soil, lying upon a clay, mixed with gravel."

Doddington and its Appendages. -" More light and gentle than Chatteris; the highland a gravelly loam, of a warm and kindly nature, lying upon a clay or gravel; the fen a light moor of various depths, and of the same structure with the level in general."

Elm. - " East of the village, taking the church for the centre, the high land is a silty, tender loam, lying upon a loam; south-west and north, a clayey loam, mixed with a small portion of infinitely fine sea-sand, or silt and vegetable matter, well stapled and lying upon a clay. The fen, a black putrid,
p.24 vegetable matter, lying upon a sub stratum at different depths of turf moor and bear's muck, which finally rests upon a clay, the natural and antient surface of the country."

Upwell. - "The highland a strong silty loam of a good staple. ' The fen is a silt mixed with vegetable matter, or fen mould lying upon a turf moor, under which in many places is found a bear's muck, though the soil or superstratum is sometimes found upon a clay."

Outwell. - "Soil similar to Upwell."

Leverington. - "The upland a deep brown under clay, or loam, lying upon a clay; the marshes are a loamy silt of a gentle nature, lying upon a silt, or sea-sand; the fen is a vegetable matter, or loose black mould, upon a turf moor, resting upon a bear's muck and a clay."

Newton. - "The highland, similar soil to Leverington, as are the marshes and fen."
Tid St. Giles. "The. highland near the village, is a strong loam or clay, of a very good staple, lying upon a gault. The marshes are a hungry silt with little or no variation."

Leverington and Parson drove. - "The more elevated part of the high land consists of a strong loam, upon a silt, and the lower part of a mild loam lying upon a silt; again a clay with a mixture of vegetable matter or fen mould, of a good depth, lying upon a buttery clay or gault. The fen of the first quality is a vegetable matter or moor, mixed with a hazel-coloured loam, or tender sea-clay, of a rich, deep staple, upon a silty clay. The fen of the second quality consists of a moor, or fen mould casually mixed with clay,"

Wisbech St. Mary, including part of Wisbech St. Peter, and the Hamlets of Guyhurn, Tholmas, Drove and Murrow. - "The inside high land of the first quality lying between the Murrow-banks and Wisbech St. Peter, and binding north-westwardly upon Leverington, Parson drove is an open loamy
p.25 soil very similar to that of the preceding parish. The low land of die same district consists of a fen mould, mixed with and lying upon a clay: the fen of the first quality similar to that of same quality in preceding parish; that of second quality is a vegetable matter or fen-mould, with little or no mixture of silt, lying upon a turf moor."

Thorney. - " The high land consists of an ash-coloured tender clay, of a good staple, lying upon a gault and gravel. The fen of the first quality is composed of completely putrified vegetable matter, with the natural clay upon which it rests, forming together, a deep, strong, black earth; that of the second quality, is a fen mould or moor, from fourteen to twenty-four inches deep, lying upon a gault and gravel. The third class of fen consists of fen mould, upon a turf moor, under which is bear's muck of various depths, which finally rests upon a clay."

Whittlesea. - "North-eastwardly of the village and adjoining thereto, is a brown, friable mould of a good staple, lying upon a clay and gravel; southwardly, a mixed brown earth and gravelly loam, of a tolerable staple lying upon a clay and gravel; the church-field is of a similar soil; westwardly of the village, the soil is similar to that north-eastwardly of it. The King's Delph-land, and extending southwardly from the village dyke, is a fen mould incorporated with clay; thence south-eastwardly the clay is gradually lost in an unmixed mass of fen-mould, upon a turf moor and bear's muck. The soil of the fen is a putrid vegetable matter upon a turf moor, under which is bear's muck of different depths."

Such is Mr. Vancouver's account of the soil of Cambridgeshire. Messrs. Britton and Bayley, in their "Beauties of England and Wales," thus describe it, " The soil of Cambridgeshire is greatly diversified. The rich marshes in the vicinity of Wisbech consist of a mixture of sand and clay, or silt. The fens of a
p.26 strong, black earth, or moor, lying on a gault or gravel, or turf moor. The uplands of chalk, gravel, loam, and tender clay, upon a gault." To these accounts it may perhaps be superfluous to add a word, the observations however of individuals are entitled to notice; I therefore, will add those made to me on this subject. The arable soil which is most esteemed in the county, is called " white-land," which is particularly adapted to the growth of wheat; the celebrated seed-wheat called Burwell-wheat, is grown on this soil, which is not only found in the fields of that parish, but in those of many of the adjoining ones, and in others in various distant districts, and is that described by Mr. Vancouver as " a deep, rich, white loam, lying upon a chalk or gault;" it is however in general, not of a deep staple but fleet, (not more than three or four inches), and it has been found that ploughing into the substratum (chalk or gault), and bringing it up, has rendered the land nearly barren for many years; this soil has been found unfavourable to turnips; they die when their root comes to the clunch; this soil, on the least rain, becomes soapy, and poaches so as considerably to injure stock (particularly sheep) feeding on it. As the Cambridgeshire farmers call this, their favourite soil, "white land," so they have a soil they call "red land," which nave indeed is too frequently applied by them to all light lands, but properly only to the soil composed of a reddish sand, with a mixture of chalk and gravel which is suitable to turnips. That the substratum of the white lands has not been found in all cases to produce the affect generally imputed to it, when brought upon the surface, appears from the following communication from Wimpole. "In digging wells at Wimpole, Lord Hardwicke penetrates one hundred and forty feet of what in Cambridgeshire is called gault, that is a pale, blue clay, seemingly free from sand, and consisting of
p.27 impalpable particles; some of it being used to level the gar[dens] allotted to cottagers, and also spread on grass lands, it was found to have considerable fertilizing qualities. As there is a prejudice against deep ploughing, lest any of this substratum should be touched, it is of some consequence to ascertain the fact. His lordship's bailiff, Mr. Patteson, from Lothian, is a friend to deep ploughing, and has yet found no evil to result from gault. Shells are sometimes found in it even at the depth of one hundred and forty feet."* The Rev. Mr. Turner of Burwell in a letter to Mr. Young, thus describes the white and red lands of that parish: "the greater number of acres under the plough are called white lands, as the appearance of the lands in dry weather, is white on account of its being a shallow soil, lying near the white-stone, and not being a spit deep in many places. There is another sort of plough land in the parish, which is called red land, lying down towards Newmarket Heath, but the quantity of this is very small when compared with the white land, and its quality is far inferior." This description of these soils is accurate, and such as I believe every Cambridgeshire farmer will assent to, as I found the generality did to that of Mr. Vancouver, of the other sorts of land in the county.

SECT. V. - MINERALS AND FOSSILS.

There are no mines in the county.

p.28

SECT. VI. - RIVERS.

The principal rivers are the Ouse and the Granta, or Cam. The Ouse enters the county between Fen Drayton and Erith, thence it runs eastward through the fens, till at some distance above Denny-Abbey, it assumes a northerly direction, and passing Stretham, Ely, and Littleport flows into Norfolk.* The Cam

---

* A.Y. Ann.Vol. 44.

* From this river, are many cuts called "loads," leading to several places in the county.

enters the county to the west of Guilden-Morden, thence flowing to the north-east, it receives several rivulets, and near Grantchester has its current enlarged by united waters which flow into this county from Essex; hence, taking a northerly direction, the Cam glides through the walk of the principal colleges at Cambridge, and having passed several villages, falls into the Ouse, at Harrimere in the parish of Stretham. The Nene is likewise a considerable river, it runs by Wisbech to the sea. The old and new Bedford rivers run upwards of twenty miles from Erith to Denver. These rivers are all navigable, and merchandize is conveyed on them by gangs of barges, from 4 to 7 and 8 each gang; the change for freight is,

For coals, from Lynn to Cambridge 6s. 6d. to 12s. per ch.
For corn, from Cambridge to Lynn 1s. per quarter
For flour, ditto. 1s. per sack
For corn, from March to Lynn 10d. per quarter
For coals, from Ely to Lynn 7s. 2d. per ch.

These freights vary in proportion to the supply of water, encreasing as the water decreases. These rivers are kept open in frosty weather, by ice-boats, drawn down the stream, by eight horses, four on each side.

p.29

CHAP. II.

PROPERTY.

SECT. I. - ESTATES.

THE estates vary very much in size; there are many large ones, viz. those of Lord Hardwicke, Duke of Bedford, Duke of Rutland, Sir Henry Peyton, Mr. Thorpe, &c. &c. The greatest part of the county is perhaps in estates from, £200. to £500. and £1000. per annum, there are however many from £20. to £50. and £400. per year, many occupied by the owners. Great part of the county (I had no means of ascertaining what proportion) belongs to colleges and other public bodies.

SECT. II. - TENURES.

Every kind of tenure is in this county; there are vast numbers of leaseholds, under the college and other public bodies; chiefly for 21 years, renewable every 7 years, paying also an annual rent, called a reserved rent; the usual fee for renewal, is from 1¼ to 1½ years rent; some are grants for a number of years, and some for life or lives.

p.30

CHAP. III.

BUILDINGS.

SECT. I. - HOUSES OF PROPRIETORS.

1 AM not aware that there is anything in these interesting to the farmer, or which suggest any particular observation; I speak of the houses of proprietors in general; those of the noblemen and gentlemen of large estates, are suitable to the rank and wealth of their owners.

SECT. II. - FARM-HOUSES AND REPAIRS.

The farm-houses and premises are in general bad, inconvenient, and of such materials as must subject the owners to heavy expence in repairs. Lath and plaster, or clay and wattle, are the most common materials; in many places, clunch-walls, which are found very warm, dry, and durable, if attended to. There are many newly erected premises on the late enclosures, most of them defective in arrangement and conveniences, and almost all over-barned. The barns all too low on the stud. Mr. Treslove on his occupation at Trumpington, Mr. Lane of Carlton, Mr. Jennyns of Bottisham afford exceptions to these remarks. Mr. Lane's open-barn, (viz. a roof on posts) for corn, deserves attention; Mr. Jennyns has erected most convenient premises for his threshing machine, which is placed in the middle of a building,
p.31 (a parallelogram), the corn is pitched on to a platform from behind the machine, and goes through it in

front, where the straw is raked, and shaked, and pitched into a large straw-house adjoining; nothing is wanted to complete these premises but to build the stacks, for the corn is brought into that part of the buildings behind the platform of the machine from stacks, on frames to run in an iron rail-way, (as has been recommended by Mr. Young) to be drawn as wanted, into the building in which is the threshing-machine. At Ely is a remarkably large barn, (Mr. Page's) it is 232 feet long, 40 feet wide in the clear, and 69 feet high. Mr. Stone (late of Leverington) observes on the subject of this Section, "The farm houses in this county are generally esteemed good; the farm yards and offices ill constructed. Situation for convenience of occupation, is little thought of."

At Whittlesea, are round the farm yards, clunch walls, seven feet high they cost 2s. per running yard.

SECT. III. - COTTAGES.

These are wretchedly bad, speaking generally. Lord Hardwicke has set an example worthy of imitation, in having built several comfortable cottages, and having attached gardens to them; some few other gentlemen have done the like; but, it is to be lamented, it is only a few.

p.32

CHAP. IV. - OCCUPATIONS.

SECT. I. - SIZE OF FARMS.

FROM 20 to 100 acres; a few only exceeding 1000 acres; many from 100 acres to 1000.

SECT. II. RENT.

Correct information on this subject however desirable, is not attainable by an indifferent person, nor indeed can it be reasonably expected from those whose interest may be, and there is reason to believe has been, affected by such communication. I have reason to believe the following nearly the real rents in many parts of the county; I had the account from a respectable quarter.

Enclosed arable from 15s. to 25s.; open field 7s. to 15s.; improved pasture 20s. to 30s.; inferior pasture, 7s. to 16s.; wood land 12s. to 16s.; improved fen 10s. to 25s.; waste and unimproved fen 1s. 6d. to 6s. 6d.; half yearly meadow 10s. to 21s.; highland common worth 10s.; fen or moor-common worth 3s.; sheep-walk 1s. 6d. to 3s.6d. The following was given me by a person in extensive business, and in high
p.33 repute as a commissioner of enclosure, land-steward, valuer, &c. &c. and who is in the receipt of large rents.

At Coveney, Mepal, Sutton, Witcham, Wentworth, Witchford, Wilburton and Haddenham.	arable field	16s. to 20s.
	fen	11s. to 21s
At Downham, Little Port, Ely, and Soham.	arable field	18s. to 23s.
	fen	12s. to 21s.
At Stretham, Thetford, and Waterbeach	arable field	16s. to 22s.
	fen	10s. to 20s.
At Whittlesea,	arable field	10s. to 30s.
	fen	10s. to 30s.
At Thorney, tithe-free	fen	16s. to 30s.

There are, however, many instances, particularly on new enclosures, of much higher rents than here stated, but it would be improper to include them when speaking of a county at large. Rents are paid mostly in money, though many by corn rents; the latter, chiefly of estates belonging to colleges; the act for which rents, requires that at least one third of the rent should be paid by a given quantity of corn, the corn however not being rendered in kind, is paid for at the highest price of wheat on a certain market-day. These rents have been a lottery-ticket to colleges, and it is somewhat remarkable that the proposer of them, should have left money to public institutions, instead of corn-rents which he had thought preferable. Land newly enclosed has been let very high, and the additional rent in consequence of its being tithe free, has been much greater than any clergyman would have demanded for tithe. Mr. Young in his notes taken on the spot, and published in the years 1804 and 1805, in Annals, v.42 and 43, reports rents in this county, as follows: Doddington, Wimlington, and March, lands formerly highland-common, now pasture and arable, 25s. 30s. to 50s. Milton, when open field 10s. since enclosed 25s. to 30s.

p.34

		When open.	Since enclosed.
Grantchester and Coton		5s. to 6s.	20s to 25s.
Barrington		5s. to 6s.	20s.
Long-Stow		6s.	16s.
Abington Pigots		7s.	16s. to 20s.
Morden - Guilden		7s.	14s.
Connington		7s. 6d.	20s.
Knapwell		6s. 8d.	13s.
Elsworth		4s. 6d. to 10s.	18s.
Chippenham.	Total rent	£1300	£2000
Little Wilbraham		6s.	16s.
Carlton		6s.	16s.
Weston Coville,	Total rent	£700 to £800	£1800
Waterbeach Fen,	severalty	13s. or 14s.	
	open field arable	23s.	
	ditto upland and enclosed pasture	20s.	

The rise of rent in this county from 1790 to 1804, is stated by seven returns to the Board of Agriculture to have been from $17^1/_2$ to 300 per cent. The rise of rents may also be judged of by Mr. Young's report of rents, as under.

In 1776, (see Annals, v. 4.)

"At Ely and two or three miles south of it, pastures very rich, letting at 20s. to 35s. and open arable field from 12s. to 20s. the fens, from 3s. to 6s. in general 7s. and 1s. draining-tax.

In 1785, (see Annals, v. 6.)

"At Trumpington, field 8s. to 10s. About Wisbeach fen 1s. 6d. At March fen 7s. Chatteris tillage and
meadow 20s. much at 40s." In Cambridge St. Giles, arable lands lately enclosed, have been let at 40s.
p.35 to £6. per acre to the inhabitants of Cambridge, for pasture, and some even at those rents are continued
arable. Dr. Nasmith of Leverington, says many of the hemp lands about Ely, let at 40s. The rents which Mr. Vancouver reported to the Board of Agriculture, as existing in 1794, may be seen in the first chapter of this volume.

SECT. III. TITHES.

These are taken in kind in many parishes, particularly in those consisting of open field, the hirer giving from 3s. 4d. to 5s. 4d. statute acre for the great tithes. Where tithes are compounded for, an equal composition is paid on the average of the county, in many instances a much higher. Under the late acts of enclosure, tithes have been abolished for one-fifth of arable, one-eighth of pasture, one-ninth of fen, allotted and fenced in at expence of proprietors at large. Mr. Shepherd of Chittenham thinks land owners and tenants wrong in wishing to abolish tithes by giving land as a compensation; as the farmer's estate requires nearly as many buildings, &c. &c. and the latter's occupation nearly equal capital, attention, &c. &c. for the whole of any given quantity of land, as for four fifths of it. Mr. S. would rather the tithes should remain than give land for them. Mr. Sawyer of Cheveley, would prefer giving a corn-rent; Mr. King of Bottisham is of the same opinion, as are the farmers of Islesham. The rise of tithes in this county from 1790 to 1804 was stated to the Board of Agriculture, to have been from 2s. 6d. to 5s. per acre. At
Wisbeach, tithes are compounded for by the acre cropped, but at what rate I could not learn on
p.36 satisfactory authority. The Rev. Mr. Fiske, of Fulburne, thinks tithe-owners would be more inclined to
compound, had they the same security as the land lord. Where tithes are gathered in this county, they are rated to the poor-rate at one-fourth to one-fifth of what the farmer is rated, generally at one fifth. Doubtless each party should contribute to the maintenance of the poor, according to his respective

profit; if those, who maintain that the clergyman should pay one-fifth and the farmer four-fifths of the expence of the poor, act on this datum, they tell us that the farmer's profit is four times that of the clergyman's. It would be desirable to have this subject ably elucidated, not only for the sake of justice, but for preventing the perpetual altercations between the clergy and laity, arising from the erroneous opinions and mutual distrust between them respecting it. Mr. Young has told the world that the farmer's profit is not more than 10 per cent, on his capital employed (on an average of situations); what do they say it is, who assess him four times the amount of the clergyman?

SECT. IV. - POOR-RATES.

These were stated by six returns made to the Board of Agriculture in 1804 to have risen, from 1790 to 1803, from 2s. 11d. to 4s. $8^3/_4$d. in the pound. The information I received on this subject in 1805 and 1806, warrants my stating them at much more than even the latter sum, at 6s. to 7s. and in many parishes at 10s. to 12s. and even higher. By an "abstract of returns relative to the expence and maintenance of the poor' published in Mr. Young's Annals, v. 53, it appears that the expense of the poor of this county from
p.37 Easter, 1802, to Easter, 1803, amounted to £55,954 14s. 11d. and is stated under the following heads.

1st, Money expended out of any house of industry, or workhouse	44,137	15	$3^1/_2$
2d, Money expended in any house of industry or workhouse	10,248	6	$1^1/_4$
3d, Money expended in suits of law, removal of paupers, and expenses of overseers and other officers.	1,568	13	$5^3/_4$
Total	£55,954	14	11

Mr. Vancouver in 1794, stated the poor-rate of Cambridgeshire to average through the county 2s. 6d. in the pound. It should be remembered that a more blind guide than a pound rate, cannot be taken to ascertain the rate per pound on a fair rental, it being the universal practice to assess to the poor-rate at a certain part of a fair rental, and this part is scarcely the same in any two parishes, and always a secret in all. Now supposing Mr. Vancouver's report of the total rental of the county in 1794, £226,009 to be correct, and that the rates were then as he stated them, 2s. 6d. in the pound, it follows that the then expenses of the poor, were £28,251 2s. 6d.; now the expense from 1802 to 1803, we are told was £55,954 14s. 11d., that is nearly double, in nine years; a proof of an alarming, and an enormous encrease, or that Mr. V.'s return, and that in 1803 are not correct.

p.38

SECT. V. LEASES.

In great part of the county none are granted, this system (if it may be so called) cannot however continue, if the benefits looked- for from enclosures are to be realized. Where enclosures have taken place, leases have in general been granted, and the usual covenant respecting cropping has been two crops and a fallow, viz. the course allowed before enclosing, and the course observed by many since. Mr. Custance (an eminent land surveyor, &c. &c. at Cambridge) requires, Where the course of cropping is four "shifts," one-fourth layer, one-fourth fallow or turnips fed, or tares fed. Where the course is five " shifts," one-fifth layer of first year, one-fifth layer of second year, one-fifth fallow or turnips fed, or tares fed; not more than one-fourth of layer to be mown, and that only once. Mr. Wedd of Trumpington thinks the more simple and fewer the covenants the better; he thinks merely restricting the tenant from taking more than two crops and a fallow, would secure the estate from injury, and supersede the necessity of any other covenants; he would however forbid the mowing layers oftener than once. Mr. Edis of Wisbech recommends that the covenants of a fen farm be two-thirds of farm corn; one-half of one third cole; one-half layer. About Wisbech and its neighbourhood lands are frequently let by auction for twenty years. The covenants allow cropping, without restriction. for the first fourteen years, but require that the whole breadth be in grass during the last six; under these covenants, a needy speculator ruins the land. Mr. Waudby of March thinks that the best covenants for a fen farm are two-thirds to be under grass, one-third of the other one-third cole, and two thirds corn; he would not restrict as to
p.39 mowing or feeding. Mr. Stone of Leverington (in answer to queries put to him by Mr. Vancouver on this subject) says, "few leases are granted in this neighbourhood, but the covenants best calculated to preserve the fee-simple of the land let, undiminished, are the following." To restrain the sowing of

hemp, flax, woad, madder, and mustard-seed, as no manure arises from them; the restraining cole-seed from standing for a crop, is founded on the like objection; where the first five of these are grown the land ought to be expressly let for the purpose, and an extra rent set upon it, because it must necessarily be the worse for what it produces, which is never the case with a farm properly let, and skilfully managed. Forbid ploughing the highlands in general, if water can be got to render them fit for grazing. Of the proportion of land belonging to any farm, not more than one third of the land permitted to be ploughed, should be in corn every year, and the same as to the marshes, and from neither more than two successive crops should be taken. To restrain the laying manure on the ploughed lands is very expedient. I have seen instances (where leases have been silent as to the routine of the crops, and the lands on which the manure should be laid), of bad tenants manuring the ploughed lands, and cropping them without intermission during the terms of their leases: by this abuse the ploughed lands at the expiration were extremely foul, and wanted fallowing and laying down, and the grass land not improved as it would have been with proper manuring. Fewer crops of corn, and timely fallowing are therefore insured by forbidding the ploughed lands to be manured, moreover the best species of pasture in every grazing farm, ought to be restrained from being mown. Mr. Vancouver writes on this subject, "there is no greater error in the whole
p.40 economy of country business than that which the gentlemen of Cambridgeshire are too apt to fall into, respecting the tenures they grant of their estates. Few are inclined to give their tenants such assurances of the certain and quiet enjoyment of their improvements, as reason dictates, and justice demands. Had the same jealousy prevailed in Norfolk on the early improvement of that county, in vain would the landlords in conjunction with their tenants have expended such large sums in claying, marling, and otherwise improving their estates, if the tenant had not been assured of an eventual benefit and reward for his expense and labour, under the protection and encouragement of a lease for twenty-one years. The general state of the husbandry in the county of Cambridgeshire, demands the like assistance from the proprietor, as to the means, and the same indulgence in point of possession, as to reward for the industry and labour of the tenant, who will otherwise be little inclined to bury his property in the earth, or improve the surface by the sweat of his brow."

SECT. VI. - EXPENSES AND PROFITS.

I did not meet with farmers enough in the county, keeping sufficiently accurate accounts from which any valuable information on this subject could be extracted. To the question, "what per cent, per annum on the capital employed, is cleared in *addition to common interest* by the generality of farmers in the county;" Answer, from 5 to 10 per cent; now nothing less than the latter appears adequate to the maintenance of a family, much less to the getting a fortune, except on very large occupations; for supposing the opinion prevalent in the county, to be well founded, viz. that not more than £7 per acre is
p.41 employed on the average of arable occupations (though much more, is employed in many instances), the following will be the profit, taking it at 10 per cent, on farms of the sizes specified.

Number of acres.		Capital £7, per acre.		Profit being 10 per cent
		£		£
50	-	350	-	35
100	-	700	-	70
150	-	1050	-	105
200	-	1400	-	140
250	-	1750	-	175
300	-	2100	-	210
350	-	2450	-	245
400	-	2800	-	280
450	-	3150	-	315
500	-	3500	-	350

Shewing that farming on a small scale deserves not the attention of men of skill and ability. The farmer, however, whose capital is his own, would have to spend one-third more than the above sums, viz. the 5 per cent, on his capital, made in addition to these profits, viz. the farmer having 50 acres, would have an income of £52. 10s. he with 300 acres, £525 per annum. By having these sums to spend, is to be understood he would have them for the purpose of paying such of his domestic and other expenses, as

are not absolutely chargeable to his farm; for when it is said that a profit of 10 per cent is made, no other part of the farmer's house expenses, &c. are supposed to be charged.to the farm, than the board of servants, &c. kept for the express purpose of carrying on the farm, and who are solely employed thereon; it is not meant that he clears 10 per cent, after paying all the expenditure of himself and family, whether chargeable to the farm or not ; it is, however, notorious, that a farmer calls that profit which he has at the year's end to spare, and he who has had a profit, however large, if he has expendcd the whole,
p.42 will say" he has made nothing" that year. If it be true that the profit of farming is in proportion to the capital employed, it follows that grass farms are more profitable than arable ones, for the capital requisite on the former, is double, in many instances treble, that of the latter : but it is not generally allowed that the profits vary in this degree, indeed it may be safely asserted that they do not, and that the idea that profit varies with the capital is therefore incorrect, it may however be safely asserted that profit varies with the sum judiciously applied, viz. where a greater or more valuable product is obtained, but not where no such benefit arises; of the latter description is ploughing with a 60 guinea horse, where a 30 guinea one would answer the same purpose, expending money for ornament instead of use, &c. &c.*

Let us take for granted, that the farmer is to make 10 per cent. profit, viz. that sum in addition to common interest, and that the following statements are nearly facts:

1st, Produce per acre	£.	s.	d.
Turnips, worth on an average of applications	3	0	0
Barley, 8 co. at 18s.	7	4	0
Clover, worth on an average of applications	3	0	0
Wheat, 6 co. at 35s.	10	10	0
Beans, 6 co. at 18s.	5	8	0
Pease, 6 co. at 18s.	8	8	0
In 6 years	34	10	0
In one year	5	15	0

p.43

2nd, Suppose a fallow every 4th year.	£.	s.	d.
Fallow	0	0	0
Crop as of above	5	15	0
Ditto	5	15	0
Ditto	5	15	0
In 4 years	17	5	0
In one year	5	18	0

3dly, Suppose the old system of two crops and fallow.	£.	s.	d.
Wheat	10	10	0
Barley	7	4	0
Fallow	0	0	0
In 3 years	17	14	0
In one year	5	18	0

---

* Under this head I might place a return made to the board exhibiting the expenses per acre on turnips, barley, wheat, oats, and manure in 1790 and 1804, but it appears only calculated to mislead, and certainly affords no valuable information, as the authors of it no doubt did not all understand the question which produced this return in the same light; consequently, no conclusion can be drawn from their answers. The return I allude to is entitled "cultivation".

4th, Crop and fallow		£.	s.	d.
Wheat		10	10	0
Fallow		0	0	0
	In 2 years	10	10	0
	In one year	5	5	0

p.44

5th, The Norfolk course		£.	s.	d.
Turnips		3	0	0
Barley		7	4	0
Clover		3	0	0
Wheat		10	10	0
	In 4 years	23	14	0
	In one year	5	15	0

Recapitulation		£.	s.	d.
1st Course		5	15	0
2nd		4	5	3
3rd		5	18	0
4th		5	5	0
5th		5	18	6
	Number of courses 5	27	2	9
	In one year	5	6	6½

	£.	s.	d.
Hence it appears that the annual acreable produce of lands suitable to the above crops, is	5	8	6½
Remain for outgoings per acre	4	14	6½

Is this sum really expended on the average of arable lands at the present (1807) time, producing these crops? It may be presumed it is, for in 1803 it amounted in Suffolk on the average of the returns made from that county to the Board of Agriculture on farms of loo acres of arable land, to £4 15s. 6d.¼ per
p.45 acre.

N. B. No similar return was made from this county, but the expenses in it, certainly are not less than in Suffolk.

The returns from Suffolk here alluded to, were made under the following heads:

	£.	s.	s.	
Rent	0	18	2½	Now higher
Tithe	0	5	4¾	
Rates	0	4	0	Now higher
Wear and tear	0	5	0	
Labour	1	6	4¼	viz. 4½ men at £30. each, or 100 acres arable
Seed	0	8	4¼	Now higher
Team	0	17	7	viz. 4½ horses at £20. each, now higher
Manure Purchased	0	5	2¼	on some farms none, on others more
Interest 5 per cent	0	5	4¼	Now 7s. viz. on £7. capital per acre
	£4	15	6¼	

From this view of the subject it appears that there is left for profit at a rent of 18s. 2¼d. per acre, 12s. 11¼d. per acre; thus, average of produce per acre, per annum.	£.	s.	d.
	5	6	8½
Outgoings per acre, per annum	4	15	6¼
Remains for profit	0	12	11¼ Per acre

p.46 It may be asked if there be any accuracy in these calculations, how account for the avidity which lands are hired, at rents considerably above that here stated and subject to many higher expense? I answer, many no doubt hire on speculation, hoping for better times, and that they shall grow more, or obtain higher prices, than can be calculated upon as averages; no doubt some do this, and they are talked of, while those who suffer are unnoticed. It may also be true that individuals may farm at less expense than here stated; but it is equally true, that more farm at much greater. There is some trifling produce from arable lands not noticed here, such as feed of stubbles, &c. from which some money is also raised, but it is not of sufficient amount to form part of the calculation on produce; part of the straw also raises what it is worth for keeping cattle lean; its other application, viz. for muck is necessary for the production of the crops, and raises no money but in that shape.

The *income* of a farmer on 100 acres of arable land would be from a profit of 10 per cent on		£.	s.	d.
	£7 per acre, profit	70	0	0
	and 5 per cent on his capital	35	0	0
		105	0	0

Also, what he might shorten the outgoings by his own labour, &c. shewing that no less profit than 10 per cent is adequate on occupations under 100 acres arable. On very large occupations than 10 per cent, no doubt would produce a handsome annual income.

p.47

CHAP. V.

IMPLEMENTS.

IN the fens is the common foot-plough with a running coulter, which with the share is kept constantly bright, and filed particularly sharp; to these ploughs is frequently annexed an appendage called a " boy," to lap in the rushes, &c. &c. which it does completely. The half and three-quarter Dutch plough, together with the common swing and foot-ploughs, are used in the highland parts of the county. The dagger whole and half winged shares are variously employed. The harrows, carts, waggons, and other implements of husbandry in general use in the county, merit neither notice nor imitation. Mr. Shepherd of Chippenham has invented many implements, which do him credit, such as harrows, rolls, dibbling-machines, &c. &c. and he has also contrived an engine for sowing small seeds; it is a drill without hoppers, the cups delivering the seeds broadcast directly on to the land; I saw some layers sown by this machine, beautifully regular and a full plant. Mr. Shepherd claims the invention of the drill for drilling oil-dust and turnip-seed together, and for which Mr. Burwell of Thetford in Norfolk, undeservedly as Mr. Shepherd terms it, obtained a silver cup of Mr. Coke, in 1803. Mr. Burwell as confidently asserts he was the inventor. The Rev. Mr. Brown of Connington has an excellent implement which he calls a "cleanser." I viewed some fallows made by it which far surpassed any I saw in the county, being free
p.48 from weeds, and of a fine deep tilth. Mr. B. speaks of this implement justly thus; (A.Y. Annals, vol. 42.) "it will work upon any soil, but more particularly upon light, and it has been used, and that continually, upon the heaviest; it is worked by either two, three, or four horses, according to the roughness of the tillage, and will raise upon bean-stubble on the strongest soil, sufficient tilth in a mild season to harrow in wheat without any ploughing. It requires only one person to attend it, and that is the driver, as it will keep steady to its work by itself. By employing two sets of horses, it will cleanse from six to eight acres each day. This implement is to be regulated so as to cut any depth with the greatest ease. The price of

* Mr. Philips of Bourn-bridge approves it for wheat and barley on light soils.

this machine, which Mr. B. offers to the public is with wheels £21.; without wheels £16. 16s. Mr. Filby of Snailwell, has a mill for thrashing clover and other small seeds, a two or three horse power; the cob is put into a cask, in the middle of which is placed an upright iron, having through it pieces of wood in the form of flyers to a jack, which are full of nails, the heads standing about a quarter of an inch out; the seed is beaten out by the revolution of these flyers (affected by a wheel at the top of the upright iron, communicating with the horse-wheel); it will thrash about 12 fans an hour. The drill-roller has been tried on "white lands," and found not to answer the purpose, the harrows will not take out the grooves made by the roller, consequently the seed can not be covered by them. Mr. Wedge of Wesley-Bottom uses it on light soils and approves it.* The Kentish nidget is also used by Mr. Wedge, on summer lands instead of the plough. The mole-plough has been tried on pastures at Madinglay, by Sir C. Cotton and approved;
p.49 the saving is great, 10 to 12 acres may be done in a day, with 12 horses; expense men and horses about 3s. 4d. per acre ; but Mr. Young, (Annals, Vol. 42.), gives an account of this implement drawn by a windlass, turned by eight women; this method would be executed in the best style, were it adopted at Madinglay; the admiral would certainly be at home, while directing it. It is spoken of highly by Mr. Y. and consequently deserves attention; the working this plough by horses is such an objection (on account of the great danger of injuring them) that very few farmers use it. Sir Charles Cotton, has also tried a "hoe-plough," which is drawn by four horses, the hoe one piece of iron, about $3\frac{1}{2}$ feet long, and about three inches broad, and sharp in front; is used on fallows when in tilthe, and answers well, will do the work of six ploughs, cuts six inches deep, this like all other large hoes, cannot work where there is any grass or weeds of any description as it would choke. Rev. Mr. Leworthy of Harston has carts for harvest work, low, long, and light; his harrows are very powerful, are drawn by four horses, can be regulated to any depth, and have coulter-teeth; he uses them on fallows instead of the plough. Mr. Boyce of Whittlesea has an excellent dressing machine by Couch of Harlston, near Northampton, costs 18 guineas, will dress 30 Co. of wheat per hour, and well attendance, two men, one boy, one woman. Mr. Edis, of Wisbech, has all Cook's machines, also a powerful scarifier which he uses instead of the plough, on his fallows, and approves it. The double-furrowed plough has been used by Mr. Darnton of Babraham on a light Soil; he has laid it aside, thinking he gained nothing by it; he has tried cast iron plough-breasts only, and approves them.

Mr. Mortlock at Abington has a sheep-rack of which his bailiff speaks highly; it is formed by splines
p.50 about six or eight feet long, across which and at right angles to them, are nailed half hoops. This rack is placed in a concave position on the ground, and when filled is inverted. Less waste is said to be made in feeding out of this rack, than out of any other, and the hay is less exposed to wind.

Mr. Mortlock's Sheep Rack

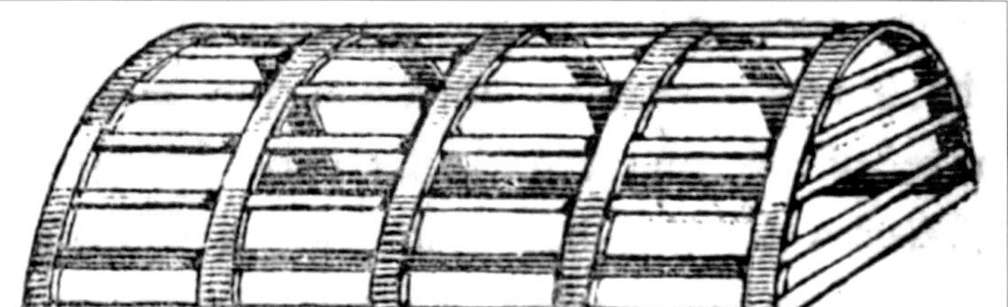

The one-horse Norfolk foot plough has been used by Mr. Tharpe of Chippenham, and by Mr. Barker of Swaffham for ploughing in barley, and are approved. Shims for shimming fallows are coming into use; 1 observed them on both sides of St. Ives's road. Threshing machines are becoming general, I saw none however differing from those which are to be seen in every county, excepting that of Lord Hardwicke, worked by water, of which it is to be lamented, it has not sufficient supply, except from about Michaelmas to Lady-day; it will thresh 60 Co. per day, and well; there are annexed to it, stones for grinding corn, a dressing machine and chaff-cutter. His lordship has also one worked by four horses, will do about 15 quarters of wheat, 30 of oats, beans, or pease, and about 20 of barley in a day; cost about £250. Mr. Lane of Carlton has a threshing machine by Rennie, on a most tremendously large and expensive scale; to it are attached a flour mill, dressing machines, apparatus for dressing small seeds, &c. &c. &c. and is worked by six horses; Mr. Lane talks of working it by wind. 1 was not informed the cost of this machine, it is doubtless such as will deter any body (having profit in view) from having one.
p.51 I saw also threshing machines at the following places. At Harston (Rev W. Leworthy's) by Bossmore of Doncaster, Yorkshire, will thresh 24 Co. of barley, 25 Co. of wheat per day, and is worked by four

horses, it will not thresh beans and pease, it splits them and reduces bean straw to dust; it cost £100; a winnowing machine, a chaff-cutter, and a steel-mill (for breaking-corn,) are attached to it. Mr. Edis of Wisbech, has also one of Bossmore's threshing machines worked by six horses, will thresh 21 Co. of wheat, 42 Co. of oats, it cost £80 to £90.

He has also one (by Burwell of Thetford, Norfolk), to which he applies four horses, although originally intended for two. It answers as well as Bossmore's, and costs about £70. Mr. E. observed they both starved his hogs. Mr. Jonathan Page of Ely, has one (by Yellowly), which, together with expences to which it led, cost £500. and yet does its work badly; it is too hard work for six horses; it separates straw from chaff. Colonel Adeane, of Babraham, and Mr. Wedge, of Westley Bottom, have threshing-machines. The Rev. Mr. Jennyns, of Bottisham, has one by (Hart of Brinkley), of which he speaks in high terms; it is worked by four horses, will thresh 20 Co. of wheat in five hours. The portable threshing machines common in Suffolk have not found their way into this county; they cost about £63. and are worked by four horses; will do (taking one grain with another) about 25 Co. per day; they are in repute.

There are various opinions of threshing machines; the following calculation may perhaps shew nearly that which they are entitled to, I will take it for granted that four horses and eight people are necessary to work the generality of them, and that their original and average cost, (including expences to which they lead in making conveniences for working them) is £80. and that they will (taking one grain with
p.52 another and stoppages by accident, &c. &c. into the account, thresh 20 Co. per day, where more is done, it is by more horses and more expensive machines. The portable ones will not do more, including the time of removing and fixing them, nor will any other of £80 cost, as I found.

Expense per day working	£.	s.	d.
Four men at 2s. each	0	8	0
Four boys or women at 1s.	0	4	0
Four horses at 2s. each	0	8	0
	1	0	0

This number of persons will certainly be wanted, if the straw be loaded on to waggons, and an equal number will be wanted on the generality of premises, which are not calculated to get the straw, &c. to and from the machine, and out of the way to the best advantages; many are worked by more men, and fewer boys or women, and it is contended to greater benefit. To these expenses, are to be added others, which I am at a loss to reduce to a daily charge on the number of days a machine is worked ; first, interest on first cost of machine ; secondly, annual repairs; thirdly, decrease of its value.

	£.	s.	d.
The first interest on cost, viz. on £80. at 5 per cent.	4	0	0
The second repairs per year at least	4	4	0

The third is a serious one, and is that which I have never seen (why I cannot tell) in any calculation on this subject. Is it included in the charge usually made per annum, for keeping it in repair, taking it for granted that is sufficient to keep the machine as good as when new? Be it so; does it therefore follow that the machine having had annually such sum laid out upon it, will be, at any future time of the same
p.53 saleable value? By no means ; instances are innumerable of their fetching not one-fourth of their original price, after having been used (and received no injury), only a year or two; this must inevitably happen to machines which are rivalled every day, by those which succeed them; Now when a man calculates on the probable result of any undertaking, does he not consider the value of stock from time to time employed in that undertaking? So surely should he calculate who is about using a threshing machine and consider its probable value at any future period. To state this point in the most favourable way (not to offend the advocates for these machines), I will suppose that the generality of farmers are from various causes liable to be obliged to decline business, or part with their stock, or that it will from deaths be alienated every fourteen years, under such a probability it would be advisable to consider what

would be the probable worth of any threshing-machine at the end of such period. This cannot I think be set (when the improvements in them are considered) at more than one-fourth of its original cost. It is to be doubted whether it ought to be set at so high, though in such repair as to be as good as new. However, to call it one fourth, viz. in fourteen years £60. will be sunk by a machine which cost £80.; £60. in fourteen years is nearly £4. 5s. 9d. per year; query, what is this per day on the number of days a machine is used on an average of occupations? It may perhaps be fairly supposed they are purchased by farmers occupying 150 acres and upwards of arable land; small farmers hire portable ones. Taking a farm of 150 acres arable, cropped one-fourth fallow, one-fourth barley, oats, beans or pease; one-fourth clover, &c.
p.54 &c, there will be grown yearly $37\frac{1}{2}$ acres of barley, oats, beans, or pease; call the average of these $7\frac{1}{2}$ Co. per acre, viz. 271 Co.; of wheat, at 5 Co. per acre, on $37\frac{1}{2}$ acres, 187 Co; together, 458 Co., that is at 20 Co. per day, 23 days work; an expense therefore of £4. 5s. 9d. annually being incurred on 23 days work, is 3s. $8\frac{1}{4}$d. for each of those days; it appears then that the expense per day of a threshing-machine, on a farm of 150 acres arable, is as follows:

	£.	s.	d.
Four horses	0	8	0
Four men	0	8	0
Four boys or women	0	4	0
Interest on first cost of machine £4. per year equal on 23 days, to per day	0	3	$5\frac{1}{2}$
Repairs of machine £4. per year, equal on 23 days, to per day	0	3	$5\frac{1}{2}$
Decrease of value of machine in 14 years, is per year, 4/. 5s. 9d. equal on 23 days, to per day	0	3	$8\frac{1}{4}$
	£1	10	$7\frac{1}{4}$

Total expense, therefore, of threshing 20 Co. of corn by the machine, and on the farm assumed, is £1. 10s. $7\frac{1}{4}$d viz. 1s. 6d. per Co. round, much above the price by hand. Do the advantages of these machines make amends for this extra expense?

This statement, it must be allowed, does not shew much in favour of machines of this sort, and on the size-farms assumed; they would no doubt cut a better figure on large occupations, but it appears they are of no advantage on others; nor can the small farmer hire to advantage; the expense being equal to
p.55 that here noted. It should however be remembered that the calculation here made does not apply to threshing machines which also grind corn, dress seeds, &c. &c. But perhaps the comparative expense between threshing by hand, and by a machine, is not the most weighty consideration, and though the latter be greater than the former, it may be preferable from the many attendant advantages; these no farmer wants to have pointed out; a material one is, that it protects him from imposition of workmen, where they are plentiful, and affords him a resource where they are not; in short, a threshing machine is as necessary to a farmer, as a tithe barn to a rector.

p.56

CHAP. VI.

ENCLOSING.

CAMBRIDGESHIRE has gone far into this measure since 1770, and in consequence its farmers have an opportunity of redeeming the county from the imputation it has so long lain under, of being the worst cultivated in England, and of proving (the fact) that the same industry, spirit and skill which have been manifested in other parts of the kingdom, exist also in this, the open-field state and system precluding the possibility of exercising them. It is somewhat singular, and is a striking proof of the snail-like progress of improvements in agriculture, that the very same ideas which are now entertained by the advocates for enclosures, existed and were published in 1650 by Walter Blyth, who has pointed out the evils of a "Champion country," and the benefits to be expected from its enclosure, with as much zeal and ability as any writer of the present day. In 1783 queries were sent to the parishes in this county, which had been enclosed in his present Majesty's reign, up to that time, with a view of ascertaining the effects of enclosures. It is necessary to state these queries and the answers to them, and to make some observations on them.

Queries.

1st, What number of acres in your parish were enclosed under the act passed?

2nd, Was the land then enclosed, heath, down, fen, waste land, common, or common-field.

p.57 3dly, What number of acres then enclosed were annually sown with wheat before such enclosure, according to the best information you can obtain?

4thly, What number of acres then enclosed have been annually sown with wheat, since such enclosure?

5thly, Is the annual quantity of wheat grown in your parish, increased or diminished since the enclosure, and in what proportion?

6thly, Is the produce in other articles in your parish, increased or diminished since the enclosure? State which are increased, and what diminished, and in what proportion.

Answers to above Queries.

From Abington Pigots (enclosed 1770) by Rev. Alern, the rector.

To query 1st, About 1000 acres.
2d, Chiefly arable, open field dispersed.
3rd, About 350 acres.
4th, About 40 acres increase.
5th, Not at all increased.

From Knapwell (enclosed 1775).

To 1st, About 1100 acres,
2d, Common field 1000, common 100 acres.
3rd, About 150 acres.
4th, About 170 acres.
5th, Increased about one-fourth.
6th, Barley increased one-filth, oats and pease decreased one-fourth by introducing clover and other grass-seeds; sheep increased.

From Weston Colville (enclosed 1777) by Rev. H. A. Lagden, rector.

To 1st, 248 acres, 1 rood, heath; no acres, common; 1547 acres, 2 roods, common field.
2d, 30 acres, 1 rood, wasteland, total 1936 acres.
p.58 3rd, About 200 acres.
4th, About 410 acres.
5th, Increased one-half.
6th, Pease fewer ; oats, increased one-third; barley, double ; feeding-grass, decreased two-thirds, seed-land for feeding increased one third; mowing land less, artificial grasses more; sheep increased from 1000 to 1200, before enclosure wethers kept, since ewes.

From March (enclosed 1792) by Rev. A. Jobson, curate.

To 1st, About 3400 acres.
2d, All commons.
3rd, None.
4th, About 400 acres.
5th, Increased.
6th, Cows decreased, butter advanced 4d. per pound,

Chippenham and Wimlington, (the latter a hamlet to March) were enclosed in 1792 also; I was not furnished with the answers to these queries from either of these parishes, if any were sent.

From Barrington (enclosed 1796) by [*blank*]

To 1st, About 2000 acres.
2d, Common-field land.
3rd, About 300 acres.
4th, About 300 acres.
5th, Expect increase.
6th, Sheep the same, they are now dry stock. Cows two-thirds less, other articles much the same.

From Little Wilbraham (enclosed 1797) by Rev. W. Butts, rector.

To 1st, About 1800 acres.
2d, About 900 acres field, 500 acres common, 300 acre heath.
3d, About 170 acres.
p.59 4th, More than 300 acres.
5th, Increased in number of acres, nearly double quantity per acre.
6th, Other grain more. As many sheep, and much better fed from introduction of turnips, and artificial grasses; cows rather diminished, but those remaining better kept.

From Great Wilbraham, (enclosed 1797) by Rev. T. Stevenson, vicar.

To 1st, About 2800 acres.
2d, Heath, fen-common, and common field.
3d, About 280 acres
4th, About 300 acres.
5th, Increased about 80 quarters.
6th, Barley increased about 100 quarters, rye diminished about 80 quarters, pease diminished about 20 quarters, oats diminished about 30 quarters; an increase is expected in all.

From Swaffham-Bulbeck (enclosed 1798) by James Barker, Esq.

To 1st, 3260 acres (statute measure).
2d, Heath, fen, waste lands, common fields, and common.
3d, About 450 acres.
4th, About 500 acres, in 1799 and 1800.
5th, Decreased on average of the two years, nearly one half.
6th, Barley, oats and pease increased.

From Harston and Hauxton (enclosed 1798) by Rev. W. Leworthy, Rector of Harston.

To 1st, 1000 acres arable, 800 acres pasture.
2d, Common field, and commonable land.
3d, One-third, viz. about 333 acres.
4th, Not known.
5th, Increased about one-sixth, and will still more increase.
p.60 6th, Sheep diminished one-third, but they will increase as well as every other article. N. B. These answers are also applicable to the parish of Hauxton, except the number of acres which did not exceed 600.

From Long-Stow (enclosed 1798) by Rev. R. Heighton, rector.

To 1st, about 1500 acres, statute measure.
2d, Old enclosure, small part, of it arable, about 200 acres common, open field, arable, about 40 acres (part of old enclosure) woodland.
3d, About 150 acres.

4th, About 66 acres in 1799.

5th, Diminished in the proportion of 80 to 150.

6th, Every produce diminished, the breed of young cattle and lambs will be diminished. There will not in future be so much corn grown.

From Pampisford (enclosed 1798 or 1799).

To 1st, 1240 acres.

2d, Common and common-field,

3d, 127 acres.

4th, About 124 acres.

5th, Will increase one-sixth.

6th, Will doubtless increase corn; sheep decreased one-third, cows decreased about one-fourth.

From Grantchester and Coton (enclosed 1799) by Rev. W. Butts, vicar.

To 1st, About 1500 acres.

2d, Mostly common field.

3d, About 300 acres.

5th, As much as before enclosure.

6th, Clover and artificial grasses increased considerably, also barley and oats. N.B. These answers relate only to Grantchester.

p.61 From Carlton with Willingham (enclosed 1799) by D. Berguer, B. D. rector.

To 1st, about 1050 acres.

2d Heath, waste-land, common, and common-field.

3d, About 300 acres.

4th, About 70 acres.

5th, Probably quantity will increase.

6th, Barley will increase, artificial grasses and turnips will increase, sheep will be doubled at least.

From Milton (enclosed 1800) by Rev. S. Vince, minister.

To 1st, 1378 acres.

2d, 937 acres common field, 213 acres enclosed pasture, 228 acres common and waste.

3d, About 300 acres.

4th, About 100 acres.

From Guilden Morden (enclosed 1800) no answers, allotments not made.

From Elsworth (enclosed 1800) by Rev. M. Holworthy rector.

To 1st, No allotments yet made.

2d, 2000 acres arable, 1000 acres commons, 700 acres old enclosures, and woodland and meadow.

3d, One-third of arable, viz. about 666 acres.

From Connington (enclosed 1800) by Rev. T. Brown, rector.

To 1st, From 1400 to 1500 acres.

2d, Down, which was sheep common, waste and other common for sheep or cows, about 1000 acres common field.

3d, About one-sixth arable, viz. about 164 to 170 acres.

4th, Not one acre, the allotments not being made.

p.62 5th, Neither increased nor diminished, less wheat and every sort of grain will be grown; examine strictly your returns, and you will find my words true.* Population is decreasing where enclosures

* The reader may judge whether these returns speak this language

take place.+ Fewer calves will be fattened and raised by half, fewer sheep by half, fewer cows by half. Enclosures will be the ruin and destruction of this country.
6th, Nothing yet sown this spring.

Observations on the above answers.

Every farmer knows that it requires some years to bring lands exhausted by cropping, deluged by water, matted by spire grass, and filled with weeds of every description, (the situation of many hundred acres of land in this county) into that cultivation and heart, and into that course of cropping from which the greatest produce is to be obtained. It is also well known that from the moment an idea of enclosing prevails in any parish, not only all improvement ceases there, till the allotments are made (a space in some instances of three or four years), but the common and annual manuring, weeding, &c. &c.; hence, *immediately after* an enclosure, less corn will be grown, fewer cattle supported, and every product lessened, but it does not by any means follow that in *future* such will be the case; when therefore it is asserted *immediately* after enclosing, that less corn is grown, less stock is kept, and in short that every product is decreased, it may be remarked in return, this may be the case, and yet enclosure a good thing;
p.63 no one however would be so bigoted as to retain such opinion, had sufficient time elapsed, and the requisite steps been taken, and these facts the result. Of the eighteen parishes where inquiries were made in 1780, and from which answers were obtained, only four had been enclosed long enough to give any in formation, from which conclusions for or against enclosures ought to be drawn ; they were Abington Pigots, enclosed 1770, Knapwell, enclosed 1775, Weston Colvill, enclosed 1777, the next (Barrington) was enclosed in 1796 and the others after that period. It will be observed that the answers vary in a great degree, and it may perhaps be safely asserted, they are as much for as against enclosures, indeed nothing can be determined from them on either side of the question, unaccompanied by explanation, and further information. Suppose query to parish A. Is the wheat grown in your parish increased or diminished since the enclosure? Answer, Increased; same query to parish B. Answer, Decreased. Does it follow from hence that the parish A. has benefited, and the parish B. suffered by enclosure? surely not: unless the application of the land in both cases were the same before, and after enclosure; were it otherwise, no conclusions can be drawn, and answers unaccompanied by the necessary explanation, tend only to deceive. The comparison should be between the *total product* (of whatever nature) on a given quantity of land, a number of years before and after enclosure; if the result of such comparison be not favorable to enclosures, it will be difficult to account for the avidity with which newly enclosed lands are sought for at a great advance of rent, and the tenants expending even under these considerable sums for improvement.

We have seen the opinions and information given on this subject in 1780; I will now add those I collected in the county and have since been furnished with.

p.64 From Great and Little Abington and Pampisford. Great tithes increased in value considerably, vicarage doubled, enclosed by contract for less than one fourth of usual expence: Rents considerably increased.

Weston Colville, rectory much improved, rents much advanced, more corn grown, stock of better quality, fewer cows. "Has been enclosed 23 or 24 years, quantity 2400 acres, of which 500 old pasture, and about 150 common, 300 heath, all the rest open arable, rent between £700. and £800. and paid tithe; now about £1800. tithe-free. Land given for tithe. Sheep before from 40 to 50 score, very badly kept, merely for fold and wool, todded, coarse wool; now 60 score ewes, and finer wool; Norfolks. Mr. Houghton has a little cross of South Down. Corn a great deal more than before. Commons and heath twice as much as before enclosure, more wheat acre for acre on lay than before on fallows; cows considerably more before than now. Before 100 head of cows and young stock, now not more than 50 or 60. Old enclosures where cows went over, are broken up. The cows were very ill-fed on the common, are now as well kept, as the county will permit. Before the enclosure the farmers could not live at the old rents, much land given up at 1s. per acre. Poor - there are several parcels of land laid to the cottages, some large gardens, others two or three acres, according to their rights; and join their houses, and are now in their occupation. They had during the scarcity a trifle allowed them, otherwise never thought of putting them in the parish books at all. They are very comfortable and much better off by this means;

\+ Nine out of ten of the persons with whom I conversed in the county on this subject were of a direct contrary opinion

but they do not all keep cows; they join, among themselves for ploughing and have bits of corn; the land is good, and one man has cropped it 10 or 12 years together. They are proprietors; others, who before
p.65 the enclosure hired farms, upon the land being allotted together for the landlords, of course lost their occupations and could keep cows no longer. Population decreased." Annals of Agriculture, v. 43.

March (a hamlet of Doddington). Tithes remain as before enclosure; are compounded for. Population increased, poor more comfortable, rents increased $1\frac{1}{2}$ of former rent, sheep increased. A common right before enclosing let for £8. per year, allotment in lieu of it for £20. expense of enclosing 20s. per acre. "Quantity, 3440 acres. Soil—near 1500 high-land, that is not subject to floods; the rest fen; the whole common never ploughed, much overrun with rushes, thistles, &c. &c. Rent. - There were 180 commonable rights, the average was about £7. per year to let, each for six cows and one horse, on the highland commons; four horses or eight neat beasts, or thirty-two sheep, on the fen from May-day to Michaelmas. From Michaelmas to May-day they stocked four horses or eight beasts, or thirty-two sheep, to run over the whole of both commons. Except from Lady-day to May-day, the highland commons were laid for pastures. The land now lets on an average at £20. a right, and per acre over the whole, at 25s. It was a limited common, there were eight cottages besides, with rights for two cows from May-day to Michaelmas, for which an allotment of $2\frac{1}{2}$ acres were made. The 3440 acres produced in the first seven years £163,000; in cole-seed, at 42s. per acre, oats at 16s. to 24s. per quarter, and eight to ten quarters per acre; pasture from 50s. to 70s. per acre; cole seed £40 per last, five quarters per acre; wheat £50. to 70s. per quarter, three to four quarters per acre.

About 1000 sheep were kept in summer before the enclosure, and in winter perhaps 2000, but it can be only a near guess, probably 1500 for the year. The sheep were good, and would give four to the tod:
p.66 now not 1000. Cows, 1090, were regularly kept as the stint stock, now not 100. Horses. - The same for dairy men, and others kept teams for their business and for hire. Labour amounts to 25s. per acre, viz. 4300 on the 3440 acres. The houses are all full, and several new ones built. Tithe. - the composition 2s. 3d. for oats, 3s. 3d. for barley, 3s. 9d. for wheat, 5s. cole seed cropt, but fed and for pasture 4d. per acre. They had a composition by decree, of 7s. 6d. for every common right previous to enclosure, and therefore they would not go to parliament on any other condition. Cottagers. - The enclosures have been beneficial by giving a very great increase of employment. On the 3440 acres there was nothing worth attention. In 1667 there was a decree obtained for setting out nine acres of mowing ground to each commonable house, thus they were able to keep their cows in winter as well as summer, and they paid about £5. per cow. There were about twenty families or dairy men, who made an entire livelihood, brought up their families decently; after the enclosure, they were reduced to day labour or to emigrate; these men were mere hirers, and had no common rights themselves, those who had are all greatly benefited to the amount of above 100; Expenses. - Part of the common sold, to the amount of £2600. to defray the expenses of the act, and of the commissioners; the whole expense came to about 20s. an acre, roads included; rates nearly doubled; population increased. A.Y. Annals. V. 42.

Wimlington, also a member of Doddington. Common rights before enclosure let for £1. allotments in lieu of it for £20. Rents, advanced more than at March; cows decreased; quantity—800 acres, all open common, stinted like March; soil - black fen, about 50 rights of common; let before enclosure on an average at not more than 20s. each, fourteen acres on the enclosure for each right. Produce after
p.67 enclosure, same as March; improvement greater than at March; lets for 30s. an acre, one with another. Expense, £1200. for act, commissioners, surveyors, roads, &c. £2000. banks, engines, drains, &c. &c. Laid a drainage tax not exceeding 20s. per acre; a banking tax, 7s. for the first two years, which sums were sufficient for engines, &c. .&c. The mill - £1400.; banks and drains £600. afterwards 3s. per acre for repairs of drains and banks; Tithes. - Oats 4s. wheat and cole cropt 5s. pasture 4s. the composition, previous to enclosing, 7s. each right; Cottagers, - the dairymen to the amount of ten families, lost their employment as at March. Rent: 300 acres let at 34s. for first four years, and at 22s. for next four, to be kept in grass; the landlord to pay all taxes.

Doddington. - "This rectory consists of 32,000 acres, including its appendages, March and Wimlington, just noticed. Of this rectory, Rev. Mr. Jobson, "(then of March) thus writes, March 1794, to the Board of Agriculture. " Since the reign of Henry VIII. this living has been advanced from £22. 10s. per year, to £2000.* effected by drainage and enclosure, which have advanced the commons in this parish and its appendages, in value from 2s. to 30s. per acre."

* Now at 3s. per acre £4800. At what let I was not informed.

Little Wilbraham. Rents, doubled; rectory, much improved; no effect on population; more of all grains grown; sheep, as many as before enclosure, and of better quality; fewer cows. Before enclosure their own poor could not find sufficient employ; since, have employed more than their own. Common, before enclosure, of little value; two-thirds of it now worth 10s. per acre, one-third 20s. Expenses of
p.68 enclosure about 30s. per acre; poor benefited; two acres of land allotted to each cottage. "Enclosed 1797, quantity 1970 acres, including a common of 469 acres. Rent before enclosure £680., now £1600.; openfield arable before enclosure about 6s. per acre, and tithe gathered; now about 16s. and tithe free. Rates before enclosure 4s. per pound on the old rental. The last year they were on the new rental as 2s. 2d. this year they will be 4s. Given for tithe one-fifth of arable, nine elevenths of the sward, they came to 323 acres, £323.

Commissioners' valuation for tithe, and 435 acres of glebe;

Expenses					£.	s.	d.
Solicitor					802	0	1
Surveyor					304	19	$4\frac{1}{2}$
Ditto for Board					56	7	2
Drainage					504	5	5
Ditto					74	4	9
Public fences					742	9	0
Ditto					70	0	0
Engineer					95	15	10
Roads					150	0	0
Commissioners,	Dugmore	£126	0	0			
	Watford	163	13	0	489	13	0
	Stone	200	0	0			
Contingencies					50	0	0
					£3339	14	$7\frac{1}{2}$

"Sheep. There were four flocks kept before enclosure, one of 400, and three of 200 each, todded thirteen or four teen, miserably starved. Now 400 ewes in one, and about 600 in others, in all nearly the same as before, and tod nine or ten and far better kept. Cows not so many, but so much better kept that there is probably as much butter and cheese; 35 years ago, about 100 cows. Poor. - About 25; common
p.69 rights were allowed, and 30 acres allotted for them, and a clause in the act which deserves great attention; it ordains that no person occupying twenty acres of land, shall ever occupy a common right; if they should possess they cannot occupy it; by which this common right is secured for ever to the poor, let the rights be bought and sold as they may, it deserves universal imitation, but it did not go far enough. I viewed this common, and found it a wretched desert in the midst of the finest crops; the poor who occupy ought to have permission to take each one-fourth of an acre of potatoes, and one-fourth of an acre of wheat, paring and burning for the potatoes and laying down with specified seeds amongst the wheat, by this method there would be every year, at fifteen rights, $3\frac{3}{4}$ acres potatoes, and $3\frac{1}{2}$ wheat, in all $7\frac{1}{2}$ acres cropped, and $22\frac{1}{4}$ of grass, five or six acres of which grass, would be much more valuable than the whole thirty at present; now I counted but seven cows and a couple of asses on it; the other poor are too indigent to use their rights. 1 cannot but recommend the parish to lend £10. to each of the remaining families (one per annum) to buy a cow, and to be repaid 20s. per annum. It would be a great assistance, and spread much comfort, and at the same time to assemble all having rights and propose the culture each of one-half an acre of wheat. Population rather increased."

Great Wilbraham. Rents, doubled; vicarage, greatly improved; lay impropriation, injured. Expenses, about 23s.per acre. "Enclosed 1797; quantity, 2400 acres in the parish; improvement nearly equal to that of Little Wilbraham, except in fen; corn increased. Population increased.

p.70

Expenses	£.	s.	d.
Solicitor	816	16	2
Surveyor	390	2	10
Ditto for Board	82	1	0
Drainage	231	13	1
Ditto	86	14	11½
Public fences	554	8	0
Engineer	95	15	10
Roads	200	0	0
Commissioners	486	13	0
Contingent	50	0	0
	£2994	4	10½

"Fen improved by drainage so much, that what before enclosure let only at 2s. 6d. per acre, has been sold since at £25. per acre. Fences. This enclosure was not fenced, only allotted in severalty." A.Y. Annals. V. 43.

Little Swaffham or Swaffham Bulbeck. Rents much advanced; vicarage greatly improved; lay impropriator not benefited, expenses on buildings being too great. Fenlands advanced in value beyond any other.

Long Stow. Where there is not a considerable quantity of common, enclosures do not answer. Fewer sheep kept; former privileges of the poor greater than the compensation given them; rectory improved; less arable land; rents doubled; expenses nearly 30s. per acre; population increased. "Enclosed 1796; soil, poor stiff wet clay or gault; quantity, the whole parish including old enclosures, 1400 acres, 422 old enclosure, 200 common, 800 open field, arable total enclosed by act 1000 acres. Rent. Open arable
p.71 before enclosed, about 6s, supposed to be worth now 16s. corn increased. Sheep, 800 kept before enclosure; since between six and 700 sheep, cows lessened, three acres given for a right of two cows and a bull, and ten sheep. Cottagers. Several who hired the cottages, that had common rights and kept cows, kept them no longer. Expenses. The whole expense of the measure, including fences, £1500. or 30s. per acre; tithe, one-fifth of arable, one-eighth of grass, one-tenth of woodland; population increased." A.Y. Annals. V. 42.

Carlton. Rents increased nearly three-fold, a corn-rent, (the particulars of which I was not informed of) given in lieu of tithe, sheep increased, cottagers right improved four-fold. "Quantity. Whole parish 2100 acres, enclosed by the act 1100 open field, arable and heath, the latter 140 acres. Rent, one farm advanced from £160. to £427. taking the average of parish at 6s. before, now 16s. tithe free. Tithe. A corn rent given; sheep before enclosure in whole parish 400, one occupier (Rev. Mr. Lane) intends to keep 500 ewes. Corn will be increased very greatly. Poor, some of them before kept cows, not more than 10, they had an allotment in lieu, of two acres each, of the best land, and they plough it, thinking it more profitable than cows; they have gained much by it. Cottagers with rights which would have sold for £10. now will sell for £50.
A.Y. Annals. V. 43.

Elsworth. Rents doubled; rectory improved; expenses 20s. per acre, including fences, and roads, &c. &c. "Act passed 1800; soil, clay; quantity 3659 acres in the whole parish of which 1037 common."

p.72 Rent, valued in 1794.

	Acres	£.	s.	d.
In-field open arable	1938	969	9	0
Out-field, ditto	250	62	11	0
North-meadow	14	8	10	0
Tithable meadow	163	163	0	0
Meadow compounded	54	68	0	0
Old enclosures	159	278	8	0
Wood closes	44	26	15	0
	2622	1576	13	0
Commons	1037			
	3659			

The in-field arable is let at 8s. to 10s. per acre, the outfield at half. Common rights. - Every plough has a common right of six horses, three beasts, and thirty-two sheep, on the lot grass common, whether mown or fed. The commonable right houses, eight sheep and three cows. There are sixty-two rights, but not more than two belong to real cottagers. Expenses. -The enclosure is put out to the solicitor of the bill, who is to pay commissioners £150. each for time and expenses. Surveyor, 3s. per acre, including map, reduced map, attendance on commissioners, &c. &c. for all these and other expenses, he contracted at 10s. per acre, excepting the expenses of roads, bridges, drains, &c. &c. which are put under the management of five commissioners, named from amongst the inhabitants; the expenses of these works it is supposed will amount to about £3. per acre more. Sheep - There are 110 score in the parish; improvement, expected to be very great, the quality price is expected to be 18s. an acre. Tithe. - One-fifth of arable, one-ninth of pasture.

p.73 *Connington.* Here I met a formidable enemy to enclosures, the Rev. T. Brown, rector of this parish, retaining the opinion he gave in 1780 (see page 138.). He believes the proprietors of estates have not benefited 5 per cent, per annum on the sums they have expended in enclosing, &c. &c. The gentleman who acts for a considerable part of the property in this parish spoke to me on the enclosure of it, in much more favorable terms. An advance of 10s. per acre rent, on the four-fifth left the proprietor, equal to 8s. per acre (on his former breadth), will pay 5 per cent, for £8. per acre expenses on former breadth; now, heavy as the expenses are, they cannot surely exceed this sum, for supposing the expenses from outset of business to signing the award, to be

per acre	£1	10	0
There remains for buildings, fences, &c	6	10	0

The advance here assumed is much below that in most cases, (see chap. Rents.) The expenses assumed much more than those which from the preceding information appear to have been incurred. The greatest charge of enclosing I heard of was that made on Professor Harwood of Bartlow, namely, £3. 19s. for enclosing one-half an acre; to make it palatable, the commissioners, he says, reminded him his land was made tithe-free; unfortunately for this observation it was so before. To return to Mr. Brown, his opinion on the subject of enclosures appears to have the merit of being disinterested; as his rectory is considerably improved by it, his allotment being worth as he informed me more to be let, than he could have let the tithe for before enclosure, or than they on an average of years paid him by occupying them.
p.74 He thinks the poor more comfortable having an acre of land to each dwelling, and a general common. Expenses of enclosure £2000. act passed 1800; quantity about 1500 acres, viz.

	Acres
Open-field arable	981
Common-meadow	41
Lot-grass	93
Common	246
Old enclosures and town	104
	1465

Rent, open-field arable, about 7s. 6d. statute acre, will be 20s. Some convertable lands will be worth 30s. or 40s. Tithes. Now pay 4s. 6d. per acre, but commuted for at one-fifth of arable, one-eighth of sward. Sheep, 13 to every 20 acres. Mr. Brown conceives they will not be lessened. (N. B. in 1780 this gentleman thought they would decrease one-half, see page 138). Poor, have no commonable rights, only the farmers and the rector. Population increased. A.Y. Annals, 42.

Bottisham. Lay impropriator and vicar benefited, the latter very considerably; rents more than doubled; expenses about 23s. per acre; common rights worth before enclosure £20. have sold since for £200. On prospect of enclosing, fen land advanced six-fold; more sheep kept by twenty score, and better fed from the introduction of artificial grasses in lieu of dreary fallows.

Balsham. Rectory considerably improved, rents very much advanced.

Trumpington. Rents advanced two-fifths of old rents; no benefit to lay impropriators; vicarages improved at least two-fifths of former income; labour and products increased; one occupier (Mr.
p.75 Treslove) keeps, and *well*, more sheep than were kept in the whole parish before enclosure; my informant here, spoke of enclosures in general in the county. A gentleman in this parish observed to me, that he thought enclosures are beneficial to vicars, and that they might be made so to others interested in them, if they were conducted in a different and less expensive manner than they generally are.

Westley. Mr. Wedge put this parish into severalty by consent of parties interested; expenses £30. rental doubled; population not decreased, sheep fewer, but of better quality; corn more.

Sawston. Vicarage more than doubled, rents higher than I heard of in any parish in the county, of similar soil.

Milton. Rents and products very much increased. "Enclosed 1799, quantity 1300 acres, 230 of it common, the rest open-field. The rent was about 10s. will be 25s. to 30s. improvement in every respect will be great; the common will be well drained by a very small mill, and then ploughed." A.Y. Annals, 42.

Grantchester and *Coton.* Great and general improvement. "Quantity about 3000 acres of open-field arable, very little common. Rent will be 20s. to 25s. per acre." A.Y. Annals, 42.

Barrington. Enclosure answered well, tithes remain, expenses £3000. on 2034 acres. " Enclosed 1796, quantity about 2500 acres. Rent before enclosure 5s. to 6s. now 20s. tithe taken in kind before and since; compounded for in a few cases at 4s. to 5s. per acre; common rights about 100, for each of which an acre was given, they were for three sheep and two cows, or five sheep and no cow; about half a dozen poor families had rights, and some were let at 5s. each to farmers; a green of fifteen or sixteen acres is
p.76 left for the poor, for a pig or anything else, except asses or geese; sheep fewer than before, cows fewer, corn hitherto less than before, and will be so for some time; but it is to be noted that Mr. Bandish's allotment of one third of the parish, lies much of it in a state of waste, and has done so for four years past; conceiving himself injured he refused to accept it, and this of course has had a very ill effect, for as attempts have been made to set aside the whole arrangement, it has given an ideal uncertainty to every man's possession, which could not fail to influence the husbandry." A.Y. Annals, v.42.

Chatteris. "The act for enclosing part of the common of this parish, and keeping it in tillage for a given number of years, did not stipulate that the layer should remain long enough. Poor. -Their rights swept away by a clause in the act, requiring them to prove their rights, which they could not; an act for enclosing this whole parish talked of, no parish would pay better for it, having a fine and extensive common of excellent land, now of little value and in a miserable state, from weeds of every description, and from water." Poor. - A cottager's right, the run of two cows, a commonable right the run of six cows. The enclosure of the common of this parish has not answered, owing to the occupiers not being obliged to carry muck on to the part under tillage. When the act for perpetually ploughing the same common was obtained, three rights were bought by a gentleman, who has since sold them for £2180. Rent.—This common has been let at 35s. per acre.

"In 1792 the price of each commonable messuage was about £110, in general; and in consequence of an act of parliament six years ago, to enclose part of the common, an allotment of four acres to each house, and to plough about 1600 acres of the common, divided into allotments to 163 houses, the value of the
p.77 property has been improved from £110, to £700. each messuage, and the parish thereby made exceedingly wealthy, and the poor have had much more regular employment. The Rev. Mr. Jobson is a proprietor and speaks from his knowledge." The act of regulation obtained 1773, &c. Tillage. - Applied to parliament in 1773 for powers to regulate the rights of commoners, and to enable them to plough their commons, especially the fenny parts, and then lay them down again open to commonage; they ploughed for four years and then laid down, and the experience: was so favourable to the practice, that in 1783 they went again to parliament for fresh powers to extend the time of ploughing. In 1793 again to parliament to have a perpetual power to plough. There are 3000 acres of the fenny part; 1500, or about half, were broken up directly and ploughed for four years; the course: 1, Pare and burn for cole (some stands for seed). 2, Oats. 3, Oats, (some wheat). 4. Oats; but where the cole is seeded, there are only two crops of oats. Then laid down again for four years to grass, being then limited common, produce oats from 7 to 10 quarters, cole fed 50s. to £3. per acre. Seeded 8 Co. per acre. Improvements. - There are 163 houses enjoying common rights. Mr. Gardner has nine, which he lets for 35s. per acre, for nine acres ploughed, and £11. or £12. for the right of herbage; £27. a right, so far as the common is concerned. Also £6. a year for 3½ acres of a several fen, called acre-fen, and £10. for the house or homestead, in all £40. 10s. for each right; the rent of £27. per right, on 163 common right houses, is £4401. or something better than 20s. per acre, on the extent of the commons, which are stated at

3000 acres arable and grass alternately
1320 always fed
4320

p.78 The common rights have risen in value from £100, to £500. Comparison with enclosure; -whatever the benefit of enclosure may be in cases very different from this, and which my informant, Mr. Gardner, is not disposed to dispute, he contends that now at Chatteris there is no want of one, as he considers this system as much superior in some respects, particularly relating to the lower order of renters. These men at present have a business which enables them to bring up their families decently, by means which secure a very large produce of corn, &c. to the public; but under an enclosure they would be turned adrift, and their farms thrown together, as has taken place so often. There are no unstinted commons, they plough as others, and all is converted to profit. They are not troubled with the rot, for the act provides for draining, gripping, mowing thistles, &c. &c. and providing for grass-seeds for laying the land after the arable course, that all may be done alike; enclosure could not, he observes, render a place more flourishing than this, as the people increase and are comfortable, new houses are every year built, and the tradesmen and farmers are wealthy. Limitation on feeding. -This is on the running out common, either forty-eight sheep, or twelve beasts, or six horses, or twelve asses. On the cow-pasture, five cows or heifers. Cows. -Before the act passed there were about 1000. The rights now admit 744, and twenty-four bulls. There is no doubt but the number is considerably lessened by ploughing. Sheep, lessened. What are kept, todd fives." A.Y. Annals, v. 42.

Knapwell. "Enclosed 1775. quantity 1100 acres. Soil - clay; rent, before enclosure, - 5s. three roods. In 1791 it was 10s. Now on an average 13s. Tithe-free; expenses about £4. per acre, did not answer so well as expected. Sheep, more kept before than since, and the breed but little improved. There used to
p.79 be about forty score, now about twenty. Cows, forty or fifty before, half as many now. Corn, their crops of some sorts better than before, but the improvement is not supposed to have been so great as it ought to have been, and no wonder, as they cultivate the land nearly as before enclosed. Fences, are very fine quicks nine or ten feet high; probably this strong land is too much shaded, and kept from the free play of the wind. Improvement, by hollow draining, or clover seed. Rates three or four years ago, only 2s. in the pound, and not much higher at present. Population decreased." A.Y. Annals, v. 42.

Whaddon. This parish has had all the benefit of an enclosure without its expense. Lord Hardwicke, the sole proprietor, some years ago, having laid the farms together, and the tenants having drained their lands in a masterly way, which they were enabled to do by his lordship having also made open drains, &c. at a great expense; this step, followed by a judicious and spirited change of husbandry, (particularly on the farm of Mr. Beaumont) has wrought a great improvement, doubtless to the advantage of all parties. Sheep increased, and improved in quality. Mr. Young observes, (Annals, v. 42.) "This system of allotting lands to farms for convenience and contiguity, is in many cases preferable to dividing wet soils by high hedges, which prevent the play of sun and wind to dry the land and corn in ticklish harvests.

Mr. Beaumont had no objection to make in comparison with enclosures, except the expense of hurdles,
which amounts upon his farm of 300 acres, to about £20. per year; call this 1s. 6d. per acre, and it may
p.80 be conceived that the loss by high hedges would equal it. * However such hedges are not necessarily
the consequence of enclosing, and certainly in many cases the land would be much better without them,
Population increased. Poor.—There are two small commons to the amount of 30 acres, inter-
commonage, with another parish; now Whaddon takes one; this is not enclosed, only drained, and Lord
Hardwicke, with that humanity which characterizes all his actions, has assigned eight acres of the best
land in the parish, to three poor families for their cows.

Chippenham. Act passed 1791; soil, light and sandy on a chalky bottom, and good marly white land; quantity in parish 4040 acres, of which

Mr. Tharp's park contains	350	4040
Fen	300	
Small occupations	20	
Seven farms from 300 to 700 acres each	3370	

Of which 2240 open-field arable enclosed by act. Rent of parish, before enclosure, £1300. after, £2000.
and farmers now flourishing. Fen. - This before Mr. Tharp's improvement was constantly flooded; when
fed, it was with cow and young stock to little profit: formerly there was a mill for draining, but it
decayed, and the whole the residence of snipes, wild ducks, and herons; cows and horses mired and lost,
and their skeletons found when the drains were cut. By Mr. Tharp's effective draining the mill proved
to be unnecessary, for a fall of five feet was gained; the copyholders fed it and made nothing, their
p.81 allotments now let at 20s. per acre. I viewed this drainage and cultivation with great pleasure; the cuts
are numerous and deep. Powerful springs cut into, and the water conveyed away and running now,
(August, 1800) after a long drought, a good stream. Plantations formed. Paring and burning, and
cropping, and everything looking well and thriving. A farmer had a part of this fen, that was not
common, which he offered at 2s. per acre, for which he would now give 20s. Sheep—before enclosing
there were 2000 kept or rather starved, dying almost every winter by scores, todding fourteen to
eighteen to a tod; now there are 2160 that tod tens, 400 are now fattened annually; before none, except
a few crones for harvest; on the whole, not one fourth of the produce from sheep which there is at
present. The breed Norfolks, except Mr. Tharp's, whose flock is South-Downs, and he has some very
good ones. Some half-breds with Leicester are mixed; which he intends weeding out, as they do not
answer. Cows—certainly fewer kept now; there used to be sixty or eighty, now thirty; it is, however, a
question whether there is any real defalcation in this article; as before they produced little. One
respectable occupier assured me that he kept eighteen and was forced sometimes to buy butter for his
family's use, which he never does at present, keeping only four.—Bullocks before the enclosure none,
now forty are fattened annually. Poor. -The only benefit the poor derive from the common-fen was to
cut turf on it, for which use forty acres are allowed them. The cattle were the farmer's. Rates doubled,
but this, as every one knows, depends on other circumstances; militia men's wives and increase of
population—increased very much. The number to whom a charitable donation is given, is doubled in
ten years; and there are twenty new houses built in the last seven. This astonishing increase of
p.82 population must not, however, be attributed to the enclosure ; the residence of a man of very large
fortune must have had in this respect a much greater effect; but from this a conclusion of no slight
importance is to be drawn, that there is a vast difference to the population of the kingdom between an
income spent in London, or in the country; in the latter here is an instance how much it favours the
population of the vicinity: at London it may and certainly has some effect, but probably to a degree
extremely inferior, and it may be there so spent as to injure population. Every shilling that promotes vice
is prejudicial in this respect, and it is too often found that the accumulation of people, is an accumulation
of profligacy. Tithes. - Mr. Tharp has the whole parish and the great tithes. The vicarial remain as they
were." A.Y. Annals, v. 43.

---

* The loss by hedges and ditches in enclosed heavy lands, is estimated generally at one-tenth, on Mr. B's farm, therefore, (if this deduction be correct) it would be thirty acres of much more than 20s. value. I think the fences alone are a charge of at least 1s. 6d. per acre on most farms; the tenant having also to pay rent for the land which they occupy.

The present state of this parish (1806) I found such as might be expected from this account of Mr. Young's; in short it is not possible perhaps to find an instance of such improvement in the value of property, or a farm, the management of which does so much credit to the director of it (Mr. Shepherd), as Mr. Tharp's. Crops large. Sheep (South-Downs)—unrivalled in the county. Layers—capital. Land—improving; the whole arrangement masterly.

Harston. The Rev. Mr. Leworthy (a modern, skilful, and spirited farmer) of this parish, thinks enclosures benefit vicars, but that they injure lay impropriators; he thinks one fifth of arable, (the usual compensation for tithes), not adequate to their value; he thinks (and could prove) that the tithes of this parish before enclosure, were worth as much as the then rent, viz. 10s. per acre. Poor - In this parish an acre of land was allotted to each cottage, but as most of the cottages belonged to the owners of the large estates, they laid the land to them instead of attaching it to the cottages; but where the cottages were the
p.83 property of the occupiers of them, many have been sold or let; Mr L. thinks that instead of granting to a cottager his full due, subject to the expenses of enclosure, he should have a less quantity, free of expense and properly fenced in, and money to enter upon his occupation; for under the present system they mortgage to great disadvantage. Mr. L. does not think land that advantage to a cottager, which it is generally supposed to be; the farmer will not assist him with horses, &c. he has therefore ploughing. &c. to pay for at the dearest rate; and few of them have proper buildings for their crops. Poor allotments in this parish have sold for £50. per acre, the purchaser paying expense of enclosing. This parish and Hauxton were enclosed under one act. Expenses, £ 4620. on 1960 acres, of which expense £150. were for public drains, £780. for public fences. Tithes. - The vicar of one of these parishes was allowed one fourth of the one fifth granted for great and small tithe of arable land, and that proportion, was stipulated for in the act. The vicarage was consequently greatly benefited, and the lay impropriation much injured. The vicar proposed to let his tithes remain rather than accept even at this rate for a compensation.

Abington Pigots. "Enclosed 1770. Quantity 1000 acres, of which a common of eighty acres. Soil, clay; but being on adjoining parish of chalk, partakes of a calcareous disposition and colour. Rent-before enclosure at 7s. quality price 16s. now raised to 20s. Course—the same as before enclosure, an extraordinary fact; corn-increased; sheep much the same; cows-greatly lessened. Poor A very bad and melancholy account; before the enclosure they had no rates, and were forced to find out an old woman to take 6d. a week, in order to escape being rated in aid of other parishes, but since enclosing the rates
p.84 have gradually risen to 2s., 2s. 4d. and 2s. 6d. in the pound, on the new rents; formerly every poor man had a cow, some by right, others by permission; on the enclosure the whole parish belonged to one person, the rights had allotments assigned them, and were thrown to the farms. Tithes - Commuted at 90 guineas (in 1770)." A.Y. Annals, v. 42.

Morden-Guilden. "Act passed 1799. Quantity about 3000 acres, at three roods per acre, of which about 200 common and waste; old enclosures about 100 acres; rent 7s. will be doubled. Tithe, paid in kind; rates, in 1774, 2s. 6d. in pound, in 1787, 1s. 9d. in pound. Common rights—these are 191, some cottages have a right to keep one cow, some two, some three. Some farmers have six of these rights. They winter their own labourer's cows in the straw yard for 6d. a week, instead of the real value 1s.6d. The rights will receive allotments, these thrown together to the respective proprietors, and there will be an end of cow-keeping amongst the poor, as in the neighbouring parish of Abington-Pigots. The poor are therefore greatly alarmed, and view the steps taken for enclosure with terror. When an evil could so easily be prevented, and enclosure converted to their advantage, as well as to that of every other class, it is to be lamented that measures are not taken with this view. Sheep, about 1200 kept at present, Cows, about 100 kept. Population increased. A.Y. Annals, v. 42.

The expenses of enclosing this parish were £4,404. on 2,508 acres.

Cambridge, St. Giles. Expenses £3,250. on 1360 acres. Sir Charles Cotton was at the expense of £700. on 125 acres in this parish, the cost of fences included; the fields are about twenty acres each; Sir Charles advanced six per cent, on the expenses incurred by enclosing and fencing. The expenses stated
p.85 in the preceding instances are those incurred from the outset of the business to the signing of the award, and may be termed the public expenses of the measure, in opposition to the private ones which individuals, landlords, must also experience; such as fences and buildings, the former if done as the public ones have been, are a heavy charge; and the latter in many instances, such as an outward allotment, are much more so, and yet it appears from the preceding observations on Connington, the

advantage is equivalent to them, assuming a moderate advance and large expenses. The fences on the new enclosures, cost 36s., 42s., 44s. per chain, of four rods; they consist of some two, some three rails on each side a bank (there is no ditch, only a slope) on which is set a double row of quick; if two rails the price is 36s. if three 42s. to 44s. The reader will have observed that an increase of produce in corn is stated in most of the parishes here mentioned, but in some of them the degree is not mentioned. I made this inquiry generally, and found the prevailing opinion to be about a fourth of former produce; now supposing the average produce of the open field of the county to be per acre, wheat, 5 Co.; barley and beans, 6 Co.; pease, 5 Co.; the produce on these lands when enclosed must be, of wheat, 6c. 1b.; barley, 7c. 2b.; beans, 7c. 2b.; pease, 6c 1b.; Mr. Vancouver writes, the average produce of enclosed lands, exceeds that of open field, taking the whole county, as under, wheat, 3b. 1p.; rye 3b.; barley, 15b. 1p.; oats, 1b. 1 p.; pease, 2b. 1p.; but if a single instance be adverted to, and a comparison made between the parish of Childersley which is enclosed, and Hardwicke which is open; and which parishes consist of perfectly similar soils, and are divided only by a hedge-row, the excess of the produce in favour of the enclosed will appear infinitely more abundant.

p.86

	Childersley enclosed.		Hardwicke open.		Excess of produce.	
	c.	b.	c.	b.	c.	b.
Wheat	6	0	4	0	2	0
Barley	9	0	4	2	4	2
Oats	9	0	4	2	4	2
Pease and Beans	5	0	2	0	3	0

It may perhaps be said, that if the open-field course be abandoned, and the Norfolk one (which is recommended) be adopted, although one fourth per acre more will be grown, it being only on half the breadth instead of on two-thirds, less corn will on the whole be produced; in answer the opinion is, that the half will produce 2 fourth more than the two-thirds, from the introduction of artificial grasses and turnips, &c. &c. to do so, the half must exceed the former produce on the two-thirds in the degree shewn by the following statement; thus

One acre open field,	c.	b.	p.
Fallow produce	0	0	0
Wheat ditto	5	0	0
Barley ditto	6	0	0
In three years	11	0	0
per year	3	2	0
say	3	3	0
Add one-fourth, which it is supposed will be grown on these lands, in addition, in consequence of enclosure	0	3	3
Total	4	2	3

p.87 The future annual produce will then be after enclosure 4c. 2b. 3p. per acre; now to obtain this under the Norfolk system, the produce must be in four years, 18c. 3b. which perhaps may be apportioned thus:

	c.	b.	p.
Fallow, (turnips)	0	0	0
Barley	11	3	0

Clover		0	0	0
Wheat		7	0	0
	In four years	18	3	0
	Per year	4	2	3 as above.

That these products will be grown, many may doubt, but that the new rents and present expenses require them, none will ; for assuming (for a lease of fourteen years) 15s. as an average price per Co. for barley, and 30s. for wheat, and the value of clover to be consumed on the premises £50. (it ought not to be set at more, when the frequent failings and the profit on its application, depending on markets, &c. &c. are considered) the value of these products will be per acre per annum, £5. 11s. 6d. thus,

	£.	s.	d.
Fallow	0	0	0
Barley 11 Co. 3b. at 15s. per Co	9	6	3
Clover, value on farm	2	10	0
Wheat, 7 Co. at 30s.	10	10	0
In four years	22	6	3
Per year	5	11	6¾

p.88 The communications cited appear to warrant the conclusion that enclosures benefit private property (in fee simple) and church preferment; but that the advantage to lay impropriations is doubtful; this subject requires consideration. For every five acres of great and small tithes of arable land, one acre of it has been given as a compensation. This acre has been variously apportioned; taking it for granted that the division which was acceded to by the respective parties in the parish of Bottisham, (and which division made a part of that act,) was fair, it may perhaps be taken as a datum on which to calculate. In that parish nine tenths of the acre were given for the great-tithes, and one-tenth for the small tithes; hence the nine-tenths ought to be of the same annual value, as the great tithes of the five acres before enclosure; now these were stated to me to be 3s. 4d., 4s., 4s. 8d. and 5s. 4d. per statute acre, therefore the great tithes of five acres, at these rates amounted respectively to 16s. 8d., £1, £1. 3s. 4d. and £1. 6s. 8d.; nine-tenths of the acre must in consequence be of the annual value of these several sums taken separately; to be so, the land must be worth per acre; £1. 2s. 2½d. £1. 5s. 11d. and £1. 9s. 7½d. for if from each of these sums be deducted one-tenth of them; the remainders will be equal to the former tithes of five acres. The average tithes before enclosure at the rates here stated, will be found to be 4s. 4d. per statute acre, and the average rent here stated also 24s. per acre, and they are equivalent to each other; thus,

	£.	s.	d.
Five acres of tithe at 4s. 4d. per acre	1	1	8
Nine-tenths of an acre of land, at 24s. per acre (barring a fraction)	1	1	8

Next let us compare the proprietor's former profit , supposing him to have occupied the tithes, and that
p.89 which he will probably reap from the occupation of the land given him in lieu of them, with the result" indeed of which comparison, it may be said neither the commissioners of enclosure nor the public have any concern; (they have only to consider the value to be let), it does not however on that account, the less affect the individual. Upon making a calculation with a renter of tithes in the county (a man of judgment and integrity), we made a probable profit of 2s. 2d. per acre,* by the occupation of tithes,

* Thus:

Dr. One acre of tithes gathered. Cr.

	s.	d.		£.	s.	d.	s.	d.
To rent	4	4	By one-tenth of annual produce of one acre					
Rates 5s. in the pound on 4s. 4d. say on 5s.	1	3		£.	s.	d.	9	0
Gathering	1	0	viz. Fallow	0	0	0		
Carting to market a bu[shel] at 6d per Co.	3	0	Wheat 5½ Co. at 30s	8	5	0		
			Barley 7 Co. at 15s	5	5	0		
	6	10	In 3 years	13	10	0		
Balance, profit	2	2	Per year 10	4	10	0		
	9	0	Tithe	0	9	0		
							9	0

N.B. No charge is made for threshing, as the straw is not valued in the produce. The product and expenses were fixed by the gentleman who assisted me in the calculation. The charge of 1s. per acre gathering is made, that being the annual charge, 1s. 6d. being the charge on the two-thirds usually cropt.

That is, 6d. per acre on the land cropt, is expended in gathering tithes in this county, was thus shewn to me by a tithe-gatherer.

Suppose the extent, crop and fallow, 1000 acres, and two-thirds annually cropt (the usual practice) viz. 666 acres, call it 670 acres, the expense of gathering would be 1s. 6d. per acre, on these 670 acres, thus :

	£.	s.	d.	
Three tithing men, at 5s. each per day	0	15	0	including beer, &c.
Three carters at ditto	0	15	0	
Four pitchers and stacking men, at ditto	1	0	0	
Three waggons and six horses at 10s.each waggon and two horses per day	1	10	0	
Expences per day	4	0	0	
Continues about 12 days	12	0	0	
	48	0	0	
Incidentals	2	5	0	
Total	50	5	0	
on 670 acres, is 1s. 6d. per acre.				

---

p.90 debiting the account with 4s. 4d. rent, (the average as above stated) this consequently is equal to 10s. 10d. on five acres of tithes; now the probable profit on the occupation of, nine-tenths of an acre of land given in the lieu of five acres of tithes, debiting it 24s. per acre, (the above average) rent, (equal to 4s. 4d. former tithes), cannot be presumed to prove more than 12s.7d. equal to 14s. per acre, that is, 10 per cent, (in addition to common interest), on a capital of £7. per acre. The question then is, whether this extra profit by the occupation of the land, is sufficient to meet the expenses to which the proprietor must be put in buildings which will be necessary to occupy the land? Another material consideration is, that the property in question (lay impropriations) is granted in general for twenty-one years, the expenses therefore must be calculated on that number of years, or on such part of it as the lease may have to run,
p.91 as the proprietor's interest in it such as will require a large rent. It appears that the following (as far as we have compared them) are equivalent to each other.

	£.	s.	d.		£.	s.	d.
Land worth to be let	0	18	6	to a former tithe of	0	3	4
Ditto	1	2	2½	Ditto	0	4	0
Ditto	1	5	11	Ditto	0	4	8
Ditto	1	9	7½	Ditto	0	5	4

Mr. Bunn of Burwell, thinks the present rent of the great tithes is more than the rent of the allotment would be, unless the fen were added; Mr. Jonathan Page of Ely, Mr. Cooper of Isleham, Mr. Hart of Swaffham, think directly the contrary; these gentlemen are all renters of great tithes in their respective parishes. Having regard then to advantage by giving tithe of arable land for land, it may be doubted whether there be any great inducement to lay impropriators to go into enclosure, unless allotment should be let at a very high rate; but where there are pasture and fen, (as well as arable), place his allowance
p.92 for these to the account, and he may perhaps on the whole have a handsome compensation; of pasture there is generally, I am told, given the lay impropriator three-fourths of an acre for eight acres of tithes; of fen, three-fourths of an acre for nine acres of tithes, viz. for great and small tithes are given one-eighth of pasture, and one-ninth of fen; out of these the vicar has one-fourth. It should also be remembered that many allotments of arable of similar quality to those we have been calculating upon, as averaging 24s. per acre, to render an equivalent for tithes, have been let since enclosure, from 25s., 30s., 35s. &c. &c. per acre, whether a sufficient quantity to give a larger average than 24s. may be doubted.

Mr. Darnton, of Babraham, thinks that laying lands into severalty, is preferable to enclosing them by fences, the expenses of which he thinks greater than the advantage. Mr. C. Pemberton, of Cambridge, has found cottagers much benefited, and their comfort greatly promoted, by land being let to them; he has let from three to five acres to each, and on rent day they meet him with chearfulness and gratitude, their money in their hand. This gentleman advises the allotment to the poor under an enclosure, to consist of a general common for their cows; a piece of pasture to mow, and a piece of arable, thus the cow will be provided for in winter, as well as in summer.

Mr. A. Young writes, (Annals, v. 43). "Cottenham in Cambridgeshire has very extensive fens, some thousand acres which are constantly under water in winter. They have 1500 cows, besides dry stock and horses, they mow sedge, &c. for winter, and hire land at a distance. The rights of keeping several cows,
p.93 (five or six the informant thought), lets at £9. per year, this shews the real value of these commons in their present state, yet a surveyor would be knocked on the head, that went there with a view to enclose." "At Waterbeach are three commons of 2500 acres, and at Landbeach 1500 more; they call loudly for enclosing, and proposals have been made to the rector and Bishop of Ely, but without success."

Mr. Vancouver writes, "the laying the intermixed property together, and in severalty and enclosing, appear to be indispensably necessary, as previous steps to the general improvement of the highland part of the county. To this measure, a few have given unqualified *dissent*, but they were flock-masters; others have concurred under certain limitations; but the mass of the farmers are directly for the measure. Mr. Vancouver attributes the disappearance of the rot in the sheep, in enclosed parishes in this county, to the effects of enclosure; he says the rot has "desolated the sheep-walks in most of the neighbouring parishes, whilst in Childersley and Knapwell, (both of which are enclosed) not the least shadow of the disease has made its appearance." As to the effects of enclosure on population, and the condition of the poor, I found the more general opinion to be, that they were favourable to both, and the extracts I have made from Mr. A. Young, who appears to have given this subject his particular attention, warrant this conclusion. In short this measure has so great a majority in its favour, that it may safely be taken for granted it has advantages, else how account for its rapid progress under the general cry of too large, and the equally general opinion of unnecessary expenses. There is no doubt were the expenses reduced, and expedition in the execution of the business secured to the concerned, all objections to enclosures would
p.94 vanish, and the measure would become general. The expenses and delay, notwithstanding they be in the end repaid, do not sit easy, not only from their weight, but from the idea that they are unnecessary. Lest gentlemen, solicitors, commissioners, &c. &c. should imagine I mean to cast a reflection on them, I beg to disclaim any such intention, I only (as is incumbent on me in the execution of this work), faithfully report what I heard in the county; I am no judge of their charges, and do not therefore presume to give

any opinion on them; I am equally ignorant of the justice of the complaint on the score of delay, and therefore do not censure it; I have greater pleasure in testifying that as a lay impropriator under an enclosure in the county, I have no reason to join in the complaints I have represented as being general in the county on this subject; on the contrary, I have no doubt, but the parish I have alluded to, the practice of the solicitor and commissioners, (Messrs. Pemberton, Dugmore, Stone, and Treslove), was such as became gentlemen of their ability and respectability.

p.95

CHAP. VII.

SECT. I.—TILLAGE.

PLOUGHING is done on light soils and in the fens by two, and in some instances in the latter, by three horses abreast; on heavy soils (up-lands), by three and sometimes by four horses at length. When more than two horses at length are used, a boy is also employed to drive them. From three-fourths of an acre to an acre is a day's work in the uplands; and one and a half acre in the fen. They plough very fleet; deep ploughing is reckoned destructive to "white lands." Lord Hardwicke, however, has tried it on them, and found no evil from bringing up the gault, (the substratum of these lands).

Harrowing and rolling. - Nothing peculiar in the method of performing these operations, except that in the fens rolling is often done by the roller being drawn by a boy and pushed by a man, expense 6d. per acre; in harrowing the boy generally leads the horses instead of driving them. Ridges. - The lands for wheat are generally laid on four furrow ridges; for soft corn, on stetches of various sizes, generally about two rods, on stiff soils the stetches are "upset," which, says Mr. A. Young, (Annals, v. 4. p.139) "is the most excellent way of all others of laying wet soils dry, if the furrows are kept free from water." A singular opinion for a Suffolk farmer: I should add he gave it thirty-one years ago. Stetches are said to
p.96 be upset when they are considerably higher in the middle of them than in the furrows; this form is for the purpose of surface draining, the furrows being intended for conductors of the water; one effect is visible, that is, too much straw on top of stetch, and neither straw nor corn on the sides. An opinion prevails that levelling these stetches, (which are also called "high backs,") even after ditching, enclosing and draining, would be injurious, as the tops (now a deep soil,) would become thin and poor. Mr. Leworthy's (of Hauxton) lands were all " high backs," they are now level, and he found only a temporary injury. The fens are always ploughed level. Mr. Wedge, of Wesley-Bottom, (on a very light soil), has his stetches contain an acre, for the more easily seeing if his men have done a day's work.

SECT. II. — FALLOWING,

Is practised through the county with very few exceptions, which are on what is called (in consequence of such exemptions perhaps) "every year land." The fallow has four earths, viz. at Lady day, Midsummer, after harvest, and seed earth; harrowing and rolling are mostly given after each earth, if the land be cloddy.

Sir Charles Cotton's steward, (a Suffolk farmer), thinks fallows necessary at Madinglay. Although they break up whole and hard, they slake and become moulds, upon the first rain. Mr. Francis, of Childersley,
p.97 is of the same opinion. His fallows are often *hoed* before the first ploughing them; never ploughs any thistles, &c. &c. in; ploughs first time in spring, or so late as May. Mr. Wedd of Trumpington thinks fallow should lay whole all winter, even if intended for turnips, and that the first ploughing should not be later than May. Dr. Nasmith says, "fallows are very sparingly introduced in the Soham husbandry. I believe on an average not so often as one year in six; hence their crops are remarkably foul. The soil is the best in the district, and the husbandry the worst." Mr. Scott, of Chatteris, calls fallowing a " barbarous system;" and that the best crops are produced where it does not exist; viz. where the course is beans, wheat, and barley, (see Chap, on Course of Cropping.) Rev. Mr. Leworthy, of Hauxton, never fallows, and gets better crops than those who do. Mr. Lawton, of Wisbech, gives the first ploughing to his fallows before Christmas, gives seven or eight earths more, says he cannot plough too much, and lays on manure about Midsummer. Mr. Edes of Wisbech also, gives the first ploughing immediately after wheat sowing, and lays his land on the ridge. I met many fen farmers who were against fallowing their lands, because it made them " too light," there are, however, many who say that objection does not exist. Mr. Darnton, of Babraham, gives the first earth between Michaelmas and Christmas, contrary to the usual custom of giving it after barley sowing. Many would give the first earth in autumn, were it not

for the winter-feed, which they would lose by it, and which feed they reckon, valuable. Mr. Lane, of Carlton, gives the first earth in autumn; upon my observing that the autumn ploughing would assist in destroying the black grass they answered, " We don't mind black grass." No experiment on the subject on this chapter.

p.98 **SECT. III.**

COURSE OF CROPS.

1st, In open field.

The common open-field course is fallow, wheat, barley; upon the stronger and more valuable soils, and where pease and beans are cultivated, the following courses are observed, (preceded by a fallow, with the exceptions noted).

At Wichin - Wheat, barley, barley.
At Soham - Wheat, barley, beans or pease; or wheat, beans, wheat, beans.
At Ely - Wheat, barley, beans and pease, barley ; or wheat, beans, wheat, beans.
At Chatteris - Beans, wheat, barley.
At Waterbech }
At Stretham }Wheat, beans, barley, or wheat, barley with clover, then "bastard fallow;" or
At Over }wheat, barley, beans, wheat.
At Littleport - Wheat, barley, beans, barley or wheat, beans, barley.
At Mepal - Wheat, barley, beans.

Mr. Young (in his Annals) confirms my notes on the cropping of the above parishes, and reports the following.

" At Fulburne - Wheat, beans, or pease."
" Two or three miles south of Ely—Wheat, beans, barley."

Eversden and Kingston—Wheat or barley, then oats or beans. Again, barley, grasses, mown 1st year, fed 2d year, then wheat.
At Upwell, &c.—Flax, wheat, hemp, wheat.
p.99 At Whittlesea }
At Witcham }Beans, wheat, barley, barley, some potatoes instead of barley or beans
At Haddenham }

Foreign as these courses are to every idea of modern Farming, and clearly as they carry their own condemnation with them by their products, there are numbers of farmers who still retain the opinion that the lands will not in future be made more productive by the introduction of turnips and seeds; in spite of this opinion, however, rents are advancing, so as to warrant the conclusion that the hirers expect much greater produce by some process or other; and that merely laying each one's occupation together will obtain it, is not easily to be believed. Under the field system it is almost universally allowed the lands are impoverishing; Mr. Wedd, of Trumpington, nevertheless is of opinion, that the "present mode of cultivating the county is very good and suitable to the soil." Surely the acreable produce from the present field-system warrants a suspicion of its defectiveness. If the adoption of courses of crops in which turnips and artificial grasses may be introduced, do not give a greater produce than hitherto, a lamentable disappointment will ensue where enclosures have taken place. What course of cropping should be adopted, the skilful will soon discover; that it should not be the modern and improved one of *Suffolk*, (called the Norfolk husbandry) I found some Cambridgeshire farmers of opinion. To give two instances. 1 accompanied one over the lands of three as modern farmers as any in Suffolk, and of as high repute; he was told their system, and the expected produce from the crops he was shewn; he appeared to think they dealt in the marvellous, and returned home with as high an opinion of his own husbandry
p.100 (the common field) as with theirs. The farm of this gentleman (well managed, admitting the system good) afforded a striking proof that some defect existed in his plan of cropping; for, with an appearance of corn crops when I saw them (in the grass) that would cause a Suffolk farmer to expect 10 Co. per acre

of wheat, he expected, he told me, (and he was a clergyman; little more than half that quantity. Another Cambridgeshire gentleman, (a land valuer, Sec. &c.) was lately in the centre of Suffolk, and pronounced a man who is there esteemed a remarkably good farmer, a very bad one; such is the force of prejudice or attachment to practices of early life.

In enclosed uplands, and uplands in severalty.

The Norfolk system (turnips, barley, clover, wheat,) is practised on many of the turnip soils of the newly enclosed lands, and on those newly laid into severalty, and with great success, from the abundant crops of artificial grasses (chiefly red and white clover, and trefoil). These plants are largely cultivated since enclosing, though not always in the Norfolk routine, and have justified the expectations entertained of them. I met, however, a few instances of the open field course having been retained since enclosing. The Rev. T. Brown, of Connington, though he has varied a little from it in his practice, believes no other can be adopted which will grow more corn; his field course was 1st, fallow; 2d, wheat or barley; 3d, oats or beans. This gentleman does not look upon clover as any acquisition on the new enclosures (soils similar to his); he grows, indeed, a little for sheep feed. His course since enclosing; 1st, fallow; 2d, wheat; 3d, tares; 4th, barley; 5th, beans, (with clover for sheep feed, which must be off in the following spring, in time for making the fallow for) 6th, wheat. Mr. Brown thinks clover, beggars lands, and encourages
p.101 twitch. I found others in the county of the same opinion. If it stand for two years, (as it often does) it then goes off, and is succeeded by twitch ; but if it stand for one year it will prevent twitch.

Mr. Wedge, of Westley, whose lands are in severalty, crops thus: turnips, barley with seeds (red and white clover, and trefoil) for two years, wheat, barley or pease, or tares, fed by folding a piece at a time, then wheat; his first course after paring and burning his heath, is wheat, turnips, layer without a crop, to continue, the seeds, red clover, Dutch clover ,trefoil, and hay-seeds; mows, apart the first year, and feeds a part by folding a piece at a time; intends the next year it should stand till the seeds will shed, then to feed it with sheep. Sows his layer just before barley sowing, but recommends after that time, as there is danger of frost in the former season. Mr. Wedge has also had the following course. "Pare and burn, wheat, turnips, barley and seeds two years, wheat, turnips, barley; and this course he contends is the best of all, and founds his opinion on experiment and observation; he has remarked that the ashes work much greater improvement when they lie spread for some time before ploughing in. In his wheat crop this year there are three preparations; first, pared and burnt in the spring 1799, and the ashes left spread and exposed to the weather till wheat sowing; second, pared and burnt late, and the ashes left in heaps till wheat sowing, and spread before the plough; third, pared and left so from the season preventing burning. The crop varies greatly, the best by far is No. 1, the next best No. 2; and No. 3, is in comparison so inferior as to shew the immense consequence of burning. Hence he concludes it is much better to leave the ashes much longer than can be done if turnips be the first crop, but he further remarks that the turnips after the wheat are much superior to what they are on one earth after burning, which he attributes
p.102 not only to the ashes being turned in too soon, but to a deficiency of tillage for that root; and as a great crop of turnips is of much consequence, whatever the system, he thinks that the means of securing one, ought in the first instance to be attended to." (Annals, vol, 40. A.Y.) The more general practice in Mr. Wedge's neighbourhood, on the late sheep walks, is, pare and burn, and take as much corn, and as quickly as possible.

In Carlton - (Rev. Mr. Lane), turnips, barley, tares, barley, or pare and burn—turnips, barley, barley. N.B. Second barley good; or, tares cut or fed, turnips, barley, clover, wheat. Mr. Lane finds clover more certain after the second barley, than after the first.

Coton - Mr. Casborne, tares, wheat, tares, barley, clover, wheat; if clover fail, substitutes beans or pease.

At Elm - Flax, turnips, (same year) or cole fed, oats, wheat; or flax or oats, if flax then turnips or cole-fed; oats, wheat, cole-seed, beans, hemp, or oats.

Leverington and Parsondrove—Oats on flag-oats, wheat, cole fed.

Outwell - Hemp, hemp, flax, turnips, oats or hemp; or hemp, hemp, flax, wheat, hemp, oats or barley. Wisbech—Flax, wheat, beans, oats or wheat, (Mr. Lawton).

Wimpole - 1st, cole fed, barley, clover, wheat.
2d, Fallow, ditto, ditto, ditto.
3rd, ditto, ditto, beans, ditto or turnips. 4th, Tares fed, wheat, barley, fallow.
5th, Cole, barley, pease, fallow.
6th, Crop and fallow.
7th, Cabbages, tares fed, cole, oats, beans, wheat.
8th, Crop and layer.

Whaddon—Beans, fallow, barley, beans, wheat and layer.

p.103 "Mr. Beaumont crops also, fallow, barley, clover, wheat, sowing seeds on half the barley, by which these courses divide the farm. If the seeds fail, winter tares, spring tares, then fallow for wheat." (A.Y. Annals)

Long-Stow. - "Dr. Thompson's courses: fallow, wheat, beans, barley layer two years. Oats or fallow, wheat, clover, wheat, beans, barley layer two years." Oats. (A.Y. Annals) I could not procure the result of these courses, Dr. T. having left the parish; his example has not been followed.

Chippenham - " Four, five, or six shifts; four turnips, barley, clover, wheat, five add barley, &c. six add barley, &c. but the clover mixed with seeds and laying two years." (A.Y. Annals)

Little Wilbraham - Turnips, barley, clover, wheat. Weston Coville, same as Little Wilbraham, adding trefoil with the clover. Some here retain field course.

Abington Pigots and Guilden-Morden. - Same as before enclosure.viz. 1st, fallow; 2d wheat; 3rd, oats or barley; or 1st, fallow; 2d, barley; 3rd, pease or beans. Mr. A. Y. observes, "this is an extraordinary fact." (Annals)

Babraham - Colonel Adeane, on lands esteemed foul; 1st, tares fed by sheep; 2d, turnips fed by sheep also; 3d, barley and layer; or 1st, pease (on layer) 2d, tares fed; 3d, turnips fed also; 4th, barley and layer. Mr. Darnton, of this parish; 1st turnips; 2d, barley; 3rd, clover and trefoil , 4th, wheat or pease; if wheat, then tares, for crop, if pease, then wheat. Mr. Phipps, (at Bourn-Bridge) 1st, tares fed; 2d, turnips or cole fed; 3d, barley and seeds; 4th, wheat; or, 1st, turnips; 2d, barley; 3d, seeds; 4th, wheat or pease; 5th, tares for feed; 6th, turnips, N.B. Sows the pease every third furrow,

Childersley. " Mr. Francis; 1st, fallow or cole fed; 2d, barley; 3d, tares; 4th, wheat; or, 1st, fallow;
p.104 2d, wheat and clover; feed clover in spring after the wheat is off, and sow oats on one earth; success great. Again fallow, barley, clover, wheat or fallow, barley, fallow, wheat; does not repeat clover oftener than once in eight years. His cropping after burning; is, 1st, cole fed, 2d, barley; 3d, rye; 4th, oats and clover; 5th, wheat or cole, barley layer. Rev. Mr. Leworthy; 1st, cole for crop; 2d, barley; 3d, wheat; 4th, tares; 5th, tares or clover; if tares feed them, then wheat. Sufficient time has not elapsed since enclosing many of the parishes, to ascertain the advantage of the newly adopted courses, but no doubt is entertained by the generality of persons, of their superiority over the old field ones.

In fens.

The perfection of fen husbandry is to be seen at Thorney, under the direction of Mr. Wing, whose management is so superior, that it is to be lamented his jurisdiction as superintendant of draining and embanking, does not extend over the whole level of the fens. His cropping process is; "pare and burn, and spread the ashes immediately; 1st, crop, cole fed by sheep; 2d, oats; 3d, oats or wheat; with either, layer for as long time as it remains good. The layer ray grass two bushels, white clover eight or ten lbs., and on lands not liable to be flooded in winter, one sack of hay-seeds, six or seven lbs. of ribgrass, seven to ten lbs. of white clover, a small quantity of ray-grass; on the latter lands, the seeds are sown on the wheat."

Occasional variations.

1st, Sow red clover with first or second crop, feed it, or mow, sow wheat in autumn.

2nd, When the wire-worm is suspected, sow cole-seed two first years, which is an admirable practice, and tends more to destroy that insect than any other known by Mr. Wing.
p.105 3rd, Lay down with cole seed the year after the second crop of corn, sowing the ray-grass and hay-seeds with the cole, feeding it in the winter, and sowing the white clover in the spring: this method has been found to answer extremely well.
4thly, Lay down without a crop of corn, this esteemed a good plan.
5thly, Sow one bushel of ray-grass, with first crop of corn, for sheep feed in winter, it causes the land to plough stiff, and makes it more adhesive.

Mr. Wing writes as follows to the Board of Agriculture.

" On the convertible system in the management of fen lands."

"The following observations on the convertible system of management of fen lands, which with the greatest deference are submitted to the honourable Board, are founded on an attention to facts, and the experience with which a situation of most honourable trust and confidence wherein the writer has been long placed, has furnished him, aided by authentic documents, and the information of his immediate predecessor, comprising the result of attentive observations for at least half a century. The district which has been the object of their care, contains about forty thousand acres, the whole of which may be called fen land; there are intermixtures of high and permanent pasture, but at least thirty thousand acres may be deemed convertible land. Of the whole forty thousand acres, about one half has more particularly engaged the writer's notice, though with the whole, and with the interests of individuals throughout the whole, he has from time to time been acquainted and connected. It is about thirty years since a system
p.106 for the management of this description of land was first introduced, before which there was not any that could be called such; a strong prejudice against the plough under any management, prevailed amongst the great proprietors; and the general practice of those who were unrestrained, was to crop the lands as long as it would produce anything, then to let it be overrun with twitch (or couch) grass, to which all fen land is prone; and after it had rested a few years to break it up again, paring and burning it without care or discretion. The use of grass seeds was then so little known, that on their introduction on the establishment of the system before mentioned, and for some time after, they were the ridicule of the old fen-farmers, nothing in their opinion being so desirable for either grass or hay, as twitch (the triticum repens). Their rents, rates, and taxes were then low; their ideas confined, possessing but little, and not being ambitious; to avoid expense was their chief object. From the fen land not permitted to be ploughed, nothing was experienced but poverty and disappointment. Twitch and goose grass (or clivers), were the general herbage; the rents were unpaid, the cattle unhealthy, the inhabitants few, and the occupiers of the land continually changing without property, hope, or exertion. These are facts too well known to the writer, from his situation, and from such unerring records as he has officially become possessed of. But it may be unnecessary to descend to particulars, further than to shew what was the general state of the fens, previous to the introduction of the convertible system, and the nature and good effects thereof, in the management of those lands. The system is as follows:

About one-third part of such of the land as is not reserved for permanent pasture, is permitted to be ploughed in each year, taking into the account both cole and corn, the remainder is kept in a succession of grass and tillage.

p.107 First year—Pare and burn for cole seed, (the depth ploughed for burning being about one inch and an half;) to be fed off with sheep, which will in general fatten six or seven to an acre; hoeing it has of late been introduced to great advantage, but not set out so thin as for turnips. The most approved season for sowing cole, is any time in the first fourteen days of July, and it should be sowed in the evening of the day on which the land is ploughed, in which case it hardly ever fails to grow. Unremitting attention should be paid during the time of burning, and the ashes spread as soon as made. From neglect alone proceeds the land taking fire, which has furnished objections to the process, but it may always be prevented by proper care. Second year—Oats, for which they usually plough about three inches and a half deep. Third year —Oats, barley, or wheat, (ploughing about one inch deeper than before), with which it is laid with grass seeds for five, six, or seven years, the longer the better; the quality of the corn being always found to be superior in proportion to the length of time the land has been in grass. Beans, turnips, &c. have all been tried, but have not been found to answer. Produce of oats, from six to seven quarters an acre, weighing nine stone a sack of four bushels, or thirty-three pounds each bushel. Wheat,

from three to four quarters, but of which little comparatively speaking, is sown, weight, sixteen stone a sack, or fifty-six pounds a bushel. The broad cast is the prevailing husbandry; dibbling wheat is sometimes practised but not so generally as might be wished on account of the saving in seed; in other respects it does not yet appear here to have any advantage over the former mode, the expenses attending
p.108 it being more; and from observation and comparison on the produce at harvest, not greater than from that sown and managed in the ordinary way. If an objection should arise to taking two crops of corn successively after cole, it may be observed that fen land will not bear much stirring. A fallow, by exposing the soil to the sun and air pulverizes it, and destroys that compactness so necessary to fen ploughed land, and to obtain beneficial cole, on a fallow, you must manure; this tends to lighten the soil, to encourage weeds, and to cause the succeeding crop to be too luxuriant and too abundant in flag or leaf: of course the grain will be thin and light, and the grass seeds which are usually sown with that crop (the second) will be choaked and smothered, and by this method the grass land would be deprived of its full quantity of manure, where it might be employed to much more advantage. Nothing lightens fen land more than frost, nor is more injurious thereto, and to wheat sown thereon. In the spring after a long frost it is customary to trample wheat with men, as closely as possible, the expense of it is about 4s. an acre, and it is found to be of great utility. The grass seeds usually sown on the inferior or low fen lands, are rye-grass, and white clover, two bushels of the former with eight or ten pounds of the latter on an acre ; on the higher, or such as are not liable to be flooded in the winter, of high land or good meadow hay-seeds, one sack, rib grass or narrow leaved plantain six or seven pounds; white clover from seven to ten pounds; a small quantity of rye grass; all which the tenants themselves provide, and indeed no expense is spared by them, in this part of their business. On land of the latter description, a wheat crop is thought to be the most favourable for the growth of the grass seeds, the land so laid down is fed the first year with sheep, the second it is manured; but if mown, not till after the grass is cut; it is then occasionally
p.109 fed and mown until it is again taken up, and undergoes the course before mentioned, of paring and burning for cole, for sheep feed, taking two crops of corn in the years immediately following, &c. &c. On some of the high land parts, red clover is sometimes sown with the first and second crop, and either fed or mown the next summer, and wheat sown in the autumn. Some, when the wire-worm is suspected, sow cole-seed the two first years after breaking it up, which is an admirable practice, and tends more to the destruction of that noxious insect than any other that has come within the writer's knowledge; others lay their land down with the cole-seed the year after the second crop of corn, sowing their rye-grass and hay-seeds with the cole, sheep feeding it in winter, and sowing the white clover the next spring, a method which is found to answer extremely well; and some without a crop of corn, which is esteemed the best mode for the seeds of any. It is frequent too to sow rye-grass, (about a bushel an acre,) with the first crop of corn, for sheep feed in winter; which causes the land to plough stiff, making it more adhesive; but these are only occasional variations of the general system. Experience shews, and the writer has with very great satisfaction convinced himself thereof, that on every time of taking up and burning the land, the quality of cole for feeding sheep is not deteriorated, but is as good as that obtained at a former period, and that from very old land, unhealthy, and apt to kill the sheep put upon it; it is also worthy of observation, that by no other means hitherto used, can cole of equal quality, or even that will fatten sheep, be procured on fen land; which being the foundation for all the ensuing succession for crop and grass, the necessity for obtaining good, may easily be conceived: indeed the so doing is the grand desideratum in fen-farming. Such is the present convertible style in the management of fen lands, no
p.110 part of which appears defective, it is attended with no difficulty in its execution, may be continued for ever, and the land kept in a constant state of fertility, requiring no other manure than that, which it is in itself from time to time capable of producing. The good effects of it are, that the rents have been progressively more than doubled, and that such an increase of population, prosperity, the various kinds of cattle, wool, and of animal and vegetable food has arisen, as to give to the country where it is established, which before was depressed far beyond its due level, a degree of importance and respectability, which few of the like extent, exceed, or perhaps equal."

To compare Mr. Wing's practice with that of others,

1st, On lands of the first quality, as stated by Mr. Vancouver; pare and burn, cole for sheep feed, oats, wheat, oats, wheat, cole, seeded and layer, sometimes the layer omitted, then oats, layer.

2nd, Lands of the second quality, by Mr. V. also:

Pare and burn, cole, oats, oats, wheat, cole fed, oats and layer. Mr. Scott, of Chatteris, gives the following as the more general cropping of the fens. Pare and burn, cole, fed or crop; more generally the former; oats or wheat, oats or wheat again, for four, five, or six years successively, then layer for three to six years.

Mr. Scott writes as follows to the Board of Agriculture on the management of fens: "To convert coarse fens, moist moors, aquatic mosses, and very rough low grass lands into tillage; and afterwards into fine, rich permanent pasture; such lands should be ploughed, burnt, sown with cole seed or some other ameliorating crop, and a crop or two of grain, and artificial seeds, having been previously well drained.
p.111 All low lands that are intended to be burned, should be ploughed in May, or at least as early in the year, as the surface is sufficiently dry to bear the horses to draw the plough; because such lands give a much better opportunity for their being burnt and sown with cole-seed when ploughed early in the year, than when they are ploughed late in the summer. But in wet seasons, sooner than miss a crop, fen farmers sometimes plough for cole-seed, as late as the middle of June, or even the beginning of July. With respect to the thickness of the furrows designed for burning, they should always be ploughed as thin as they can, without balking any part of the land; and they are sometimes ploughed, where the surface is even, and the sward tender as thin as one inch, or an inch and a half in thickness ; but if the surface is very rough, uneven, and tough, the surface in general must be ploughed much thicker, or the plough will miss more than half the surface. However, the rougher, coarser, and more impregnated the surface is with the roots of rushes, reeds, and aquatic rubbish, the less injury the land will receive, from the furrows being ploughed thick; but where the land is too soft for horses or oxen to walk upon, or the surface too rough for the plough; such bogs should be pared with a turf spade, or rather with an instrument made on purpose. Respecting burning, as soon as the sods are sufficiently dry, the furrows or parings should be placed in heaps. In fens, the labourers or servants make the heaps for burning commonly about two feet, or two feet and a half broad, and about twenty inches or two feet high; and the instrument they are mostly made with is a strong hay fork. As many balks or spots will unavoidably be missed by the plough, especially where the surface of the land is very uneven, some heaps should
p.112 always be placed on such patches, and the sward there will be burned, as well as that which was ploughed. In the fens, some farmers have introduced a cheap instrument drawn by a horse, to heap furrows for burning. After the heaps are made and are sufficiently dry for burning, the persons who set fire to them generally begin in the evening, for such fires burn best in the night, and they always begin to fire those heaps first that are on that side of the land that is farthest from the wind, because the wind then wafts the smoke from them; for if they were to begin to burn on the windward side they would be almost smothered with clouds of smoke. And as soon as one row of heaps is on fire, the persons who manage the burning, carry fire with their forks from those heaps that are burning, and set the next row on fire, and so on, till all the heaps are in a general blaze. In dry weather the heaps burn very furiously, the fire soon consumes the vegetable furrows, pernicious aquatic seeds, and many injurious insects; it provides also a plenty of the richest ashes to manure the land; which when spread over the surface seldom fails to produce an extremely luxuriant crop of cole-seed, which smothers such weeds and seeds as had escaped the burning. As this prodigious bulky crop is always eaten on the ground, it amazingly enriches the lands, and leaves it in a fertile state, for a crop or two of grain and artificial seeds. If such surface should again, through such a breach of banks, or mismanagement, acquire a sour sward, it may be burned again with care, not only without any injury, but with greater advantage. There is fen land in the parish of Chatteris, that has been ploughed and burned several times, that lets this spring at three guineas per acre, a plain proof that ploughing and burning a few times, with good management does not
p.113 injure the land. And many other specimens might be pointed out in the fens, where the land has been really improved by being ploughed and burnt several times; but where land has been ploughed and burnt from time almost immemorial, and the tenants have ploughed the furrow deep, and frequently permitted the fire to burn the moor much lower than the land was ploughed, and have repeated such burnings very often, there are instances where the surface is lowered, and the land greatly injured by such barbarous burnings; nevertheless, it is not burning in a proper manner that injures rough, sour, aquatic swards, but burning them too frequently and too deeply; for burning rough fens, aquatic moors and bogs once or twice in a proper manner, is certainly the most excellent mode of bringing such rough surfaces and moory swards into cultivation. The heaps of ashes should always be spread about the land immediately, because if the weather be hot and dry, and the ashes not speedily spread, the fire often burns too deeply under the heap bottoms, and materially injures the land. The instrument used in the fens to spread the ashes about the land, is a piece of board about eighteen inches long, and ten or twelve inches broad; the top corners of this board are a little rounded, and the bottom edge is thinned, and a hole is boared into

the board about the middle, and a stick about five feet long, and as thick as a small fork, is fastened in the hole. With this simple cheap instrument, the ashes are drawn or pushed about the land very expeditiously. When labourers take the work they have commonly about five shillings per acre, for heaping the furrows, burning the heaps, and spreading the ashes. Immediately after the ashes are spread, the most prudent farmers plough the land to turn the ashes under, and prevent them from being blown away; for it is a great loss to have such valuable manure as the ashes are, blown into the dikes, ditches,
p.114 and drains. * And when the land is thus ploughed over, and the ashes thus turned under, about Midsummer the farmers sow their cole-seed (rape-seed), and rejoice if they are favoured with the appearance or commencement of rain about the time when the seed is sown. But if the cole seed does not come up well after the first sowing, the farmers sow over again. The fen farmers very uniformly sow about half a peck or a gallon of cole-seed to a statute acre; of late years, some of them sow a quarter or half a pound of turnip seed, with the half peck of cole-seed on an acre, and it answers very well, especially if the cole-seed misses growing. Sometimes in the fens and adjacent high land cole-seed is sown on fallows, swards, and stubbles, without the land being either burnt or manured, and the crops are sometimes very good. When the seed is sown, some farmers only draw a light roller over the land and cover the seed, but many draw a hurdle with bushes under it for the same purpose, and others draw a light pair of harrows with bushes under them, over the seed, which covers it very properly. Respecting the young cole-seed plants, they very seldom require either weeding or hoeing; a few plants are some times transplanted from thick spots to thin patches. When the cole-seed is a fair average crop, an acre will feed eight large Lincolnshire sheep, or a greater number of smaller sorts. The sheep are commonly put to the cole seed about the 11th of October, and have liberty to go into the whole field as soon as they are turned in, because the sheep commonly eat the grass round the outside of the fields, and then the
p.115 outleaves of the cole-seed, and the heart and stalks of the cole-seed last. A few sheep in a hundred sometimes die of the garget, when nearly fat, the best remedy for which is bleeding; but it is a common custom in the fens, to slaughter such sheep, as soon as ever they are perceived to be affected with the disorder. A good crop of cole-seed will commonly sell for two guineas per acre, to be eaten on the land; this year an average crop sold readily for three guineas per acre. After the sheep have eaten the cole-seed, the stalks are often permitted to stand for seed, and will frequently produce twenty-six to forty bushels per acre, but where the land is designed to be laid down with artificial seeds for permanent pasture, the cole seed should never be permitted to stand for a crop of seed, because such a crop greatly exhausts the land. If the best modes of cultivating this most excellently ameliorating crop were adopted on all rough fen lands, rushy moors, wet mosses, and rough bogs in the kingdom, it would improve the land in a superlative degree, amazingly enrich the tenants, and provide a much greater supply of mutton and meat, at the season of the year when it is most wanted for the great metropolis, and all the country markets also. It is therefore much to be lamented this most excellent crop is not more generally propagated in the united kingdom. The fen farmers are certainly backward in other branches of agriculture, but in the culture of cole-seed, in which they have long had the most extensive practice, they certainly excel most other farmers in the kingdom, perhaps in the world. The most common place in England of raising this crop is in the fenny counties. When the cole-seed has been eaten on the ground, especially after a fallow, the fine fen moory soil is in a most rich fertile state, and never fails to produce a prodigious crop of any grain that is sown upon it. Fen farmers commonly sow oats (five bushels per
p.116 acre), on cole-seed fallow land, the next after the cole-seed, and not only obtain a very heavy crop, but abundance of grain, for the produce is seldom less than eighty-four bushels per acre, and frequently more. About Wisbech and Well, hemp is frequently sown next after cole-seed; and the produce is generally forty stone and upwards per acre, but hemp is too exhausting a crop for any land designed to be preserved for permanent pasture. Now that oats sell so well, the bulk of fen farmers sow oats the first year after cole-seed."

I heard of the following courses in fen:

At *Whittlesea*. Pare and burn; 1st, cole fed, and some times then seeded; 2d, oats; 3d, wheat; 4th, wheat or barley, and seeds from five to ten years. Another: 1st, cole; 2d, oats; 3d, wheat and layer, four to eight years. On foul land, 1st, fallow; 2d, wheat and layer.

At *Elm*. Pare and burn; 1st, cole fed; 2d, oats for two or three years; then layer for five or six years. Again (Mr. Saffory), pare and burn ; 1st, cole fed; 2d, oats; 3d, oats or wheat; 4th, cole; 5th, oats and

* See Mr. Wedge's opinion on this point.

layer, viz. clover; 7th, wheat. Again, not pare and burn, but 1st, fallow for cole; 2d, oats and clover, then wheat. Again: pare and burn; 1st, cole fed; 2d, oats; 3d, wheat; 4th, cole; 5th, oats; 6th, layer, for five years, if good.

Chippenham. Pare and burn; 1st, cole or cabbages for sheep; 2d, oats and layer. N.B. The cabbages succeeded wonderfully, and were very valuable, double the value of cole or turnips on land the most adapted to either.

Chatteris. Mr. Fryer on fen worn out; 1st, cole fed, and with the cole grass seeds, feeds the cole in about three weeks after sowing, keeps feeding close all summer, gets excellent layers thus. Again 1st, cole; 2d, oats; 3d, wheat and layer. N.B. Finds layers often smothered by the corn.

p.117 *Wisbech.* (Mr. Lawton); 1st, cole fed close, and with it harrows in layer. The layer will be fit for feeding the May-day in next year.
Mr. Edes pare and burn; 1st, cole fed; 2d, 3d, 4th, oats; 5th, layer. Again: 1st, turnips; 2d, barley; 3d, clover; 4th, wheat; with great success.)

Soham. Mr. Wedd recommends pare and burn; 1st, cole; 2d, oats or spring wheat; 3d, ditto and layer. Again, 1st, cole fed; 2d, spring wheat and layer.

Little Wilbraham. Pare and burn; 1st, cole; 2d, oats or barley, or wheat; 3d, ditto and layer.

Mr. A. Young, (who has been over every inch of the fens), gives his opinion on the husbandry best suitable to there; thus,

" The best system for the fens may be thus described. Pare and burn for cole, pare thin as possible with the French plough, and sow cole upon the first earth, a shallow one; feed the cole with sheep only, then sow oats twice on one earth each time. Then muck for cole on two earths or three, according to circumstances, feed the cole with sheep, then sow oats and lay down for three or four years as the seeds remain; suckling ray and hay seeds, then pare and burn for cole. The common practice is to lay down with the second or third crop of oats, after the first breaking up; but three crops are too much, and exhaust the land. By laying down with the second crop, after the first breaking up, the land is not brought into sufficient tilth to have rotted the roots of the spontaneous growth, which would be apt to vegetate again, and damage the sowing grasses in order to destroy such weeds; laying down is postponed till after another crop of cole and oats, by which means the seeds will last longer." Mr. Young
p.118 is silent on cole-seed crop, and on ray-grass seeded, two articles of extensive cultivation in the fens; it may also be remarked that the preceding courses of cropping do not shew, that " the common practice is to lay down with the second or third crop of oats, after the first breaking up," as Mr. Young observes; it appears many more crops are often taken.

Fen layers.

At *Wisbech.* Ray-grass one bushel, white clover seven lbs. red clover, seven lbs., rib grass five lbs. (N.B. Rib grass is called also lamb's tongue.) It is said water will not kill white clover, it will red. Another: ray grass only two bushels; stands for seed and layer, remains four years, then burn again.

At *Wisbech.* (Mr. Waudby). Ray-grass, one bushel, white and red clover, and rib-grass together, twelve lbs. disapproves of ray-grass only ; but where it is so sown, should be mown first year for seed, fed second year. If stands for seed will not remain above another year, and is then sometimes mown again for seed. Mr. Edes, Red clover and rib-grass, or ray-grass, only two bushels: when it is generally seeded.

At *Waterbeach.* Ray-grass, two bushels, Dutch clover, seven lbs.

At *Littleport.* Ray-grass, one bushel, Dutch clover, red clover, rib-grass, each four lbs. Another, ray-grass one bushel, Dutch clover and rib-grass, of each half a bushel.

At *Chatteris.* (Mr. Scott says). "The fen commons after having been ploughed three or four years, are laid down with red clover, white clover, (Dutch clover, or honey-suckling), trefoil, (or black nonsuch) narrow leaved plantain (or rib-grass) of each three lbs. and one bushel of clean ray-grass. N.B. two bushels of high land hay seeds are preferred to the one bushel of ray-grass.

p.119 At *Elm.* (Mr. Safory.) Ray-grass one bushel, white clover, ten lbs., one or two lbs. red clover.

At *Soham.* (Mr. Wedd.) Ray-grass, Dutch clover, red clover, trefoil. Mr. A. Young recommends suckling ray grass and hay-seeds.

Thorney. Hay-seeds, rib-grass, red and white clover, and ray-grass. See Mr. Wing's (of this parish) layer, page [181] and [182].

SECT. IV.—CROPS COMMONLY CULTIVATED.

1st. Wheat.

Preparation. Tillage in open field; fallow of four earths, after two or three crops, spring corn. In uplands in severalty, or enclosed, where seeds have been introduced; wheat is generally grown after clover, on one earth; otherwise, as in open field, after fallow; or after beans or pease, on one earth. On heath lands, wheat is often the first crop after breaking up by paring and burning on fen. Wheat is sown on one earth after two or three crops of oats, and is put in in spring as well as in autumn, Mr. Leworthy of Hauxton has had wheat after tares, but did not succeed, though he mucked for the wheat.*

Manure. In uplands, lay on (at seed time and plough it in), eight to ten loads (60 bushels per load), of
p.120 muck, having been thrown up in yard, or carried to a hill and turned over; this if after a fallow, and sometimes also if after a crop or layer. Sir Charles Cotton of Madinglay, folds for wheat after fallow. Many farmers use oil-dust for this crop, eight to ten bushels per acre, at 3s. per bushel, sow it at the time of sowing the wheat; is supposed to last only one crop; if season prove dry does no good even to that, and is thought by many farmers injurious to land. N.B. 1000 cake will produce 88 bushels of dust. Rev. Mr. Lane of Carlton, folds and top dresses all his wheat he can.

Rev. G. Jennyns, folds his clover land wheat immediately after sowing it, and gets better crops by that, than by any other method.

Mr. Mortlock of Abington practises the same. Soot is often sown on wheat, it is found to check the wire-worm: many farmers believe it an absolute preventative to the effects of that insect so destructive in the fen; about twenty bushels per acre are sown. When (in the fens) wheat is the second, or more than that number of crops after burning, it is mucked for.

Sorts. In uplands red and white, of the former Burwell produces a quality much esteemed and used not only in this county, but in many others. Of this wheat and of the process of getting what is wanted for seed, the Rev. Mr. Turner, rector of that parish, thus writes to Mr. A. Young. "It is the white lands which produces the seed wheat which is in great request in the north, on account of its becoming ripe much sooner than any other seed that is sown, and consequently makes an earlier harvest in a cold climate. This wheat bears the highest price in the market, and is threshed as soon as it is got into the barns, that is, it is only topped out, not threshed to straw, and the sheaves are tied up again, and laid up for some time before they are threshed again to straw, so that it is the ripest and best part of the ear from which
p.121 the seed is obtained in the early threshing. The reason why this white land wheat is so beneficial for seed, I humbly think is owing to the saltpetre with which the soil is impregnated arising from the white stone underneath it, and what has confirmed me in this opinion, is that my house is built with the same stone dug out of the pits, and the walls in damp weather, are always wet with saltpetre, and produce a great deal of moisture after frost."

Mr. Darnton of Babraham tried white wheat but did not succeed.

---

* Mr. Wedd on fen land at Soham; 1st, ploughing and burning; 2d, cole fed; 3d, spring wheat.

Mr. Francis of Chidersley, grows great wheat and gets ten bushels per acre more than of any other sort. Spring wheat is grown in great quantities in the fens. Mr. Wedd, at Soham, had this year 83 acres of it, this sort succeeds generally with the fen farmer. Rev. Mr. Leworthy, of Hauxton, never changes his seed of any grain; he always sows "tail" wheat, and never dresses it. "Mr. Ground, of Whittlesea, and his father, for sixty years together, have never changed their seed-wheat, except from fen to upland, and from upland to fen; and to this day have been as free from blacks as the crops of any other farmers whose practice varies; the management and produce of Mr. G. equal to his wishes." (A.Y. Annals, 44) This plan of Mr. G. is almost general in his parish. Mr. Shepherd, of Chippenham, always sows ordinary seed, and has succeeded equal to those who have used the best. Mr. Fryer, of Chatteris, has had a most striking confirmation of the doctrine of Sir Joseph Banks on the subject of seed wheat; Mr. F. had a crop so bad from mildew that his workmen would not accept it for the cost of threshing it, nor would any stock eat it; he cut the ears of this wheat into two pieces, and dibbled a piece into every hole, he had a great crop and of excellent quality.

p.122 At Burwell they never change their seed-wheat, except some few who are tempted by price, to sell their own and buy cheaper.

At Swaffham (adjoining parish to Burwell) they change frequently.

Preparation of seed. Mr. Wedd, of Trumpington, dresses his wheat in the usual way, preparing the night before wanted, enough for the succeeding day's use. Mr. Hart, of Swaffham, washes in pure water, uses one lb. of salt to one bushel of wheat; then limes it.

Mr. Houlton, of Weston Coville, uses lime after having watered the wheat in Bombay water, never washes in pure water, never had burnt wheat; is a farmer of long experience.

Mr. Wedge, of Westley Bottom, limes and washes, but does not salt.

Mr. Ingle, of Little Swaffham, washes only, never had smut for twenty years.

Mr. Treslove, of Trumpington, thirty gallons of water, twenty-eight lbs. of salt, boil them an hour, add half a lb. of arsenic, boil all together half an hour, steep the wheat in this.

Quantity of seed. On uplands, two bushels; on fens, three bushels per acre.

At Abington, Mr. Mortlock three bushels. At Harston, Rev. Mr. Leworthy sows less seed than his neighbours by half, and is sure he gets as good crops as they, and gets as full a plant. Rev. Mr. Lane, of Carlton, prefers less seed than the usual quantity. Mr. Darnton, of Babraham, prefers a full seed. Mr. Wedd, at Soham, less than two bushels of spring wheat; if early, sows less.

Mr. Edes, of Wisbech, one bushel, drilled at nine inches.
Time of Sowing. Autumn, October and November; Spring, March and April.

p.123 Mr. Wedge, of Westley Bottom, prefers early sowing, has had repeated proofs of its superiority, he shewed me a remarkable one, where only one day intervened between the sowing the two adjoining pieces.* Rev. Mr. Lane, of Carlton, is against early sowing wheat, says he always gets much more from late sowing, the later he sows the less straw he gets, but the more corn. Mr. Darnton, of Babraham, sows earlier than his neighbours, and thinks he has an advantage over his neighbours, on an average of years.

---

* Mr. Wedge writes to the Board of Agriculture on this subject. "I must mention that on the 1st day of August, which was the day I began to sow rye, I sowed an acre of wheat, which was by far the best of any I had that year; it was quite free from mildew, and I have found by experiment for many years, that sowing early and pretty thick is the only way to prevent wheat from mildew." (Com. v. 4).
Mr. Scott, of Chatteris, writes, (also to the Board). "All loamy soiled grass lands that lie low on a clayey substratum, will bring excellent wheat if sown early in the spring, when a bushel will do as well as two bushels in autumn." (Com. v. 4).

Mr. Wedd, at Soham, has sown spring wheat in April, and autumn wheat in December, and has succeeded; but prefers earlier sowing.

How put in. On uplands generally broadcast, ploughed in on four-furrow ridge; do not wish to have land fine at sowing, because it is then apt to bind. Mr. Leworthy, of Harston, dibbled one bushel per acre of spring wheat on an old pasture, on one earth in February; crop twenty-five bushels per acre. Mr. L. prefers dibbling wheat on stiff soils, and broadcasting on others. Mr. Edes, of Wisbech, has (in fens) dibbled and drilled wheat, but prefers the latter; drills at nine inches. Mr. Darnton of Babraham, has dibbled wheat, but did not think the advantage sufficient to induce him to repeat the practice; he has also
p.124 drilled wheat at nine inches; but docs not continue it, he thinks it improves the sample, but that it does not increase the produce. Mr. A. Young writes on Mr. Darnton's drilling. "Mr. Darnton has found the drill better than broadcast for all corn, when seeds arc not to be sown, but is clear that it is disadvantageous if clover, &c. &c. arc to be raised; the last year (1790) lost his crop entirely by trusting to it, but draws his conclusion not from that experiment only, but from others. Wherever he sows seeds of any kind, the corn is broad cast. He is of opinion that if the whole farm is under drill, it would require more horses than if under broad cast. His drilled wheat this year is better than broad cast in the same field, but both have lost plant greatly (Annals, v. 18, p. 226). Drilling wheat is practised by Lord Hardwicke at Wimpole, when the land can be got in order for it, distance nine inches, and supposed to beat broadcast. Mr. Philips, of Bourn-Bridge, has drilled wheat and discontinued it, as have many of his neighbours. Why Mr. P.? "Because we could get nothing from it."

Mr. Wedge, of Westley Bottom, says " drilling will not do, our lands are not good enough;" and "the corn thus deposited will not shade them enough. Mr. W. approves drilling on heavy good lands. Professor Harwood, of Bartlow, is of the same opinion. Mr. Shepherd, of Chippenham prefers the drill to broad cast, and assures me it beats it. Mr. Waudby of March, drills fen lands with wheat, and approves its distance six to nine inches.

An opinion prevails that drilling white lands would not answer: they require too much seed to be deposited that way. Rev. Mr. Hicks, of Wilbraham, says that dibbling gives less wheat than broad-cast, but of better quality.

Culture while growing. Hoeing by the best farmers, but far from the general practice, crops are therefore
p.125 generally foul, though after complete fallow. Where plant is too thick, rake with a drag, rake such as is used for raking stubbles. Mr. Darnton, of Babraham, did not hoe his drilled wheat; his reason is it would have let in the drought, and have made it subject to root-fall. Mr. Edes, of Wisbech, hand hoes, and horse hoes. Rev. Mr. Leworthy, of Hauxton, harrows his wheat in May with very heavy harrows drawn by four horses, teeth of harrows only three inches asunder, and cutting six inches deep, succeeds so well, intends continuing the practice; but recommends doing it in March. In fen if much frost, during the winter, the wheat is trampled in spring by men (thrcc or four) abreast, price 4s. per acre. Mr. Darnton, of Babraham, used to feed his wheat, but is sure he suffered by it.

Harvest. Reaped, and generally by "acre men," viz. strangers (mostly Irishmen) who come over in large companies, and do that work only. Is shocked in the usual method. Do not cut early.

Produce. Five Co. per acre average of county. Mr. A. Young, in his account of average produce of Great Britain," states that of wheat in this county, at 23½ bushels per acre. (Annals, v. 36) Mr. Vancouver states produce of high-land of county at 24 bushels; of fen, 24½ bushels per acre. I could get no confirmation of either Mr. A. Y.'s or Mr. V.'s reports; it may be suspected my information is nearest the fact, if it be true, as Mr, V. states, that the open-field do not produce so much per acre, by three bushels one peck, as the enclosed land does, as the former breadth exceeds the latter so much.

Mr. A. Young gives the following produce of wheat.
At Whittlesea, three to four quarters. At Islesham, 15 to 16 Co. At Connington 20 to 25 bushels. At
p.126 Waterbeach five loads, (viz. 25 bushels). At Chippenham before the enclosure, 5 Co. since 6 Co.
At Soham, (Mr. Wedd, 1805), three to four quarters. (In fen).

Stubbles. Generally ploughed in. Some few haulm them.
Mr. Darnton, of Babraham, used to do when in business.

Disorders. Here as in other counties, the mildew is prevalent, and opinions on this subject are not peculiar to the county.

Mr. Edes, of Wisbech, thinks drilled wheat as little liable to it as broad-cast ; he always cuts early if he sees the mildew.

Rev. Mr. Leworthy, of Harston, thinks it proceeds from drought in June, succeeded by heavy rains. In 1805, Mr. A. Young put the following queries on this subject.

Queries.

1st, What soils have yielded the crops most affected by the mildew?

2d, Have early or late sown crops suffered most?

3d, What situations have been most exposed to it; high and ventilated ones, or low and sheltered vales?

4th, Have thin or thickly sown crops escaped the best; and thin or thick from other circumstances, drilling, the red worm, &c. &c.?

5th, Has the use of old or new seed been attended with any effect?

6th, If from your observations you conceive the causes to be atmospheric, of what sort; late frost; fogs; severe or open winters, &c. &c.?

7th, Have crops on fallows, or layers escaped the best?

8th, Has manuring whether by lime, dung, fold, &c. had any effect?

p.127 9th, Have you made any observations on the barberry bush as locally affecting wheat?

10th, Has there been any difference from the sorts of wheat sown, bearded, red, white, spring, &c.?

11th, Has early cutting been found useful, and how early in point of the milk of the grain being coagulated?

12th, What proportion in your opinion does the late crop bear to a common average produce? With any other circumstances you may think applicable to the inquiry?

Mr. Wedd, of Trumpington, answered these queries; thus,

To 1st Query. "In general, gravelly soils have been most affected by mildew. To 2d. I think there cannot be a doubt but late sown crops have always in seasons subject to mildew, been found the most injured. To 3d. The vales of the highlands have been most damaged in such years as the last. To 4th. I cannot decide upon, but rather think thick sown crops have escaped the best. To 5th. The old seed has proved most productive, but I apprehend not on account of its being old wheat, but being earlier sown. To 7th. In general, layers suffered the least by mildew. To 8th. Folded land has been most affected by mildew. To 9th. The land near the barberry is in general evidently affected by the mildew. To 10th. I think the bearded wheat was less injured by mildew last season than either the white or red wheat, but spring wheat the least hurt of any. To 11th. Early cutting very advantageous when wheat is mildewed. To 12th. I apprehend not more than two-thirds of a crop; Observations by Mr. Wedd. Wheat that was fed off in spring by sheep, was more injured by mildew than lands not fed.

Mr. Shepherd, of Chippenham, answers Mr. Y.'s queries; thus,

p.128 1st. All loose or chalky soils enclosed, and sheltered, having been pasture, or sainfoin layers; not limed or marled, after breaking up were most affected, but the late season affords instances of general mildew. 2d. Late sown crops suffered most, but in many instances the effect is general. 3d. All low and sheltered, but in many instances general. 4th. Thin plants escaped best, but many instances as above. See observations. 5th. I have heard that old seed has escaped in some instances; but I tried several acres drilled in rows, alternately old and new; but found no other difference, excepting that of the new vegetating quicker by six or seven days than the old. 6th. From my observations it does appear that the Causes of mildew are various, are chemical and mechanical, any of which producing a very sudden, change in the plant, a superabundant fertility, too rapid vegetation from frequent showers and warm weather, either of these causes produce diseased luxuriance, and a consequent mildew, as appeared the case in last May, during the frequent rains; for I observed that the wheats in general never promised a more abundant crop, (as far as could be judged by their appearance at that time), but from the beginning of that showery season, the wheats in general turned pale and unhealthy; very cold weather, heavy fogs,

late frosts, may by producing that change which their different influence is capable of, produce mildew,
but more especially any sudden change during impregnation, and after the grain is formed by
preventing that necessary and regular supply of nutriment, which the plant cannot receive in a state of
obstructed circulation; it appears certain that the cause of mildew may happen during the months of
May, June, July or August, but that it is not likely to originate in winter. From severe winters and
p.129 backward springs it frequently happens, that we cannot form an idea of the wheat crop till the middle of
May. Perhaps a severe winter, and backward spring, succeeded by a rapid vegetation, subject to be
checked by the changes of this uncertain climate, may occasion mildew. Nor does it frequently occur
that open winters produce mildew. 7th. In different places the effect is quite the reverse; but altogether
I think the wheats on layers the best. 8th. I have long considered that the barberry bush is certain as to
injuring wheat planted near it, but that the injury it sometimes produces is not simple, but compounded
with other causes. I never saw a single instance of wheat growing near a barberry bush, not being injured
more or less. 1 have seen instances of wheat not being injured after the bushes were destroyed, and
where the oldest man (near 90) had never before seen wheat, but what was mildewed. On these lands I
left two bushels as an experiment, the following effect and particulars were foretold by the old man as
near as possible; in a semicircle of half an acre or thereabouts, near each bush the wheat turned quite
black, the straw quite rotten, and not a single grain could be found a fortnight before harvest, which
would vegetate; in a line across the field also issuing out of this semicircle, the wheat was much injured,
but least furthest from the bush; the whole of the wheat of the field was injured, and weighed only 15
stone per Co. (14 lbs. to the stone). In the parish of Moulton, near Chippenham (but in Suffolk) Barberry
bushes abound, near which wheat has not been sown for many years, the occupiers having experienced
the certain effects. A similar instance may be found in Landwade, (in this county and near Chippenham
also.) In the field of Fordham, adjoining Landwade, barberry hedges, never escape mildew, more or less.
It does frequently happen that all other corn growing near these hedges, is also affected. In the parish of
p.130 Fettwell (Norfolk) a similar instance may be found of general mildew from barberry bushes, so as to
induce the occupiers not to sow any wheat near them. Mr. Simpson, of Nowton, Suffolk, Mr. Worledge,
of Inglam, and Mr. James Slutter, at his Bury farm, have assured me of the effects of barberry-bushes in
the last crop nearly similar to what I have stated. 10th. Bearded and white wheat have escaped the best,
the common red and spring wheat is most injured. All my observations relate to red. 11th. Early cutting
produces the best grain, vis. when the grain begins to harden, but it requires a longer time in the field,
or it will not separate from the straw. 11. Below one-half an average crop.

Observations by Mr.Shepherd on the crop harvested 1804.

1st, Sixteen acres of deep, rich chalky loam, rather lowand sheltered, well dunged with good horse dung, drilled early in October, at twelve inches, seed three bushels per acre, nicely hoed and weeded on the 1st of May, shewed a prospect of 10 Co. per acre; on that day fell a heavy rain succeeded by following showers, from that time this plant changed produce two Co. per acre, very much mildewed.

2nd, Twenty acres of gravelly loam, high, dry, and open, a two years layer of white and yellow
clover, fed with sheep each season, and well folded before and after sowing, dibbled at eight inches, first
week in October, two bushels per acre, nicely hoed and weeded; the same observations as above, 1st
May, and a prospect of seven or eight coomb per acre, produced two Co. per acre, very much mildewed,
as much as the first. 3d. Thirty-five acres of thin stapled chalky loam, on a sterile, yellow, chalk bottom,
a clover seed stubble, manured with ten bushels of rape dust per acre, drilled in with the wheat at eight
inches in the second week in October, three bushels of seed per acre; the land high, dry, and open, nicely
p.131 weeded, hoed, &c. not so much mildewed as the two preceding cases. Produce three Co. per acre, and
14 lbs. per Co. heavier. At the beginning of harvest this field exhibited a singular appearance, for certain
small spots looked bright and were not mildewed; this induced me to examine the substratum, and I
found those spots differed from the general soil, a thick stapled loamy sand, on a gravelly bottom;
therefore suppose that the difference in the dryness or innate warmth of the subsoil, occasioned the
escape from mildew, but when I ascertained that the whole of the parish suffered so generally, that the
difference of the times of sowing of the variety of manures, treatment of lands, quantities of seed, &c.
afforded no criterion by which to form any decisive ideas, I know not what to think on the subject. I find
however by the information of others, that the above circumstance was by no means singular. In the
adjoining parish of Snailwell, the mildew was general, excepting only a spot of land of considerable
fertility; a hazel loam, a southern aspect, chalky bottom, low and rather wet, but open; this spot affords
great variety in the times of sowing, the different manures, in treatment of lands, in quantity of seed, &c.

&c. yet all escaped the mildew; the crop is short, only four Co. per acre. Two miles distant from this. spot, Fordham field, soil and aspect as similar as possible, exhibiting all the variety of times of sowing, manures, quantity of seed per acre, treatment of lands to be expected, where there are perhaps fifty different occupiers, and the lands under common-field husbandry, all mildewed, with so little difference as scarcely to be imagined. In the adjoining parish to this latter (Frekenham) the Wheats are less mildewed, on the lightest and worst lands. Go two miles further, to Heringswell; quite the reverse is the
p.132 case, the wheats are worst on the best lands; unless the chemical properties of the different substratum of the different soils to which I have alluded are more different in their properties than the appearance warrants; we behold quite the reverse effects from the same probable causes." (Annals, v. 43)

Mr. Edes, of Wisbech, says wheat in fens is apt to be very "strawy and full of blacks." The wire-worm is a great enemy to wheat in fens, the lands in Landwade (similar to Burwell) are particularly subject to the mildew. The rich lands round Ely are also very subject to it.

Gleaning is a general evil in this county, and is unlimited, extending to every grain and without any regulations, the gleaners going amongst the shocks of wheat, and following the rakers of soft corn so closely, and in so disorderly a manner, as to cause perpetual dispute and complaint. Dr. Nesmith of Leverington thus expresses him self on this subject. "Quere. Would it not be worthy the attention of the Board to consider how the custom of gleaning might be so regulated, as to protect the property of the farmer, and to secure to the poor that portion of the grain which is necessarily left on the ground? A short act giving the magistrate a summary jurisdiction, and prohibiting the poor to glean till the land was cleared, under a penalty of 10s. or one month's imprisonment, and prohibiting the farmer to turn any stock on the ground for [*blank*] days after it is cleared, under a penalty of £5. to be levied by distress, would I think answer the purpose. The depredations committed by the gleaners are very great, and the undefined right which the poor claim of gleaning amongst the sheaves, and even amongst the gavels before tied up, (for I have known even this insisted on), is a source of perpetual disputes and dissentions. Such an act must be local, because custom varies, but I believe throughout the open-fields of this county,
p.133 the custom of gleaning all grains is uniform. It would also be expedient to restrain the right to the resident poor of each parish; for the want of such a regulation, the wheat crop is almost always cut too late, and carried too quickly after being cut, because the farmer dares not trust it in the field, while the poor are perpetually amongst the sheaves."

SECT. II. - BARLEY.

Preparation. Tillage, in open fields; barley succeeds wheat, two earths are given, the first before Christmas, laying the land unto the stetch; the second, the seed earth, and seed ploughed in on heavy, and harrowed in on light soils. On lands in severalty and suitable to turnips, barley follows them with seeds; three or four earths are given; the first before winter; by some, but by the majority not till spring. Where turnips are not grown, the preceding crop is usually pease, tares, or beans, and two or three earths are given.

Mr. Wedge of Westley Bottom has given the following preparation for this grain, and reported them to

Mr. A. Young, who thus relates them.

"Thirty-two acres of land, the soil a good barley loam, deep, on a chalk bottom, worth 16s. per acre, were thrown into eleven divisions.

No. 1, Spring tares, mown for soiling.
No. 2, Spring tares, mown for hay.
No. 3, Spring tares, seeded, produce five Co. per acre.
p.134 No. 4, Summer fallow, four earths.
No. 5, Beans, broad-cast hand-hoed, but the season being very dry at the time, the work was not done well. Produce six Co. per acre.
No. 6, Summer fallow, four earths.
No. 7, Spring tares mown for soiling.
No. 8, Winter tares, ditto.
No. 9, Winter tares, seeded.

No. 10, Clover fed.

No. 11, Clover fed and then seeded, produce six bushels per acre, worth 20s. per bushel. The tares of No. 1 and No.8, worth 40s. per acre. Two earths were given before winter; except the tares, divisions mown green, which had one ploughing extraordinary, being stirred as soon as cut. All sown with barley in 1787, at the same time, on one spring earth.

Result. No.10, was the best of all. No.11, was the next best. These two clover divisions produced eight Co. per acre of barley, and were better than any other by two bushels an acre; Nos. 1, 4, 6, 7, 8, equal; and the next best to the clover; no difference between spring and winter tares. No. 2, next. Nos. 3 and 9 equal, and next No. 5. The worst about four Co. per acre. In 1788, the field was summer fallowed. Manure seldom any, unless the barley succeeds turnips folded, then it has of course the benefit of that operation. Mr. Mortlock, of Abington, folds for barley, whether it succeeds turnips or not. About Harston, oil-cake dust is sometimes applied for this crop; eight to twelve bushels per acre, sown with the barley. Sir Charles Cotton, of Madingley, dungs for this crop ten to twelve loads per acre.

Sort. The common barley is in general use. Mr. Mortlock of Abington sows the barley of the Isle of
p.135 Thanet, and thinks it preferable to the common. It is earlier. About Swaffham, a barley called Staffordshire barley is preferred, it is grown at Wickin, (in this county,) is forwarder by nine or ten days than the barley of this county. Mr. Wedge, of Westley Bottom, sows an early barley from Shropshire, it comes earlier into ear, and is more productive than any barley he knows of. The barley of the parish of Cottenham is said to have a strong perfume, but is only the common sort. The Rev. Mr. Leworthy, of Harston, cuts the barley he intends for seed, very green, finds it (in consequence as he supposes) vegetates quicker, and is more productive. At Burwell and Swaffham seed barley is changed every two years.

Quantity of seed. About three bushels per acre, the usual quantity.

At Whittlesea. One Co. is sown. Mr. Mortlock, of Abington, sows one Co.

Time of sowing, March, till middle of May.

How put in. Broad cast, generally. Mr. Darnton, of Babraham, has drilled barley at nine inches, but discontinued it. Lord Hardwicke at Wimpole, has also drilled it, and his bailiff (a Norfolk man), prefers it to broad cast, distance eight inches. Mr. Wedge, of Westley Bottom, has also drilled barley, and does not approve of it on his soil. Mr. Shepherd, of Chippenham, drills barley in a masterly manner, and is convinced of its superiority over broad-cast, but does not drill where he sows seeds.

Harvest. Mown and turned on swarth.

Produce. Open-field six Co, per acre. Lands in severalty, where the course of cropping may be chosen, eight Co. and often more. Mr. A. Young's," Account of the Produce of Great Britain," says nine Co. that of this county.

Mr. Vancouver states it at nine Co. uplands. In fens seven Co. one bushel. N.B. Very little barley
p.136 grown in fens. At Whittlesea some is grown instead of wheat and the preparation the same as for oats in fens.

SECT. III. - OATS.

Preparation. Tillage. In open-field. Oats are not often grown, but when they are, it is after two or three crops of corn.

On lands in severalty. By the best farmers the same preparation, and in the same order as barley, and seeds also sown with them, by others as an extra crop, before fallowing.
On fens. Oats are sown after cole, which cole was the first crop after burning ; sometimes two and three crops of oats are J1ere taken successively after cole. One earth only given.

Manure. Oats are sometimes mucked for in fens, when the second or more crop after burning.

Sorts. The common white oat. The potatoe oat has been tried, and has not succeeded; it degenerates. There are two sorts of white oats, the best called " short smalls," the worst" long smalls."

Mr. Edes, of Wisbech, uses the Poland oat, which Rev. Mr Leworthy, of Harston, thinks the greater impoverisher of any, Mr. Edes also sows in fen, seed from clay soil; he finds the potatoe oat more productive but of less weight, and that it degenerates more than any other. The Poland oat is sown on the best lands.
Mr. Edes says all grains are found to degenerate in fens.
p.137 Mr. Mortlock, of Abington, has also found the potatoe oat degenerate on his lands.*

Quantity of seed. On uplands one Co. per acre. On fen five bushels.

At Whittlesea. Six bushels short oats, eight bushels long oats, they sow an additional quantity in fen, on account of the wire-worm. Mr. Mortlock, of Abington, sows five bushels, and the poorer the soil the more he sows.
Mr. Edes, of Wisbech, drills in at six inches one Co. Mr. Lawton of the same place drills eight pecks, at six inches, five pecks at nine inches.+

Time of sowing. Uplands, March and April ; fen, April and May.

How put in. Uplands and fen, broadcast, with a few exceptions.
In fen. At Wisbech, Mr. Edes and Mr. Lawton, drill them.
At March, Mr. Waudby; distance by these gentlemen six to nine inches.
In uplands. Mr. Shepherd drills them, and has done for many years. Mr. Edes trench-ploughs for oats, if first crop after a layer, and considers it essential.

Harvest. In uplands as barley. In fens, reaped and tied in sheaves as wheat.

p.138 *Produce.* In uplands, six, eight, to ten Co. per acre. Mr. A. Young in his "Account of average Produce of Great Britain," says that of this county is for this crop nine Co. one bushel. Mr. Vancouver states it at six Co. three bushels, on uplands. In fens my notes say ten to twenty Co. Mr. Vancouver says average $47^{1}/_{2}$. bushels.

SECT. IV. RYE.

Preparation. Tillage. This grain is grown as in other counties, on lands not good enough for wheat, to which however it is giving way. Rye is generally sown on a wheat stubble, for sheep feed; on one earth, immediately after harvest, ploughing in the stubble, and har rowing in the seed. When this grain is intended for a crop, the same preparation (a fallow) is given as for wheat, on lands in severalty. Mr. Darnton, of Babraham, has grown rye instead of wheat, on lands subject to mildew. Some rye is grown, on fens about Wisbech, for sheep feed.

Quantity of seed. One and a half to two bushels per acre.

Produce. Four to six Co. per acre. Crop. Worth of feed 20 to 30s.

Mr. Wedge, of Westley Bottom, has grown ten Co. per acre.

p.139

SECT. V. —BEANS.

Preparation. *Tillage.* In open-field beans generally succeed barley or wheat, and are put in on one earth. In uplands in severalty, they are grown often in the same course as in open-field, but where clover has

---

*. Mr. Scott, of Chatteris, says Poland oats are ripe much before any other, and that a loamy soil suits them.

\+ Mr. Scott recommends $4^{1}/_{2}$ bushels, Poland oats broad-cast, and three bushels drilled, and the poorer the soil, the more the seed.

been introduced, they are often sown where that plant failed, or as a substitute to it, when it is wished to avoid its too quick repetition. In fens, beans are grown on an oat stubble, or the first crop after a layer. Autumn tillage is seldom given, even on uplands, for beans ; the reason assigned is, that lands ploughed previously to winter, "pan" more in the spring, than those which had laid whole all winter.

Sort. Ticks, those generally sown.

Quantity of seed. If broad cast, one Co. sometimes more.

Time of sowing. Beginning of February to end of March.

How put in. In open-field, broad-cast and ploughed in, on ridge, sometimes on stitch. In lands in severalty same as in open-field, generally speaking. Dibbling. Mr. A. Young gives the following account of dibbling beans in 1800, at Long-Stow. "Mr. Moscrop, bailiff to the Rev. Dr. Thompson, of Long Stow, dibbled in 1800, four acres of beans; he ordered three in a hole, but this was changed after a time for one in a hole; throughout the drought of that year, plants, where only one in a hole was set, were poor and puny, much inferior to three; nor was this the first time that he made the same remark. These succulent plants, he observed, attract moisture when they grow together, and assist each other.

p.140 "Mr. Moscrop, (who came from Tweed-side), has had many years practice in drilling, in various of its branches, and assured me, (A. Y.), that all the best farmers have found that instead of drilling taking less seed than broad cast, it requires rather more, and it is the same with dibbling beans," (Annals, v. 42 and 44.) Rev. Mr. Leworthy of Harston has dibbled beans one row on a flag on an old layer, and had great crops. Mr. Lawton, of Wisbech, puts them in every fourth furrow. Mr. Fryer, of Chatteris, has put them in (on uplands) every other furrow, but did not succeed better than by broad-cast. I saw many which were put in every third furrow. Lord Hardwicke, at Wimpole, drills beans at 20 to 22 inches. Mr. A. Young speaks of some his lordship had in 1800, drilled on two feet on ridges, and that they were very fine. (Annals, v. 42).

Culture while growing. In open-fields, generally only sheep fed; it is said sheep will not touch a bean, while there is a spire of anything else to be had; they keep this crop in appearance, in garden neatness; but at harvest it is far otherwise. In lands in severalty hand-hoeing is given; but the crops are here also generally very foul, owing to their being broad-cast and so thick a plant. Mr. Lawton, of Wisbech, horse-hoes his beans (put in every fourth furrow), but sheep-hoeing is preferred by nine out of ten Cambridgeshire farmers.

Harvest. Reaped or pulled, by some mown; all tied up in small sheaves, some with their own straw, some with other straw, and by a few with rope-yarn.

Produce. Mr. Vancouver says four Co. one bushel per acre. From 10 to 12 Co. are frequently grown. Mr. A. Young, in his " Account of average Produce of Great Britain," states beans in this county six Co. The
p.141 straw of this crop, esteemed in other counties of great value, being excellent for horses "and lean cattle of any kind, is in no estimation here, and is applied to littering yards only.

SECT. VI - PEASE.

Preparation. Tillage. In open-field pease are usually grown instead of barley or beans, on one earth. On lands in severalty, they are grown after barley, and frequently on light lands upon a layer.

Sort. There are no sorts peculiar to the county, the white, grey, and dun are common.

Quantity of seed. About five bushels broad-cast, drilled and dibbled, and not more than two to two and a half bushels, per acre.

Time of sowing. February and March.

How put in. In open-field, almost universally broad cast. On land in severalty also broad-cast, but some are dibbled, and some few drilled. Mr. Mortlock, of Abington, puts them in every third furrow, and has found them a very uncertain crop, liable to be taken off by the fly, &c. Mr. Darnton, of Babraham, has drilled them at nine inches. Mr. Shepherd, of Chippenham, also drills them, and both speak well of the practice.

Culture while growing. When broad-cast none, of course are very foul, and many I viewed, miserably so, not promising a crop sufficient to pay rates and taxes. The dibbled crops somewhat better, but not sufficient hoeing bestowed on them; indeed on lands subject to weeds, this crop can be kept clean only when drilled at wide intervals, a plan the Cambridgeshire farmer has not yet adopted.

p.142 *Harvest.* Taken up by a pease-make, and left in small heaps, and turned as often as the weather may make it necessary.

Produce. About five Co. per acre, vary from three to eight Co. Mr. Vancouver says, four Co. three bushels. Mr. A.Young, in his "Account of Produce of Kingdom," says average of pease in this county, five Co. per acre.

SECT. VII. - TARES.

The county is indebted to B. Barker, Esq. of Little Swaffham, for the introduction of this valuable plant, the culture of which, however, does not spread equal to its merit; no reason assigned, but it may be presumed the partiality for corn in the sack is the real cause.

Preparation. Tillage. Usually a wheat stubble, ploughed in immediately after harvest, seed harrowed in broad cast. Drilling them, which in Suffolk has been proved an excellent plan, is not here practised. A spring crop of corn usually succeeds them, and turnips sometimes follow them in the same year (on a small scale).

Sort. Common winter and spring tare.

Quantity of seed. Two bushels per acre.

Time of sowing. Autumn. August and September, the former better. Spring, March and April.

Application. Cut green and given to horses, beginning those sown in autumn, about the middle of May; there are few farmers who have more than a spring and an autumn sowing instead of two or three of
p.143 each, for providing a succession through the summer. They are sometimes seeded, and produce from three to six Co. per acre, they are seldom made into hay, as they receive more injury from rain than any other grass does. They are very often sown for sheep feed, and by some few are made a regular shift, (thus applied) in their course of cropping. Instance, Colonel Adeane, (and formerly Mr. Darnton), and Mr. Philips, at Babraham. Horses can no way be kept so cheap and so well as on green tares; and where straw is plentiful, an immense quantity of valuable muck, may during summer be raised by feeding them in a well littered yard, the practice of the best farmers in Norfolk and Suffolk.

N. B. Rev. Mr. Leworthy, of Harston, thinks tares great impoverishers of land, even when cut green. I have heard the same observation in Suffolk, from an occupier of a lightish soil.

SECT. VIII. - COLE.

On uplands. This plant is in some few places grown on uplands, where the preparation for it is the same as for turnips, and wheat generally succeeds it when it stands for a crop, but the great cultivation of cole is in the fens, where it is usually the first crop after paring and burning.

Manure. Mr. Edes, of Wisbech, mucks for cole, when he does not burn for it. When a second crop of cole is grown, it is mucked for out of yard, 12 to 14 loads per acre.

Quantity of seed. One-fourth to one-half a peck per acre.

Time of sowing. About Midsummer if for feed, if for crop, about August.

p.144 *How put in.* On one earth if after burning, immediately after which the ashes are spread; the seed harrowed or bushed in, by some rolled in. Many farmers spread the ashes as soon as burnt, and directly plough them in, and give another earth at seed time, others spread them as soon as burnt, but not plough them in, till seed time. There are various opinions on these methods, the observations on them by individuals of the county, are placed in the chapter of Paring and Burning, and I had occasion to insert some observations on them, when speaking of cropping the fens. (See Chapter on Course of Crops.)

Culture while growing. If for a crop is set out by hoeing, as turnips are, but at less distance. Is seldom weeded, but is often transplanted from thick to thin places.

Harvest. When cole stands for a crop, it is reaped carefully and laid on a stubble, and threshed in field, being drawn on sledges having sail cloth lining, to the place of threshing; plenty of help is employed, only fine weather suiting the business, and notwithstanding all possible care, much of this crop is lost by shedding. The work is generally done by the day.

Produce. Four to six and seven Co. per acre, some times more. Worth to feed, about 4s. per acre, on average; but varies from 20s. to 60s. Improves from six to eight sheep about 10s. each. Is of more value than turnips; is improved by that which destroys turnips, i. e. frost. Begin feeding it about Michaelmas. Is given to ewes after they have lambed, (will injure them before lambing), and to fattening sheep. Mr. Wedd of Trumpington, thinks cole should be fed by hurdling it off, a piece at a time, and that it should
p.145 be given to old sheep. Mr. Scott, of Chatteris, thinks the sheep should be turned into the whole field of cole at once. Mr. Boyce, of Whittlesea, hurdles it off if he gives it to store-sheep, but turns into the whole at once, when he gives it to fattening ones; for when hurdled off and fed bare, the sheep bite so close as to eat the crown of the plant; which they prefer to the leaf, and will not eat the latter afterwards, but "pine for the former, and will not in consequence get on well." When intended for a crop, if fed first, it must not be after February. It is apt to garget sheep while they are in young; the usual remedy is bleeding them; most farmers, however, do not attempt a cure, but kill them. The cole also affects the lambs before yeaned. This crop is the sole dependance of fen-farmers, their whole success depends on it, as that of the Norfolk farmers does upon the turnip.

Disorder. When cole it stands for a crop in fen, is subject to blight.

SECT. IX.—TURNIPS.

The cultivation of this plant has hitherto been very confined in this county, owing to so great a part of it having been in open field, the system of cropping which, and the flock masters' right of going over the whole fallow-field, precluding it; the Cambridgeshire farmers, however, appear as sensible of the value of this root as the Norfolk ones, having introduced it into the rotation of cropping adopted on new enclosures, on suitable soils, where it is likely to prove, as might be expected, a great acquisition; one
p.146 circumstance is indeed to be lamented, namely, that this plant does not succeed on the best lands of the county; namely "the white lands," the soil of which is very fleet, and the substratum a clunch; at which when the root arrives, the turnip dies; another objection to turnips on this soil, is, that on the least wet they rise very dirty, and the land poaches on the tread of sheep, even so as materially to injure them; hence did not turnips on such lands go off in the manner stated, they could not be fed a season through, either on or off them without injury to Stock and land. Mr. Wedd, of Trumpington, says "turnips will not answer on white lands." Mr. Darnton, of Babraham, has had his turnips go off when the root comes at the substratum of his soil, a chalk, and this crop has always been a very uncertain one with him, owing to the fly and locust.

Preparation. The usual one of four or five earths; the preceding crop generally wheat; fine tilth and garden cleanness are aimed at. The best farmers give the first earth before winter, but it is not the general practice.

Manure. Fold or muck; if the latter, that of farm-yard, ten to twelve loads per acre ploughed in at seed time. Mr. Shepherd, of Chippenham, manures for them with oil-dust drilled in with the seed, about eight bushels per acre. Rev. Mr. Lane, of Carlton, cannot get a fine tilth after folding, therefore mucks for turnips. Mr. Darnton, of Babraham, mucks for turnips. Rev. Mr. Leworthy of Harston, manures for them with mold and lime, and says that plan secures a crop.

Sort. None peculiar to the county; Mr. Shepherd, of Chippenham, has largely cultivated the Swedish turnip, and he speaks highly of it. Mr. A. Young, (Annals) mentions a fine crop Mr. Shepherd had of this sort in 1803, and attributes its escaping the fly to manuring and folding amply. Rev. Mr. Leworthy, of Harston, has also grown it, and for seed. Mr. Edes, of Wisbech, is a cultivator of the Swedish turnip, and
p.147 has found it more subject to the fly than any other. Game prefer them to any sort.

Quantity of seed. About a quart an acre.

Time of sowing. Through June.

How put in. Broad-cast and harrowed in; and when mucked for with long muck, are rolled in. Mr. A. Young speaks of the Rev. Mr. Lane having in (1799) drilled one acre at eighteen inches; and that it kept 100 sheep three weeks and four days; large Cambridgeshire sheep that had been at turnips before; the crop far superior to the broad-cast adjoining. Mr. Shepherd, of Chippenham, drills turnips at twelve inches; and has proved that it matters little whether they be put in deep or fleet; if the former, the only difference is, that they come to the hoe a few days later. Mr. Wedge, of Westley Bottom, sows broad-cast, and cuts them into drills by horsehoes, at the usual time of hand-hoeing.

Culture while growing. Hoeing twice, but as the art is not well known by the inhabitants, the work is done by persons who travel the country for that purpose, and who make great earnings; it cost a farmer in the neighbourhood of Wimpole 25s. per acre in 1803, for hoeing his turnips by his own people, who would not take them by the acre, but did them by the day, and it was thought wrought hard; the usual price in turnip countries is 5s. to 7s. per acre for twice hoeing. The Rev. Mr. Jennyns, of Bottisham, always has his turnip-hoers carry each a bag of cole-seed, when hoeing the second time, to sow vacancies in his turnip crop.

Application. On light soils fed by sheep; on heavy lands drawn for bullocks, &c. Rev. Mr. Leworthy, of Harston, grows turnips for seed, has had 10 bushels per acre, and sold them at 30s.to 36s. per bushel;
p.148 and retail at 8d. per lb. sold some to London at 28s. per bushel; has grown of Swedish turnip 8 bushels per acre seed; then wheat.

SECT. X. - CLOVER.

Preparation. This plant is sown in this county as in most others; usually with the first crop of spring corn, after a fallow or after turnips, and by some persons in the open-field, where that system will not allow any other application of it; it is sown with the last crop in the course, for a little sheep feed (in the spring) after feeding which, the land is fallowed; it is also occasionally sown on fallow-wheat, in the spring after the wheat is sown; good clover is thus obtained, the wheat stubble nursing it in the winter.

Mr. Shepherd, of Chippenham, says the best layers are from seeds sown on wheat or rye crops. The "white lands" are very favourable to clover, and produce abundant crops of it. Mr. King, of Bottisham, says clover will not stand on the heath lands about Newmarket, lately broken up; whether it will after they have been in tillage some years, is to be proved.

Manure. The best farmers muck their young clovers, and say it pays well for it.

Quantity of seed. 10 to 12 lbs. per acre.

Time of sowing. With the crop if a spring crop; if on wheat, about March or April.

How put in. Harrowed in with the spring crop, rolled in if on wheat.

p.149 *Produce and application.* A ton to a ton and a half each mowing on lands, upon which it is newly cultivated, on those where it has been often not near so much; it is however more generally fed, and will keep four to seven sheep per acre, from about May Day to wheat sowing. It is also by some few, cut green and given to horses; much also is seeded, and has occasionally paid well, but it is a lottery. I heard of no experiment by which the comparative value of these applications could be ascertained, nor after which process is obtained the best wheat. The Rev. Mr. Leworthy, of Harston, mows and then seeds; had two tons per acre in 1804. In many of the new enclosures great breadths of clover have been thus managed and succeeded, although it is deemed an exhausting system, and one that on an average of years would not succeed. If the second crop has a good make, it has been found little inferior in quality and weight to the first, but it is not thought this will be the case on a repetition of the plant. Mr. Francis, of Childersley, has better wheat after clover mown, than fed.

SECT. XI. - TREFOIL.

Preparation. It is generally sown with clover and ray-grass, and often by itself, instead of the former.

Seed. When sown alone 10 to 12 lbs. per acre, if with clover and ray grass, from 6 to 8 lbs. of trefoil.

Manure. Good farmers wish to manure this layer, (which they do in the winter,) if intended to be succeeded by wheat, which crop as well as the trefoil is benefited by it.

p.150 *Time of sowing.* Same as clover.

Application. Generally fed by sheep, if not seeded; produce inferior to clover, and when seeded equally uncertain as to produce. Wheat is not so good after trefoil, as after clover.

SECT. XII. - RAY-GRASS.

Preparation. Is sown on the uplands of the county with clover and trefoil, on mixed and light soils; and in the fens, it forms the greatest portion of seeds of their layers. It is often sown by itself in fens, and is the great dependance of the fen-farmer.

Quantity of seed. On uplands, when sown with clover and trefoil, half a peck per acre. On fen, where it is often sown with other grasses, one bushel of this is sown, and when with Dutch clover only, or by itself, two bushels.

Manuring. In fen where the layers consist, as I have observed, chiefly of this grass, manuring is given generally immediately after the hay of the first year is off.

Time of sowing and how put in. As clover.

Application. On uplands, generally fed by sheep, as it is sown there on lands applied to that stock chiefly, and lays from two to five years. In the fens it is applied to all kinds of stock, and lays there also from five to seven years; being however when sown by itself, seeded as well as fed; on this point there are various opinions, but the more general practice is to feed with sheep the first year, and mow for seed, the second.

p.151

SECT. V. - CROPS NOT COMMONLY CULTIVATED.

1st, Sainfoin.

This valuable plant is cultivated in many parts of the county, and with the success and profit everywhere attached to it under judicious management on suitable soils, viz. such as are dry and have a chalk bottom.

Preparation. Usually fallow or turnips, succeeded by barley, with which the sainfoin is sown. Mr. Darnton, of Babraham, used to sow it on rye, viz. the spring after sowing the rye, and is then rolled in. Mr. D.'s neighbour, Mr. Philips, of Bourn Bridge, sows it also with rye, but at the same time he sows the rye. Mr. Wedge, of Westley Bottom, sows it with rye. Professor Harwood, of Bartley, sows it with barley. Mr. Sanxter, of Horse Heath, sows it on summerlands without a crop.

Manure. Cinder dust the best manure. Professor Harwood lays on about 100 bushels per acre in the frost, cost 1d. to 2d$^1/_2$. per bushel, including carriage 12 miles.

Quantity of seed. Five bushels per acre alone. Professor Harwood three bushels sainfoin, trefoil, half a peck. Mr. Sanxter four bushels alone.

Time of sowing. In the spring, with barley, with the exceptions noted.

How put in. Harrowed in with the barley, rolled in if on rye, sown the preceding autumn, and the sainfoin sown in the spring.

Application and produce. First, Mown for hay, which is excellent; great care is necessary that it be not
p.152 made too much. It requires only turning on the swarth, is gotten up so green, and heats on the stack to a degree that would alarm one not used to. it. All stock are fond of it, and it is as valuable as the best meadow hay. The after grass is fed by sheep, but many think it should not be very closely fed. When it stands for seed, produce three to six Co. per acre. When for hay, from one to two tons per acre. It is a remark of a gentleman of Landwade, that, "sheep ruin it. I make it into hay, and get a ton an acre." Mr. Wedge, of Westley Bottom, "sheep destroy it. Professor Harwood, makes it into hay. Feeds the rowen till Michaelmas. Mr. Sanxter mows it and does not feed the rowen. Mr. Hammon, of Ashley, mows about two tons per acre, and feeds after grass with sheep; he has grown eight Co. per acre seed.

Mr. Eaton, of Stetchworth, says, sheep injure it if fed near winter.

About Babraham neighbourhood it is made into hay, and never fed close. The Rev. Mr. Lane, of Carlton, gives it made into hay, and cut, to horses; grows great crops of it.

Duration. At Landwade, remains about nine years.

At Ashley. About seven or eight years. (Mr. Hammond).

At Stetchworth. If it remains more than four years, the crop which succeeds it, (oats) is likely to fail. (Mr. Eaton).

At Babraham. Lasts about seven years. (Mr. Darnton).

After management. At Landwade, it is broken up in February, and fallowed for cole, for crop; then barley twice taken, and returned to field course of cropping At Stetchworth, Mr. Eaton breaks it up, and sows oats, then fallows. Sainfoin is sown again after one course of cropping of the district is taken. At
p.153 Babraham, Mr. Darnton, used to break up for pease, then took rye and lays down again with trefoil only.

SECT. II. - LUCERN.

I heard of none except from Mr. Darnton, of Babraham, who formerly grew it, and with great success; used to mow it four times, had each time equal to a crop of clover, yet discontinued it. It was too much trouble to keep it clean, he sowed it broad-cast with summerland barley. Gave it to horses in a yard; had made no experiment to prove its real value, &c. &c. the soil light, and gravel bottom. The Rev. Mr. Lane, of Carlton, intends growing it on a large scale.

SECT. III. - SCOTCH KALE.

The Rev. Mr. Lane, of Carlton some years back grew this plant on both light and heavy lands, and speaks highly of it, but does not now cultivate it; he gave it to sheep, of which he then kept a large quantity.

SECT. IV. - POTATOES,

Are cultivated largely in the fens and uplands of this county, and are as profitable a crop as any grown. At Whittlesea, Chatteris, Soham, &c &c. they are grown on a large scale; almost all small
p.154 occupiers cultivate them. March is also noted for their cultivation.

Lord Hardwicke, says Mr. Young, (Annals, v. 43) "in 1799 had 58 bushels of wheat per acre, after potatoes, on strong, wet land, but well hollow-drained." *

* At Whittlesea, labourers give 50s. Per acre for the use of land for growing a crop of potatoes, and often get 100 sacks per acre.

Preparation. Two or three earths. They are generally grown instead of beans or barley. Mr. Boyce, of Whittlesea, has them in place of wheat. Mr. Wedd, of Trumpington, after cole, fed off. At Soham, wheat is taken after them. Many grow them for several years in succession.

Manure. No crop pays better for manure. Farmyard muck usually applied, about fourteen loads per acre ploughed in at planting the crop.

Sort. Red nosed kidney, rough red, ox noble, &c. &c.

Quantity of seed. About six sacks per acre, cut into pieces about the size of an egg, each piece having "an eye" to it. Mr. Fields, of Upwell, plants eight sacks per acre; Mr. Boyce, of Whittlesea, twelve sacks.

Time of planting. Latter end of April, or beginning of May.

How put in. By many placed in every third furrow, each piece at about four inches asunder, and ploughed on to. At Soham they are dibbled in. Mr. Fields, of Upwell, puts the sets in at twenty-three inches asunder in the rows, and thirty inches from row to row, and on the ridge. Mr. Edes, of Wisbech, rows at three to four feet asunder.

Culture while growing. Horse and hand-hoeing. Mr. Field hoes them three or four times.

Harvest. Ploughed up and surface harrowed, and are gathered by women and children. At Soham are
p.155 taken up by three-tined forks. At Whittlesea in the same way at 6d. per sack. Are protected from frost by being covered with straw, then earth, then straw again and thatched, laid in a pit, or on a dry spot, so that water runs from them.

Application. Sell if possible, as no stock will pay nearly the usual sale price of them. If cannot sell, give them to all kinds of stock, as all do well on them. The best system for consuming them is in the spring. Mr. Field, of Upwell, gives them to cows and sheep, and esteems them a very profitable crop thus applied. In the time of scarcity this root was recommended as a substitute for flour in bread, and the general opinion was in favour of the measure, that it was economical; the following letter on this subject, being from a gentleman of the county, may not perhaps be improperly placed here; the letter alluded to was by the Rev. Mr. Metcalf, of Ely, and is as follows. "To ascertain the value of potatoes, in making bread, a loaf was made of five pounds of good flour, and another of three pounds four ounces, of the same flour, mixed with one pound twelve ounces of potatoes; when boiled and mashed, equal quantities of yeast, salt, and water, were put to each loaf, but in making up, it was found that the loaf of flour required more water, which was accordingly added, and as the mixed loaf had already too much, three ounces of flour were added to remedy the defect. On weighing them when cold, after baking the same time in the same oven, it was found that the flour loaf weighed eight pounds six ounces, and the mixed one only five pounds fifteen ounces. Now as five pounds of flour produced eight pounds six ounces of bread, in the same proportion the three pounds seven ounces of flour would have made five
p.156 pounds twelve ounces of bread, hence the one pound twelve ounces of potatoes may be said to have produced only three ounces of bread." (Annals of Agriculture, v. 25, p. 538) Mr. Edes, of Wisbech, thinks hogs pay better for potatoes than any other stock does. Mr. Darnton, of Babraham, gives them to stock when he cannot sell them at 8d. per bushel, as he says no cattle will pay more than that for them; he thinks, except they are prepared by some culinary process, they improve stock very little. At Wimpole, they are given to all stock. Lord Hardwicke in the scarcity relieved the poor greatly by selling them potatoes at 1s. 6d. per bushel, when the price was 4s. to 5s. per bushel. Mr. Boyce, of Whittlesea, gives them to bullocks, calves, and pigs; and says, a bullock that will fatten to about 50 to 60 stones, will eat about two bushels per day and hay; he never gives them till spring. Bullocks should be kept warm, while eating them; calves do well on them, but they should be cut.

Produce. In fen from 80 to 150 and 170 sacks, of three bushels each.

In uplands, 170 to 180 sacks have been grown, but these are extraordinary and rare crops, the average produce not more than one-third of them. Price from 8d. to 2s. 3d. per bushel; in the scarcity, 10s. 6d.

per sack. At Whittlesea, produce about 84 sacks. Mr. Wedd, at Soham, in 1804 had sixteen acres, and sold part of them at £16. per acre. Mr. Boyce, of Whittlesea, values them at 2s. 6d, per sack on an average of years, the purchaser to take them up. Mr. Edes, of Wisbech, would sell at it. 2s. 6d. per sack, rather than give them to stock. Lord Hardwicke has grown 166 sacks per acre.

Distempers. Potatoes (particularly the finer sorts), are subject, (says Mr. Scott of Chatteris), "to be
p.157 curled rooted, by which the produce is much reduced" when thus affected, (Mr. S. says) "the main root is eaten off from the sets, by some worm or insect." Mr. S. has an idea that this disorder might be prevented by steeping the sets in some nauseous preparation.

SECT. V. — CARROTS AND PARSNIPS.

I saw none of either forming part of the farmer's course of cropping. Lord Hardwicke tried them some years back on a small scale on his strong clays, and obtained great crops, but the particulars were not known by my informant, the bailiff.

Mr. A. Young, (Annals, v. 42) thus writes on carrots, at Wimpole. "On the strong clay of Wimpole, the Earl of Hardwicke tried in 1798 half an acre of carrots, to see if they would succeed on a soil deemed so utterly improper for that root; they succeeded well, and produced a full crop, but the number of bushels could not be ascertained, from the depredations of people stealing them; wheat succeeded and produced a great crop. In 1799 the trial was repeated, and a comparison made with parsnips, these succeeded well, but the carrots were eaten by the white snail; the parsnips were sold to the poor at 1s. a bushel, and proved a great assistance to them in the scarcity; they wisely took the hint, and have many now in their own gardens. Lettuces and radishes were scattered amongst them, which afforded the poor many sallads. The wheat that followed this root as great as after any other preparation. Mr. Edes, of
p.158 Wisbech, says, carrots are so subject to the worm, that it does not answer growing them on his farm.

SECT. VI. - CABBAGES,

Are not grown to that degree in the county they might be expected to be, when the quantity of land suitable to them is considered. Mr. Ground, of Whittlesea, Mr. Edes, of Wisbech, Mr. Jennyns, of Bottisham, and Mr. Thorpe, of Chippenham, grow them, and I saw a few at Wimpole.

Preparation. Same as for turnips.

Manure. Is always given for them. Farm-yard muck, twenty to thirty loads per acre.

Sort. Drum-headed. Mr. Jennyns, of Bottisham, plants the red cabbage, and finds that caterpillars will not attack them, so soon as they will the drumheaded.

Seed. About 6000 plants per acre. Mr. Field, of Upwell, sows the seed; it costs 3s. per lb. in London; one-fourth (9d.), will produce plants enough for an acre; the usual price per 1000 of plants is 2s. 6d. (some times much more); cost of plants therefore for an acre is at least 15s. shewing that raising the plants answers well. Mr. Field plants in the middle of June, 7000 per acre.

Time of sowing. July after rain, some sooner.

How put in. Generally on four furrow ridge, at two to three feet distance on the ridge, Mr. Field, of Upwell, (in fen) puts them in at 2½ feet square, and on the flat.

p.159 *Expense.* The work being usually done by the day, I could not come at the expense per acre. A Suffolk cultivator thus estimates it (on a heavy wet loam) exclusive of rent, tithes, rates.

	£.	s.	d.
Five ploughings	1	0	0
Two harrowings	0	0	6
Manure 20 loads	2	0	0
Seed raised	0	1	6
Planting	0	3	0
Deficiencies	0	0	6
Hand-hoeing	0	4	0
Horse ditto	0	4	0
Cutting and carting	0	15	0
	4	8	6

N.B. Mr. A. Young, observes that, "only 15s. of the £2. charged for manure, should be charged to the cabbages, as the succeeding crops receive the remainder."

Here a charge for cutting the cabbages; they should be drawn, or they shoot again, and injure the land.

Culture while growing. Hoeing by hand in the rows, in the intervals by ploughing from the plants with a common plough, and to them with a double-breasted one. Mr. Field moulds up his (on the flat), by a double plough, and hand-hoes the rows three times.

Value and application. Their value estimated at much more than that of turnips, most growers think double. Mr. Shepherd, of Chippenham, has had them on a poor moor, (which would scarcely bear a man), worth £10. per acre. They may be given to every kind of stock; if to cows the outside and decayed leaves should be taken off. Mr. Edes, of Wisbech, gives them to sheep in the spring, and prefers them to turnips. They are thought better than turnips for weaned calves.

p.160

SECT. VII. - HEMP.

This plant is cultivated largely, and appears to pay so well, that it is not easy to account for its growth not being still more extended. It is found at Upwell, Guyhorn, Ely, March, Manea, Chatteris, &c. &c. Its being now almost generally esteemed a great exhauster, and requiring constant mucking, may perhaps be the great check to its cultivation; formerly, however, it was not esteemed an exhauster, for Dr. Nasmith, of Leverington, informed me he had seen old leases stipulating that in the last two years the land should be cropped with hemp. The growth is supposed to be at this time increasing. Mr. Vancouver says, in parts of Cambridgeshire, this plant is not now esteemed an exhauster; but an ameliorator. I did not find this opinion acceded to generally; I met indeed individuals who thought it did not impoverish land which "suited" it.

Preparation. A fallow, with all the ploughing, harrowing, picking, &c. that can be bestowed from the preceding autumn; when one deep ploughing is given till May; it is then sown, the preceding crop having been flax, beans, or wheat, and the succeeding one often wheat, sometimes barley; and hemp is occasionally taken twice successively, then wheat. Flax sometimes succeeds hemp, then wheat; and better wheat after seeded hemp than after maiden hemp, as the former affords a manuring from its leaf which is left on the land. The land when sown should be in garden cleanness, and as fine as if for onions; free from every weed, rubbish, &c. The soil which best suits it, is a strong loam. This crop leaves the land perfectly clean, having killed everything in it.

p.161 *Manure.* Fifteen, twenty, to thirty loads per acre, from farm-yard, and ploughed in at sowing the crop.

How put in. Broad-cast.

Quantity of seed. 3 1/2 bushels to one Co. per acre.

Time of sowing. Middle of May.

Culture while growing. None. It smothers everything.

Harvest. Commences about August. Is pulled about twelve or thirteen weeks after sowing by women, tied up at both ends in bundles as large as the two hands can grasp, and is immediately "dyked," or as it is called, "water-retted," i.e. sunk in a ditch and covered by flags (called sods); the water should be about ankle deep above the sods; should lay from four to ten days in water, till it works like new beer and rises up, when the bark will strip off the stalk; should be a standing water, or water made so by being "stanked" at each end; some water will bring it forwarder than other. When taken out of the water, (on doing which to a *moment* of the proper time, depends everything), it is untied and set on an end to dry, then spread on grass land (short grass) parallel to each other; turned after every rain, or the worm will injure it, for four or five weeks, then is tied into sheaves and shocked, one in the middle and four round; it stands till dry (requires turning) the[n] barned or stacked, is dressed in sharp frost, or dry time in spring. By some it is only dew-retted, that is laid on the grass in the way, and for the time mentioned above, the dyke being omitted, but hemp thus managed is from 1s. to 2s. per stone less value. If seeded, stands till October, viz. about five week's longer than if not seeded; it is not then water retted, but when pulled, shocked till dry, threshed in field, and the sheaves stacked till spring, then spread on grass (as here described) and dressed.

p.162 Separating male from female plant, or as it is called, selecting, is not now practised, owing to the expense, and to the carelessness of the labourers. Male used to be pulled when in flower. Mr. Low, of Wisbech, observed to me that the management of hemp is so difficult, that he believes it can be understood only by practice, not by the *best written directions*. Crows and pigeons are great enemies to this plant.

Produce and value. Forty to fifty stone, (14 lbs.) per acre from the break, from which the farmers sell it. Mr. Vancouver says average 48 stone. Average worth per stone 5s. to 7s. Is sold at Wisbech and Ely. Short hemp worth about half of long hemp. If stands for seed, produce about three Co per acre. Crops vary from 20 to 100 stone, says Mr. Scott, of Chatteris. Mr. Lawton, of Wisbech, thinks average crop worth about £6. per acre, the purchaser pulling and being at every subsequent expense. The produce is sometimes reckoned by bunches, and 550 bunches were stated to me as an average crop. 100 bunches equal about nine stones, consequently 550 bunches equal $49\frac{1}{2}$ stones. In 1805, at Wisbech, the prices were, shorts, 2s. maiden, 7s. 6d, seeded, 5s. to 6s. per stone. The merchants buy it at the farm-houses, and sell it at monthly markets at Wisbech. Dew-retting produces more, and the expenses are less than water-retting, but the hemp sells from 1s. to 2s. less. Standing for seed lessens the quantity as well as the quality. Maiden-hemp 1s 6d. to 2s. per stone more than seeded hemp, and produces one-fourth more. Another informant says, average produce forty stone. Male plant worth 2s, per stone more than female; but, he says also, the former practice of separating them discontinued.

Application. Maiden-hemp sold for cloth. Seeded hemp for ropes.

p.163

Expenses per acre.	£.	s.	d.
Rent *	2	0	0
Tithe (by act of parliament)	0	5	0
Rates 5s. in pound on two-thirds of rent	0	7	6
Manure +	0	7	6
Five ploughings and harrowings	1	5	4
Seed one Co	1	1	0
Sowing	0	0	4
Pulling about ±	0	17	6
Watering about	0	15	0
Grassing about	0	10	0
Breaking, 1s. per stone on crop	2	5	0
Carriage to market and expenses §	0	2	6
	£9	16	8

p.164

	£.	s.	d.
Expenses brought forward			
Produce			
Say 45 stone at 6s. **	13	10	0
Profit per acre	3	13	4

* Dr. Nasmith, of Leverington, says £5. per acre are given often for liberty to sow hemp, the hirer having possession no longer than till the hemp is off. The farmer sometimes takes turnips the same year.

\+ Half expenses, (viz. labour only) on 30 loads, which is thought to be as much as ought to be charged to the hemp, as wheat succeeds it to advantage without muck.

± 3s 6d. are given for pulling 100 bunches, (the bands of which are 2½ feet long) and it amounts at that rate to about 17s. 6d. per acre, viz. 500 bunches at nine stones per 100 bunches, is 45 stones. At Wisbech, I was told pulling was only 2s. 6d. per 100 bushels.

§ Supposing this 20s. on a waggon load, and that 40 cwt. (equal to 20 Co. of wheat at 16 stone per Co.) may be carried on a waggon, 45 stone, 5½ cwt. the produce of an acre will cost about 2s. 6d.

** Bounty, 3½d. per stone, never claimed.

It appears from these data that hemp being sold by the farmer from the break, pays him a profit of £3. 13s. 4d. per acre. A deduction however perhaps ought to be made for the value of the muck, as I have charged the labour on it; only my reason is, that in many of the districts where hemp is grown in this county, muck is so plentiful, that it lays year after year in mountains, unemployed, and with out sale; and may therefore be said to be of no saleable value; the reader may make such deduction from the profit here stated, as he may think proper. I should have been glad of being able to carry this account of hemp, through the manufacturer's hands, had I been furnished with materials.

To compare the farmer's profit on hemp with that which he would probably receive from the application of the same land to other crops, usually grown on it, I inquired the average product on hemp-lands when under wheat, barley-big, (which is grown instead of common barley), oats and beans, and was told at Upwell, as follows, on an average ; barley-big, 10 Co.; wheat, 8 Co.; oats, 15 Co.; beans, 8 Co.; and the expenses on these crops ; as under,

	£.	s.	d.
Barley-big. Rent, rates, tithe, and manure, as for hemp.	3	0	0
Three ploughings and harrowing	0	15	4
p.165 Seed three bushels, at 12s. per Co.	0	9	0
Harvesting	0	10	0
Carriage and expenses to market on 10 Co.	0	5	0
	4	19	4
Produce. 10 Co. at 12s.*	6	0	0
Profit	1	0	8
Wheat. Rent, &c. as before	3	0	0
One ploughing and harrowing	0	5	4
Seed, two bushels	0	15	0
Harvesting	0	12	0
Carriage and expenses to market on 8 Co.	0	4	0
	4	16	4
Produce 8 Co. at 30s	12	0	0
Profit	7	3	8

* Usually sells 3s. Per Co. Under common barley, straw set against threshing in this and following crops.

		£	s	d
Oats,	Rent &c. as before			
	Three ploughings (sometimes only one) and harrowing	3	0	0
	Seed, one Co.	0	10	0
	Harvesting	0	10	0
p.166	Carriage and expenses to market on 14 Co.	0	7	6
		5	2	10
Produce, 15 Co. at 10s		7	10	0
	Profit	2	7	2
Beans,	Rent, &c. as before	3	0	0
One ploughing and harrowing		0	5	4
Seed, five bushels, at 16s per Co.		1	0	0
Harvesting		0	12	0
Carriage and expenses to market on 8 Co.		0	4	0
Produce, 8 Co. at 16s.		5	1	4
	Profit	1	6	8
	Recapitulation			
Profit on Barley-Big		1	0	8
Wheat		7	3	8
Oats		2	7	2
Beans		1	6	8
	Profit on four crops 4)	11	18	2
	Average profit on four crops, per crop	2	19	6½
Average profit on hemp, as shewn		3	13	4
Ditto on average of four crops, per crop		2	19	6½
	Per acre more by hemp	0	13	9½

It appears from this comparison that hemp is more profitable than barley-big, oats, and beans, and less
p.167 than wheat only; and that it is more profitable than the average of the four crops, per acre 13s. 9½d. yet the cultivation small, when the quantity of land in the county suitable to it, and its national importance are considered; add also what is often obtained, a crop of turnips or cole, in the same year, and hemp will appear an article far more lucrative than most crops. Taking the course, (a not uncommon one) wheat, hemp, repeated often, and the profit will be greater than from any other, being equal to £5. 8s. 6d. per acre per year; thus profit on wheat, £7.3s.8d. profit on hemp, £3. 13s. 4d. together £10. 17s. in two years; being £5. 8s, 6d. per year. In the above estimates I have charged no interest on capital, nor other incidental expenses; such as muck, &c. as they equally affect all the crops. Great as the advantage of hemp appears, it is not sufficient to cause any considerable increase in the growth of it; it is thought, the difficulty and trouble of managing it, as well as the opinion that it is an exhauster, are the grand checks to it. It should also be remembered that the rent here charged is much below that given by individuals, and that muck if bought at a dear rate, (as it is in many districts), is another great deduction: notwithstanding however, all these circumstances, hemp is undoubtedly an article of profitable cultivation.

SECT. VIII. - FLAX.

Preparation. Tillage. This plant and hemp are cultivated on similar soils, and they have nearly the like preparation as to tillage, &c. it will therefore be only necessary to notice wherein they differ. If flax
p.168 succeed hemp or wheat, only one deep ploughing is given, and that at seed time, the land being then made perfectly clean, by picking, &c. &c. and fine by rolling and harrowing. Hemp is however often the first crop, on one earth, upon breaking up grassland. A crop of cole for feed, or turnips are taken the same year, after the flax is off.

Manuring. None.

Quantity of seed. Seven to eight pecks. Riga seed, called also barrel seed, and that of a year old, called "rested seed," is preferred.

Time of sowing. About Lady-day.

Culture while growing. Weeded by women crawling upon their knees, the pressure by the weeders supposed beneficial; rolling would be injurious.

Harvest. Is pulled if crop be not seeded, commences about the latter part of July, viz. about fifteen weeks after sowing, when berry is yellow, if stands to be seed; is harvested about August, when it is red. In the first case it is taken immediately after pulling to dyke, in which it remains about 10 days, and is trampled daily by three men abreast, when taken out it is grassed for about [*blank*] being turned after every shower, till it is of a blueish colour, and then barned. In the second case it is dyed for a few days, then stacked for about a fortnight, when the seed is whipped out against a post.

Produce, value and application. - 40, 50, 60 stones, or 2000 to 2500 beat, equal from 50 to 70 stones per acre. Mr. Vancouver states average produce 46 stones. Mr. Scott, of Chatteris, says 20 to 80 stones, i.e. 50 stone average. Value 9s, to 12s per stone. Maiden-flax is made into cloth. Seeded-flax into ropes. The cloth finer than hemp cloth, but not so strong. Much cloth is sold (by persons who do not value their reputation), as made all of hemp, which has a mixture of flax in it; to those unacquainted with the nature
p.169 of these articles it may be difficult to account how it should answer the purpose to substitute that which is dearer (by nearly half), than the article itself, yet this fraud is lucrative, for,

Flax, seeded, produces from six to twelve bushels per acre.

Expenses per acre.

Weeding		1	10	0
Pulling +		0	10	0
Watering and grassing		1	5	0
Breaking ±		5	0	0
Carriage to market and expenses §		0	3	6
		12	14	10
Produce, say 50 stone at 8s. 6d.‖		21	5	0
Expenses.		12	14	10
	Profit	8	10	0

* Land has been let by the farmer to the flax grower for growing one crop of flax at six guineas per acre, I heard of even £7. and £8., the flax being off in time for the farmer to have a crop of cole, or turnips the same year.

\+ 6d. for 100 beat, (alias sheaves) 2000 beat an average crop

± 1s. 6d. to is. 6d. per stone, say 21. per stone, on 50 stones.

§ If 40 stones of hemp cost for these expenses 2s. 6d. 50 stones of flax may cost 3s. 6d.

‖ Bounty 4d. Per stone, never claimed

p.170 If this statement be near the truth, it may be asked of this plant as well as of hemp, why is it not more cultivated; and the same answer may be returned, and in addition, that flax is acknowledged by all to impoverish land- Although a rich loam, in short the best land, be recommended for flax, it has succeeded on a strong clay at Wimpole, as appears by the following communication of Mr. A. Young. (Annals, v. 42)

"On the strong clays of Wimpole, the Earl of Hardwicke in 1797, tried half an acre of flax for experiment; produce 350 lbs. or 50 stones per acre which is a very great crop; it was seeded and then dressed, and spun, &c, the lands sown with barley and grass seeds, and those crops were full as good as in any other part of the same field, after other preparations. In 1798 another piece, crop very good, but not ascertained; oats succeeded, which were equal to other crops of that grain, in the same field. In 1799, sowed half an acre more, which was as fine a crop as any, but lost by the wetness of the season; the rest of the field was under potatoes and turnips; after the flax was pulled, dunged that part as for the other crops; at present the wheat appears to be the best in the field."

SECT. IX. - BARLEY-BIG,

Is grown at Wisbech, Outwell, and neighbourhood, instead of common barley, and has the same preparation, tillage, &c.

p.171 *Produce.* From 10 to 15 Co. per acre, and is worth generally 3s. per Co. under the best common barley.

Winter barley.

Not much cultivated. Mr. Francis, of Childersley, thinks it will be when more known, as he has succeeded with it to his wishes.

Preparation. Mr. Francis, of Childersley, has fallowed for it, and has also had it after common barley.

Quantity of seed. Same as common barley.

Time of sowing. Directly after harvest.

How put in. Broad-cast on one earth, if after another crop.

Produce and application. Fed by sheep in spring, till about the latter part of May, then is saved for seed, and produces three to four Co. more than common barley price when in demand for seed, three to four Co. above common barley; when not wanted for seed, about 2s. under it. It produces much more feed than rye.

SECT. X. - LENTILS.

Some few grown.

Preparation. Are sown instead of barley, on any second crop; sometimes on a fallow. One ploughing at seed time is given.

Quantity of seed. Two to two bushels and a half per acre.

How put in. Broadcast, harrowed in.

Time of sowing. About Lady day.

Application. Made into hay for horses, or any cattle.

p.172 Cattle having water directly after eating them, are apt to be hoven. Are of less value than tares.

SECT. XI. MUSTARD.

This plant is grown in the neighbourhood of Wisbech and Outwell.

Preparation. Often on grass land, on one ploughing. Sometimes in lieu of any second crop. Plough once at seed-time.

Quantity of seed. One half peck, or one pint per acre.

Time of sowing. Latter end of February, or beginning of March.

How put in. Broad-cast, harrowed three times before, and twice after sowing.

Culture while growing. Hoe if necessary.

Harvest. When blossom is red, (which is about August) reap it in about fourteen days, stack it in field, covering it with stubble. At Michaelmas thresh it.

Produce. About five Co. per acre, worth about £50. per Co. A second crop is obtained from what shells of the first.

Effects. It always remains in the land, and by many I was told it is an impoverisher.

SECT. - XII. WOAD,

This plant is not now cultivated in the county, it was some years since at New Barns, Ely, by Mr. p.173 Tattershall. I had the following information on this subject from the person who then lived with Mr. T. and saw the management of it, and who, though not absolutely the director of the business, appeared to be well acquainted with it. Mr. Tattershall had 120 acres under woad.

Preparation. Pasture land (that which Mr. T. applied to this plant was most excellent, worth as much as any in the county), broken up in January or February, by ploughing as deep as possible, barley succeeds it, then the usual cropping of the farm.

Time of sowing. February, dibble in at vacant spots.

Quantity of seed. About five bushels per acre.

How put in. Broad-cast.

Culture while growing. Weeded twice by women on their knees. Expense 40s. per acre first time; second time, not quite so much.

Harvesting. Pull off the leaves into skips, which are emptied into large tumbrils, and carried to mill;* which grinds them (as small seeds are ground). They are then made into balls about five inches diameter, and laid on to frames (made of splines at small distances), placed one above another, in open shed; when dried (when they will be reduced to one-fourth of their original size), they are piled together in an airy place to prevent their heating. In winter they are taken to mill again, and broken to pieces, then are removed to couch-barn, (which has a brick floor and brick-sides four feet high, and latticed windows and shutters); are there watered and turned frequently, (turned as muck is) which causes a heat, stench, p.174 and smoke to such a degree, that only persons who have been accustomed to it can bear it; this operation requires a month or six weeks, and when "enough," the woad has the appearance of mouldy sheep-dung. A hogshead will hold 20 cwt. It is sold to Northamptonshire or London,

Produce. From one to two tons per acre per year; at four crops; by the time the pulling of the first is finished, the second is ready, and so on.

Value. About £20. per ton.

Application. Dying.

Expenses and profit. The former I could not obtain, but the person of whom I had the above information, assured me that Mr. T. informed him; he cleared £10. per acre, after charging every expense, even to the shoeing of the horses employed, as he expressed himself; £5. per acre were charged as rent. The woad sold from £20. to £25. per ton.

* One mill is necessary to every forty acres.

Mr. A. Young thus writes on the culture of this plant on this farm.

" Woad was cultivated some years ago, to a very considerable amount, on the fine farm of New Barns near Ely. The land was very fine pasture, some of the richest I have anywhere seen, and valued at two guineas an acre, rent. It was ploughed up (a bold undertaking) five inches deep and sown in April and May with this plant. Weeded with great care and attention, the weeders on their knees. In July the crop made; this as is well known, consists of the leaf, which is pulled thrice in a season; and ground under mill wheels that cut with wooden edges. It is then worked into balls, two men doing as much as two horses can grind. These balls take from six to eight days in drying. The same mill grinds the balls to powder, which is placed on the floor of a room, to the depth of 3½ feet, and water thrown in at the windows every day for seven weeks; this seemed an irregular way of doing it, machines might be
p.175 invented that would neither be drunk, nor careless. When the fermentation is over, it is removed, packed into barrels or tubs, and is then merchantable. The price £20. to £25. per ton; one acre of land has produced (but mentioned as extraordinary) a ton and half, at thrice plucking the leaves. There are 120 acres of it on this farm; twelve men are kept in the house for the culture, besides many women hired for weeding. One hundred hands have been at work at once; and twenty-four horses employed; but these probably do the work of the farm. If £30. or £35. is a great crop; it requires very few figures to demonstrate that the old grass was a more profitable cultivation. It is a biennial plant."

SECT. XIII. - TURF.

So great is the value of turf, that land growing it has been sold at £50. and £80. per acre; and even at higher prices, and it appears that the land could not be applied to so lucrative an application.

Expenses.
Digging at different places, 2s. 6d. to 31. 6d. per thousand.

Drying, ditto, from 1s. 3d. to 1s. 9d. per ditto.

Rent 1s. to 3s 6d. per thousand of turf dug.
Getting from where grown to yards of retailers, stacking there, &c. &c. vary so much that no average price can be even guessed at. At Whittlesea these expenses are estimated at 5s. per thousand.

Produce. Turf is cut of various sizes, viz. three, four, four and a half inches square, and from eighteen
p.176 inches to twenty inches long. At Islesham, two inches and a half square, and eighteen to twenty inches long. At Whittlesea, eleven inches long, and six and a half inches by five inches. Many (in different places), very ordinary and of no regular dimensions. From one to three turf deep are obtained, in some places the length is cut perpendicularly, in others horizontally. In many parts of the fen the cutting is repeated in about twenty or thirty years, as the turf pits are known to grow up. There are persons living at Islesham, who remember the same ground having been dug for turf three times; good turf land may be dug three or four feet deep. Produce of an acre of turf at Whittlesea, about 222,000; in many places 300,000. A complete acre will produce 392,000 turf, four inches square, and the length taken perpendicularly.

Prices.

At March, if, good, 7s. to 9s, per thousand.
At Ely, 6s.
At Cambridge, best Islesham turf, 8s.
At Whittlesea, 10s.

Turf lands often produce sedge after they have been dug for turf. One gentleman informed me he gave for a turf land £450. that he sold the turf off it, and reaped a nett profit of £1400. and has now the land which is worth £500. This gentleman says coals are cheaper firing, than turf. I made inquiries on this subject at many places, and found that 5000 turf are supposed "to go as far" as forty bushels of coals in firing; hence, coals at 40s. per chaldron, (the present price of coals) and turf 8s. per thousand, are equal in value. Let us see what an acre of turf land will produce, calculating on the lowest of the above data.

p.177 1st, The lowest price. 2d. That only one turf deep be taken, and that four inches square, and the length cut horizontally, 3d. That no future produce be obtained. 4th. That the expenses be those of the present day,

Recapitulation.

	£	s.	d.
Produce per acre; 392,000 turf, (viz. four inches square), and the length taken horizontally, and one turf deep only taken, say at 5s. per thousand	98	0	0
Expenses per acre. Digging, drying, and rent, together 4s. 6d. per thousand on 392,000	88	4	0
Profit per acre	9	16	0

Now calculate upon the prices above 5s. per thousand, that two, and sometimes three turf deep are taken, that the cutting is repeated, that sedge is also obtained, and a profit will appear, accounting for the high price of turf land.

SECT. XIII. - SEDGE.

Lands appropriated to this purpose vary so in their value, that no average worth per annum can be with accuracy stated; some idea, however, on this subject may perhaps be formed from the following account of their produce, and the attendant expenses.

Produce. From five to fifteen hundred per acre. Price 7s per hundred, and it is advancing. Cut about every five years. At Chippenham, £4. per acre have been made of sedge. At Cambridge, retail price, for
p.178 best burning sedge, 12s. for thatching 14s. per hundred. At Whittlesea, 21s.
per thousand.

Recapitulation,

	£	s.	d.
Produce—Say every five vears, ten hundred at 7s.	3	10	0
Expenses ditto ditto cutting at 1s. 6d.	0	15	0
Profit per acre	2	15	0

£2. 15s. for five years, is 11s. per year per acre. From this 11s. are to be deducted rent, rates, and getting crop together for delivery. These expenses vary so much, I could get no average of them. The value of sedge is so increasing, owing to the rise in the price of straw and seed, and the improving state of the fens, (which decreases this crop), that it is the general opinion that land producing it, will not yield so great profit from any other application, after improvement.

SECT. XIV. - REED.

Nothing pays the occupier equal to this crop. Its cultivation, however, is rapidly decreasing, owing to the improvement of the fens.

Expenses. Cutting 4s. to 4s. 6d. per 100 bunches (six score).

Produce. Per acre 200 to 500 bunches (twenty-eight inch bands) worth £6. to £8. per 1000 bunches. At Whittlesea, 14s. per 100, viz. £7. per 1000 laid in. At March, seven guineas per 1000; bands formerly an
p.179 ell, now twenty-eight inches. At Downham (adjoining Cambridgeshire), seven guineas per 1000, a few years ago, Only £2. At Ely, seven guineas per 1000.

Produce per acre (taking price at £6. per 1000.)

		£	s.	d.
Three and a half hundred at 12s.		2	2	0
Expenses on ditto, at 4s. 3d. per 100, cutting		0	14	$10\frac{1}{2}$
	Profit per acre	1	17	$1\frac{1}{2}$

Here are £1. 17s. $1\frac{1}{2}$d. per acre to pay rent, rates, &c. &c. shewing that at seven guineas and the advancing prices the profit is handsome. Ice and wind are great enemies of this crop.

SECT. XV. - WHITE-SEED.

White-seed is the produce of ordinary fen land, and frequently of such as has been dug for turf; it is produced in many parts of the fen at Waterbeach, and Cottenham, &c. &c. A great deal of it grows in the Wash. White seed may be called fen hay, and is esteemed as valuable as any hay for cows, causing them to produce much milk. It is mown twice, and two tons are frequently produced each time. Mr. Young (in his notes taken at Cottenham) calls this produce a reed. It appears more like sedge. The soil that grows it, is "a black turf or moor, two to three feet deep." (Annals, v. 4. p. 143) The land is purposely inundated till the crop appears above the water, then (where it can be effected) the water is let off.

p.180

SECT. XVI. - OZIERS.

Oziers are grown in the Wash, as well as in-many parts of the fen, and their culture appears a most profitable application of land, paying far beyond any other to which the greatest improvement could make it suitable. Land which has been dug for turf is sometimes applied to this crop.

Culture. Put sets in April, twenty to twenty-four inches asunder; eighteen inches into ground, the same out, 8 to 10,000 sets wanted to plant an acre; cost of sets 10s per thousand. Cut sets from holts, viz. stubs of two years growth. Want renewing yearly to amount of about 1000 sets per acre. They are cut in March and May, those cut in the former month are dyked till May to make them peel, those cut in May will peel without dyking. Both cuttings are sold together, and at the same price. Are cut the second year after planting, then every year. Ice and wind destructive to them.

Produce. A load to two and a half loads per acre. A load is eighty bunches, price £18. to £20. per load. The produce from holts under four years old, of little value. The bands of the bunches are forty-five inches long in general; at Mepal only forty inches. Produce at Mepal one load, at Sutton same, and price £17. to £20.

Expenses per acre. Planting 10,000 sets, two feet each way, done by day. Weeding 12s. to 14s., cutting
p.181 and tying 1d, to 2d. per bunch. Putting into pit, done by day. Peeling 4d., per bunch. Binding, $1\frac{1}{2}$d. per bunch. Rent, 2, 3, to £4. Freight and expenses to London £4. per load, paid generally (and under all the prices I have stated) by the purchaser. To these expenses are to be added hire of premises (a barn usually) and other incidental charges, which vary so much that it is not easy to state an average of them: but as the whole expenses per acre (on an average of fen situations) are estimated at £10. I have in the following annual account of the outgoings per acre, added incidentals to make it up that sum.

Annual expenses per acre from above datum, assuming as an average crop, one load and a half viz. 120 bunches.

		£	s.	d.
1000 sets, renewed annually		0	10	0
Cutting and tying, 120 bunches, at $1\frac{1}{2}$d.		0	15	0
Peeling 120 bunches, at 4d		2	0	0
Weeding.		0	13	0
Binding after peeling 120 bunches, at $1\frac{1}{2}$d.		0	15	0
Incidentals—Rent, and rates, planting the 1000 sets renewed annually, putting into pit, hire of barn, boating, (in many situations), carting, &c &c.		5	0	7
		10	0	0
Produce one and a half loads at £17. per load, (the lowest price which I heard)		25	10	0
	Profit	15	10	0

p.182 Oziers have risen to their present price only a few years; formerly they were at £7. to £10. per load. It should also be remembered that great losses are sustained by wind and ice; the crop being often totally destroyed by them. Mr. Bull, of Ely, has been a successful, spirited, and judicious cultivator of oziers; his method may be seen in the following letter addressed by him to the secretary of "the Society, for the Encouragement of Arts, Manufactures, and Commerce," claiming their premium for planting oziers.

"Sir,

On reading over the list of premiums offered by the Society for the Encouragement of Arts, &c. for the year 1801, I beg leave to claim the premium for planting oziers. It may not be unnecessary to premise, that in the year 1801, I purchased a piece of waste land that lies contiguous to the river Ouse, and is liable to be inundated by every flood. I mention this circumstance, because the value of such land is very little indeed for any other purpose than planting, and on account of its situation for moisture, and the accumulation of fresh soil by the winter floods, is the most proper for that purpose. This land, which was more than eight acres, and was dry during the summer of that year, which was very favourable, I prepared by throwing it up into bars or beds, each being about a pole in width, and raised them more than a foot higher than" the natural soil, for the reception of the sets or plants in the spring of 1801; and in the months of March and April last, I planted each of them, at the distance of exactly twenty-one inches, that is 14,223 per acre. The season was fine for the purpose, and I have the satisfaction to add, that they have grown beyond my most sanguine expectation, the greater part being more than nine feet in height, and proportionably thick. I have spared neither expense nor care to keep them perfectly free
p.183 from weeds, and well fenced; and almost all of them will be in the spring fit to cut for the basket-makers' use, which is, I believe, an unexampled precedent for so large a quantity. The sorts consist of French, New-kind, West-country, Spaniards, and a few Welsh, and oziers all of the best quality."

I am, Sir,
Your most obedient Servant,
Seth Bull,"

Two certificates, viz. one from Thomas Page, Esq. of Ely, and the other from the Rev. Charles Mules, and Mr Lutt, jun. accompanied this letter, and confirmed Mr. Bull's statement. Mr. Bull's present ground (1806) is flourishing; it is cut into beds of twelve feet wide, between every one of which is a ditch nine feet wide, the earth out of which raises the beds so high as to secure them from inundation.

p.184

CHAP. VIII.

GRASS.

THIS county contains a great quantity of grass lands. Some under no management, and of so little value in their present state that the town charges of many parishes in which they are, would be a high rent for them; indeed from their appearance one would conclude they are not deemed by the farmer worthy his attention; there are, however, many thousand acres of pasture of the first qualify, and under the best management. Mr. Vancouver speaks of the quality of the pastures of the county, thus: "the principal division of the pasture grounds which are noticed, are first, those which produce a rich tender grass and herbage, from a loose black soil proper for feeding or grazing cattle, and worth from 25s. to 30s. per acre. The second a more coarse but luxuriant grass and herbage, produced upon a close moist soil proper for the depasturage of milch cows and store cattle, worth from 15s. to 20s. per acre. The third class produces very coarse, short, sour grass and herbage, vegetating very late in spring, from wet, cold, and compact clays, worth from 5s. to 10s. per acre; this last division owes its inferiority to the wet, cold, and compressed state in which it has lain for ages.

I. Inferior pastures.

These are dispersed chiefly over the upland part of the county, on heavy, wet soils; they are
p.185 miserably poor, and abounding with everything but what they ought, yet capable of vast improvement, with the prospect of paying amply. Opinions vary on the mode of improving them, many (the majority) being for paring and burning, keeping them in tillage a few years, and returning them to pasture again.

Others are for improving them without breaking up, viz. by clearing them of bushes, ant-hills, &c. &c. draining, mucking, and by occasional mowing. Others instead of occasional mowing, are for constantly feeding them by sheep. Mr. Sawyer, of Cheveley, is against breaking them up, as is Mr. Sanxter, of Horse-heath; the latter gentle man has an idea that he can effect every improvement of which his pastures (as miserable ones as need be) are capable, without fire, or plough, he shewed me a piece on which he means to make his trial, and which if he alters at all it must be for the better. Mr. S. will state his process to the Board, through which the public will no doubt be put in possession of it, if it be thought worthy of imitation. Mr. Vancouver observes, "these" pastures are to be relieved only by hollow draining, breaking up with the plough, and exposing the soil to the meliorating influence of all those external powers, the benign effects of which long experience has clearly proved to communicate fertility. By previously hollow draining and breaking up with the plough, in two or three years every remnant of the former surface of this class, together with the roots of all the weeds and beggary it produced, will be completely putrified. The soil thus opened, becomes pulverized, mellow, open, free and ready for the reception of the following grass seeds, proper for permanent pasture.

Six pounds of perennial red clover, called cow grass (trifolium alphistre); four lbs. of Dutch white clover, called honey-suckle, (trifolium repens); three lbs. of narrow leafed plantain, or rib-wort; four lbs.
p.186 of yellow trefoil, called black nonsuch; three lbs. of burnet, and one bushel of rye-grass per acre. In place of the latter article, two bushels of clean light hay seeds, which when properly sifted, and well cleaned, ought to weigh twenty pounds to the bushel, or four gallons of timothy (cat's tail) and four gallons of fescue (dog's tail) may be recommended in preference to the rye-grass. The crops, which should not exceed three, and which may be taken from the old pasture, before it is again laid down, will amply repay every expense that may arise in the hollow draining, stubbing, levelling the ant hills, and purchase of grass-seeds; when this description of land will be thus improved from 5s. or 7s. 6d. to 15s. or 20s. per acre. Mr. V. is an enemy to paring and burning these lands; his reasons may be seen in the chapter on that subject. These pastures afford a miserable support to various kinds of lean stock.

II. Superior pastures.

The greater part of these is situated in the parishes of Soham, Ely, Chatteris, March, Wisbech, Outwell, Upwell, Thorney, Whittlesea, and other parishes in and bordering upon the fens. The district called the "Wash," is also most valuable pasture; it is the receptacle of the upland waters, it is called in the map the "100 foot Wash," running by the side of the old Bedford river, being nearly twenty miles long, and from one-fourth of a mile to three miles wide. This land has been sold at £10. per acre, for growing oziers, but it is chiefly applied to feeding; some mow it, running the hazards of floods. Its quality is such that in six weeks it will fatten a bullock or horse, though put unto it bone lean; it rots sheep. Its fertility is attributed to the earth of the upland arable lands, brought and deposited at every
p.187 flood. Formerly the growth of oziers was prohibited in this spot, it being then thought prejudicial to drainage, preventing the waters getting off so soon as they otherwise would; now, that the waters are thought to get off too soon, the growth of oziers is encouraged here.

Culture. Frequent mucking, by some with muck only, by others, with muck and manure.

Application. First, grazing bullocks and sheep.
2nd, Breeding and rearing neat stock, sheep, and horses.
3rd, Dairying.
4th, Mowing.

Stock per acre. Bullock, half, one, one and a half to two per acre. Sheep, five to twelve. Growing neat cattle, horses and colts in proportion.

Management. The sheep pastures are fed all the year, reducing the number in March, for a week or two, to about half the summer-stock. Bullock-pastures are spared about a month or five weeks in the spring. Mr. Jennyns, of Bottisham, sows on his pastures, where they fail of plants, ray-grass in autumn; and folds after it directly. About Madinglay the pastures abound with mole-casts, and not a mole catcher near; the hills are cut level with the surface, the mould spread, and the flag returned to its place.

Mowing. No greater breadth of pasture is mown, (where stock is kept) than is wanted for winter food. All the improvement on stock is in fact from the pastures, as the winter keep, (excepting a few instances of corn grazing) is hay; one, one and a half, two, and two and a half tons of which are mown per acre. Nothing singular in the making process, except that the grass is gotten together for cocking by a horse and rope. Mowing and making in fen from 6s. to 8s. per acre. The rich pastures, called grazing grounds,
p.188 are never mown. Mr. Edes, of Wisbech, mows his grazing grounds when they become full of thistles, then mucks them. About Babraham, where the meadows are highly rented, they are much neglected, owing to an idea that they require no mending, though mown yearly; but it is notorious that they need mucking, though regularly flooded; much more then do they require it, when they have not the benefit of the latter operation.

The returns from the various applications of these pastures vary considerably, from an almost incredible profit, to great loss, owing to the great fluctuations of London markets, to which most of the stock and firkin butter go. Some idea, however, maybe formed of the value of Cambridgeshire fen pastures by the following account of a lordship in the county.

		Profit £.	Increase Pounds
3000 acres, say 1000 beasts cost £14. each, weight in, thirty stones; out, fifty-six stones; increase twenty-six stones sold for £21.		7,000	364,000
3000 sheep; weight in, 161b. per quarter; out, 20 lbs. increase 16 stone.		1,200	4,800
Wool of ditto, at $3^{1}/_{2}$ to a tod, say 856 tods, at 21s. or 9d. per lb		900	
Average profit £3. 0s. 8d. per acre.			
Animal food 137 lbs. per acre.			
7000 acres to keep sheep	24,500 in summer.		
	5,000 In winter		
	29,500		
p.189 of which	20,000 shearlings will increase 20 lbs. each	10,000	400,000
	4500 lambs hogs, 12 lbs. each	1,350	54,000
	5000 winter stock, 6 lbs. each.	750	30,000
	20,905		
200 store beasts, increase 10 stone each		700	28,000
And the 24,500 summer stock will clip $3^{1}/_{2}$ to a tod, or 7000 tods of wool, at 21s.		7,350	
		29,250	924,000

10,000 acres, average £2. 18s. 6d. per acre.
Average of animal food, 92 lbs. per acre.
Average rent of said 10,000 acres, 18s. 6d. per acre, viz.
Of the 3000 acres, £1. 2s }
Of the 7000 ditto, 17s } 18s. 6d. an acre rent:
producing 92 lbs. of food, is in the proportion of five lbs. of meat for every shilling rent. (A.Y. Annals, v. 38. p. 3.)

The perfection of grazing is reckoned to consist not only in the choice of stock, but in nicely proportioning it to the breadth of land; being under-stocked is considered a great evil, as long grass is found prejudicial to any cattle. On grazing, the farmers of this county with reason pride themselves.

Many of the pastures will not fat stock, but they pay well by rearing it.

p.190 Laying down to grass. Nothing singular on this head. A few years hence will probably afford some useful information on it, as many of the new enclosures will doubtless be applied to grass, instead of the plough. Lord Hardwicke intends laying down to permanent pasture with ray-grass, and Dutch clover only. Breaking up old pastures, has been done by the majority by paring and burning, though many individuals, as 1 have remarked, are against it. When not burnt, beans or oats are the first crop.

The following list of grasses natural to the county, was given me at the Botanical garden, Cambridge.

N.B. Those marked thus* are most esteemed for pasture.

			Called
	Anthoxanthum	odoratum,	sweet-scented vernal grass.
	Alophecurus	pratensis,*	meadow-fox tail grass,
		agrestis,	mouse-tail grass.
		geniculatus	
	Agrostis	spica venti	
		canina	
		vulgaris	
		stolonifera,	creeping bent grass.
		alba	
	Aina	cristata	
		aquatica	
		coespitosa	
		flexuosa	
		praecox	
		caryophyllea	
	Avena	fatua,	wild, or bearded oats
		pubescens	
		pratensis	
		flavcscens,	yellow oat grass.
p.191	Arundo	phragmites	
		epiggos	
		calamagrostis	
		colorata	
	Briza	media,	middle quaking grass
	Bromus	seculinus	
		multiflorus	
		mollis,	broom grass, soft.
		arvensis	
		erectus	
		asper,	broom grass, rough,
		sterilis,	broom grass, barren.
	Bromus	sylvaticus	
		pinnatus	
	Cynosurus	Cristatus *	dog's tail grass, crested.
	Carex	divica	
		pulicaris	
		stellulata	
		curta	
		ovalis	
		remota	
		axillaris	
		intermedia	
		muricata	
		divulsa	
		culpina	
		teretiuscula	
		paniculata	
		pendula	
		strigosa	

			Called
	Carex	prascox	
		flava	
		extensa	
		distans	
		panicea	
p.192		sylvatica	
		recur	
		palbesceus	
		pseudocyperus	
		pilulifera	
		casspitosa	
		stricta	
		riparia	
		paludosa	
		acuta	
		iesicaria	
		ampullacea	
	Dactylis	glomerata,	cock's foot grass, rough.
	Eriophorum	angustifolium	fescue, sheep's.*
		duriuscula	
		myurus	
		giganteus	
		coliacea	
		pratensis,*	fescue, meadow.
		elatior*	
	Holcus	canatus	soft grass, meadow
		Avenaceus *	
		mollis,	
	Hordeum	murinum	barley-grass, wall.
		pratense,	rye -grass,
		maritinum	marsh barley-grass.
	Lolium	perenne *	perennial darnel,
		temulentum,	annual darnel.
		arvense	
	Luncus	glaucus	
		conglomerate	
		effusus	
p.193		squarrosus	
		articulatus	
		uliginosus	
		bulbosus	
		buffonius	
	Luncus	pilosus	
		campestris	
	Milium	effusum	
	Milica	uniflora	single-flowered wood.
		coerulea	
	Nardus	stricta	mat grass, or mat weed.
	Phalaris	arenaria	
		phloeides	
	Panicum	i iride	
	Phleum	pratense*	cat's tail grass, meadow.
		paniculatum	

			Called
	Poa	aquatica	
		fluitans	
		distans	
		maritima	
		rigida	
		compressa	
		trivialis	
		pratensis*	
		annua,	annual, meadow-grass
		memoralis	
		decumbens	
p.194	Scirpus	palustris	
		Coespitosus	
		aciculare	
		lacustris	
		setaceus	
		maritinnus	
	Tricum	repens	couch-grass
		caninum	
		loliacum	

p.195

CHAP. IX.

GARDENS AND ORCHARDS.

Gardens.

AT Ely, Soham, -Wisbech, &c. are many large gardens, producing so abundantly of vegetables and common kinds of fruit, as to supply not only the neighbouring towns but counties, the produce being sent to a great distance, to Lynn, &c. &c. by water, and by land, affording employ for many hands, labourers, retailers, carriers, &c. &c.

Rent, Expenses, Produce, and Profit. - The tenants of these occupations are not of that description of men, who are either able or willing to give correct information on these points; I learnt, however, from other quarters, that the rents were from £3. to £7. per acre. The occupiers labour hard themselves, and every part of their families, and at all hours, doing in a day, what would be called amongst labourers, a day and a half's work, and hire much help too; the profit notwithstanding must be great, as a garden of two or three acres affords a decent maintenance for a family. Mr. Middleton, in his Report of Middlesex, has communicated much valuable and interesting information on this head; shewing the immense value of the produce of lands thus applied; but it is not to be expected that the gardeners of Cambridgeshire
p.196 should be so communicative as those Mr. M. met with, who were doubtless men of education and independence; regardless of their individual interest.

Orchards.

These are numerous and large in the same districts as the gardens; the chief growth, apples and cherries; Soham is remarkable for the latter.

Rent, Expenses, Produce, and Profit. On these the same observations are applicable as made on gardens; the rents excepted, which are double at least.

p.197

CHAP. X.

WOODS AND PLANTATIONS.

WOODS are not extensive in this county. Many plantations have been made where enclosures have taken place; they have not only considerably improved the face of the country, but promise to prove a source of profit, exceeding, it is thought, on poor light soils, any other application to which such lands are suitable. The Rev. G. Jennyns, of Bottisham, has planted with great success, as has Tharpe, Esq. of Chippenham. Mr. Jennyns has planted,

on clays, oak and spruce-fir.
on white lands, beech and birch.
on gravel, larch.
on light land, Scotch fir.
on fen, spruce fir.

In planting oaks, Mr. Jennyns does not cut off the straggling roots in the usual way, but digs sufficient space to receive them, and has found, that thus managed, they thrive considerably faster. Mr. Pemberton, of Trumpington, has planted a broken moor at about £10. per acre; the contractor, (Mr. Mackie, of Norwich) engaging to leave all alive at the end of three years.

The woods are felled at twelve or thirteen years growth, the produce made into hurdles, splints, spits, &c &c. Labour, making hurdles per dozen, 20d.; splints, per hundred, 6d.; spits, per thousand, 6d.; produce, per acre, worth about £18. at thirteen years growth (exclusive of timber) i.e. per year £1. 7s.
p.198 8$^{3}/_{4}$d Mr. Vancouver states woods as paying 15s. per acre. In Stetchworth he says "there are about 335 acres of wood (oak); the undergrowth of which, consisting of hazel, ash, black and white thorn, sallows and maple, is filled every twelve years, and produces from £8. to £10. per acre."

Observation. I was told, as I have stated, which difference may in part be accounted for from the great advance in prices; many of the homestalls in the fens are surrounded by handsome and thriving plantations of larch, firs, beech, oak, birch, black alder, poplar, ash and willow.

Mr. Tharpe, of Chippenham, has remarkably thriving plantations on very poor fen, a direct bog. Dr. Harwood, of Bartlow, has in his plantations a striking profit, that trenching previous to planting, repays the expense; the difference where he has followed this method, and where he has not, is remarkable.

Annual profit. This is supposed equal to that which would arise from any other application of the land, at a fair rent, the profit on the timber excluded. Ozier plantations are noted under the section Crops not commonly cultivated.

p.199

CHAP. XI.

SECT. I. - WASTES.

Mr. A. Young, in his account of "Waste Lands by Estimation in Great Britain," (published 1795) states those of this county at 185,300 acres. Mr. Vancouver, in 1794, calls them 158,500 acres, under the following heads.

	Acres
Waste and unimproved fen	141,000
Half-yearly meadow	1,500
Highland-common	5,500
Fen or moor common	6,000
Heath, sheep-walk	4,000
	158,500

I found great doubts entertained in the county of the accuracy of Mr. V.'s report on this subject; various opinions exist on it. The fact is, no dependence can be placed on any communication on this head; very

few persons are in possession of sufficient information on which to form a correct opinion; every one will, however, allow that the quantity is sufficient to merit the attention not only of individuals but of the legislature. Greater inducements cannot in reason be desired, or safer grounds on which to act,
p.200 expected, than the result of experience from what has been done in fen and upland, in this county. Compare the value of the former improved, with that inundated or in danger of it, and the latter enclosed, with that open, and pasture neglected with those improved. Mr. Vancouver is very full and correct in his descriptions of these waste lands; he writes. " Upon this subject, the want of opportunity to revisit the great level of the fens, and the parishes bordering upon them, is a circumstance much to be lamented, as the quantity of fenland, that is in an improved and profitable state, and that which is drowned and of little value, would thereby have been more correctly ascertained. Reference however may be had to Chatteris, Elm, Leverington, Parson Drove, Wisbech, St. Mary, and Thorney, for a comparative view of what the lost country of the fens is capable of in point of improvement by recovering the natural outfall of the middle and south level waters. The fenny land in the above parishes under improved cultivation amounts to about 50,000 acres, and yields a produce far beyond the richest highlands in the county, averaging a rent of more than 15s. per acre. Whereas the waste, the drowned and partially improved fens, amounting on a moderate computation to 150,000 acres, cannot be fairly averaged at more than 4s. per acre. Hence in this county only, an increased rent of 10s. per acre, amounting to £75,000. annually, may be reasonably expected from a complete and effectual drainage of the fens; and restoring to the country a tract of far more beautiful and productive land than is to be met with of the like extent, in any part of the island."

"Fen or moor common. In the highland part of the county, there are about 8,500 acres of this description, which at present contribute little to the support of the stock, though greatly to the disease
p.201 of the rot in the sheep and cows. These commons generally lie well for draining, and are otherwise capable of very great improvement; but until a court of sewers shall be established with powers to oblige the mills upon the several streams which pass through these moors, to be pitched lower so that the mill dams shall not hold the water up to its present height, and over-ride the surface of the commons as they now do; no remedy can be applied to this very serious evil, which must necessarily be removed before any improvement can be undertaken."

"*Half-yearly meadow land.* There are about 2000 acres of these lands lying dispersed through the hollows of the open-fields, and receiving the richest juices of the surrounding lands; even in their-present neglected state, they are rented on an average at 12s. 6d. per acre only, but would by proper draining, and being put in severalty readily be improved to 30s. per acre, as the crop which is now only mown twice in three years, would then be annually secured."

"*Highland common.* There are about 7,500 acres of this land in the county, which in severalty would be readily improved to the annual rent of 21s. per acre. In its present state it cannot possibly be valued at more than half that sum; though no alteration in the present mode of depasturing, can apparently be made to encrease the present estimated value."

"*Heath sheep walk.* Of which there are about 6000 acres." This land appears to be chiefly appropriated to the original design of nature, the surface or skin forming a tender and wholesome food for the sheep which are generally depastured thereon. The staple of the land is in general so very dry and thin, that once broken it will be ages before it can acquire an equally valuable turf or covering with that it now
p.202 produces. The substratum is generally a chalk, though in some places there is found a deep rank sand, abounding with flints, and where the surface is broken, the sand in the dry season of summer is very liable to be driven by the wind, to the inconvenience not only of the adjoining lands, but of those at some distance. Were these plains in severalty, and were it practicable to raise live fences upon them, trefoil, cinquefoil, and rye-grass would be found the most profitable grasses to cultivate. The less however, that this kind of land is disturbed, the better." On these lands the Rev. T. Hall, of Bartlow, observes, ten Co. per acre of oats, and twelve Co. of barley were produced from land formerly heath, this season (1805): "A sufficient proof of the advantage that would result from the proper management of this species of soil now let for 3s. per acre, as sheep walk."

Many of the sheep walks (in the neighbourhood of Newmarket in particular), have been converted in consequence of enclosure, to arable, by first paring and burning; and the success has been great. There are, however, those who think with Mr. Vancouver, and pronounce this only a temporary benefit, and that should it be intended to return these lands to sheep-pasture again they will never be so valuable for that purpose. Such indeed may be the case from injudicious and unmerciful cropping succeeding it, but it is not easy to conceive it will under proper management; what that should be (if success may be taken as a safe criterion) may be seen by the method which has been adopted of cropping these lands.

p.203

CHAP. XII.

IMPROVEMENTS.

THE fens of this county form so prominent a feature of all that concerns improvement, and the particular operations going forward in them embrace so many of the heads stated by the Board under this chapter, that I consider it will be the best arrangement of the subject, here to introduce the state and capability of the

Fens

A district meriting the particular attention of its owners and occupiers, even if their views be confined solely to their individual interest. Lord Hardwicke in his pamphlet on the Eau-brink business, well observes on this tract of land: "It is an object of great importance in a national view to bring into a state of more certain cultivation, a considerable tract of country, the produce of which is comparatively small, and to render fruitful other districts that now produce neither corn nor herbage, and are incapable of any cultivation at all. So great indeed is the importance of increasing the products of the country at large, that if grants of public money were ever made for local purposes, there is no object that could form a more proper ground for an application to parliament." Great as have been the returns made on sands, by the clay cart and on clays by the draining spade, much greater may be reasonably expected from judicious and spirited exertions on this tract, if experience be allowed a fair criterion from which to
p.204 augur future improvements, or, as Lord Hardwicke observes in his pamphlet I have alluded to, "unless one can suppose a number of professional men, either to be deceived themselves, or to deceive the public wilfully, and without a motive." The instances given me of the improved value of fen by cultivation and drainage, would be incredible, were not the authority most respectable. The accounts I had of money saved by buying, improving, and selling, are equally astonishing; it must not, however, be concealed, that numerous as are the instances of vast fortunes accumulated in the fens, many speculators there have met utter ruin: this indeed has chiefly befallen persons wanting skill or capital, or has arisen from accidents not now to be apprehended under a proper system of drainage.

It was the opinion of Mr. Atkins (a commissioner of sewers in the reign of James I. 1604, &c. &c.) that these fens were once "of the nature of land-meadows, fruitful, healthful, and very gainful to the inhabitants, and yielded much relief to the highland countries in time of great drought." Sir W. Dugdale (who was born 1605, and died 1686) was of the same opinion, adding as a proof, "that great numbers of timber trees, (oaks, firs, &c. &c). formerly grew there, as is plain from many being found in digging canals and drains, some of them severed from their roots, the roots standing as they grew in firm earth below the moor. The firs at the depth of four and five feet. The oaks at three feet; they were lying in a north west direction not cut down, but burnt near the ground, as the ends of them being coaled, manifested. The oaks in multitudes of an extraordinary size, being five yards in compass, and sixteen yards long, and some smaller of a great length, with a quantity of acorns near them." In marsh-land he says, "about a mile westward of Magdalen bridge, at setting down a sluice, there were discovered at
p.205 seventeen feet deep, several furze and nut-trees pressed flat down, with nuts sound and firm lying by them, the bushes and trees standing in the solid earth below the silt." The Rev. J. Rasbrick, of King's Lynn, (see Philosophical Transactions, No. 279.1702), and Mr. Elster, (see Historical account of Bedford level), gives the like testimony, respecting the former existence of trees in the fens, the latter remarking that those he saw, appeared to be sawed off. To this day (1806) are found in every part of the fens, many at so short a distance from the surface, that the plough frequently touches them; I witnessed this many times. Mr. A. Young (Annals, v. 37, p. 451), says "in every part of Europe, where marshy fens and bogs are found, if the soil be peat, trees are commonly discovered at various depths. It is the same in the lordship of Thorney (in this county); in the upland parts all sorts of trees, and in the lower fen-lands they are all firs; and it is a fact, that Mr. Wing (of Thorney) has often ascertained, that many have been met with sawn off, and lying as they fell by the stump." The horns of red deer have been dug up, and are preserved at the abbey. "The commissioners under a law of sewers made 1596, and called "neat

moor law," speaking of the fens say, "which in former times have been dry and profitable, and so they may be hereafter, if due provision be made."

Sir H. Hobert, (Attorney-general to James I.) says, "the grounds now sought to be drained (1604, &c.) are such as naturally and anciently were dry grounds." Dugdale mentions a gravel causeway three feet deep, (supposed to be made by the Emperor Severus, who was born 146, and died 211), from Denvor in Norfolk, to Peterborough in Northamptonshire, twenty-four miles, and which is now covered with moor five feet in thickness. In deepening the channel of Wisbech river, 1635, the workmen at eight feet below
p.206 the then bottom, discovered a second bottom which was stony with seven boats lying in it, covered with silt. And at Whittlesea, on digging through the moor at eight feet deep, a perfect soil was found with swaths of grass lying on it, as they were at first mown. Henry of Huntingdon, (who lived in the reign of Stephen, 1135) described this fenny country "as pleasant and agreeable to the eye; watered by many rivers which run through it, diversified by many large and small lakes, and adorned by many woods and islands." And William of Malmsbury, who lived in the first year of Henry II. (1154) has painted the state of the land round Thorney in the most glowing colours, he says, "it is a very paradise, in pleasure and delight, it resembles heaven itself, the very marshes abounding in trees whese length without knots do emulate the stars." "The plain there is as level as the sea, which with the flourishing of the grass, allureth the eye;" " in some parts there are apple trees, in others vines." It appears then on the authority of the authors quoted, that the fens were formerly wood and pasture. The engineers were of opinion that the country in question formerly meadow and wood, now fen, became so from partial embankment, preventing the waters from the uplands going to the sea, by their natural outfall; want of proper and sufficient drains to convey those waters into the Ouse; neglect of such drains as were made for that purpose; and that these evils increased from the not embanking the river Ouse, and the erection of sluices across it, preventing the flux and reflux of the sea; and the not widening and deepening where wanted the river Ouse, and from not removing the gravels, weeds, &c. &c. which from time to time accumulated in it. The first attempt at draining any part of the fens (Dugdale) appears to have been made
p.207 in the time of Edward I. (1272. &c.) many others with various success followed. The famous John of Gaunt, (or Ghent who died in 1393), and Margaret, Countess of Richmond, were amongst the draining adventurers; but Mr Gough in his addition to Camden, says "the Reign of Elizabeth (1558) may be properly fixed on as the period when the level began to become immediately a public care." Many plans were proposed and abandoned between that time and 1634, when King Charles I granted a charter of incorporation to Francis, earl of Bedford, and thirteen gentleman adventurers with him, who jointly undertook to drain the level on condition that they should have granted to them, as a recompense 95,000 acres (about one-third of level). In 1649, this charter was confirmed to William, earl of Bedford, and his associates, by the convention parliament, and in 1653 the level being declared completely drained, the 95,000 acres were conveyed to the adventurers, who had expended £400,000. which is about £4. 4s. per acre, on the 95,000 acres, and about £1. 8s. on the whole breadth, if the whole level contain 285,000 acres; (it is generally supposed to contain 300,000 acres). In 1664, the corporation called "conservators of the great level of the fens," was established. This body was empowered to levy taxes on the 95,000 acres, to defray whatever expenses might arise in their preservation, but only 83,000 acres were vested in the corporation in trust for the earl of Bedford and his associates, the remaining 12,000 were allotted, 10,000 to the king, and 2000 to the Earl of Portland. At first the levy was an equal acre tax, but upon its being deemed unjust, a gradual one was adopted, which is now acted upon. In the year 1697, the Bedford level was divided into three districts, north, middle, and south; having one surveyor for each of the former, and two for the latter. In 1753, the north level was separated by act of parliament from the
p.208 rest." * In addition to the public acts obtained for draining the fens, several private ones have been granted for draining separate districts with their limits, notwithstanding which and the vast sums expended, much remains to be done; a great part of the fens is now (1806) in danger of inundation, this calamity has visited them many times, producing effects distressing and extensive beyond exception, indeed many hundred acres of valuable land, are now drowned, the misfortune aggravated by the proprietors being obliged to continue to pay a heavy tax, not withstanding the loss of their land. Mr. A. Young describes the state of the fens when he visited them, + thus: " I found a very great portion of them in so dreary a state, that waste was the only appropriate term to be given, and the whole appeared to be in such manifest danger of inundation, that 1 could not but agree in the propriety of being particular in

* "Beauties of England and Wales," by Briton and Brayley a work much esteemed in Cambridgeshire. Colonel Armstrong's History, &c. &c. of the Fens.

\+ Mr. Young published the following in 1805. The communication is without date.

the examination 1 took of this interesting country. The last great breach of banks which inundated the north level, and laid the whole seven or eight feet under water, happened in 1770; it was 130 yards long, and 36 feet deep. In 1795, all the other banks gave way, and flooded.

	Acres
By slips in the banks	83,500
By downfall	57,000
	140,500

p.209 N.B. Calculated at the meeting at Ely, 27th February, 1795.

Much about the same quantity flooded in 1799 and 1800, by downfall and breaches in the interior banks. "For the last thirty years many inundations have taken place, and lately with increasing power and immense mischief. The remedies that have been applied by numberless acts of parliament, obtained with merely local and distinct view's, have been vain and nugatory, but the burden by taxes immense. In 1749, over a great district 1s. 6d. an acre was laid on; in 1772, 3s, added, and in 1798 above 150,000 paid 5s. an acre, upon inundated lands. In 1799 above 85,000 acres were under water till May 1800, and all much annoyed by the flood; and it was a melancholy examination I took of the country between Whittlesea and March, the middle of July, in all which tract of ten miles, usually under great crops of cole, oats and wheat, there was nothing to be seen but desolation, with here and there a crop of oats or barley, sown so late that they can come to nothing; a great loss by seeding the land at so high a price. Some crops on rather higher spots looked well; but very late. Of wheat there is not an acre; the grass itself is very much damaged, produces where mown, miserable crops of sedge, instead of good grasses; and where fed, keeping very little stock, and that badly. Yet the average rent of these ten miles is 14s. per acre, and the landlord has a drainage tax to pay of 5s. per acre, and in some districts 7s. In Ramsey Fen, I examined more melancholy instances of the want of a better drainage, and more speedy conveyance of the water to sea. Middlemoor in that parish, is a tract of 2,500 acres, which remained for more than twenty years a watery desert." Towards Ramsey New enclosed Common and Whittlesea
p.210 Moor, a spectacle still more, mortifying is to be seen to the left, on the other side of the river or had; now a tract of water, sedge, and frogs, which Mr. Pooley remembers thirty-six years ago in a state of cultivation, and producing ample crops over hundreds of acres. It joins another similar tract called Holm Fen, all under water; that twenty years ago, had buildings, farmers, and cultivation; on part of it, near Whittlesea Moor, fine crops of wheat were grown, only three years ago. One man had five quarters of wheat two years running per acre, on this land, now all waste and water. Another twenty-eight Co. of oats per acre, followed by a second crop of a last. Another had as good a dairy of cows as any in Huntingdonshire, the land is excellent and would graze a large ox." "I was shocked at the sight of this desolation. A people starving, and 1500 acres of fertile land left in such a condition, in such a kingdom, is a spectacle that ought to be instructive to politicians. We are told of the national wealth; here is a field for the exercise of it. The efforts of individuals can do nothing, this immense region of the fens depends for drainage on the outfalls to the sea, and on measures for deepening the rivers, and raising the banks which must be general. "Such is the present state of this most fertile country;" "but the evils great as they are, which have been hitherto felt, are not the whole of this melancholy business, for no doubt is entertained of the whole, or nearly the whole country being lost, if it remains in the present state. The enclosures of the upland country, the waters of which are all discharged into the fens, increase every year, and not one takes place without adding to the evil; with so powerful a cause constantly increasing, the rivers and cuts in the fens silting up, and the outfalls remaining unimproved, must in the nature of
p.211 things gradually increase the influx of water, and lessen the capability of conveying it away. The consequence is obvious. The total ruin of the whole flat district must ensue. Mr. Ground, of Whittlesea, calculates the uncultivated lands and moors, &c. at 10,000 acres. Mr. Waudby, of March, at 6000, and also a further deduction of 12,000 acres more, (at 4 in 100) for ditches, in all 18,000. To keep on the safe side, I shall suppose 20,000, and that there remains 280,000 capable of cultivation, and which are or have been cultivated but subject to inundations."* "The fens are now in a moment of balancing their fate; should a great flood. come within two or three years, for want of an improved outfall, the whole country, fertile as it naturally is, will be abandoned." Such being the melancholy state of this district,

* Mr. Golburn of Ely, informed Mr. A. Young, that the quantity of land affected by the drainage was about 400,000 acres. Mr. Gardener, of Chatteris, thinks about 300,000.

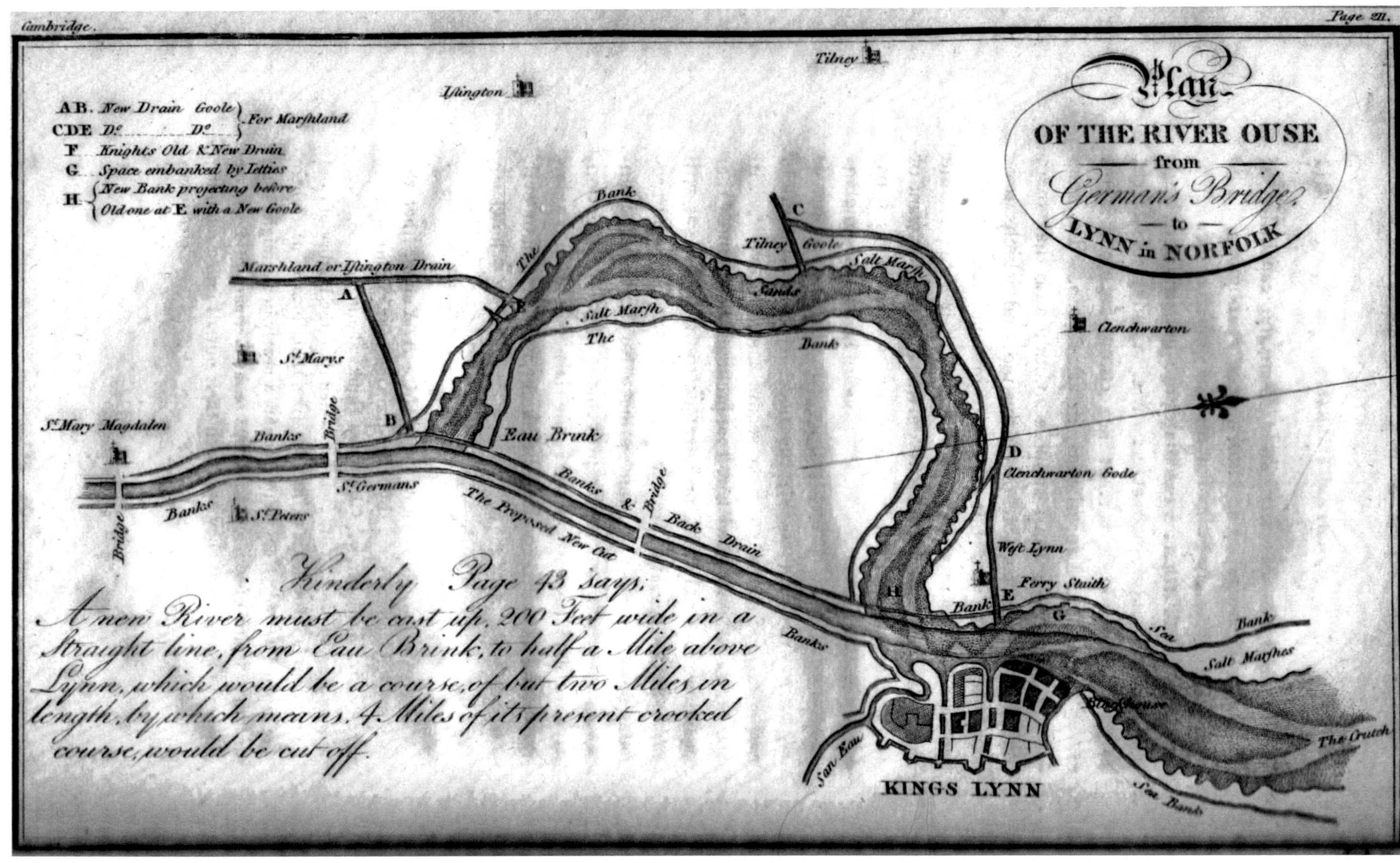
Cambridge.
Page 211.
Plan
OF THE RIVER OUSE
from
German's Bridge
to
LYNN in NORFOLK
AB. New Drain Goole } For Marshland
CDE Do. Do. }
F Knights Old & New Drain
G Space embanked by Letties
H { New Bank projecting before Old one at E with a New Goole
Tilney
Islington
Marshland or Islington Drain
St. Marys
St. Mary Magdalen
St. Germans
St. Peters
Banks
Bridge
The Bank
Tilney Goole
Salt Marsh
Sands
The Bank
Eau Brink
The Proposed New Cut
Banks & Bridge
Back Drain
Clenchwarton
Clenchwarton Gode
West Lynn
Ferry Staith
Bank
Sea Bank
Salt Marshes
The Crutch
Sea Bank
San Eau
KINGS LYNN
Kinderly Page 43 says;
A new River must be cast up, 200 Feet wide in a Straight line, from Eau Brink, to half a Mile above Lynn, which would be a course, of but two Miles in length, by which means, 4 Miles of its present crooked course, would be cut off.

and its value being so immense (which I will soon shew), the necessity and wisdom of taking some effectual steps to secure and improve it, will not be disputed, nor will it, I apprehend, be doubted that such measures only will be adequate to the object, as will embrace the several interests of the concerned, and promote them mutually. Many projects for the better drainage of the fens, and the improvement of the navigation, have of late been proposed; the last passed into a law 1795, and is called the Eau Brink
p.212 cut, + the benefit or evil, however, of which is yet to be known, a difference of opinion after passing the

\+ 1794. Eau Brink cut. It is presumed that the history of tidal rivers does not furnish an instance like that before us, where the upland waters from being confined nearly in a straight line, and to a width of 200 feet (as they are at Germans bridge, are suffered to wander as they approach their outfall into a rambling circuitous course, expanding to a width of nearly a mile, and thence returning to the same line that was before deserted.

As the case is singular so are the consequent evils. Internal navigation is rendered so defective, that boats cannot pass from Germans to Lynn without pilots, by means whereof great delays and a vast increase in the expence of freight are occasioned; and in blowing weather many lighters have been sunk, and lives have been lost.

The banks guarding the lands contiguous to the wide part of the river are supported at an enormous expense.

Drainage is so impeded that 300,000 acres of land dependant on the outfall of the Ouze, are in the greatest danger of being overflowed, nay many thousand acres of them are now under water.

Navigation from the port of Lynn to sea is injured by beds of sand, which are constantly becoming stronger and stronger for want of a proper scower, insomuch that no vessels can navigate, but such as are of a particular form and structure.

Hence foreign trade is enjoyed by a small number of merchants who are their own carriers, and the price of coals, raft, &c. is considerably higher at Lynn than it ought to be.

The remedy. It is proposed to desert the present wide circuitous bason above Lynn, and to confine the upland waters by means of a new cut to the same width at its commencement as the river now is at Germans, and to widen it gradually until it enters the old channel again a little above Lynn.

The effect. The upland waters and tidal waters flowing and refluxing through the new cut, when conveyed in half the time that is now required, will act in one uniform compact body, and with a force increased to so great a degree as to carry away all impediments.

Internal navigation will become safe, cheap, and expeditious, the weight of waters, and its lashing force against the banks will be wonderfully lessened.

Drainage, which is now impossible to be had, will be easy and practicable.

Foreign trade will be open to all the world, and monopoly, the sworn enemy to fair dealing, will no longer exist.

In a word, navigation, drainage, agriculture, will be amazingly benefited, and trade and commerce so diffused, that coals, raft, and other goods, will be infinitely cheaper, to the great benefit of the consumer, whose interest alone ought to be the main object of consideration, where trade is concerned; and, above all, the lives of his majesty's subjects will be secured.

p.213 act, having arisen between Sir Thomas Hyde Page, and Mr. Milne, (the engineer named in the act), for determining the dimensions of the cut, and there being no power in the act to compel these gentlemen to name a third engineer as umpire; nothing has been done but tracing the lines from the dimensions in the act at the lower and upper ends of the cut, and collecting the tax imposed by act ; but as this project has long engaged the public attention, and is thought a subject of importance to the county of Cambridge in particular, I have been solicitous to obtain the best information on it. The advocates for the work assert,

1st, That upwards of 300,000 acres of land will be better drained.
2d, That the harbour of Lynn will be rendered safe and commodious.
3d, That the foreign and coasting-trade of the port will be extended.
4th, That the danger and uncertainty of the navigation between Lynn and Eau-brink, by the present channel will be avoided, and the remainder of the inland navigation improved, &c. &c.

The opposers of this measure contend that none of these benefits will be the result, but that the reverse of them will ensue.

p.214 Regarding the maxim, "audi alteram partem;" I will state the opinions I am in possession of, for and against the measure.

In 1775, Governor Powell. "The quitting the old river in this crooked, ruined, irrecoverable part of it, is become at least a matter of necessity; and the cutting a strait cut is the only measure left, by which to carry on a real drainage, by which to maintain for any great time longer, a practical communication of navigation between Lynn and the inland country, by which to preserve for ever Lynn itself as a great maritime town."

In 1777, Mr. John Golborne. "It cannot fail to give immediate relief to both those (the south and middle) levels, and to lower the surface of low water at least four feet at Salter's load, Old Bedford, and Denver Sluice, and at the mouth of the New Bedford river."

In 1791, Mr. James Golborne. "I can form but one opinion, which is, that if such a cut should be carried into execution, it would be of more benefit to the middle and south levels, and also to all other low grounds discharging their waters into the river Ouse, in any part of it above the harbour of King's Lynn, than any work that hath ever been yet executed for the purpose of draining. This work seems to hold out as fair a prospect as any of so great an extent can, of doing as little private injury as may be, and will at the same time distribute its favours impartially with the hand of kindness to many worthy proprietors, and industrious occupiers of fen-lands."

"An inspection only seems necessary to convince every reasonable, disinterested, and unprejudiced person of the great advantages that will arise from it to both (i.e. drainage and navigation). It cannot fail
p.215 to operate in a degree highly advantageous to the navigation above Lynn, highly advantageous to the general drainage of all the country, above that port, and particularly advantageous to the port and harbour itself. With respect to the navigation above Lynn, I presume that it would be an insult to any person's understanding to inform him that by the proposed new cut, the gangs of lighters may at all times navigate either up or down, with much more expedition, and with infinitely less danger than they now do, all the present wide, difficult, and uncertain channel from Eau Brink to Lynn. The risque that the gangs at present run in a passage at all times dangerous, but especially in tempestuous weather, will by this proposed cut be avoided. The expense of bridge pilots saved, the wear and tear of craft, the labour of men, boys, and horses lessened; the voyage performed with greater certainty, and in much less time than at present. The proprietors and occupiers of lands on each side the proposed cut, together with every person interested in the event, may rest with security, and not be under the least apprehension for the safety of such new erected banks. In a little time after the completing such cut, the landowners will be exonerated from a very heavy expense, at which they now are, and must be liable to, for the maintenance and support of their seabanks and counter shores. In a little time after the finishing of this work, the present channel will very rapidly silt up, and become marsh. The tides will, if the cut be made, rise higher at Denver sluice, but not materially so. It is therefore most probable, under these circumstances, that the tides will not by the new cut be raised at Denver sluice above six inches. I am yet of opinion that a very high tide will not have that effect; but supposing on this account it should be found necessary to raise the lower part of the 100 feet bank, as far as Welney, for instance, being six
p.216 miles, that may be done by the Honourable Corporation of Bedford level, without any expense to individuals, or additional expense to that body. The navigation up the Ouse, &c. might be assisted by ebb-doors, and by deepening the river in places, so much as to give them a lasting and uninterrupted navigation up to Clayhithe, as perfect and as complete as most of the canal navigations in this kingdom, and the gangs would not then have occasion to wait in different parts of that river, on many different shoals, and for several days together, when they have a scanty head of water from above. The same method of relief may be given to Mildenhall river, and the result would be that craft would go with ease and expedition at all times, without unloading their cargoes as they are now obliged frequently to do."

Expense, viz.

	£.	s.	d.
Conveying water of marsh-land into new cut	1887	4	6
New cut	38098	2	0
	39985	6	6*

---

* Since this many other estimates have been made some amounting to double this sum.

In 1791, Mr. Wattie. "It (the new cut) would be a certain drainage to all those border lands which have their outfalls into the river Ouse, below Denver sluice, and would prove effectually so to that valuable tract of land called marsh-land, except the low parts of the fen, the drainage of which could easily then
p.217 be compleated by the assistance of an engine mill. I would therefore recommend the deserting of the present channel (making a dam across the same) and the opening of a new cut or channel, from Eau-brink, across the old lands and marshes to about two furlongs above Lynn. By the making of such new cut, and turning the channel, it would prove of very great advantage to those who have banks to support against the present channel, below Eau brink, which heavy expenses, in a little time, they would be released from. The old channel in a few years, would be quite silted up, and become good and firm land, the sale of which would in great measure pay the purchase for lands used in the new cut, its banks and forelands. The effect which the proposed cut would have upon the navigation in the river Ouse, would be of great importance to trade, as shortening the distance would accelerate the passage of the craft, going thereby to and from Lynn, and render the same safe at all times ; they would then be conducted by a channel sheltered between banks, and not liable to be exposed to the violence of the winds and tides, and danger of the sand-banks which now attend the navigation, through that dangerous river, or rather bay, from Lynn to St. German's bridge, where merchants and traders meet with so many disasters, losses, and frequent delays, that trade is now carried on thereby with great hazard, much difficulty and considerable expense. As to any idea or fear the traders may have of the craft being rendered unmanageable by the rapidity of the current, that would be extinguished a little time after the intended cut or river was opened, particularly if a land flood should quickly follow, as the current shortly after that would run smoothly, or in the same manner as the upper part of the river above German's bridge
p.218 now does. The effect it might have upon the harbour of Lynn, I cannot conceive would be attended with any of the dangerous consequences as some are so much alarmed at; but on the contrary would be great use thereto. If the waters coming through the cut were properly pointed down the channel through the harbour; and exertions used to assist it by throwing out jetties, &c. &c. at proper places; by such means there would be a great probability of bringing the channel along by the town at such distances as desired, § and to fall down to the crutch in nearly a straight direction. As to the danger of the current raising sand-banks or bars across the channel, as seems to have been suggested by some, I cannot by any means agree to it. They (the tides) would certainly flow something higher in still tides, against the banks above, than they now do. The banks above would be in no more danger of being overflowed, after the new cut was made, upon the dangerous tides, than they are at present, but this I think admits of a demonstration."

In 1793, a member of the committee in a pamphlet called "Reasons attempting to shew the Necessity of the proposed Cut." + "The great impediment to both drainage and navigation, I apprehend to be, the wide, shallow, and crooked channel of the river Ouse, between St. Germans' bridge and Lynn. I do not
p.219 pretend to say that this is the only one, but it seems to be the first and greatest, and that all interior works can be of little use while this remains unremedied. The cut in question was first proposed by Mr. Kinderley, about the year 1720,* and again by his son in 1751. The father was himself a conservator of the great level of the fens, and had devoted the greatest part of a long life to this particular study, and it is the scheme which he recommended and invariably adhered to. The son is no less confident of its necessity, and ventures boldly to assert, that whatever other schemes may be invented or remedies proposed, they will in the end prove ineffectual, and that how much soever prejudiced people might be against it then (1751), yet at one time or other, when driven by necessity, they will be forced to make use of it, other wise this whole country, together with the navigation of those rivers which pass through it, must in time be inevitably lost."

In 1793, Mr. Rennie, "to remedy these (the existing) evils, there cannot be a more effectual way than by directing the whole waters of the river Ouse (assisted by the returning tide of the last half-ebb) against the sand banks in the harbour, which will be completely done by the proposed cut. By this cut, the tide and river water at the last half ebb will have a greater scouring power than before. I would also recommend jetties on the shore at West Lynn, they are likely to open the east channel to sea. By scouring

---

§ "It is to be hoped Mr. Wattie will take our granaries, &c. to this channel." Thomas Brome, Lynn.

\+ "This pamphlet with the abstract of the reports and opinions upon both sides of the question, contains the substance of almost all the material information that exists upon the subject, plainly and impartially stated." See Earl of Hardwick's Observations on the Eau-brinkcut.

* Mr. Hodgkinson says, " the Eau-brink cut is only a part of Mr. Kinderley's plan."

away the sand banks in Lynn harbour, the water will be deepened; ships therefore of greater burden will
p.220 come to the town, and ride in safety. The surface of the water in the Ouse upwards, will be lowered for a great distance, until it expires in a point; hence every load, river, or drain, connected therewith must be proportionably benefited. Islington and West Lynn drains, will then have a much better outfall, and the drainage of marsh-land greatly improved. By lowering the water at Denver's and Salter's load sluices, the middle and south levels will be equally benefited, as well as Stoke, Brandon, Mildenhall, Soham, Reach, Swaffham, and Bottisham loads, with the country drained thereby, and I think it unnecessary to open St. John's Eau. The flood-waters will find an ample passage to sea, by the proposed cut; the inhabitants of Marshland will be relieved from a very heavy expense in supporting their banks. The navigation from Lynn will be more safe and expeditious, and the banks of the 100 feet are so strong, and at so great a distance, that they will have little to fear from the increased tide. "The navigation above Denver sluice may be preserved and improved by shutting the ebb doors of sluice, and deepening the river upwards. The navigation between Upware and Clayhithe will be injured, which may be rectified by a lock placed near Upware." If Swaffham and Bottisham loads should not have a sufficient declivity for carrying off the waters of their respective districts, they may be carried along the inside of the banks to Reach load, where they may jointly empty themselves into the Ouse. I do not see a more effectual way of improving the outfall than by the proposed cut, which therefore ought in my opinion to be supported by every person interested in the drainage of marsh-land, the grounds adjoining the Ouse, the south and middle levels, and the improvement of Lynn harbour."

p.221 1794. The Earl of Hardwicke, in Observations and Proposals, &c. &c. "From everything that I have heard and read upon the subject, I cannot help thinking but that the intended cut will be of great advantage to the Isle of Ely. Undoubtedly some lands will be much more benefited by it than others, for the advantage will be in proportion to the state in which they (the lands) now are. It is to be expected, however, that some advantage will accrue to every part of the isle, and that when once a good outfall is obtained at Lynn, the expense of banks and of mills, without which many estates would be under water a considerable part of the year, will gradually diminish, and probably come at last totally unnecessary.

Mr. Hudson. "I am therefore of opinion that if the old neglected river, from its junction with the Cam through the hermitage sluice or lock, into the upper end of the 100 feet river, were restored to a proper width and depth, the drainage of the fens in Haddingham would be greatly improved, and also the fens in the south-side of the said old river." "And if the shallows in the river Ouse from the Cam to Denver sluice were lowered, and the proposed new cut effectually made, I am of opinion, that in all ordinary seasons, Haddenham, Wilburton, and Streatham fens, will be drained without the use of engines." "The fens in Littleport, though lying much lower than Haddenham, being much nearer the outfall, will receive the same advantage." "Of course it (the new cut) will very much improve the drainage of the Littleport district." (His lordship offers a subscription of £500. to enable the smaller landowners to pay the tax, and when £2,500. is raised for that purpose, will give £500. more). Upon a general view of the question,
p.222 I was of opinion from the beginning, that the scheme (the proposed cut) promised the greatest advantages to the whole level of the fens; and everything that I have since read and heard upon the subject, has tended to con firm me in that opinion. Indeed if the plan is properly executed, with a fair view to the public benefit, without any part of the fund being diverted from the main object, it is likely to prove in its consequences the most effectual plan that has been suggested for the improvement of the fens, since their original drainage in the last century, by the Earl of Bedford." "To the town of Lynn the benefits will be so evident, that it is difficult to account for the opposition of so many of the respectable merchants of that place. The operation of the new cut, would in the opinion of the different engineers that have considered the effect of it, not only improve, but absolutely preserve the harbour of Lynn. The improvement of the harbour must of necessity increase the general trade of the place, by opening the door to new enterprizes, and of course to the introduction of new ship owners, and new merchants. At present the shipping of Lynn is calculated for their trade only, and for the present mouth of the channel, and no vessel with a sharp floor, and which is not of their own peculiar construction, can venture into the harbour, or at least remain there with any safety. * The consequences of this must be the exclusion of ships from other ports, which is so evident a disadvantage to the trade of a maritime town, and so great an obstacle to the increase of the general wealth and prosperity of the inhabitants, that it is scarcely
p.223 to be believed they will concur (if in truth they have concurred) in op posing the plan. With respect to Cambridge, the alarm originally conceived by the merchants and navigators must be considered as a

* "It is not necessary to have ships of any particular construction for our harbour." Thomas Brome, Lynn.

fortunate circumstance; the inquiry that it has. produced, and the provisions that are inserted in the bill, will eventually not only secure, but considerably improve the navigation of the Cambridge river."

In 1729, Mr. Humphrey Smith. "It (the new cut) will (in my opinion) be the utter ruin and total loss of the port of Lynn, for the wide space between German's and Lynn, gives room for the tides, and serves as a large receptacle for a back water to scour out their haven, which if confined by the methods prescribed, the silt and sand of the sea water would raise such a bar, that their shipping could not get over."

In 1745, Mr. Labelye. "I am of opinion, and ever shall be till better reasons be given than any of those which I have seen hitherto, that such a new cut, (the Eau-brink cut) would prove of more detriment than service to the draining the fens, by its lessening one of the means of preserving a good outfall to sea, and prejudicial to the navigation of the port of Lynn." .

In 1767, Mr. Smeaton. "I cannot agree in recommending the expedient (the proposed cut) for if the cut be not made equal to the mean capacity of the old river, it would check the influx of the tides, and if so made the event must be uncertain."

In 1775, Sir Thomas Hyde Page, Knt. "I am of opinion that if (the cut) had not at the first receiving of the water a very considerable breadth and depth, particularly near the outfall, the run of water from the sea into it, being very violent, would carry great quantities of silt, &c. from its sides and bottom, which
p.224 might be dropped higher up the river, and as the ebb at Lynn is so much slower than the flood, it probably would not have sufficient force to carry it out to sea. This danger might be the greater in a dry season, upon a want of fresh water in the river to counteract the inlet of the tide. Although in general I condemn a winding channel, when a straight one can be obtained; it has its advantages when the sea comes into it in a shorter time than it requires to go out again, the case at Lynn."

In 1778, Mr. Elstebb. "The tide waters filling so large a bason as Lynn harbour, and endeavouring to continue their whole motion, a great part, by the opening of the new channel (the Eau cut) being directed towards it, will (by the smallness of its dimensions) be compressed into it, and impelled through it with so great a rapidity, especially in spring tides, that the trains of small boats they navigate with in that river, either with or without horses, will be entirely unmanageable, will run foul, or break from one another, swinging across the river, be frequently overset and sunk; and they will for some time be obliged to wait the approach of high water, that the rapidity of the current may be abated, before they obtain a safe passage through it; consequently it will be so far from being at all times a ready passage, that great and constant delays may be expected from it, and how long they may continue, is not easy to determine. And besides the disadvantage to navigation by the interruption of the passage, there are other effects which may be reasonably apprehended from it, so long as Denver sluice is left standing. The acceleration of the motion of the great part of the tide water, in Lynn harbour tending towards the new cut, and the rapidity of the current through it, will carry large quantities of silt into the upper parts of the river, which will plentifully subside in those parts of the channel which are now the deepest, and will soon fill them
p.225 up to a level with the most shallow parts. In vain, therefore, are the expectations of great advantages to the navigation from the new cut, while Denver sluice is standing, and in vain are the hopes of a perfect recovery, and a full improvement of the fens, until the levels are properly and sufficiently embanked."

In 1792, Mr. Hodgkinson trusts "he shall convince every unprejudiced person that the execution of the pro posed scheme (the Eau-cut) will be productive of very alarming consequences to the trade and navigation of Lynn, Ely, Cambridge, and country adjacent. The tide having a less distance to flow, it will be high water at German's bridge much sooner than at present, and of course the waters will return to sea much sooner also, and before the tide at Lynn is fallen sufficiently to give them that grinding effect which they now retain by having a greater distance to come, so that Lynn harbour will not only be deprived of twenty millions of tuns of back water, but the remainder will be partly deprived of that scouring effect which it now possesses. It has been repeatedly asserted, and I believe never denied, that upon the erection of Denver sluice, and opening the 100 feet or new Bedford river, the tides being stopped by means of that sluice, occasioned a stagnation in the water against the sluice; thus a great quantity of silt being brought up by the tides was deposited there, which the tides in their reflux, being so much diminished could not scour away, by which means the bed of the river in a short time became silted up; just so it will happen at Lynn. I am aware it will be argued, that the silting up of the river below

Denver, was owing to the new Bedford river not being so deep as the river below, but that the new cut
p.226 being intended to be of equal depth with the harbour below it, the same consequences which followed the stopping the tides at Denver, are not to be apprehended here. I beg leave to observe that it was not owing to the new Bedford being so shallow, but to the great checks which the tides met with at the sluice which occasioned the silting up below. The channel from Lynn Deeps to the harbour, is preserved in a navigable state by the influx and reflux of the tides; every diminution, therefore, in the quantity of that influx, or check to its velocity (both which will be the consequence of embanking the wide space between St. German's and Lynn) must lessen the very great assistance it now affords towards keeping open that channel. That inundations will be rendered more frequent and more dreadful in their consequences, from the sudden check these raging tides will meet with in entering the New Cut, must be apparent to the meanest capacity. The current will be forced up this straight, narrow channel, with such increased velocity that the gangs navigating at that time will be rendered totally unmanageable, and be frequently overset and sunk. This scheme (the New-cut) is only part of Mr. Kinderley's plan. The late Mr. Golborne was the only engineer prior to Mr. Wattie, who publicly recommended a part only of Mr. Kinderley's plan: every other engineer (whose works have come to my knowledge), has uniformly condemned it, amongst whom are Labelye, and Elsteb."

Sir Thomas Hyde Page to Sir Martin Folks, Bart. "Whether the cut would really save or ruin the country, does not seem to be proved. We now find Messrs. Golborne, Wattie, Hudson, Milne, and Rennie, engineers, in favour of this cut. I doubt not from their experience and character of their believing it would be materially beneficial. Against it are the names of Smeaton, Hodgkinson, Nichols, and other
p.227 engineers of former times, these gentlemen from experience and character also have a right to notice; they have judged that the Eau brink cut would not only ruin the drainage, but inland navigation and Lynn harbour. These gentlemen having upon a point of science in long written reports, been so directly opposite in opinion I own, I see no way for the country gentleman or merchant to make up his mind, and at last I fear conviction, as to the propriety or impropriety of this measure, must be the effect of some dangerous experiment, which by rendering the country much worse than it now is, will shew the necessity of a general plan of drainage, of which I conceive the Eau brink cut would be no part. I think it ought to be considered as a measure in which infinite public danger is involved, while the benefits remain exceedingly doubtful. I am of opinion that it would be wrong to make any work that would lessen the quantity of water brought up by the tides, too much mischief having already been experienced by Denver sluice, which stops the tides from passing as they formerly did; the indraught was considerably lessened by that sluice, and Lynn harbour must have suffered a loss of depth. I fear the loss of the great space from Lynn to German's for a back water upon making Eau-brink cut, would bring after it the loss of Lynn harbour, for ships of the size that now trade there. My opinion, such as it is, I have expressed to be against the Eau-brink cut, as I fear its effects would be injurious to navigation, to the free lands, and also to the corporation lands of the Bedford level."

In 1793, an inhabitant of Lynn remarked. "The rapidity with which the present upper ebb current runs, in the deepest part of the bay of the haven at Lynn, from the Ball point to Common South Quay,
p.228 sometimes drives ships from their moorings and puts them in danger of stranding; more probably, therefore, neither the moorings in their present state, nor others of a stronger construction, will be able to withstand the force of it, should the new cut be made. Instead of the current through the new cut scouring the harbour, as it is pretended it will do, the reverse will probably happen. The haven above the Ball is protected from the violence of the land floods, accompanied by the strong ebb at spring tides, by that very point or neck of land intended to be cut through, which at present, by giving the river a curved direction, and a circuitous course round it, lessens the impetuosity of the current, and shelters the ships at anchor from the violence of the torrent. The banks most probably will not stand, because the gault must be dug through, and the quagmire exposed to the rapidity of the torrent. If the wide expanse of that part of the river, in the vicinity of which the new cut is to be made, and which in many places is three-quarters of a mile in breadth, was unable to receive and contain this sudden and vast accumulation of water in any of those inundations, (enumerating many) how is it possible that the narrow cut intended to be made, could carry even the waters of land flood combined with the ebb of a spring tide, with safety? and how much more must be the danger of inundation, when the two powerful agents, a high spring tide of flood, and a storm of wind at N.W. operate with impetuous force against the current of the land flood in this narrow cut. The water will, beyond a doubt, soon be raised to an immense height overflow the banks, and carry destruction over the face of the neighbouring country." He attributes all

the mischief which has arisen to drainage and navigation, to the erection of Denver and other sluices. "To prove this we shall shew,

p.229 "1st. The good state of the Ouse, and of navigation and drainage, till Denver dam and Hermitage sluices were erected, and the New Bedford river made.

"2d. The sad condition of navigation and drainage since those works were made."

"In 1423, The river Ouse was so deep between Salter's Lode and Lynn that its bottom was fourteen feet under soil. It was then famous for navigation and draining the adjacent country."

"In 1605, low water mark "was ten feet lower than the superficies of the fens at Salter's Lode, but there wanted drains to convey the fen-waters into it."

"In 1618, The commissioners of sewers found the river Ouse from Salter's Lode to the outfall at Lynn, much increased in breadth and depth, and that it had a very quick current."

"In 1619, The outfall of the river Ouse, ample and great, gave large passage for the fresh waters from the inland counties, and also to the tides from sea, inso much that the haven of Lynn had been worn wider and deeper in memory of men."

In 1645, ships rode in Lynn haven at anchor in twelve feet water at low water. The channel to sea-ward was so wide and deep, that the biggest ships could sail between Lynn and the sea with neap tides."

"In 1649, the inland navigation was so good in all the rivers, viz. Ouse, Stoke, Brandon, Mildenhall, and Grant, that keels could sail with forty tons freight, thirty-six miles from Lynn towards Cambridge, at ordinary neap tides, and as far as Huntingdon with fifteen tons."

"As the rivers were thus famous for navigation before those sluices were built, so were they also good sewers for the fens to run through." E.G.

"In 1618, Mr. Atkins says, "had the river Ouse been deepened between Erith and Ely, by removing the
p.230 weres, the fens would have been good meadows," so says Lord Popham.

In 1610, Sir Clement Edmunds said, that "the country all along by the river Ouse both in Cambridgeshire and in the Isle of Ely, being a very rich soil and well habited, was not much troubled with water, but in time of floods caused by weeds, weres, and gravels, but would not have been drowned if those stops to the floods had been removed, because below Ely the river has a swift current, and gives a large passage for the fresh water."

"In 1650-1, Denver dam and sluices were erected. Immediately after this the rivers silted up from the said sluices quite to sea, insomuch that in two years ships could not sail between the sea and Lynn, but with spring tides only, whereas before they could with neap-tides. In the haven there was then but the depth of two feet at low water, where ships used to ride in twelve feet at low water. The river between Lynn and the sluices had its bottom raised with silt sand ten feet high in two years. As to drainage they (the sluices) were more pernicious, and losses to the amount of £100,000. were sustained during the time Denver sluice stood."

"In 1713, The tides undermined Denver sluices, and blew them up (but not the eight feet dam), and since that time the spring tides, which do put up into the rivers of the south-level, drop their silt in those rivers, and the land-floods drown the south level, and drop their sullage, and choak up the Ouse towards Cambridge above one foot every year. Thus spring tides and land-floods, these which used to keep open the Ouse, do now by means of works choak it up, insomuch that the bottom of the Ouse (which was before the adventureship fourteen feet under soil is now raised higher than the superficies of the fens,
p.231 and yet, part of the south-level is usually three feet under water at May day. Thus that level (south-level) which was before the adventureship good and profitable summer land, has long been and is now drowned and impoverished; so also is great part of the middle level, and 60,000 acres of land in Marsh land and Freebridge, and Blackclose, which were before rich meadow and pasture. As these artificial

works have been by fatal experience found to be the ruin of draining, as they will also of navigation in four or five years time, the Ouse ought to have that natural course given it again which it had before the adventureship, when it was famous for navigation, and wanted only to have been embanked in some places and cleared of gravels, to have it made absolute for draining, and when the freshes have their natural course again, and the tides free admission into their ancient receptacles, and the rivers embanked, as Lord Gorges, and Colonel John Armstrong advised, the river Ouse,* Lynn haven, and the channel to seaward, will be reinstated in their ancient depth, and become famous both for navigation and draining in a short time. The promoters of the intended cut, expecting that the making a dam across the river at Eau-brink, will cause a depositing of silt, which will soon fill up the curved expanse from Eau brink to Lynn, is in fact acknowledging that Denver sluice is the cause of the subsiding of silt, and forming sand-banks from thence to the mouth of the river, as repeatedly observed ever since it was erected."

In 1777, Mr. Creasey. "It is not easy for any one to assert positively that this work (the Eau-cut) will
p.232 answer. The width of the present outfall at Lynn, being at the narrowest place near 300 yards, we ought, agreeably to what nature will require, to give at least the same width to the lower end of the proposed cut, and the upper part of it should be equal to the old channel at the German's bridge. Then it may be safe to make it, but not other wise, as under smaller dimensions the indraught of the tides, would soon destroy its banks, and might probably carry the silt, &c. and form dangerous bars higher up the river. There would certainly be great risque, as the tides come in very rapidly at Lynn."

"Correspondence between Sir Thomas Hyde Page and Mr. Milne, 1801 and 1802. "Mr. Milne agrees with the Bedford level corporation, in their opinion expressed in a paper of their Minutes, wherein they express their serious apprehensions, that if the proposed cut should be too wide, the expectation of the country with regard to the scouring and keeping open the outfall, will be disappointed. Mentions another estimate by Messrs. Golborne and Wattie, amounting to £53,000. Mr. Milne's estimate by his plan for Eau-cut, £40,000., for ditto, Marshland upper ground, £2,400."

Sir Thomas Page, says "the narrow cut proposed by Mr. Milne will not serve Lynn harbour, but that the direct reverse will be the certain consequence, aid that instead of scouring away the present shoals, they would be increased. The flood tide would be suddenly checked in entering the cut, and the velocity of the stream lessened there; while the torrent through the narrow cut above would be too great for any kind or navigation upon it. Immense quantities of sand or soil would be carried with the flood tides from the sides and bottom of the cut, and from bars and shoals higher up the old river, which the returning
p.233 ebb might not carry back again, before the upland waters had risen above the banks, and inundated the country." Sir Thomas observes, Mr. Milne's estimate of expense of executing the cut, is not more than one-third of the real expense. Sir Thomas is of opinion, that drainage and navigation require a strict observance of the dimensions in the act for the proposed cut. At a meeting at the shire-hall, Ely, April 19th, 1777, three estimates of the expense that would attend the proposed works, were proposed, viz. of £145,000. of £150,000. of £180,000. each. Such are the opinions (of which I am in possession), of professional gentlemen on this subject; I will add those of others which have come under my notice.

Mr. Vancouver. "The proposed cut presents to us a probability of lowering the water twenty-five inches at Denver sluice, and an hope that in time the advantages resulting from that measure may be greatly improved. The result, however, from the whole of these considerations ought to be regarded more as the probable consequences than the certain effects of the proposed measure. The good effects cannot possibly extend to the complete and effectual relief of the middle and south levels, these can only be relieved through the channel at Wisbech."

Mr. A. Young, (Annals, v. 43, p. 547, &c) "The commissioners (of Eau-cut), were by act empowered to borrow £78,000. and to lay a tax of 4d. per acre, on 300,000 acres, to pay the interest and sink the capital. This tax would of course raise annually £5,000. viz. interest of £100,000.; and we have seen that in the opinion of engineers, from £145,000. to £180,000. will be required, and now (1807) it is said a still larger sum. Mr. Ground, of Whittlesea, observed to Mr. A. Young, that if the Eau brink cut was
p.234 made, Whittlesea meer (1.500 acres) might be easily drained, but that the drainage of the meer without that cut would be a ruinous business, for it would demolish all their banks on every flood that came. Mr.

* Lord Gorges in 1682, Col. Armstrong in 1724.

Ground is perfectly satisfied of the great importance of the Eau-brink cut, and remarked that it must be followed by a complete scouring out of the rivers. Messrs. Edes and Nichols, (of Wisbech and Elm) assured me that all their country would be lost, if something effective is not done, for its better drainage. They are of opinion that the Eau brink cut would render the outfall all that is to be wished, and after that was executed a scouring out the rivers, and heightening the banks would finish the work. They lament the delay of putting the work in execution, having suffered dreadfully by inundations. Mr. Saffery, of Downham, contends strongly for the Eau brink cut, and is clearly of opinion that if it is not made, the whole 300,000 acres will be lost. Among other proofs that the Eau-brink cut would have the expected effect in draining the fens, Mr. Saffery remarks a circumstance that is certainly striking. At Setchithe bridge there are two drains, one the Puny drain which empties itself near Lynn; the other the Polver drain emptying near St. Peter's church, between Magdalen and German's, their mouths six miles asunder. The lands on the former will be dry, while the latter are under water. The first enjoys the same outfall as the proposed Eau-cut, but the other pursues the course of the present river, this is an experiment in constant action or the present and proposed outfalls. To convince me of the necessity of a better outfall, Mr. Saffery proposed my taking a boat to Lynn, and examining the channel below German's bridge, and he had the goodness to accompany me. I sounded every where, and the general fact without exception, that wherever there is a contraction of the channel by sand banks, or a comparative narrowness of space,
p.235 there are at low water, six or seven, or more feet of water; but wherever the channel expands, there it shoals to three, and two, and even less than two feet: this was the result of above a hundred trials; and the conclusion is palpable, that if the stream was confined to a channel of a proper breadth and in a straight line, it would scour itself a free deep passage, and the shifting evil of these sands would give way to the regulated effect of a limited and properly directed current. Mr. Gardner, of Chatteris, thinks that the Eau brink cut will effectually assist in draining the two levels but not to the greatest perfection without scouring out the river. Mr. G, asks whether the fact that the small rivers have no outfall, till the great wash is free from water, does not prove the necessity of the Eau brink cut. That cut would speedily clear the old Bedford and other interior drains, and consequently give a fall for the water of the small rivers. Mr. Bateman, of Chatteris, is clearly of opinion that the Eau bank cut would answer the purposes expected, and give such an outfall as would secure the future drainage of the fens. If the Eau brink cut was made, it would, alone, and unconnected with any other object have immense effects, but these would not go to their full extent without scouring out the rivers. Mr Custance, a surveyor at Cambridge is of opinion that the Eau brink cut would be a most effective measure, and that if it is not executed, the whole, country will be lost. He considers the effect of the late great floods as proving this, for they scoured out the outfall so much, that it has not of a long time been in so good a situation as at present. This idea is quite consistent with Mr. Kinderley's, of uniting different rivers in one channel, for obtaining a great flow of water for scouring.

The Earl of Hardwicke. "On the 15th of December, 1794, Mr. Yorke, Mr. Bell, Mr. Saffery, and myself,
p.236 went down the river at time of low water, from German's bridge to Lynn. The following are the observations that I made of the depth of the water in different parts of the channel. From German's bridge to the point where it is intended to begin the new cut, the river is narrow, between good banks, and of a sufficient depth, but as soon as it expands over the channel half a mile or more, it becomes shallow, and forms those obstructions that have been so long complained of as the great impediments to drainage: opposite Tilney Goole, where the channel was half a mile from bank to bank, the depth of water was only two feet four inches. It was of the same depth opposite a mill near Islington shore at twenty minutes past eight, and in the middle of the river opposite Tilney shore, looking into the Delph, it was only one feet ten inches, in the middle of the river at thirty-one minutes past eight. In the Delph, where the river is 100 feet wide, the depth was six and a half feet, and as the river widened, the depth diminished to two feet, and from that to three feet. At Hull's ball it was four feet one inch. At Clenchworton Goole, two and a half feet, and at the point where the cut is proposed to come into the river near Lynn, it was six feet deep. These observations were made at the time of low water, or within half an hour of it, and it is remarkable that from the observations made by a person at Denver sluice, the water fell only one inch from seven to eleven o'clock, and when it was at the lowest, it was nine feet eight inches deep. This circumstance clearly shews that there is no impediment at that place, and the soundings of the river from thence to Eau brink, prove distinctly that the impediment does not begin till the channel of the river begins to widen, and the water of course to lose its force. Such were the most
p.237 prominent features of the information which I received in favour of the proposed works at Eau brink, and, united with a great mass of other circumstances produced before parliament, were of weight sufficient, notwithstanding a very hot opposition, to carry the measure through both houses. It should

not, however, be concealed that opinions, to this day, vary considerably on the effect which would result were the cut made. Of the objections to it which I heard, the following only deserve attention. Messrs. Rayner and Hardwick, of Wisbech, contended that the deficiency in the present drainage is not the want of a better outfall, but that of better keeping the interior rivers and cuts, which through neglect are silted up, and as a proof of this they observed there being a considerable fall into the new Wisbech canal, at the same time that the lands about Whittlesea were under water, that canal began to run in assistance of the drainage, when the water in the sluice at Wisbech was at the eight feet six inches mark, it sunk to three feet ten inches; consequently with a fall of four feet eight inches, while the Whittlesea district was still under water; shewing that an outfall is not so much wanted as interior scouring, and reparations. The next objection was from Mr. Thomas Malin, of Southery, who asserts that the great impediment in the outfall is not below German's bridge, but between Denver sluice and that bridge, arising from a hard bottom of the river, which wants removing, and from the contraction of the bridges being too great for the admission of ice floods. These removed, and the interior drainage improved, he conceives that the Eau-brink cut would be unnecessary." (N.B. It is conceived these objections are answered in the preceding observations.)

Such are the opinions on this important subject; *all* agreeing that *something must be done, or the country*
p.238 *will be lost*, encourages, the hope that some effectual steps will, before it is too late, be taken. Hope may now with more reason than hitherto be entertained on this subject, the dispute respecting the dimensions of the cut, &c. &c. being adjusted, and power obtained (by act of parliament), to collect five years more tax from Lady day 1805. N.B. The tax is 4d per acre, and the extent subject to it, is 308,000 acres, as ascertained by a late measurement, consequently it amounts annually to £5,133 being interest at five per cent, on rather more than £102,000 not nearly sufficient to pay interest on the sum said now (1807) required.

If further testimony be wanted to convince any one of the importance and value of the fens of this county, I would refer him to Mr. Young's account, of which the following; is an extract. (A.Y. Annals, v 43. p. 551)

		Produce, supposing the drainage secure.	
Oats	52,739 acres at	7 quarters	Per acre
Wheat	33,036 at	3½ quarters	
Cole *	33,036 viz seeded.	3 qrs. fed 35s	
Grass	161,189	From l6s. 25s. to 40s	
	280,000		
	20,000	moors, ditches &c.	

This produce Mr. Young values at £1,000,000. per annum, and Mr. Ground, of Whittlesea, from different data, makes about the same amount.

Having considered the works thought necessary for the effectual improvement of the fens in general,
p.239 those required on particular districts of them are next to be noticed; these are their drainage individually, which, according to the arrangement of the Board, will be the subject of the next section.

SECT. II. - DRAINAGE.

The interior drainage of the fens is performed on particular districts by mills, whose working depending on wind, they are often useless when most wanted, and the proprietors consequently sustain material injury; to remedy this, steam-engines have been recommended; and I found many persons in the county entertaining an opinion that they would answer. Mr. A. Young, (Annals, v. 43, p. 569) gives the following account of one. The Rev. Dr. Cartwright informs me that one of his improved engines, at the price of £1,400. (building included), would lift six feet high, one thousand acres of water six feet deep, in eight

---

* 9000 acres seeded.
24036 acres fed.
33036

days and a half, working day and night, and consuming forty bushels of coals in twenty-four hours, cost therefore, interest on £1,400. at ten per cent. £140. and if erected for a work equal to,

		£.	s.	d.
	Four such drainages in a year, the proportion of 1,000 acres once cleared would be	35	0	0
	425 bushels of coals, at 45s. per chaldron	21	5	0
	Attendance 5s. per day	2	2	6
p.240	Suppose repairs	10	0	0
		68	7	6
	Say	70	0	0

At this rate £70 clears 1000 acres of water six feet deep, and the work done with certainty at the time when most wanted. The gentlemen of the fens are the best judges whether their present mills equal this operation of steam + Mr. Wright erects engines of various powers, and at proportionate prices, from £180. to £1000. &c. &c. Mr. E. Savory, Jun. of Downham, Norfolk, (bordering upon the Cambridgeshire fens) thus writes on steam engines to the Board of Agriculture. "From the best information I can get, a steam engine complete, I understand would cost about £1,500. having a twenty-horse power, which is supposed to be capable of discharging as much water, as a mill with a forty feet sail when in full velocity. The quantity of coals to work a steam-engine of this description, from the same source of information, I learn would be about twenty bushels consumption in twenty-four hours. This expense may be reduced, however, in a principal degree, by the collateral heat of an oven so constructed, that in the operation of turning coals into cake, or cinders, it may afford a considerable share of the heat required, and it is supposed to be worth about three-fourths of the price of the coals. The advantage that are to be derived
p.241 from steam to the fen country are almost incalculable. In case of intense frost, the uniform velocity, with the opportunities of communicating heat, would prevent the engine from freezing, to which, from the uncertainty of winds, the other engines are very much subject. The consequence is, that a great fall of snow coming at the same time as the mills have not been in a state to prepare the ditches to receive the waters which it occasions, an inundation very generally takes place in the fens; and as the waters rise very rapidly under these circumstances, after a thaw, it consequently occurs that when the mills are set at liberty from the effects of ice, they are for some days incapable of throwing against the head in the rivers, owing to the freshes from the high country preventing a discharge of water from the small into the great rivers. On the other hand, by adopting the means of steam, the engines would be working in full effect during the continuance of frost, if necessary, and therefore the ditches would be in a state adequate to the reception of the waters upon a thaw; as what they previously contained would be discharged into the rivers and at sea, at the time of its taking place; and as they usually are low in the continuance of a long frost, the circumstance affords another advantage. Until a power can be commanded at will, for the drainage of the fen country, it can never attain its full prosperity. Whether the motion is acquired by the power of steam independently of wind mills, or by attaching steam engines to those of wind (which I am informed is very practicable) to work only when the weather is calm, I must assert it as my positive opinion, (which experience and observation daily strengthen), that the benefit to the public will never be equal to two-thirds of what it would be from this description of
p.242 country, as if the means of steam were resorted to for the drainage of it. As to a district of country which requires draining, without any engines upon it at the time of its being undertaken, it is a matter of doubt in my mind whether it could not be drained more economically by steam than by the means usually adopted, although the expense of fuel must certainly be very great. Taking the average of winds, the mills in the winter season do not throw so much water in a week, as they would in one third of the time, if they went in all the velocity of which they are capable. It follows, that one steam-engine with equal powers, would do as much execution in the course of a season as three windmills; and consequently, a great saving would accrue in the first expense, and afterwards in attendance and repairs."(Communications to the Board of Agriculture, v. 4, p. 52)

Necessary as drainage is to fen-lands, there are instances of its having been absolutely ruined by it; a remarkable one is at Chippenham, at Mr. Tharp's mill, where a very deep cut was made to carry off the tail water; the effect on the land on each side (a fen moor) is, it cracks in summer to that degree that it produces nothing, and no cattle can go upon it in safety; when, therefore, fen is drained, it is necessary

+ A fen wind-mill for draining, costs about £1000. and is supposed sufficient for 1000 acres.

to have a command of water to be kept within a foot of the surface. Mr. Tharpe has done this with great judgment by sluices.

On the subject of drainage of uplands, by hollow draining I collected the following:

At *Cambridge St. Giles*. 1st, Plough as deep as you can with common plough, then take out one spade with common spade; fill up with stones and bean-straw on the top of them; drains a rod asunder, lead all into ditch; effect very great; expense 5s. per score rod, labour.

At *Madinglay*. 1st, Plough, then one spit with draining spade, distance of drains, one rod; fill up with blackthorn bushes and sedge, answers well. Expenses 2s. 6d. per score, labour.

p.243 At *Childersley*. Drains cut in furrow, fill up with wood and straw. Expenses, labour 3s. to 3s. 6d. per score, answers well, and the practice is gaining ground apace.

At *Harston*. Rev. Mr. Leworthy, puts haulm (tied at each end by barley-straw), upon the top of the cut made by draining spade, not into it, shovels mould over it. Expenses, labour 4d. per pole, answered well. Mr. L. also used wood in the same way as he did haulm, but prefers the latter. He cuts his drains across the fall of the field, regardless of the furrows; his land lays on the flat; they were formerly, high backs; he thinks the injury from levelling them only temporary, leads all the drains into ditch. Mr. L. plants in his open drains, on his low grounds, oziers, and finds they prevent the drains filling up.

Mr. Vancouver speaks of the following hollow draining.

At *Horningsay*. Some hollow draining has been lately done, in the wet parts of the open fields, between the lands; made eighteen inches deep below the bottom of the furrow, and two inches deep at the bottom, they are filled with bushes and sedge, and seem to answer extremely well, the labour and materials for this work cost $2\frac{1}{2}$d. per rod.

At *Stow cum Quy*. Some hollow draining has been done, and has hitherto answered extremely well. The lands skirting upon the fens, are a dark coloured close clay, upon which the underdrains were laid off, one pole apart, eighteen inches deep, and one inch and a half wide at bottom, part of these drains were filled with stones, the whole cost of which was 4d. per rod, the other part filled with a straw rope, the whole cost of which is $1\frac{1}{2}$d. per rod. At this time they both draw and work well, the lands thus hollow drained, are now richly worth a guinea, which, previous to this improvement were not worth 8s. per
p.244 acre. Much more of this underdraining would be performed were it not for the wretched state of the general drainage of the low lands, which absolutely forbids further attempts.

At *Steeple-Morden*. Mr. Stirtland, one of Lord Hardwick's tenants, has drained 200 acres, some with straw, some with the turf reversed, and no other filling, the whole has answered greatly, and is much to his credit. A. Young, Annals, v. 42, p. 492.

At *Carlton*, Rev. Mr. Lane, has benefited old rough pastures much by hollow draining; he draws his drain eight yards asunder.

At *Coton*, Mr. Casborne placed the top spit inverted upon the drain made by draining spade, stampt it down; it has been done seven years and stood well; he put nothing in.

I found a few persons asserting that hollow draining of uplands is no improvement, that it had been tried, (in the parish and neighbourhood of Waterbeach), and no benefit derived; others confident that surface-draining is preferable; but if I may judge from the effects I saw of the latter, much cannot be said in its favour. Mr. Treslove, of Trumpington, is completely at home at hollow draining, and has wrought great improvement by it, on his own farm. He laughs at the idea of any wet land not being benefited by it, and engages (it is part of his profession) to drain effectually any land upon which he may be employed.

At *Madinglay*. Sir Charles Cotton has used the mole-plough with success on pasture; draws the drains at about a rod distance; each drain goes into an open ditch; depth of drain about a foot only; they have been done seven or eight years, and are now perfect, and work well; have made the pasture perfectly

dry; twelve and fourteen horses did fifteen acres a day; attendance one man to hold the plough, five men
p.245 to attend horses, &c. the expense therefore in labour, may be estimated at 3s. 1d. per acre, thus;

	£.	s.	d.	
6 men at 2s.	0	12	0	£2. 7s. on fifteen acres,
14 horses at 2s. 6d.	1	15	0	viz. 3s. 1d. per acre

I never heard of so much per day being done by this plough; its going so fleet and the land lying remarkably convenient, account for it in some measure. This plough is now worked by Mr. Lambert, of Risington Wick, near Stow on the Wolds, Gloucestershire, at eighteen to twenty-four inches deep, by one horse only, having a power equal to twenty horses. Expenses 1½d. per rod, Mr. L. finding assistance wanted, and his own horse; he has now forty of his ploughs out in different counties, and Mr. A. Young, who has seen one work, speaks highly of it in his Annals, v. 42, p. 4132. Although the expense of working this plough by horses, is so cheap, it has been discontinued where tried, owing to the hazard of injury to the horses, from their stamping on each other, and the greatness of the weight drawn by some of them, and which cannot be prevented.

SECT. III. —EMBANKING.

This measure, when applied to the fens, is in fact only a part of the process of draining them. On this subject Mr. Smith, of Chatteris, has made the following valuable communication to the Board, and I found his plan becoming general and highly approved. "I find from the public papers that the premiums offered by the Board of Agriculture, include draining low lands; and indeed if stagnant water is not well
p.246 drained off such lands, no improvement of any value for either corn or grass can ever be adopted on any fens or low lands. But previously to my describing a valuable and improved mode of banking, I will concisely observe that the great level of the Fens is divided into three large levels, and that each of these levels is subdivided into numerous districts by banks; but as these banks are made of fen-moor, and other light materials, whenever the rivers are swelled with water, or any one district is deluged either by rain, a breach of banks, or any other cause, the waters speedily pass through these bright, moory, porous banks, and drown all the circumjacent districts. The fens have sometimes sustained £20,000. or £30,000. damage by a breach of banks; but these accidents seldom happen in the same district twice in twenty years; the water, however, soaks through all fen banks every year in every district; and when the water-mills have lifted the waters up out of the fens into the rivers in a windy day, a great part of the water soaks back through the porous banks in the night upon the same land again. This land that soaks through the bank, drowns the wheat in the winter, washes the manure into the dykes, destroys the best natural and artificial grasses, and prevents the fens from being sown till too late in the season. This stagnant water lying on the surface, causes also fen agues, &c. thus the waters that have soaked through the porous fen banks have done the fertile fens more real injury than all the other floods that have ever come upon them. I have been much concerned in fen banking from my youth, and though I now farm upon a large scale, yet I am still much employed in superintending fen banking, and draining low lands; not only in the fens, but also in some highland counties, at a considerable distance. I had some time back
p.247 devised the plan which I now find to answer so well, but found it extremely difficult to prevail with any gentleman, who possessed a proper district, to give it a fair trial; however, this last autumn I prevailed with a gentleman in the parish where I reside to try the following plan, which proves equal to my most sanguine expectations.

"*Plan of improved banking.*"

"I first cut a gutter eighteen inches wide, through the old bank down to the clay, (the fen substratum being generally clay) the gutter is made near the centre, but a little on the land side of the centre of the old bank. The gutter is afterwards filled up in a very solid manner with tempered clay, and to make the clay resist the water, a man in boots always treads the clay as the gutter is filled up. As the fen moor lies on a clay, the whole expense of this cheap, improved, and durable mode of water-proof banking, costs in the fens only sixpence per yard. This plan was tried last summer on a convenient farm, and a hundred acres of wheat were sown on the land. The wheat and grass lands on this farm are now all dry, whilst the fens around are covered with water. This practice answers so well on this farm, that all the farmers in this parish are improving their banks in the same manner, and some have begun in adjacent parishes. If the plan be noticed by the Honourable Board, and published, it would soon spread through the fens, and other low lands, and produce inconceivable advantage to agriculture in many parts of the British empire."

Mr. Vancouver makes the following observations on embankments for enclosing lands left by the sea; his observations arose from considering the land likely to be reclaimed, should the Eau brink cut take place. "We uniformly find a certain point of elevation, to which the sea raises its sands before they begin to assume the appearance of salt-marsh.

p.248 Here the first dawning of vegetation is samphire and a species of grass which partakes a good deal of the same nature, and here the more loamy and divisible part of the sea sediment is deposited, which gives a consistence and strength to the surface, which the larger and more gravitating particles of sea sand below are incapable of affording; and in proportion as this matter is exhausted, and deprived of its virtues by repeated crops, so we approach to an hungry silt, and the permanent value of the embankment is lessened. There are other points, and of the first consequence to be attended to in undertakings of this nature, particularly not to be too impatient or too greedy in the embankment proposed. If the sea has not raised the salt marsh to its fruitful level, all expectation of benefit is vain, the soil being immature and not ripened for enclosure, and if again with a view of grasping a great extent of salt marsh, the bank or sea wall be pushed farther outwards than where there is a firm and secure foundation for it to stand upon, the bank will blow up, and in both great losses and disappointments will ensue. The enclosed marshes on the sea side of the old Roman embankment, in Tid St. Giles, are valued at 8s. per acre, the new embankment on the opposite and east-side of Kinderley's cut, in the same parish, were greedily sought for, immediately after the bank was raised, at 30s. per acre, which difference can only be accounted for from the adventurers in the former instance having been too early in that "inlake," or from the improper treatment it has since received."

p.249

SECT. IV. PARING AND BURNING.

So great is the majority in favour of this practice in the Fens, and such is the opinion of many on it, that they consider it the " sine qua non" of the husbandry of that district; the late Duke of Bedford ascertained this point to absolute demonstration at Thorney; Mr. A. Young, thus writes on this subject. "In the year 1797, some experiments were made by the duke's orders, to prove whether burning was really necessary. It was imagined that deep ploughing would do better, but the success was so very bad as to ascertain the point most satisfactorily; the ill effect of the trial is yet seen and will be till the soil has been in grass and burnt. There is a crop of oats now on Mr. Wing's farm, which succeeded cole on deep ploughing; and while all the surrounding crops after burning are very great, this is a beggarly one, full of weeds, except on one land which was burnt, though very late; this land is good, but inferior to the crops in the common management. A more satisfactory single. trial could be scarcely wished for. Another person in 1800 tried oats without a previous burning, the crop was destroyed by the wire worm.* When is conviction to be universal on this question? It has been ascertained again and again, till doubt is folly."

Mr. Wedge, of Westley Bottom, says "burning beats the mucking cart." He thus writes to the Board of Agriculture. "I shall mention the treatment of a very poor piece of heath-land which I wished to lay
p.250 down in sain foin as soon as possible. I pared and burned it, sowed it with cole-seed, which I let stand for a crop, with a view to mellow the land and destroy the turf as much as possible. As soon as the crop was off I made it very fine, by ploughing and harrowing it very well, and as soon at I could procure new sain foin seed, I sowed it with rye. I ploughed about half the seed in, and harrowed in the other half, five pecks of rye and four bushels of sain foin. This happened to be in the first week in August. I had a very good crop of rye, and an excellent plant of sain foin; I let the stubble remain upon it all winter, which sheltered it so much that I turned my cows out upon it in the month of March, and it was an excellent pasture all the last summer. I did not feed it down close, and it now looks extremely well. I cannot finish this account without mentioning an experiment that I made on this piece of land, when I began to pare for burning. I ploughed up an acre in the middle of the piece, and set it with early dung pease, which I got off in time to sow with cole-seed with the other, and I manured it with twelve loads of muck. The

---

* I must here remark that I was assured by many in the county, that burning will not destroy the wire-worm.

result has been that the burnt part has been twice as good in every crop, and has now greatly the advantage in appearance." (Comm. v. 4. p. 91). Mr. Wedge gives also the following valuable information on this subject to the Board of Agriculture. The greatest part of my land, is poor heath on a chalk bottom, the soil white from three to six inches deep, and in many places near the tops of the hills the chalkstones are mixed with the little soil there is, quite to the surface, which although it is of a better colour, yet is quite bare, and produces but very little herbage. In other places the soil is deeper, and rather of a red
p.251 sandy nature; this produces hawthorn bushes, furze, &c. and in some places a little fern: this land is much better than the other, both in its natural state, and when it is reduced into tillage. I had always an idea, that paring and burning was by no means injurious to land when properly managed; but never to this day having seen one course of tillage practised by others that I thought a proper one, and so much having been written and said against it, I determined to act cautiously, as I had a good deal of this sort of land to reduce into tillage, and bring into a regular system of farming with other old tilled lands of the same description worn out, and not easily to be recovered with out great exertion. Indeed nothing can be more injurious than to take after burning, three, four, or five crops in succession from poor, weak, or even from good land, which has been and still is the practice. I began first with the best land before described, which I ploughed, and with a heavy roller I rolled it down very close, and some part I set with pease, and the other part with oats, after which crop I turned the furrows back without breaking them, run a drill over it, and sowed it with wheat. This answered very well, but best on the pea-land. I then fallowed it for turnips, and I found and still find that turnips will not do very well in this course without muck. With the barley crop, about a peck of trefoil, three lbs. of red clover, and a peck of rye-grass were sown, and the land laid down for two years. When this piece was sown with wheat, I burnt a slip of it that I had left on purpose, and sowed it with wheat at the same time with the other. On this land the wheat was better than on the other, and the turnips better without muck; the barley and the seeds were also better. This encouraged me to go on, and I have found it right; it is much the practice to sow this sort of
p.252 burnt land with turnips and then with barley, and this is generally followed with two or three crops more before it is laid down. It certainly ought to be laid down with the barley crop, and if it is good land taken up merely for the purpose of improvement to get it down again as soon as possible, the course will certainly succeed; but at the present moment this ought not to be done, because a certain crop of wheat will be lost. Nor do I think it either so beneficial for the land, or so profitable to the farmer, to take turnips first. These require the land to be in good tilth, which is seldom the case with one ploughing, and this is one reason why they so often fail; another reason is, that the land is generally ploughed as soon as the ashes are spread, whereby the ashes are all laid at the bottom of the furrow, which generally is about four inches deep, without being mixed with it; and being washed into the chalk with the first shower, a great part of the goodness is thereby lost. Of this fact I have had sufficient proof; all the middle parts of the summer of 1799, were extremely unfavourable for burning. I had when the wet season set in about ten acres burnt, the ashes were spread, lay all summer, and were washed in by the rain till the land was nearly grassed over. After the rains were passed, I burned some more; and the ashes were ploughed in immediately before sowing; the wheat crop from this land was not so good as the other by more than four bushels an acre. But, to return: if a crop of turnips should be obtained, you have such part of the manure from the ashes as is not lost, and the manure from the turnips for one crop of barley. Such lands as are sown with wheat and turnips, must either have muck or the fold, or both, to produce the crops, which cannot be the case. On the contrary, if wheat is sown the first crop, the ashes make it certain, and
p.253 turnips are much more certain after the wheat than they are at first. By this means both the wheat crop and the barley crop are manured for without either muck or fold (except folding off the turnips) which is bestowed on other lands and is pushing improvement further than it can be done by any other means, when manure is not to be purchased. The course that I have pointed out, will more plainly appear by the following statement; 1800, burnt, wheat; 1801, turnips; 1802, barley; 1803, seeds: 1804, half seeds, half pease; 1805, wheat after seeds and pease: 1806, turnips manured; 1807, barley; 1808, seeds; 1809, half pease, half seeds. By this course half the second year seeds will be sown with pease or tares alternately; the wheat crops will always take the fold, and the turnip land the muck, which, generally speaking, will always secure on white land a tolerable crop of turnips; * the fold will not produce the same effect. After this statement it requires but little to be said in order to prove the great advantage of burning this sort of land. The seventh year after burning, is the first time that muck is at all required, as the land is in no one part of this process in a state of impoverishment." (Com. V. 4, p. 98.)

* Chalky land.

Mr. Hustler (Mr. Wedge's neighbour), "is a determined enemy to burning upon any poor, thin soil; fen soils, he thinks, cannot be managed without it, but for poor heaths he is utterly against it. Seven years ago he burnt five acres of heath for turnips, after that barley, then oats, then ray-grass and trefoil, rested four years. Another five acres ploughed without burning, and cultivated in the same way. Last year, he burnt the whole ten acres for turnips, the five acres burnt twice gave very moderate turnips, the five burnt but once, a very good crop. Now under barley, and full two quarters of an acre difference; that
p.254 twice burnt, is so much less than the other." (A.Y. Annals, v. 43, p. 201).

Mr. Wedd, of Trumpington, approves burning.

Mr. Harvey, of Wimpole, proved its superiority by absolute experiment. The following gentlemen are also friends to this system.

At Wilbraham, Rev. Mr. Butts.
At Chippenham, Mr. Shepherd and Mr. Causton.
At Soham, Mr. Shearing.
At Whittlesea, Mr. Ground.
At March, Mr. Waudby.
At Elm, Messrs. Edes and Nichols.
At Downham, Mr. Saffery.

Mr. A. Young collected the following from them some years back.

Mr. Butts. "Where the land was burnt, a very fine crop (barley) ten or twelve Co. an acre, in parts more; where not burnt, the crop is good for nothing, two or three Co. an acre. Mr. Butts is clear the land will not recover the want of burning these seven years to come, if he does not richly manure these parts, and questions if then they will equal the rest. Another part of this field was sown with wheat, without burning, produce nothing; then oats, produce nothing ; now under barley, and that miserable. Adjoining is a piece that was burnt for wheat, which was good, and now there is great barley on it. N.B. Mr. B.'s soil is blackish, on a yellowish marl, not fen."

Mr. Shepherd (Chippenham) and Mr. Causton, "are decidedly of opinion that fen land cannot be cultivated to profit, without this operation, and the former has had many proofs of its superiority over any other system."

Mr. Shearing is of the same opinion, and thinks that "it does not lessen the staple of the soil": so thinks Mr. Ground, of Whittlesea; "nay the latter says, that it deepens the soil as he has proved."

p.255 Messrs. Edes and Nichols, "are well persuaded from experience, that the land is not reduced by burning, but on the contrary much improved."

Mr. Saffery, is for "burning fen-land once to bring it into cultivation, but thinks the repetitions usual, both unnecessary and hurtful in lowering the staple of the soil."

Mr. Golborne, of Ely, "is clearly of opinion that this operation lowers the staple of fen land. Mr. Gardener, of Chatteris thinks the same, but allows his tenants to do it, thinking it really necessary."

Mr. Custance, surveyor, of Cambridge, "objects to the practice on highland, because the staple is too thin, but thinks it necessary on fen." (A.Y. Annals, v. 43).

Mr. Francis, of Childersley, thinks this system prefer able to any other for bringing into tillage old, rough, upland pastures; whether it be intended to return them to pasture, or to keep them under the plough; he makes his heaps about one-third of a tumbril load, spreads the ashes, and also ploughs them in immediately after they are made.

Mr. Vancouver on this subject says, [p. 201]· "This practice is admissible to a certain extent upon land com posed entirely of vegetable matter, where the water is at command, and where lowering the surface is not likely to be attended with material inconvenience. Paring and burning is here the only effectual

means of quickly bringing land of this description, into a profitable state of cultivation. In such land, wherever there is a considerable depth of vegetable matter after a few years rest, the surface becomes uneven, resembling a field covered with innumerable ant-hills, and the tops of these inequalities, producing little herbage, and that of an inferior quality, are only to be improved by a judicious application of the plough, and burning about one-third part of the thinnest of the flag, that can possibly
p.256 be spared. Even here this practice ought to be permitted under certain restrictions and performed with great care; but to extend the same thinly stapled highlands of the county, thereby dissipating the vegetable mould; and leaving a surface of cold sour clay, harsh gravel, or other inert matter, is so highly destructive to the county where it prevails, the in King's and Queen's and other countryside in Ireland, where it prevails on thin high lands, extensive and naturally fruitful tracts have been reduced to the lowest and most exhausted state of barrenness and poverty; and as the like effect must on a certainty, under similar circumstances, follow the same practice in this kingdom, it is not easy to comprehend the reasoning of those persons whose judment leads to the general recommendation of so pernicious a system."

At Cheveley, Mr V. Observes; "The destructive practice of burning these highland pastures has unfortunately been adopted in the neighbourhood, and its consequenses confirmed the dislike which landlords generally have to the breaking up of old pasture ground." *Observation:* - I did not hear of these consequences but found the farmers friendly to the measure. At Shudy Camps, Mr V. says, "a striking instance of the ill effects of burning land of a fair staple, is seen in this parish; the whole field is now ruined completely, and is reduced to the state of an absolute caput mortem." *Observation:* - I was told that cropping corn, corn, corn, without end, and that great products followed the burning here. Mr. Stone of Leverington, gave his opinion on this subject to Mr. V. "On the fen lands burning is general. The toughness of the fen-sward is such that it will not fall to decay, nor be got in pieces unless burnt. Cole
p.257 seed on fen-land will not feed sheep, unless the land producing it is burnt to prepare it for the cole-seed. An excess of this practice often consumes a great deal of the soil and when the land is laid down, a barrenness where this has taken place is very apparent. Goose grass (or clivers) is the general symptom of this impoverishment. Breast-ploughing is certainly the best method; it may be done thinner, and more uniformly than by the plough drawn by horses, though the latter is the practice of this country. And indeed I do not think the damage done by burning, arises from the burning of the sward, or the quantity pared off, so that it exceeds not one inch and a half or two inches, but from the fire getting hold of the land, from allowing the heaps to lie unspread too long, and not watching the fire carefully, and putting it out immediately after spreading, before it gets such hold of the land as to make it difficult to be extinguished; the fire then hits, as it is called, and this is very prejudicial. Mr. Scott, of Chatteris, is a friend to this system, on lands which cannot be otherwise brought into tilth, viz. on lands having a sour sward that consists chiefly of reeds and rushes, and other aquatic rubbish, but he says to plough or burn lands every five or seven years, as is now almost a general custom in the fens, is in his judgment almost as barbarous and bad husbandry as can possibly be practised. It never fails when repeated often, to reduce the land to a state of great barrenness. It never fails (even when carefully done) to lower the surface. Many lands are reduced to a third part of their value by repeated burnings. Such are the opinions of individuals in Cambridgeshire on this subject, and the arguments here advanced against the measure in question have been answered again and again, proving that the evils stated have not arisen from the burning when properly done, but from the succeeding treatment of the land, and particularly from an
p.258 unmerciful and injudicious cropping. The method in the county of performing the burning, &c. is fully related by Mr. Scott, of Chatteris, and may be seen in the Chapter on Cropping.

SECT. V. — IRRIGATION.

Colonel Adeane, of Babraham, has a large tract of meadows, which have been irrigated from the time of Queen Elizabeth. Of these Mr. A. Young thus writes: "the only watered meadows of any consequence on this side of the kingdom, are those I believe at Babraham, in Cambridgeshire, belonging to Thomas Adeane, Esq.; their history is remarkable. Pallavicino, who was collector of Peter's pence in England, at the death of Queen Mary, having £30,000. or £40,000. in his hands, had the art to turn protestant on the accession of Queen Elizabeth, and appropriated the money to his own use; he bought with it the estate at Babraham, and other lands near Bournbridge; and procuring a grant from the crown, of the river which passes through them, was enabled legally to build a sluice across it, and throw as much of the water as was necessary into a new canal of irrigation, which he dug to receive it in the method so well known, and commonly practised in Italy long before that period. In the first week of April I examined

the works. The river of which this good use is made, passes from Linton to Abington, then by
p.259 Bournbridge and Babraham, and falls into the Cam at Shelford. No similar use has been made of its waters either above Babraham or below it, though the effect has been seen in this improvement during the long course of two hundred and forty years, which is a remarkable instance of stupidity; the Granta is another stream which runs almost parallel with that of Bournbridge, and which passes by Audley End and Chesterford. I do not know if any irrigation is carried on by means of it, but I take it for granted there is none. The sluice made across the river by Pallavicino is about a quarter of a mile above Bournbridge; it is well executed, but in want of repairs; inscriptions on the stone work record to what height, by the original grant, there is a power of raising the water; the deviation is of a considerable body, a canal that carries a stream six or seven feet broad, by three deep; it is thrown over a meadow immediately behind Mr. Phipps's inn, and in his occupation, and the range watered extends from thence through Babraham, to the amount of about three hundred acres. Since the rivers run, as rivers generally do, in the lowest part of the vale, it gives an opportunity of carrying the water equally on either side. Pallavicino accordingly erected two sluices for raising the water on both sides; one as I have mentioned above Bournbridge for the lands on the right of the river, and another about a quarter of a mile below the inn, for throwing the stream over those on the left. The canals and the sluices are all well designed, and are the work of a man evidently well acquainted with the practice; but in taking the water from them for spreading it by small channels over the meadows, there does not seem to be the least intelligence or knowledge of the husbandry of watering. No other art is exerted, but that merely of opening in the bank of the river small cuts for letting the water flow on to the meadows always laterally, and never
p.260 longitudinally, so necessary in works of this kind. The water then finds its own distribution, and so irregularly, that many parts receive too much, and others none at all. From the traces left of small channels in different parts of the meadows, I suspect that the ancient distribution formed under Pallavicino is lost, and that we see nothing at present but the miserable patch-work of workmen ignorant of the business. In the regulation of the meadows by lease, and in the rules of watering, circumstances are found not easy to understand. The irrigation begins on Easter Monday, and never sooner than two weeks before; an appointed irrigator goes round the whole range of meadows, twice in seven weeks, giving every tenant his share. There are two waterings, each of three weeks; and after seven are expired, none whatever. The tenants are also excluded by lease from mowing more than once; yet such is the immense benefit of the practice, that though the irrigation is so ill understood and executed, and not withstanding the absurd regulations of the leases, these meadows would let more readily at 30s. an acre with the water, than they would at 10s. without it. I cannot well conceive why, with plenty of water, that irrigation which ought to last almost through the year, is restrained to seven weeks, or why in a kingdom where so many watered meadows are successively mown two, three, and even four times, these should be cut but once. The stream runs through Abington above a mile, it comes to Bournbridge but no irrigating. What a loss to individuals and the public, that such valuable opportunities should be so utterly neglected." (Annals, v. 216, p. 177).

I viewed these meadows, and found the irrigation still carrying on, but the benefit much lessened by the right of scouring out certain places being litigated. The land-lord covenants to irrigate in a specified
p.261 degree, and when he cannot do it, allows his tenant 30s. per acre: this shews stronger than argument, the value of the operation; not withstanding, however, it is so great, Mr. Darnton (a tenant) says occasional mucking is also necessary. Mr. W. Smith, in his "Observations on the Utility, Form, and management of Water Meadows, &c. &c." speaking of the Babraham meadows, says (p. 116 &c.) "I went purposely to see them. The feeder crosses the turnpike road from Newmarket to London at the smallest arch of the two, by Bournbridge. The water is directed from its original channel in the grounds belonging to J. Mortlock, Esq. and continued for two miles below, through the village of Babraham. The principal feeder, which follows the level of the ground in a very winding form, may be said with the hatches to constitute all the works, for nothing else can be now discovered by anyone unacquainted with the construction of water meads. The various grasses and weeds in blossom, and in different stages of growth, and of various shades of green, just enable me to discover that very small catch drains had at some time been made, but it appears doubtful if they were ever numerous or capacious enough or properly disposed; most of them do not appear to be of any service to the meadows. The above indications now clearly prove that the water does an infinite deal of good on some parts, and injury, for want of proper form, on others. The good parts, are small indeed, but sufficient to prove the practicability of making all the other equally abundant, besides the addition of an extraordinary crop of good feed in the spring, which by the present rule of putting on the water at Easter is certainly lost. I was informed that the occupiers were afraid of rotting their sheep, and they are therefore contented with

the imperfect proceedings which give them a tolerable crop of hay. These circumstances, and the form
p.262 of the works seem to prove that they were not designed by any person from Wiltshire, and that the possessors are totally unacquainted with the management and utility of water meadows in that county."

Mr. Scott, of Chatteris, recommends irrigation in the fens. Mr. A. Young says, " Mr. Scott, of Chatteris in Cambridgeshire, is of opinion, that there might be very great improvements made by this practice in the fens, to which they are exceedingly well adapted. He thinks this the great object of all, and he partly founds this observation on the fact which he has often witnessed in seventeen years residence, that a breach of banks, wherever it happens, is attended, from the deposition of the muddy sediment, with a very great improvement, however ruinous at the time. The soak of the bank is quite a different thing, for the water comes strained of its rich qualities and is left too long; but under a command at right seasons, the effect would be exceedingly great, and improve the land much." (Annals, v. 40, 0. 464). Mr. A. Young relates the following, which appears to prove Mr. Scott's ideas on this subject correct.

"A gentleman near Denver sluice, more than twenty years ago, observing the extreme muddiness of the water of the Ouse, let it in upon his land which he had slightly banked for that purpose, and used his mill for throwing it back, clear after it had deposited its silt; by this method he raised his soil above two feet in no long time. The advantage was very great, but not followed by any other person.". (Annals, v. 44, p. 186).

p.263

SECT. VI. — MANURING.

The common process with farm-yard muck, is to carry it to a hill and turn it over, or to turn it over in the yard, and then carry it on the land; very few composts are made. Some marling has been done, but to no great extent. Mr. Godfrey, of Kennett, carried that which he found on his farm, and thinks it did not answer the purpose; his soil, "a light gravel, dry and chalky, under which is a very fair marl." Pigeons dung is used as a top-dressing to wheat, twenty bushels per acre at 8d. per bushel. The following manures are also used: soot, twenty bushels per acre at 2d. rabbit's down and their trimmings, thirty bushels per acre, at $7^1/_2$d.; oil-dust, at about four Co. per acre, at about 10s. 6d. per Co. 1000 cakes will produce 22 Co. of dust, which cost 10s. 6d. per Co. when cakes are eleven guineas per 1000. Malt-chives, forty bushels per acre; at 9d, a fish called stickle-backs, twenty bushels per acre at $7^1/_2$ d. * N.B. Soot is supposed to prevent the progress of the wire worm in wheat.

Professor Harwood, of Bartlow uses cinder-dust thirty bushels per acre; cost at Cam. (exclusive of carriage eleven miles) 2d. per bushel; thinks it equal to folding, sows it on fallows immediately before wheat sowing; Mr. Wedge, of Westley Bottom, is an advocate for long-muck. Mr. Cole, of Quy, Rev. Mr. Brown, of Connington, carry muck and mould on separately. Mr. Burleigh, of Barnwell, waters his
p.264 pastures with the draining of his yard, and finds great benefit. One-tenth of the cost of purchased manures is allowed the farmer by many tithe gatherers. Rev. Mr. Lane, of Carlton, approves potash on pastures after draining them; he thinks gathering stones prejudicial, and will not suffer it even for roads. Mr. Wedd, of Trumpington, thinks no manures except dung pay for purchase and carriage. At Wisbech price of muck has risen within a few years, from nothing to 5s. per load carried on. At Chatteris, and indeed in many parishes bordering on the fens, there is such abundance of muck that the farmers know not what to do with it. At Babraham, Mr. Darnton has found composts (muck and earth) preferable to muck alone; he has tried lime, and it did not answer his purpose, he found it impoverished his lands: a light gentle soil, on a gravel. At Harston, Rev. Mr. Leworthy makes composts; has tried lime thus: to every tumbril load of moulds while laying on a heap in the field, he puts two bushels of unslaked lime, covers the lime with the moulds, lets them lie three or four days, then spreads them; cost £5. to £6. per acre, improves the soil; insures a crop of turnips. At Whittlesea, Mr. Boyce mixes the sweepings of the streets, (which are collected and delivered to him gratis) with farm-yard muck, and finds the benefit great. In the neighbourhood of Cambridge the farmers purchase the sweepings of the streets, &c. of that town, of the scavenger, at 2s. 6d. per tumbril load. The corporation of Cambridge do not now give more than one-third of the sum they gave only a few years since for sweeping the streets, &c. which shews the increase value of manures. At Childersley, Mr. Francis prefers composts to raw muck. At Leverington, Mr. Stone says, "pigeon dung and soot are sometimes sown upon marsh land and high land

---

* These are used after having been mixed, a layer of earth, and a layer of fish and turned over, and when decayed, carried on the lands. If carried on before this process, the vermin would take them off.

fallows, whereon turnips or cole-seed are sown, and sometimes soot upon wheat at spring, to embitter
p.265 the surface and upper stratum of the land, to make the wire-worms eating the wheat retreat from it; and when this has been used it has always succeeded, there having been a vast yield after it; when if it had not been tried it has been believed the crop would have been entirely destroyed; twenty bushels per acre is the, quantity generally used. Wire-worms are the greatest annoyance we experience in our husbandry, they are yellow in their colour, and resemble the centipede, from the number of their feet, but not quite so long in their bodies"; the heavy and light soils are equally subject to them. No particular attention is paid to the making of dung hills, nor do I see that our country furnishes any thing likely to give rise to the practice. To clay our light silty lands would be the first and greatest improvement, and this I fear must ever be retarded by the badness of the roads, and the dearness and scarcity of labourers; the manure in our straw-yards we are very careful of, and think it much improved by caking our beasts upon it with linseed cakes." In the neighbourhood of Cambridge, and in most upland parishes, cottagers' muck is sold at 2s. 6d. per cart load. Rubbish of buildings at 6d. per load. In the fens the chief manure is the ashes from burning, these are almost generally spread and ploughed in immediately after burning. The ashes from turf are esteemed of so little value, that those having them, can by favour only get them taken away; they are carried to the nearest arable upland. At Fenny Ditton about forty loads per acre of clay have been carried on to fen-land, and wrought great improvement.

p.266

CHAP. XIII.

LIVE-STOCK.

SECT. I. - COWS.

THESE are mostly the horned breed of the county, and are called by its name; there are, however, cows of various kinds in every parish. Mr. Vancouver has attempted to specify them, viz. the Suffolk polled, the Craven, Short horned Yorkshire, Derby, Welsh, Leicester, Fifeshire, Gloucester brown, and the common Cambridgeshire. An opinion prevails at Islesham that the Suffolk Cow will not thrive in the fens. Mr. Fuller (one of the farmers) has had, he conceives, proof of it, by having purchased some from Suffolk, and having kept them with his other Cows two years, during which they gradually declined; he sold them to the person of whom he bought them, and they were soon restored to their original health, &c. &c. I did not find the rot in cows, and their frequency of slipping calf existing to the degree mentioned by Mr Vancouver. The butchers will give more for a Cambridgeshire calf than for a Suffolk one, fancying the former whiter veal. Even the calves of one parish in the county, are preferred to those of another in it. Calves for rearing are weaned at four days old, and kept on milk, and afterwards on hay,
p.267 turnips, potatoes, &c. &c. from four to nine months, according to the time they "fall." Rev. Mr. Leworthy, of Harston, lets his calves, which he fattens, drink the milk ten weeks, and is paid about 10s. 6d. per week, selling them at five guineas.

Mr. Darnton, of Babraham, keeps the South Wales cow, and thinks they produce less milk than the Suffolk, but of so superior a quality that it yields more cream; this was acknowledged by his dairy woman, a Suffolk one. He thinks cows have paid him better than grazing. Lord Hardwicke has a fine and beautiful dairy of short-horned cows, fed in winter on hay and potatoes; they appeared in too high condition for profit, all the calves are reared, keeping them three or four months before turning out. At Cottenham (where the famous cheese called by its name are made), I inquired whether the excellency of their cheese was to be ascribed to any particular process in making them, or to what other cause; and the general opinion seemed to be that it was owing to the nature of their grass. The dairy-women of Cambridgeshire are not so communicative on the score of their art, as their husbands are in theirs; none of them know how much butter or cheese they made, or milk their cows gave. Whether Mr. Vancouver got in Cambridgeshire, the following directions for preparing the runnet, I know not; but as I am informed they are good, I insert them. "In preparing the rennet for the purpose of making cheese, which is here brought to very great perfection, nothing more is necessary than salting down the bags, in which state they remain for twelve months; about six of these bags will make two gallons of brine, strong enough to suspend a new laid egg, which being put into a jar, is fit for use in about a month, when a gill of it to every four gallons of new milk, or warmed as from the cow is sufficient; the milk should all be
p.268 of the same age or meal, and much depends upon breaking the curd with the hands, for unless that is done very completely, the whey cannot be expressed, any of which remaining in the cheese, communicates a harsh fiery taste, produces the blue mould, and leaves the cheese full of holes, or cells

like a honey-comb. In short the dairy-maid's attention should never be called off, or diverted from the very essential part of the process of breaking the curd."

The farmers whose wives attend the dairy, say nothing pays better than cows; but all agree they are unprofitable unless that is the case. The butter is sold rolled up in pieces of a yard long, and about two inches in circumference, this is done for the conveniency of colleges, where it is cut into pieces called "parts," and so sent to table; its quality is nowhere excelled. Suckling of calves, and making of butter is the chief cow system; there is not much cheese made, except the noted ones of Soham and Cottenham. The suckling season is from Michaelmas to Lady-day. It requires on an average two cows to fatten a calf. The profit of cows is said to be much lessened by the increased price of cooperage, firing, &c. and fewer are kept, owing to the difficulty of getting men to milk, without extra wages. The cows when at a distance from home are milked in the pasture, and the milk brought home by a horse or ass in tubs slung across: women could not do this work, the travelling being (after the least rain), very bad, even when there is no water to go through.

SECT. II. - BULLOCKS.

These are of various sorts; the stock of the county, and from Norfolk to Suffolk are the kinds generally
p.269 reared. Those bought at an age for grazing, are Galloway, Scots, and other north country breeds, and for the best part of the fens and superior pastures, large beasts; chiefly the short-horned, the Lincolnshire, Yorkshire, Fifeshire, and Irish. The systems with stock are various. Mr. Wedd, on his farm at Soham, rears neat cattle, and sells them lean from grass, for grazing, and thinks it pays better than fattening them; he also sells heifers just before calving, and thinks they and cows pay better than any stock. When the calves fall in autumn, they have milk or oil-cake porridge warm till spring. When they fall in the spring they have milk three or four months, then are turned out. Those which fall in the autumn have hay first and second winter, those falling in spring hay only first winter. Mr. Edes, of Wisbech, buys in at autumn, and returns succeeding autumn from grass; or buys in at spring beasts forward in flesh, and returns them with those bought preceding autumn; he also stall-feeds some, i.e. about one fourth of his stock. Mr. [*Blank*] rears his own stock, keeping a large dairy, calves falling at all times of the year. If the cows be not good milkers lets the calves run with them; otherwise gives the calves milk in the house. Sells at all ages, according to markets.

The most prevailing systems are,

1st, Wean at a few days old, keep in house four to nine months on milk, turnips, potatoes, &c. &c. put them to grazing, at three, four, or five years old, generally at three years.
2d, Wean and sell to graziers at age for fattening.
3d, Buy in year olds, and keep them till of age to graze.
4th, Buy at an age for grazing, this is generally done at autumn, and return succeeding autumn, keeping on hay and grass, in winter, and finishing them from grass.
p.270 5th, Buy at the spring, and if not forward enough to sell fat in the autumn, finish on corn, or oil cake.

Estimated returns from these processes.

From 1st, 2d, and 3d. Pay from £4. to £5. per year till put to grazing.
From 4th. Pay for a twelve months fattening £8. to £12.

From 5th. This process is not adopted, of late by choice, but is resorted to rather than sell to a certain loss, or when muck cannot be purchased or otherwise raised; formerly, however, corn and oil-cake grazing were almost universal, but the losses have for some years past been so serious, that the rage for it is abating fast. Even with corn very low it will not pay. Mr. Wedd, of Trumpington, has corn grazed frequently, and has declined it, not having found it answer, even when corn is at the lowest; he thinks he has been paid by potatoes and barley-meal, given separately. The expense of oil-cake feeding may be ascertained, when their price is known, it having been found that a large beast will eat six in a day, weighing 2½ lbs. to 3lbs. each, besides a "little hay and a little corn," as the advocates for this system call it. Oil-cakes are now £16. to £17. and £18. per thousand, viz (if they weigh 3 lbs. each), 1 ton, 3 qrs. 4 lbs. being at £16. per thousand 3¼d. each. Mr. Page, of Ely, is out of all patience with corn and oil-cake grazing, says he has suffered greatly by it, intends in future to buy small beasts that may be returned from grass; says that oil cake not only increases in price, but is of considerable worse quality than formerly, so much so that beasts benefit little by them.

Mr. Shepherd, of Chippenham, speaks more favourably of corn grazing; he cleared last year by sixteen
p.271 beasts £5. each, on turnips, oil-cake, and pea-meal, charging turnips and every other article at market-price.

Colonel Adeane, of Babraham, intends buying in London, on a falling market, and keeping for a rising one, on oil-cake, &c. N.B. Babraham is fifty miles from London.

Mr. Darnton, of Babraham, has grazed beasts on *linseed-oil* and barley-meal, half a pint of oil to one peck of meal daily, and was paid well. The oil varies in price from 8s. to 9s. per gallon. Beasts put to this keep, Mr. D. observes, should be forward in condition. Not withstanding this account of oil-cake, grazing is thought preferable to corn grazing, as the beasts on the former fatten much quicker than on the latter.

Rev. Mr. Lane, of Carlton, intends to graze all the year round; in a well littered yard, in summer on tares, sainfoin, &c. cut green; in winter, on turnips and sainfoin hay, cut into chaff.

It has been questioned whether beasts which have been at corn, will do well at grass afterwards. Mr. Cooper, of Ely, who grazes on corn, grains, &c. &c. says he has found they will.

Amongst the numerous graziers of note in, the county, Mr. Wing, of Thorney, and Mr. Johnson, of Whittlesea, are conspicuous. The former sold a pair of beasts (twins) in Smithfield, one for £100. and one for £60.; the latter sold there also on the same day, three beasts, at £82., £84. and £86. each.

p.272

SECT. III. — SHEEP.

Sorts.

The most prevalent sort in the fens (where the greatest number in the county is kept) is a cross between the Leicester and Lincoln; there are, however, many other breeds, viz. Norfolks, West-country, Cambridgeshire, Berkshire, Hertfordshire, South Down, Lincoln, and Leicester. Mr. Tharpe, of Chippenham, has the first South-down flock in the county. Mr. Shepherd (Mr. Tharpe's steward), thinks they are not so subject to diseases, that they rear more lambs, produce more wool, require less keep, and yield a profit on the whole one-third more than Norfolks. Mr. Treslove, of Trumpington, has whole Leicesters, fine and handsome, having just set them; had nothing to communicate on their merit or demerit, but has no doubt they will gain ground in the county. Rev. Mr. Lane, of Carlton, has tried many sorts, and is going to keep South Downs. Mr. Darnton, of Babraham, prefers the cross between the South Down ram, and Norfolk ewe, to whole South Down, as the former are of more value to the grazier.

Colonel Adeane sold a fine Norfolk flock, to set a South Down one. Mr. Mortlock, of Abington, has fine South Downs.

Mr. Wedd, of Trumpington, formerly kept west country sheep, and upon parting with them has tried every polled breed, and is returning to his old stock, convinced that it is superior to any other. At Madinglay, Sir C. Cotton is parting with his Cambridgeshire, and substituting South Downs. At Childersley, Mr. Francis breeds west country ewe and Leicester ram.

p.273

Quantity in the county.

Mr. Vancouver says 152,928. I can neither confirm nor disprove this opinion.

	Weight per quarter.
South Downs, Mr. Tharp's	1 year old, 12 to 15 lbs.
	2 year old, 16 to 20 lbs.
Mr. Mortlock's	3 years old, 16 lbs.

Lincoln and Leicester cross, Mr. Johnson once sold (of his own breeding) four three-shear, which weighed 45, 46½, 48½ and 52 lbs. per quarter, and three others averaged 46 lbs. per quarter. In one day at Smithfield he sold two sheep at £7. each. N.B. All these sheep were grass fed only. Mr. Edes, of Wisbech, has the same breed, and they usually weigh, shearlings 18 lbs., two shear 26 lbs.

Mr. Vancouver states the weights as under, of three years old.

Norfolks	16lbs
West Country	18lbs
Cambridgeshire	14lbs
Lincoln and Leicester cross	22 to 26lbs

Wool.

Mr. Vancouver states (at three years old).

Norfolks	2¼lbs
West Country	4lbs
Cambridgeshire	2¼lbs
Lincoln	12lbs
Lincoln and Leicester cross	8 to 11lbs

Mr. Ede's Lincoln and Leicester cross, tod 3½.

Ditto whole Lincoln, ditto 2.

Ditto whole Leicester, ditto 4.

p.274 *Folding,*

is universally practised, its value variously estimated.

At Horse-Heath, Mr. Sanxter	at 40s. per acre.
At Islesham	18s.
At Barnwell, Mr. Burleigh	26s.
At Burwell, Mr. Dunn	25s.

At Westley Bottom, Mr. Wedge. "Take away my fold, take away my flock." At Trumpington, Mr. Wedd at 30s. per acre, if done well between August and Michaelmas, when he considers it of the most value. At Abington, Mr. Mortlock's bailiff, at 40s. per acre.

Systems.

These are not peculiar to the county; they are

1st, Breed and sell lamb, fat from ewe; then fat ewe and sell her, buying in every autumn fresh ewes.
2d, Breed and rear produce, and return it fat at three years old, keeping ewes as long as they are "whole mouthed;" set ewes from own stock.
3d, Buy at one or two years old, and return fat, within the year.
4th, Keep regular folding flock.

The keep under all these systems is, (speaking of the general practice) in fens, during winter and spring, grass and cole seed; in summer, grass only. In uplands, in winter and spring, turnips and layers; in summer, layers and natural grass. Individuals, however, adopt somewhat different modes,

Mr. Mortlock, of Abington, feeds his flock on hay, morning and evening while they are at turnips; the hay in the racks described before. Mr. Mortlock feeds his layer as well as his turnips, a piece at a lime hurdled off.

p.275 Rev. G. Jennyns, and Mr. Tharpe, have excellent foldyards fenced in by open pales; in these yards well littered, they lodge their sheep in bad weather; they conceive a close fence would be injurious to the sheep.

Mr. Edes, of Wisbech, breeds and returns fat from grass, at one and two years old. At Wisbech and neighbourhood, sheep are fattened to excess; at Christmas there is an exhibition, by every butcher in Wisbech hoping to shew the fattest. In feeding upland layers with ewes and lambs, the almost general practice is, to let the lambs go before the ewes into fresh feed, through "nooses" in the hurdles, going to and from the ewes at pleasure. The lambs are found not to be so liable to be hoven by clover as sheep are. Mr. Philips, of Bournbridge, never breeds his sheep "in and in." Mr. Francis, of Childersley, breeds from west country ewe and Leicester ram, has his lambs fall at Christmas, sells them fat, and puts ewe into flock. Sheep which cannot be wintered at home, are put out to stubbles, and other hard keep in uplands of neighbouring counties, at 6s. to 7s. per head.

Mr. Waddelow, of Little-Port, feeds his sheep on beans and oats, and thinks they pay well for it. Rev. T. Brown, of Connington, gives whole beans, and recommends the practice.

All fen-farmers remove their sheep frequently into fresh feed; they say they lose many if they neglect to do it.

Mr. Wing, of Thorney, thinks bullocks and sheep should graze apart; the general practice is otherwise.

If a sheep pays under any system 20s. per year (including wool) the farmer is satisfied.

Stocking.

The following are supposed to require an equal breadth of pasture, five to six sheep, or one beast from
p.276 forty to fifty stone when fat; Mr. Edes, of Wisbech. Five sheep, or one beast from fifty to sixty stone when fat. Mr. Boyce, of Whittlesea. At Elm, on highland pastures, twenty-two sheep and one steer for five acres, are the stock for summer months, and three sheep for two acres in winter, (Vancouver).

Observation:—this is equal (calling the beast equal to five sheep), to five sheep and two-fifths summer stock, and one and a half in winter. I found the more general stock to be five to six in the summer, two in the winter.

Disorders.

Mr. Vancouver has ably and fully described the dis orders prevalent amongst the sheep in the county. I did not, however, find them existing to the degree, (or any thing like it) which he states; he says,

At Ashley and Silverly are Norfolk-sheep, amongst which a growing disease prevails equally alarming with the rot, (though these sheep-walks are happily free from that calamity) the first appearance of which is indicated by the wool changing to a brown colour; and as the disease advances it drops off at the roots, and leaves the skin quite clean and naked. At this time the animal appears extremely uneasy, constantly rubbing its head against the hurdles and fences, and scratching its back and sides with its horns, starting suddenly, running a few steps, then falling down, where it will remain a short time, and then rise and begin feeding as in perfect health. The skin is perfectly free from eruption, and other appearance of disease, nor are there any traces of the disorder discoverable by examination of the entrails, the body or head of the animal; and as no instance of a cure has occurred in any of the surrounding parishes; and moreover as this disorder is considered to be infectious, the sheep are usually
p.277 killed on the appearance of the first symptoms, though some have been known to languish under its fatal influence for ten or twelve weeks together.

At Dullingham. "In the summer there prevails amongst the sheep, a garget or gangreen, appearing between the flesh and skin: this disease has hitherto been deemed incurable."

At Kennet. Norfolk sheep are kept, and "are extremely liable to warp or slip their lambs. They are very subject to the garget or red water, the symptoms of which are so indiscernible that in two hours after the animal has appeared in perfect healfh, it is found dead."

At Tadlow, Trumpington, Dry Drayton, Barrington, Eltsley, Croxton, Caxton, Longstow, Bourne, Cottenham, the rot has prevailed to that degree that taking the numbers, said by Mr. V. to have been carried off in one year, I find it is 7,548 out of 11,885. "Another species of rot was noticed, which does not appear to be ascribable to the like cause. This is called by the farmers the blood rot. The liver appears to the eye in these cases to be perfectly sound, and as free from disease, as in the most healthy animal; it is however covered with an extremely thin transparent membrane, as tender as a spider's web, but which the smallest pressure imaginable immediately ruptures, when the whole liver resembles a mass of coagulated blood, without any cohesion whatever, the liver and intestines at this time are free from any appearance of insects, alive or dead; nor was it understood from the farmers that the liver in the state before mentioned, was offensive to the smell; though certain it is, that in its progress, it must have been rendered gradually inert and corrupt as it became disorganised."

At Badlingham, "The sheep are subject to the disease noticed at Ashley, the red water, garget, or
p.278 gangreen between the flesh and skin of the animal, warping their lambs, and dying "dunt," (as the shepherds term it) that is, dizzy; as a cure for this latter calamity, the shepherd will frequently open the sheep's head, at the insertion of the horns into the scull, with his knife and extract one, two, and sometimes more maggots, larger than those generated in tallow."

At Elm. "The sheep in this parish have been subject to a very extraordinary disease feeding upon newly laid down land; which by the farmers is considered to arise from eating a herb or grass by them called cockspire (cocksfoot) which is said to produce a relaxation of the shoulder; this calamity is most to be apprehended in moist forward seasons." Young neat cattle from one to three years old are also subject to this disease. A cure is generally effected by removing the stock to high land, on the first appearance of the disease.

At Thorney. "The breeding of sheep has in a great measure been relinquished in this parish, on account of a weakness that prevails amongst the lambs; it affects the whole frame of the animal, and seems to be an extension of a disease, similar to that well known in many counties, by the name of the rickets. The rickets however is a disease originating in the animal, whereas this disease appears to have its origin from the nature of the soil or herbage, which the animal when young, feeds upon; "is observed to prevail most generally upon new or lately laid down land, and it is the opinion of many farmers that the rye-grass contributes to this effect."

As it is so well known what description of land will inevitably cause the rot, it is not easy to account for sheep being kept on such to a certain and heavy loss. "Flying flocks," viz. sheep bought and sold within the year, the rot is scarcely heard of.

p.279 *Accidents.*

Vast quantities of sheep (the long wooled) are lost in the fens, from being cast on their backs; they are watched solely on this account, as immediate assistance is necessary.

SECT. IV. - HORSES.

The farmers in this county think themselves unrivalled in cart horses; in the fens they are a source of great profit, they are very large and bony and the greatest number black; long hair, from the knee to the fetlock and trailing on the ground, is reckoned an excellency. Mr. Johnson, of Whittlesea, shines as a breeder of these horses, perhaps as much as any gentleman in the county; he has a cart stallion for which he gave by auction 255 guineas; the colts of this horse have sold off the mare, at £60. and year olds at 100 guineas. Mr. Johnson one year sold twenty two year old cart colts (not the breed of this horse) at £40. each. Mr. Edes, of Wisbech, is also a great breeder of this stock, he sells at two and three years old;

average price of late years, two year old, £20. three year old £25: the present prices of cart-horses and brood-mares, are high beyond belief; £40. to £50. is thought a low price, for a good, strong, common, three or four year old. They are generally sold at two years old: while these prices remain, stock will pay equal to them. Farm horses are kept at great expense in the upland part of the county, being in the stable all the year at hay, corn, and chaff; very few farmers, comparatively speaking, giving them grass, tares,
p.280 clover, or any green food. The expense per year, horse £20. to £30. thus estimated,

	£.	s.	d.
Oats $1\frac{1}{2}$ bushels per week the year round, viz. $19\frac{1}{2}$ Co. at 12s.	11	14	0
Hay one cwt. per week, that is 52 cwt. at 3s.	7	16	0
Shoeing	1	1	0
Farrier	0	10	0
Interest on capital, say on £30.	1	10	0
Decrease in value in seven years, supposing the first cost £30. say £15. which is per year say	2	2	0
	24	13	0

There is also a further expense for chaff, which in general consists of cavings of corn, trodden down hard, kept in a heat by watering it; the farmers begin to get a stock at Michaelmas, but don't wish to use it till after barley-sowing; till which time, from Michaelmas use chaff or cut-straw untrodden. A horse consumes about half a fan of chaff per day.* The quantity of oats I have stated, is about the average given; it varies from one to two bushels per week. The hay is under that which many give, I heard of one cwt and a half.

Many farmers, however, do not keep so "high" as here stated. Rev. Mr. Leworthy, of Harston, reckons the expense and decrease in value on a cart-horse, £30. per year. The fen-farmers keep their horses at
p.281 comparatively no expense. Mr. Wedd thinks it so trifling, that he keeps four to every plough he works, using two horses at a time for half the day, the men going the whole day. The horses here are not shod, except those which go on the road. The expense in the fens per horse per year was stated to me thus,

	£.	s.	d.
From May-day to Michaelmas, say 26 weeks on grass at 2s.	2	12	0
From Michaelmas to May-day, say 26 weeks on hay, $1\frac{1}{2}$ cwt. per week, viz. 39 cwt. at 2s,	3	18	0
From Michaelmas to May-day, oats seven pecks per week, viz. 11 Co. at 12s	6	12	0
Interest on capital, farrier, decrease in value, as in preceding estimate	4	2	0
	17	4	0

All the expense here stated, from Michaelmas to May day, is not incurred by every horse, but by the number required for winter use, which is very few.

Quantity kept.

Mr. Mortlock, of Abington, on a light land farm, keeps seven on three hundred and fifty acres.

Mr. Francis, of Childersley, keeps twelve to fourteen on four hundred arable heavy land, and two hundred pasture. Rev. Mr. Leworthy keeps four on one hundred acres arable, heavy land.

Mr. Wedge, of Westley Bottom, thus writes to the Board of Agriculture. (Communications, v. 5, p. 98).

---

* Chaff is very subject to be destroyed by the wevil (or beatle), wormwood branches strewed in the heap will send them away. Mr. Burleigh, of Barnwell.

I think where two horses are sufficient to work a plough, one horse is kept on an average to every twenty
p.282 acres of ploughed land, and every horse will furnish employment, (exclusive of harvest) for half a man and a quarter of a boy.

	£.	s.	d.	£.	s.	d.
Half a man, cannot be set at less than				15	0	0
Quarter of a boy				5	0	0
Blacksmith	3	0	0			
Wheeler	1	0	0	4	10	0
Collar-maker	0	10	0			
Keep of horse				15	0	0
			For 20 acres	39	10	0
						5
			For 100 acres	197	10	0

The above articles do not vary in proportion to the value of land.

On the horse system of the county Mr. Vancouver writes: "Nothing in the husbandry of Cambridgeshire is more replete with error and abuse, or more capable of reform under the present circumstances of the county, than the feeding and working management of farm-horses. The scarcity of pasture ground, the want of proper attention in the farmers to the raising of green food for soiling their horses in summer, and the great neglect in the culture of artificial grasses, all conduce to an expense in supporting the farm-horses in the upper parts of this county, that is absolutely enormous. They are kept in the stable throughout the year, each horse is fed with a peck of corn per day, with as much chaff, chopped straw, and hay as they can eat; and work but one journey in the day, which seldom exceeds seven hours, but
p.283 never eight, except in the neighbourhood of Leverington, Parsondrove, and Thorney, where two journies a day are not unusual; ploughing from seven to twelve, and from two in the afternoon till night, or when the day will admit of it, till seven in the evening, doing about an acre each journey."

Hours of work.

At plough, generally one journey of seven or eight hours, when they go two journies, (which is in the spring), they are from seven to twelve, and from two to seven, viz, ten hours.

SECT. V. - HOGS.

These are as various as the county itself, and the adjacent ones produce; there are many of the Suffolk breed, viz. short, white, and short eared, which are gaining ground. Some of the Cambridgeshire are so large as to fatten to forty stone, fourteen lbs. to the stone, at two years old; twenty to thirty such stones, a common size. Nothing particular in the hog-system in the county. Fattening hogs on barley meal is supposed to pay when barley is at 10s. and pork at 7s. per stone, and the lean price in proportion. Rev. Mr. Leworthy, of Harston, has fattened hogs on steeped barley, and says he has been paid well. Rev. Mr. Lane, of Carlton, has been a very large corn-grazier of hogs, and has declined the practice, not having found it answer his purpose; neither of these gentlemen could furnish me with the result of any experiment. An intelligent and large farmer observed to me, (and I am inclined to think justly) "that fattening hogs pays a cottager, or anyone who himself attends them; as in that case less is suffered by
p.284 robbery, less waste is made, and they are not kept a moment longer than it is done to profit". They require, he observed, more attention "than servants will give them"; at any rate he said more "economical management than they would exercise." I witnessed at Shelford, a most barbarous and disgraceful way of killing hogs, viz. a man standing in the middle of a stye, and striking them on the head (by an instrument somewhat like a cricket-bat) as they run round the stye; several ineffectual blows

were given with no other regret than exposing his want of skill; another man attends to finish the business in the usual way.

SECT. VI. - RABBITS, POULTRY, BEES.

Nothing singular in these. There are no warrens in the county.

SECT. VII. - PIGEONS.

Almost every farm has a pigeon-house, and though the quantity sold is in many instances very great, and amounts to a large sum, the most intelligent farmers believe them on the whole injurious, and would not keep them but for their muck, and that they would be necessitated to feed others. They destroy thatch, and oblige the farmer to sow more seed than is necessary for his crop. Many dove-houses produce annually one hundred dozen young pigeons, which sell from 2s. 6d. to 5s. per dozen; the produce however varies much, and, in some instances amounts to a trifle.

p.285

CHAP. XIV.

RURAL ECONOMY.

SECT. I. - LABOUR.

The annexed Communications* on this subject were to the Board of Agriculture from this county, in the following is the information I received from individuals at the places noted.

Wages of Shepherds

	£.	s.	d.	
Connington	10	10	0	and usual advantages
Mepal, wages and adages equal to	35	0	0	
Upwell, ditto	35	0	0	per year
Chatteris, ditto	25	0	0	

Wages of Dairy-Maids

	£.	s.	d.	
Connington	5	5	0	
Mepal, wages and adages equal to	25	0	0	
Upwell, ditto	5	0	0	per year
Chatteris, ditto	5	0	0	

Mowing - grass

Connington, 2s. 6d. per acre. Mepal, 3s. 6d., Upwell 3s. to 4s. At Chatteris 2s. 6d. At Ely, 4s and beer.

p.286

Making grass

At Connington, by women, 1s., boys and girls, 8d. per day. At Mepal per acre, 4s. 6d. Upwell, 3s. At Chatteris, 1s. 9d.; Women, per day, 1s. 2d. and 1s. 4d. Upwell, Women, 1s. 3d. to 1s. 9d. per day.

* See Table pp.254-55. **Note:** *in the original this was one large pull-out table, it is here given as two tables.*

Turnip-hoeing.

Twice, 7s.; once, 2s. 6d. to 5s. per acre, the art not understood; has cost 20s. and upwards, having been done by gardeners, and by them by the day. There are, however, now great quantities of turnips grown, owing to the late enclosures, and there will be no difficulty of getting them hoed at the usual price of the countries growing them.

Chaff-cutting,

A general price 2d. per fan, (a fan equal to three heaped bushels). At Upwell, $2^{1}/_{4}$d. per fan. At Chatteris, one half-penny for a heaped bushel.

Hollow-draining.

Per score rods 3s. to 3s. 6d. and 5s. and more.

Washing sheep.

Per score 2s. At Chatteris, 1s. Mepal, 2s. 6d. Upwell, 6s.

Clipping sheep.

Per score 2s. to 3s. 6d.

Reaping.

At Mepal, oats, 16s. per acre; beans 2s. At Upwell, oats, 14s. to 20s. beans, 8s. to 16s. At Chatteris, oats, 12s. At Whittlesea and neighbourhood are many women reapers, who will reap a quarter of an acre per day; the price in fen 12s., in field 9s, per acre, more is often given.

p.287 *Turning over muck.*

Per load 1d.

Dibbling.

Wheat 10s. 6d. oats, 8s. to 10s. at Upwell. At Chatteris, wheat, 10s. 6d.

Threshing.

Oats, 6d. per Co. at Upwell. At Chatteris, 8s. per last of 21 Co. (about $4^{1}/_{2}$d. per Co.) beans, 9d. per Co.

Yard-man.

Per year, wages and value of board, £26.

Wages.

In hay season 1s. 6d. to 5s. per day, and more; year round, summer, 12s., winter 10s. 6d. per week; in harvest per week 18s. to 24s.

Mowing.

Beans 4s. per acre; barley, 1s. 6d. to 3s. 6d.

Weeding.

Wheat 4s. per acre.

Hoeing.

Beans 6s. per acre.

Fencing.

In fields near fens, 4s. for six yards, (including materials).

Thatching.

Per square of 100 feet 4s. to 4s. 8d. with reed; with straw, 3s. Reed thatching is done in a masterly way in this county, costs, per square of 100 feet, £1. 1s. the reed, 5s. the labour. Reed is now four guineas per thousand bunches, which will thatch four square. At Whittlesea, reed thatching is done at 3s. 6d. per
p.288 square, the thatcher finding spits and rope; straw-thatching at 4s. 2d. per square.

Paring and burning.

Per acre 30s. to 40s. including spreading the ashes.

Ploughing and burning.

Per acre 14s. to 15s. including spreading the ashes.

Ploughing.

In a few places per acre, 20d.; not often done by acre in many parts of county.

Mr. Darnton, of Babraham, during the high price of provisions, instead of advancing the wages of his labourers, allowed them in harvest six lbs. of pork, two lbs. of cheese, four lbs. of rice per man, per week at 4d. per lb. each article, this plan proved advantageous to himself, and was well received by the people; the farmers who advanced the wages have found it difficult since to reduce them.

Harvest wages.

At Wisbech, harvest-men are hired every morning at four o'clock on the bridge there, for the day only, or for two days at most. At Burwell, wages and board of a harvest man is estimated at £5. 10s. At Chippenham, at £8. 11s. thus, wages, £6. 6s.; treats, 5s.; malt, £1. 10s.; carting, firing, 10s. * Where harvest-men are boarded in the house, the following is their fare, as I learnt from a gentleman at Wimpole.

At six in the morning, one pint of strong beer, and bread and cheese.
p.289 At eight, breakfast of cold meat and beer.
At eleven, one pint of strong beer, and bread and cheese.
At one, dinner; one day roast beef or mutton, (pork will not do) and plain pudding, next day boiled beef or mutton, and plum-pudding.
At four, one pint of strong beer, and bread and cheese. At seven, hot hash or hot mutton-pies.

On Saturday night an addition of good seed-cake of one lb. covered with sugar, and a quart of strong beer poured over it. Hence each man has daily, Nine pints of beer (strong); Three times bread and cheese; Three times meat; And on Saturday night, in addition one quart of beer, and a sugared cake. The expense of these will be found great, at the present prices of the several articles.

Haulming Stubbles.

Before Michaelmas 2s.; after, 1s. 1d. to 1s. 6d. per acre. The farmers not only complain of the rapid advance of wages, but of the difficulty of procuring steady and deserving labourers; they are much less

---

* Where boarded, £2. to £2. 10s.

LABOUR

Communication to the Board of Agriculture	Price in Winter, 1790		Price in Winter, 1804		Price in Summer, 1790		Price in Summer, 1804		Price in Harvest, 1790		Price in Harvest, 1804		Head Man's Wages, 1790		Head Man's Wages, 1804			Second Man's Wages, 1790			Second Man's Wages, 1804		
	Per week.		Per week.		Per week.		Per week.		Per week.		Per week.		Per week.		Per week.			Per week.			Per week.		
	s.	d.	s.	d.	s.	d.	s.	d.	s.	d.	s.	d.	£.	s.	£.	s.	d.	£.	s.	d.	£.	s.	d.
No.1	7	0	11	0	9	0	15	0	15	0	30	0	—		—			—			—		
2	3	0	12	0	12	0	15	0	18	0	20	0	0	12	0	15	0	0	7	6	0	9	0
3	6	0	9	0	9	0	15	0	21	0	30	0	0	9	0	12	0	0	8	0	0	10	0
4	6	0	9	0	6	0	9	0	18	0	24	0	0	8	0	12	0	0	8	0	0	12	0
5	7	0	9	0	9	0	11	0	11	3	13	2	7	0 per ann	5	0	0 per ann	6	0	0 per ann	8	0	0 per ann
6	6	0	10	6	9	0	13	6	10	6	17	0	0	7	0	16	6	0	6	0	0	13	0
7	8	0	9	0	8	0	10	6	21	3	26	3	0	8	0	9	0	0	7	0	0	8	0
Places	—		—		—				—		—		—					—			—		
Conington	—		12	0	—		15	0	—		21	0	—		12	12	0	—			6	6	0
Mepal	—		9	6	—		12	0	—		28	0	—		47+	5	0	—			37+	0	0
Upwell	—		12	0	—		18	0	—		30	0	—		16	0	0	—			8	0	0
Chatteris	—		9	0	—		13	0	—		24	0	—		30+	0	0	—			25+	0	0

* For a month, also board and a load of straw

+ Wages and board

LABOUR

Communication to the Board of Agriculture	Reap Wheat, 1790 Per acre.		Reap Wheat, 1804 Per acre.		Mow Barley, 1790 Per acre.		Mow Barley, 1804 Per acre.		Thresh Wheat, 1790 Per Qr.		Thresh Wheat, 1804 Per Qr.		Thresh Barley, 1790 Per Qr.		Thresh Barley, 1804 Per Qr.		Filling Earth, 1790 Per yard.		Filling Earth, 1804 Per yard.		Filling Dung, 1790 Per load.		Filling Dung, 1804 Per load.	
	s.	*d.*	*s.*	*d.*	*s.*	*d.*	*s.*	*d.*	*s.*	*d.*	*s.*	*d.*	*s.*	*d.*	*s.*	*d.*	*s.*	*d.*	*s.*	*d.*	*s.*	*d.*	*s.*	*d.*
No.1	7	6	21	0	2	6	6	0	2	6	7	0	1	6	—		0	3	—		0	2	0	4
2	12	0	13	0	3	6	5	0	3	6	4	0	12	6	—		0	2	—		—			
3	6	0	9	0	1	4	2	6	12	8	3	0	1	2	1	9	0	3	0	5	0	2½	0	3½
4	4	0	7	0	1	0	2	6	2	0	3	0	1	0	1	6	0	2	0	4	0	2	0	3
5	5	0	10	0	1	3	2	0	2	0	4	0	1	3	2	0	—		—		0	2½	0	3
6	6	0	15	0	5	0	8	6	2	0	5	0	0	0	—		—		—		0	3	0	6
7	4	0	8	0	1	2	1	6	1	6	3	0	1	2	1	6	—		—		0	2	0	3
Places	—				—		—		—				—		—		—		—		—		—	
Conington	—		7 to 14s.		—		—		—		3	4	—		2	0	—		—		—		0	2§
Mepal	—		16	0	—		3	6	—		3	4	—		1	8	—		—		—		0	2½§
Upwell	—		16 to 24s.		—		0	0	—		4	0	—		1	6	—		—		—		0	4
Chatteris	—		12	0	—		3	6	—		2	8	—		1	6	—		—		—		0	1½§

§ Including spreasding

industrious and respectable than in many counties. In the fens it is easily accounted for, they never see the inside of a church, or any one on a Sunday, but the alehouse society, or that of their neighbours met together to drink away the day. Upon asking my way (towards the evening), in the fens, I was directed, with this observation from the man who informed me; "are you not afraid to go past the bankers at work yonder, Sir?" I was told these bankers were little better than savages; they gave me, however, civil answers.

p.290

SECT. II. - PROVISIONS.

Beef, 8d. to 9d. Veal, 7½d. to 8d. Mutton, 7d. to 8d. Pork, 5d. to 6d. Cheese, 4d. to 7d. Butter, 1s. to 1s. 4d per pound. N.B. The butter rolled up in pieces of a yard long, and about two inches in circumference.

SECT. III. - FUEL.

Coals, 40s. per chaldron; turf, 7s. per thousand; sedge, 9s. to 12s. per hundred; at Cambridge all fuel except coals rapidly advancing; cow-dung dried is used as firing for dairy purposes and by the poor; it is spread on grass, (common or waste-land) about one inch and a half thick, and cut into pieces about eight to twelve inches square, and lies till dry.

p.291

CHAP. XV.

POLITICAL ECONOMY.

SECT. I. - ROADS.

EXCEPTING the turnpikes, the roads in this county are miserably bad, owing to the scarcity and dearness of materials. Most roads running through the fens, are frequently almost impassable, even the turnpike one from Downham to Wisbech, not excepted; the "mending," being only the silt, viz. a sand formerly left by the sea, and not a stone amongst it. The turnpikes in the highland parts of the county are excellent, as is that from Cambridge through Chatteris, March, &c.

SECT. II. - CANALS.

The fens in this county are intersected in all directions, by cuts for the conveniency of districts and individuals; the last made was from Wisbech to the river Nene at Outwell, and thence to the river Ouse at Salter's Lode sluice, opening a communication with Norfolk, Suffolk, &c. &c. It was opened in 1797 and has been of great service in draining its neighbourhood, as well as having benefited the town of Wisbech, and the adjacent country, considerably, by the increase of trade.

p.292

SECT. III. - FAIRS AND MARKETS.

The fair of greatest note is Stirbich, beginning September 18th, and lasting a fortnight; it is held for the sale of all sorts of shop goods, and for cheese, butter, hops, and horses; it has been declining for many years. There are also fairs held at Cambridge, Ely, Wisbech, Soham, Caxton, Linton, Reach, and Whittlesea. At every parish is annually a "feast," viz. a meeting of the lower classes for the purposes of merriment, &c. &c.

There are weekly markets at Cambridge, Ely, Caxton, Soham, Newmarket, Linton, Mepal, and Wisbech.

SECT. IV. - COMMERCE.

None peculiar to this county; a large corn, flour, coal, and deal trade, is carried on in many parts of the county, by means of the rivers and canals communicating with them from Lynn, Wisbech, &c.

SECT. V. - MANUFACTURES.

Ely has a pottery for coarse ware; excellent white bricks are also made there, and at Chatteris, and Cambridge. Lime is burnt at Wisbech, Mepal, Cherryhinton, &c. &c. but that in greatest estimation is

burnt at Reach (a hamlet of Burwell), and is fetched many miles. Land, which at Reach would let for
p.293 farming purposes, at about 15s. per acre, will sell for sixty, to eighty, and ninety pounds; and even more, for burning lime. The expense of burning lime is 4s. for 100 bushels; ten bushels of coals will burn a chaldron of lime, viz. forty bushels. Price of lime 6d. per bushel at pit. Price of clunch, of which the lime is burnt, 2s. 6d. per chaldron, delivered to boat; there is a great demand for it, and it is sent to great distances.

SECT. VI. - POOR.

Nothing singular in the management of the poor, their dwellings in general bad. No hundred houses as in Norfolk and Suffolk. The poor resident in the fens reside in miserable huts. At Weston Colville, enclosed some years since, the poor were much benefited by having land attached to their cottages; this has been done under many late enclosing acts with similar advantages. Mr. A. Young took the following note at Chatteris. "Mr. Scott, of Chatteris, gives one account upon the subject of the poor, which is very interesting. Till within six or seven years they were permitted to build houses upon the waste; and erected great numbers, taking only the ground the cottage stood on; but the commoners complaining they were stopped from doing it, and since have not been able to procure a dwelling without purchasing a bit of land for that purpose. The ease of doing it before, was a great encouragement to industry and good morals, for a young couple who intended marrying were frugal and saving, in order to have money
p.294 enough to provide their habitation. Some of these did not cost more than from £7. to £8. to £10. and £15. They used to be in a comfortable state till the last scarcities, but since much distressed, and the class just above, who will not take from the rates, are now perhaps the most distressed of all. What are we to say to the striking fact, that the possession of a mere miserable cottage built for £8. or £10. without garden, and without live stock, keeping the proprietor from the parish. Is it possible that such a fact can be contemplated without amazement at that voluntary blindness to so palpable a mean of lessening if not doing away poor-rates altogether? There is magic, an enchantment in property, even of this curtailed and wretched nature, that works wonders in no other way to be effected. If a poor cottage will do this, what would not a good garden effect? What would not a cow in addition produce? Annals, v. 36, p. 348. Lord Hardwicke has encouraged his poor to make the most of their gardens by giving a premium to the best manager of them. Mr. Custance, of Cambridge, adopts a plan (where he has authority), which does him honour; Mr A. Young thus speaks of it. "Mr. Custance, of Cambridge, who has the management of Mr. Vernon's estate in Suffolk, has laid four acres and a half of land to each cottage; and taken the inhabitants from being tenants to the farmers to be tenants to the landlord. They pay £2. 1s. for the house, and the same rent for land as the farmers. One paid the farmer £5. rent for his house, and an acre of meadow; this man had three acres and a half more let to him. and his rent £4. 14s. 6d. They were all much delighted, and had no doubt of now doing well. Some almost cried for joy. Mr. Custance also requires the farmers to plant from one to three acres of potatoes, according to the size of their farms, and sell them to the poor. The farmers threaten to rate them to the poor, this has been done at Kingston in
p.295 Cambridgeshire, a cottager pays £5. rent for half an acre of meadow, and he is rated at £4. and has paid 20s. to the poor. This is abominable." (Annals, v. 36, p. 608).

Mr. Tharp, of Chippenham, allows his mill (a watermill) to grind one day in the week for the poor at 1s. 6d. per Co. taking no toll. The poor as well as the farmers complain of public houses being attached to brew-houses; they say those which are independent of brewers, sell much better, more wholesome, and cheaper beer than those belonging to brewers.

SECT. VII - STATISTICAL DIVISION OF THE PRODUCE OF LAND.

Mr. A. Young, in his Chapter on this subject in his " Suffolk Report," observes that he inserted it as an attempt which may in time be ameliorated in more able hands; as mine are not those hands, I must decline a similar attempt; indeed the accuracy of Mr. Young's calculations under this head may be suspected, (he himself observes they are very far from perfection), as the result of them is such as proves farming so beggarly an employ (except on a very large scale) that no man with two ideas in his head and a hundred pounds in his pocket would engage in it and that these estimates are very far from the truth, may be taken for granted from the apparent, and, it is to be hoped, real, situation of the farmers in the kingdom, and above all from the impossibility of their living, reaping such profits only.* Till accounts

* Viz. 5 per cent. Profit, on £5 capital per acre.

p.296 absolutely accurate, be produced, and those from various respectable quarters, every communication of this nature must be defective in so great a degree, as to be of little individual or national utility.

SECT. VIII. - POPULATION.

That of this county appears, by communication to the Board of Agriculture, (1801) to be 83,000, and as the number of acres is estimated at 443,300, it is five acres and three tenths to each person. (Annals, v. 36, p. 74).

An estimate returned to government in 1804, makes the population of this county in 1700, 76,000; in 1750, 72,000; in 1801, 92,300. (Annals, v. 42, p. 267). Mr. Vancouver writes that from the information he collected, the population of this county is 83,000, which he says is greatly short of former calculations, which have stated it at 140,000. The general opinion is that the population (particularly in the fens) has greatly increased of late years.

p.297

CHAP. XVI.

OBSTACLES TO IMPROVEMENT.

IN the uplands, the expense of enclosures. In the fens, clashing interests.

p.298

CHAP. XVII.

MISCELLANEOUS OBSERVATIONS.

Not one in the county.

SECT. II.—WEIGHTS AND MEASURES

THE stone is 14 lbs.
Wool is sold by tod, of 28 lbs.
Cheese, by cwt. of 120 lbs.
Corn, by coomb, or by load of five bushels.
Oats of fen, by last of 21 coomb.

SECT. - III. BLACKSMITH.

The prices in 1790 and 1804, for blacksmith's work in this county, were returned to the Board of Agriculture, as under;

		1790	1804
Tire per lb.	average of the returns	4d$^{1}/_{4}$.	5d$^{1}/_{4}$.
Plough-irons, per lb.		4d$^{1}/_{2}$.	6d$^{1}/_{2}$.
Chains per lb.		5d.	7d.
Shoeing per Shoe		4d$^{1}/_{2}$.	6d$^{1}/_{2}$

p.299 I received the following information in 1806 and 1807. At Connington, wheel-tire, 6s. 6d. per score, or 4d. per lb.

At Mepal, ditto	6d.
At Upwell, ditto	6d.
At Chatteris, ditto	4$^{1}/_{2}$d.
At Connington, plough-work	6d.
At Chatteris, ditto	6d.

At Connington heavy chains 1s. 3d. per yard, light chains, 1s. per yard.

At Mepal, all chains	8d. per lb.
At Chatteris, ditto	6d.
At Connington, shoeing per shoe	6d.
At Mepal, diito	6d.
At Upwell, ditto	7½d.
At Chatteris, ditto	6d.

Similar prices exist in most parts of the county.

SECT. IV. - CARPENTER.

Returned to the Board of Agriculture as the prices in 1790 and 1804, as follows; by day a man in 1790, average of returns, 1s. 9½d.; in 1804, 2s. 8d. The average of the returns I received in 1806 and 1807, is, per day, for a carpenter 3s. and beer, or 2d. in 1s. in lieu of it.

SECT. V. - COLLAR-MAKER.

Returned to the Board of Agriculture, as the prices in 1790 and 1804, as follows; a man per day, In 1790,
p.300 average of returns 2s.; in 1804, 3s. The average of the returns I received in 1806 and 1807, is 3s. 6d. and board.

SECT. VI. - MASON.

Returned to the Board of Agriculture, as the prices in 1790 and 1804, as follows; a man per day, in 1790, average of returns, 2s.; in 1804, 3s.

The average of, accounts I received in 1806 and 1807, is 4s. 6d. per day for mason and slab, and beer or 2d. in 1s, in lieu of it.

SECT. VII. - THATCHER.

Returned to the Board of Agriculture, as the prices in 1790 and 1804, as follows; a man per day in 1790, average of returns, 2s.; in 1804, 3s.

The average of the accounts I received in 1806 and 1807, is 3s. 1d. per day for a man.

SECT. VIII. - WEIGHT OF CORN.

Field corn is heavier than fen-corn one stone and a half to two stone (of 14 lbs). Weight of fen-corn
p.301 at Thorney, oats, nine stone; barley, fourteen stone: wheat, sixteen stone, per Co. Hence the weight of field corn is (taking the difference at two stone per Co.) oats, eleven stone; barley, sixteen stone; wheat, eighteen stone; from which it may be suspected that the fen-corn is over-rated in weight.

SECT. IX. - WATER.

At Soham very bad; at Tid St. Giles so bad that in 1803 many persons as well as cattle died from drinking it.

SECT. X. - WEEDS.

Weeds abound in the fens, and indeed in upland arable fields, notwithstanding the boasted fallow system. The most weed in fens, (if I may be allowed by the Cambridgeshire farmer so to call it) is couch grass, esteemed by farmers of the old school of as much value as ray-grass; it is not unusual to have fields so full of it, as to have the surface matted together so that it would "fork," as it is termed, viz. might be loaded by the fork; All weeds in fens, on mowing lands, wastes, roads, banks, &c. &c. are suffered to seed, and may be seen on a windy day, flying in clouds to a great distance.

p.302

SECT. XI. - FENCES.

Those on the new enclosure, (and which have been described, when speaking of enclosures), promise to be excellent.

The wall fences about pastures near home, and about yards, &c. are made of clunch, and cost 9s. 6d. per running rod four feet high.

The quick fences round March, &c. &c. and on lands bordering upon the fens are excellent, they are set on the ground and little or no ditch against them, being guarded by dead fence till they can protect themselves; the method of doing this is expensive, and in a country where firing is scarce, would be too great a temptation to those in want of and unable to purchase it.

Professor Harwood, of Bartlow, excels in the management of old fences, he lays and dips them; they are beautiful and hog proof.

SECT. XII. - DEER

There are deer in Wimpole park which are subject to a disorder similar to that to which Mr. Vancouver relates the sheep in many parts of the county are subject; he describes it, thus : "The first symptom of the disorder observable in the deer, is similar to that amongst the sheep; which is an apparent uneasiness in the head, and the rubbing of its horns against the trees, (this action however is
p.303 common to deer, in particular seasons in all countries, whether in a perfectly wild, or more domesticated state) but the most extraordinary effect of this disease is, that the animal appears to labour under a sort of madness, in pursuing the herd which now flee before him, and endeavour to forsake him; trying to bite or otherwise annoy them with all his strength and power, which soon being exhausted, he becomes sequestered from the rest of the herd; and in that deplorable state of the disease, breaks his antlers against the trees, gnaws large collops of flesh from off his sides and hind quarters, appears convulsed for a short time, and soon expires."

THE END.

Arthur Young's visits to Cambridgeshire.

Note:- *The following transcriptions are taken from Arthur Youngs published 'Annals of Agriculture and other useful Arts'. One visit made by Young to view an irrigation system at Babraham has been omitted as it was included in the Rev. Gooch's survey, Annals, Vol.19, pp.120-123 (see p.233 in this volume).*

Annals vol.6, A Months Tour to Northamptonshire, Leicestershire &c., pp.480 - 482.

1791, July 18

I have minuted notes of the country between Bradfield and Cambridge before; it affords me, therefore, no other remark than that of its want of improvement. Great tracts of land well adapted to sainfoin, but not an acre more sown than ten years ago; and streams that call aloud for irrigation, without a single acre of watered meadow: such supineness is dreadful.

The 19th. Taking the road from Cambridge to St. Neot's, view for six or seven miles the worst husbandry I hope in Great Britain. All in the fallow system, and the loss of time, and the expence submitted to, without the common benefit, these fallows are overrun with thistles, and the dung being spread over them forms an odd mixture of black and green that would do well enough for a meadow, but is villainous in tillage. Some divisions of these fallows have not yet been broken up since reaping the last year's crops. Bid the current of national improvement roll back three centuries, and we may imagine a period of ignorance adequate to the exhibition of such exertions! To what corner of the three kingdoms - to what beggarly village must we go to find in any branch of manufacture such sloth --- such ignorance-- such backwardness - such determined resolution to stand still, while every other part of the world is at least moving? - It is in the agriculture of the kingdom alone that such a spectacle is to be sought. There seems somewhat of a coincidence between the state of cultivation within sight of the venerable spires of Cambridge, and the utter neglect of agriculture in the establishments of that University.

They are ploughing here with poor implements, drawn by two horses at length, and conducted by a driver. The crops of wheat pretty good; all others bad. At Knapwell there is a parliamentary inclosure, and such wretched husbandry in it, that I cannot well understand for what they inclosed relative to management; rent is the only explanation which has risen from 5s. tythed, to 10s. or 11s. free. They sow hay feeds and clover, but little comes except raygrass and thistles; soil a strong loam, and some clay. Thence to St. Neot's, and all the way from Cambridge, must be classed amongſt the ugliest countries in England. The lands mostly open field, at 6s. an acre. The management very bad, much strong clay, and some fallows not yet ploughed; the course,

1. Fallow, ploughed thrice; breaking up 7s. 6d.
Two stirrings, each 3s. with 4 horses and a driver.
2. Wheat, produce short of statute
3. Oats or beans.

Annals vol.19, A ride from Kent &c., pp.120 - 123 (1792)

Cross the river Ouse: a very large track of land here entirely under water, and covered with reeds; it has been so for many years; are informed that it contains three thousand acres. Between Lynn and Wisbeach the lands are some under corn and some grass; the corn, much of it, very full of weeds; beans in ridges, about 2½ feet wide; many fields of wheat, very slight and full of weeds; in some fields that lie a little higher, very fine wheat; oats very backward, and much laid; hardly a day without rain here till last Sunday, for a long time; in consequence of which, the greater part of a very abundant crop of hay is spoiled. Wool all bought up here at 21s. and 22s. per tod, of 28 lb. To Wisbeach. - 10 miles.

Fine oats in the fens, but extremely backward; so very stout, that, if any rain falls a few days hence, they must inevitably fall close to the ground.

Basney -Moor. Wheat a middling crop. Turf burning here for rape ; the surface is pared about 24 or 3 inches thick, with a plough drawn by horses, and then laid up in small heaps by women, at the expence of 5s. or 6s. per acre ; the turf a mass of vegetable matter, and burns to very light ashes, which are immediately spread and ploughed in, and the land sown with rape; they grow very great crops, and after it, for many years, abundant crops of oats, and some very good wheat. They reckon their oats but a moderate crop, if they do not get above a last per acre; generally sow the last week in May, and sometimes as late as the 10th of June. The soil is so amazingly rich and fertile, that the oats come up and grow away as fast as if they were sown on a hot-bed; the soil a black moor. In riding along the wall, or embankment, from Wisbeach to Peterborough, which is 21 miles, we pass several wind-mills for lifting the water out of the fens up into the river, some of which have a little cottage withinside, for the man who attends it and his family to live in. We examine one of these mills of a very large size; it seems calculated to throw out a vast quantity of water. Such would doubtless be of great advantage to the low marshes of East Kent. - To Peterborough. - 21 miles.

Extract from the Report of the Board of Agriculture, entitled,

Agricultural State of the Kingdom in February, March and April 1816; being the Substance of the Replies to A Circular Letter Sent by the Board of Agriculture to Every Part of the Kingdom.

CAMBRIDGESHIRE.

J. Page. - The number of failures among the farmers, amounting in value to £73,000. without any dividend being paid to their creditors; the great decrease of stock of all kinds, hitherto kept by small proprietors, which is proved by the very low price of hay not saleable, which evils are produced by the weight of taxes, parochial dues, and the increased amount of tradesmen's bills that relate to husbandry, in addition to the inadequate price of every sort of grain; the depreciation of the value of cart–horses, of which great numbers have hitherto been bred with us, taken collectively, have occasioned the present state of things.

Rev. Dr. R. Thompson. - In this neighbourhood more tenants than I can enumerate have quitted their farms. Several of these of have been taken in hand by the landlords, but a much greater proportion remains absolutely unoccupied. Within a few miles of Long-Stowe, viz. in the parishes of Croxton, Eltisley, Toseland, Yelling, the Gransden's, the Hatley's, there are supposed, to be towards 8000 acres unoccupied, and more and more expected to be thrown up. This must unavoidably follow from the exhausted state of barns and farmyards. Money and corn are gone, and effects distrained and sold off to great disadvantage. Three-fourths of my own estate are on my hands; the part which I have let, is at little more than half the rent I had expected. To prevent my property becoming waste, I have for some time been sinking my capital on it, and kept from 25 to 30 labourers, and from 12 to 14 horses in regular employment. Without this expedient, ruin must have overwhelmed this parish. Of the dejection or inability under which the farmers in this country labour, I cannot give a more significant proof, than, that our wheats, from the late unfavourable weather, look most unpromising, and yet there is no rise in the market.

John Mortlock. - One farm in East Hatley unoccupied, having been thrown upon the landlord's hands since Lady-day 1815, by notice from the tenant at Michaelmas 1814. The tenant had last year's crop, as a way-going crop. The size of this farm 272 acres formerly two-thirds pasture, and one-third arable; but much of the pasture ploughed up of late. Last rent only about 13s. 4d. an acre, subject to great tithes, for which the Rector offered to take 2s. 6d. an acre. So great is the decline of Agriculture, that farming stock of various descriptions may be said to sell at half the price that it would have fetched two or three years ago. Yet scarcely a man can be found to enter upon a vacant farm; though the rents are so low. Those who remain, either bound by leases, or willing to continue in hope of better times, and not liking to give up their business, pay their rents with difficulty, reducing the work done on their farms; which brings great distress on the poor. In some parishes, able-bodied men are paid to do nothing, that they may be kept from starving. In others, more wisely, they divide among themselves the superfluous hands, according to their occupations, (I have known two or three hands per 100 acres) and thus get at least the labour of the men, for their money.

As remedies, the malt-tax, which has been aggravated to such an enormous amount, as to effect a prohibition on the labourer, and a great loss of market on the farmer; also the husbandry horse-tax, which presses most unjustly on those heavy land farms, which require most labour and expence to till. The leather-tax is a severe aggravation of expence to the farmer, in his implements, harness, &c. and to the labourer in the price of shoes. The circumstances that denote the distress of the farmer, are strongly depicted in the account of Wichford Hundred, enclosed—our gaols being full of farmers, formerly deemed respectable, and from scarce a single landlord getting his rents paid. I have not received one-third of mine.

Distress for rent and drainage tax, for the last two years, amounted to nearly £12,000. and within the same period farmers have failed, whose debts amount to £72,500 and whose creditors have at present received no dividend, neither is it likely they will; it appears also, that 19 farms are without tenants, in the above Hundred.

Several farmers concur in opinion, that a very convincing proof of their distress is evinced by every market in the kingdom being over-stocked with Agricultural produce, and selling infinitely below their absolute cost.

John Boyce,—Their not being able to pay the Parish rates without being put to trouble, and not employing the usual quantity of labourers, and not paying the tradesmen's bills.

Rev. Joseph Scott, sen.—I am fully satisfied in my own mind, that it is a chain of causes that have reduced grain below the price it can be grown for (while land is at such a high rent and taxes so heavy.) The principal causes are as follow: —Many farmers had contracted an expensive mode of living, and others, more economic, had made large purchases of land, stock, &c. so that both classes were bare of money. The peace threw enterprise and speculation into an inactive pause, and the calls for money were multiplying and irresistible. And as the late harvest was unusually good, and crops of grain most plentiful, and thrashing machines in abundance, therefore the markets have *been overstocked with grain* ever since harvest; and as speculation has not recovered its panic, and many banks have failed, and paper circulation decreased, these are the real causes, of the low price of grain; although, at this time, I believe we have not grain enough for our own immense consumption, till the produce of the ensuing harvest can be brought to market. And if Government, in its wisdom, would only bring a sufficient quantity of bank notes into circulation, (suppose half a million on an average for each county) grain would soon rise sufficiently high, without any other legislative aid. And this measure would aid manufacturers, and commerce also, at the same time. If paper money is sufficiently increased, speculation will start at full speed, now grain is so good, under value, and rather scarce, and the growing crops of wheat unfavourable; and two plentiful years and good harvests rarely succeed each other.

Sir G. Leeds, Bart.—The whole of the Hon. and Rev. Mr. Cust's tenants at Cockayne Hatley, have given notice to quit at Lady-day next. The quantity of land so abandoned, I am not able to ascertain. The Rev. Dr. Thompson, of Long Stowe, also in this county, has one or two farms thrown upon his hands; I believe, however, he does occupy them in part, and that the same is the case with the Rev. Thomas Brown, at Conington, in this county also. The partial relief proposed by Government, will, I am afraid, have no effect towards restoring confidence and credit to the agricultural interest. A curious case, in my neighbourhood, occurs at this time; the name of the party of course I do not feel at liberty to disclose, although, were it of importance, I have no doubt I could obtain his consent thereto. He is a Gentleman of landed property, and which, of late, without being high let, brought him an income of £1400. or £1500. per annum. From the establishment he usually kept, his assessed taxes amounted to about £70. per annum. At Lady-day last the whole of his property was abandoned, except a farm let for 7s. 6d. per acre, enclosed and tithe free, producing £60. per annum; of course, before Lady-day last he abandoned all his servants, carriages, horses, &c. but he is actually paying this year for the preceding one, £10. per annum more than his income; which, undoubtedly, must so involve the estate, that without a very speedy relief he must be ruined. There are other cases, though not quite so hard, nearly as desperate, and a great many indeed, where the taxes never can be collected at all. It is the dreadful pressure of the poor's-rate that will crush the remaining occupiers; of course the poor obtain no work out of their own parish, and after an absence of sixteen or seventeen years, many are returned to their legal settlement, from the impossibility of obtaining work abroad. It is the case in the parish where I reside; there is but one occupier, who must maintain the whole of the indigent poor; and, in several cases, where there is an actual difficulty of supporting their own families. I am afraid the evil is too wide spread, and too deeply rooted, to be easily cured. The gangs of depredators and poachers increase most alarmingly; the murmurs and complaints of the half-starved labourer increase in equal proportion.

James Harris.—To depict the distress that pervades the farmer, is impossible; for the man who, three years ago, was in affluence, does not scruple at every market table to say, that if he has to meet another year like the present and the last, he must be brought to indigence. This complaint is become universal. The state of the labouring poor is most distressing, as the inability of the farmer to improvement is such, that labourers, who, for years together, have found employ in neighbouring villages to where they belong, are now driven to their own parish for work, and find none, saving in the gravel pit, which has caused the poor and other rates to be higher than they were in 1811 and 1812. I am in occupation of nearly 700 acres of land, all of which is convertible land, which I have held for fifteen years, at the rent of 25s. per acre, enclosed, and tithe free, and declare, that from the two last crops I have not derived one guinea for rent.

William Custance.—The distress is denoted by men of capital being obliged to resort to their capitals to pay their way; the complete stagnation of trade, the stoppages to all improvements in land, the want of confidence, and the limited circulation of money.

John Edes.—The circumstances denoting the distress of the farmers are so very visible, by the daily issues of writs, executions, &c. for rents, debts, &c. that they are within the knowledge of every attentive observer—and arise, principally, from the very low price of the produce of land, which certainly cannot be grown for the present prices, even by farmers employed on their own estates; as the labour, parochial rates, tithes, and taxes on an acre of land, far exceed the amount of the value of produce—as there are thousands of acres of fen land in this neighbourhood, where the staple commodity, oats, do not this year produce more than from five to six quarters per acre, and the average price 12s. per quarter, being from £3. to £3. 10s. per acre only.

J. Wing.—The farmers in general have been under the necessity of thrashing out nearly the whole of their year's corn, and bringing it to market; many are in arrears with their landlords; few employ their usual complement of labourers; and, perhaps, no stronger proof of their distress can be exhibited, than the uncultivated state of many farms, and the perusal of assignments in every country paper.

The state of the labouring poor is very deplorable, and arises entirely from the want of employment, which they are willing to seek, but the farmer cannot afford to furnish. The poor deprecate the low price of corn, and say, they never experienced such bad times. A parish in the next county, (without any manufacture) consisting of 3500 acres, has, at this time, 72 men, besides boys, out of employment, and upon the parish; the poor rates are increasing, in an unexampled and alarming degree, in all other places.

Rev. Thomas Briggs.—Several farms in this parish are unoccupied by tenants. I have been obliged to take a farm of 570 acres into my own hands. There are three farms, containing, in the whole, about 700 acres, at the present time lying entirely waste.

Owing to the non-occupation of so much land in the parish, the poor-rates fall with great weight on the remaining occupiers. Should I throw up my farm, by which I am a considerable loser, the evil would be increased to an insupportable degree.

John Jones.—Several farmers have been distrained for rent, taxes, &c. &c.

Charles Wedge.—Rents remaining in arrear, requests for time by farmers who have had the appearance of opulence; loss of trade amongst every class of country tradesmen; neglect of cultivation (men being to be seen in all directions, in gravel pits, and wasting their time on the roads) are certain indications of distress.

Distress is certainly greater on arable than grass farms. Flock farms have not suffered so much as arable farms; but short-wool flocks are but little better.

The diminished circulation of country paper has put a stop to all accommodation, and all speculation.

The state of the labouring poor is now much worse than in the dear times; they were then fully employed; now their employment on the roads is a bare subsistence; and those who are not on the roads are at reduced wages. The poor-rates are higher.

The price of grain must be raised; and I am strongly inclined to think, the best way to assist it materially will be to drop the Malt Duty. Altogether, it now requires the price of more than four quarters of barley to brew one quarter of malt. This entirely prevents the poor man from brewing, and, in a material degree, the rich man too. It has been the means of the common brewers poisoning the country with substitutes for malt. It has compelled the farmer to give his labourers money (about 1s. per week) instead of beer, which he used to do, and it also promotes the baneful use of spirits. All these causes combined, induce me to think, that if the Duty on Malt was wholly taken off, the consumption of malt; would be double what it now is. I suppose it would render a number of Excisemen useless, and the maltster would then be at liberty to make his malt in the best possible way, which, under the present restrictions, cannot now be done.

Glossary

Acre	now standardised in UK as 4,480 square yards or 4 roods. Vancouver (p.20) notes that he had converted the many local measures to this standard.
Acre men	used here to denote a man able to reap an acre per day.
Adages	used here to mean additional sums e.g. additions to a wage payment.
Aftermath	the grazing that has been left after a crop has been cut (also known as eddish)
Balk, Balking	a narrow strip of land between arable lands, often raised; raising land by ploughing, soil being thrown up where the plough turns
Banker	a man employed, often as part of a hired gang, to build banks or excavate ditches.
Barberry bush	the shrub *berberis vulgaris*, with spiny shoots, and yellow flowers followed by tart red berries, believed to aid digestion, sometimes used in cookery.
Bastard Fallow	land left uncultivated with an inferior green crop taken from it.
Beans, clean	Beans (seeds) free from disease.
Bear	a machine developed to scrape from the bed of a watercourse the silt and vegetable matter which accrued there.
Bears Muck	a layer of soil found in fens, consisting of a mass of only partially-decayed organic matter mixed with soft clay and having a powerful odour.
Beat of flax	A sheaf of harvested flax plants.
Bite	feed taken from land for a short period.
Broad cast	The method of planting seed before the widespread use of the seed drill. The seed is scattered by hand by persons walking up and down a field.
Burning gravel	dry gravel which attracts the sun's heat .
Bushed	over in seed, often with a bush-arrow, to prevent its being consumed by birds etc.
Bushel	a measure of capacity used for corn etc, of varying sizes in different areas but probably used here in the form standardised in 1826 in UK, containing four pecks or 8 gallons.
Candlemas	the feast of the purification of the Virgin Mary after Christ's birth, celebrated on 2nd February.
Caput mortuum	a useless substance left over after a chemical reaction, the epitome of decline and decay.
Cavings (of corn)	straw and stalk left after threshing corn.
Chaldron	a dry measure, used mainly for coal, the London chaldron, probably that here used, being 36 heaped bushels. Note though that here (p.203) a chaldron of lime or clunch equates to 40 bushels.
Cinquefoil	a plant whose compound leaves are formed of 5 leaflets, properly of the genus *potentilla* and probably used here for *potentilla reptans*.
Clean	free from disease or weeds.
Clover or trefoil	common names for the genus *trifolium*, of which the tow most-frequently-cultivated species are white or Dutch clover, *trifolium repens*, and red clover, *trifolium pratense*.
Clunch	a soft white limestone.
Coomb	a dry measure of capacity, equal to four bushels sometimes 'comb'; the comb Winchester was some 3% smaller.
Cocking (hay)	gathering hay or straw into cocks, or conical heaps.

Cockspire, cocksfoot	A species of grass (*Dactylis glomerata*)
Cole, Cole Seed	A plant of the Brassica family. Commonly known as Rape.
Comminibus Annis	on the average of years.
Commutation of tithes	the cessation of tithe payments for land.
Couch barn	a purpose-constructed barn for laying out dried balls of ground woad to complete processing. (In malting, couching is laying out grain to germinate after steeping)
Corn rent	a money rent that varied with the fluctuating price of corn.
Crone	an old ewe (female sheep).
Depasturing	to put cattle or other animals to graze, or of animals, to graze.
Dibble	to make holes in the ground (with a dibble, a pointed stick with or without a handle and cross-bar) to plant seeds.
Drill	to sow or plant in channels or furrows, known as drills.
Dunt	an East Anglian term for a parasitic disease of sheep and other ruminants caused by the larvae of certain tapeworms (especially *taenia multiceps*) encysted in the brain, characterised by unsteady gait and loss of balance, and for the staggering and 'dizzy' behaviour of infected animals
Dutch Clover	see clover
Dyking	To soak plant matter in water for a period of time before processing.
Earth	Soil.
Ell	A measure of length, in England 45 inches.
Enter-common	For inter-common, an area of common land or fen shared between two or more parishes
Fan	a measure, apparently peculiar to Cambridgeshire, equalling three heaped bushels, used of chaff, and here also of small seeds.
Fast day	Fast days were proclaimed on several days each year in the 1790s in support of the war effort and the government.
Firkin (of butter)	a cask or other container, and thus a unit of measure equal to a quarter of a barrel, the weight varying with the content, for butter, 56 lbs; here used as an adjective probably meaning casked up for market rather than for local sale.
First cost	cost price, the initial cost.
Flag	A weight, earth or stone for holding harvested crops such as willow and hemp under water.
Flag-oats	Wild oats
Flax	The plant *Linum usitatissimum*, bearing blue flowers, succeeded by pods containing seeds commonly known as linseed; cultivated for its textile fibre and for its seeds; Maiden flax, see hemp.

Fleet	with little depth, shallow, so as a verb, fleeten, to become shallow, swift or nimble, used primarily for living beings but here for a machine.
Garget	inflammation in the head, throat, udder or elsewhere, but also used more generally as synonym for red-water, ie any virulent infectious disease of cattle or other livestock, such as anthrax or babesiosis (from ticks).
Gault	a series of thick, heavy clays and Marls forming strata in southern England. In the eighteenth century it referred to any clay.
Gavels	a quantity of corn cut and ready to be made into a sheaf.
Goole	here used in the same sense as gull: a channel, hole or bank-breach created by the flow of water.
Great, working by the	see task work.
Grip, Gripping	small open furrow or ditch, esp. for carrying off water; a trench, drain, making such ditches.
Gutter	a shallow trough or open conduit properly for the outflow of fluid, but here to take a solid infill.
Half yearly meadow land	land used as pasture for part of the year, in some cases the grass allowed to grow in the other half-year, for hay for winter feed.
Haulm	the straw of peas beans and tares, to haulm: to lay haulm upon
Heath	open uncultivated ground, naturally clothed with low herbage and dwarf shrubs, often with sandy soil.
Hemp	An annual herbaceous plant, *Cannabis sativa*, a native of Western and central Asia, cultivated for its valuable fibre, used for stout cloth and in rope-making; maiden hemp is pulled before seeds form and is used for cloth-making.
Herbage	a growth of soft-stemmed-low-growing plants which die down each year, suitable as pasture; right of herbage the right to use the herbage, usually by depasturing animals, often a common right attached to specific dwellings in a settlement.
Hollow draining	underground drainage, achieved by laying of pervious material at the foot of a deep trench, then covered over; much improved in the late 18th century by the introduction of tiles or drain bricks laid at the trench foot to form a pipe-like structure through which water flowed more readily.
Hoven	swollen, bloated by gas formed through fermentation especially of clover in the animal's stomach
Hundred houses	indoor provision for the infirm and young and for the able poor who were provided with work, made jointly for a number of parishes usually in a group of hundreds, under local acts of parliament passed in the mid-18th century ,initially in Suffolk then in Norfolk and also elsewhere.
Hurrock	used by Vancouver to denote stony ground, a word possibly of Scandinavian derivation in use in the USA.
Impropriator	see tithe
Infield	land around or near a homestead or settlement, manured and used as arable, in contradistinction to outfield, less easy of access and often used as pasture, but here also as arable.
Joist Cattle	to take in live stock to remain and feed at a certain rate, for a defined time.

Lady Day	the feast of the Annunciation to the Virgin Mary of the impending birth of Jesus, celebrated on 25th March, one of the traditional 'quarter-days' on which tenancies begin or end.
Lammas, Lammas Land	1st August; lammas land – land cropped privately until 1st August and thereafter open as common pasture.
Last	a measure of volume of dry goods, usually oats, barley and rye. The measure was variably, but in Cambridgeshire was typically equivalent to 21 coombs.
Lay or Ley	land sown with grass instead of being let lie fallow, to provide pasture.
Lay impropriator	see tithe
Layer	fast-growing crop sown between main-crop plantings, often ploughed in to increase soil productivity.
Lie land	a term used by Vancouver for Lay.
Locust Tree	A leguminous tree of the North American genus *Robinia* (subfamily *Faboideae*), also know as 'false acacia'
Lode	a water-channel, generally man-made.
Malt chives	stringy fibres, a by-product of malting.
Marl	a loose and unconsolidated earthy deposit mainly of clay; to marl it to spread such earth to improve other soil.
Meal	animal feed of finely ground plant material.
Michaelmas	the feast of St Michael, 29th September, a quarter day (see Lady day).
Modus	a money payment made in lieu of a tithe, q.v.
Mold or Mould	loose, broken, or friable earth, surface soil, especially the upper soil of cultivated land.
Morass	a wet swampy tract, a bog, a marsh; an area of very wet or muddy ground.
Mortmain	lands in: lands held inalienably by an ecclesiastical or other corporation
Muck	manure
Neat	finely proportioned, of cattle, complete i.e. retaining their horns.
Oil cake	the mass of fibrous vegetable matter left after seeds eg rapeseed, have been pressed for their oil, used as fodder for livestock and as manure.
Oil dust	oil meal, oil cake broken and ground.
Osier, Ozier	a willow with tough pliant branches used in basketwork, esp. *Salix viminalis*; a flexible branch of willow.
Outfield	see infield
Paring and burning	The paring off of grassy turf with an implement known as a breast plough to a depth of one or more inches and burning off the pared material with the assistance of brushwood, peat, or other combustible material, The practice was said to kill off diseases and pests and improve soil fertility.
Pease-make	A variant of pease meak, an implement with a long handle and crooked iron or blade used to pull up or cut down peas, bracken, reeds, etc
Peck	A measure of capacity for dry goods, equal to a quarter of a bushel or 2 gallons.

Perch	See Pole.
Poach	To become or make muddy or mushy; to trample, to be trampled eg by cattle.
Pole	A unit of length, varying locally but later standardized at 5½ yards, ie 16½ feet: also called perch or rod; a square pole, also sometimes called a perch, is 160th of an acre
Potato Oat	an obscure name for a type of oat grown in the county.
Red water	see Garget.
Rennet	curdled milk from the stomach of an unweaned calf, containing rennin and used in curdling milk for cheese.
Retting, Retted	the process of steeping Hemp in pools of water (retting pits) to remove the leaves and other soft material and expose the fibrous stem.
Rot	a highly contagious disease of sheep, causing debilitating pain and lameness.
Rowen	the aftermath of a mown meadow.
Rye grass	a tough native grass (*Lolium perenne*) commonly found on verges, rough pastures and waste ground; it was once the most commonly sown grass in leys (fields used for grazing livestock) and is now often used for reseeding grasslands.
Sanfoin	sainfoin *(Onobrychis viciifolia)* is a perennial legume that thrives on thin chalk, limestone or stoney soils.
Sedge	a course grass or rush (*Claudium Mariscus*) used in thatching.
Severalty	land held in severalty is land held in a person's own right without being joined in interest with another; land held as private enclosed property (as opposed to common).
Sewer	an artificial watercourse for draining water off land, a Commission of Sewers is a royal commission issued to a number of persons constituting them a temporary court with authority for the repair and maintenance of 'walls, ditches, banks, gutters, sewers, gotes, causeys, bridges, streams and other defences by the coasts of the sea and marsh ground lying and being within the limits of' a specified district liable to inundation from the sea or rivers'
Shackage	the turning of animals into the stubble or 'shack'; the right so to turn animals.
Sheep fold	a pen for keeping sheep together in a confined space.
Sheep hoeing	as an alternative to hoeing by hand or by horse-drawn machine the crop might be 'sheeped' or sheep hoed ie the soil cleared of weeds and broken up by depasturing sheep on it
Sheep-walk	a tract of grass-land used for pasturing sheep. Usually a set rotation of areas into which sheep are moved over time.
Shift	crop rotation. A course of cropping that varied from parish to parish.
Shims, shimmy	a Shim, sometimes called a Skerry, a kind of horse-hoe or shallow plough, used for hoeing up weeds, often between rows of beans etc; to operate a shim. The process of working the implement was known as Shimmying.
Shocks	a group of sheaves of grain placed upright and supporting each other in order to permit the drying and ripening of the grain before carrying.

Skirt, Skirt Land	the edge, margin, or verge of a wood, lake, etc., here frequently used for the fen-edge, sometimes of the land abutting a river.
Slip (lambs or calves)	of animals, to miscarry with; to drop or bring forth prematurely.
Smut	a fungal disease affecting various plants, esp. cereals, which are spoiled by the grain being wholly or partly converted into a blackish powder; also, one or other of the fungi (often ustilago tritici) causing the disease.
Soiling	feeding (horses, cattle, etc.) on fresh-cut green fodder, originally for the purpose of purging.
Staple	a term used by Charles Vancouver to indicate a the quality of soil and its consistency.
Stank	here used in the sense of damming a stream to create a pool of stagnant water.
Stanked	to leave in standing or stagnant water.
Stitch or Stetch	A ridge or balk of land; esp. a strip of ploughed land between two furrows; also, a narrow ridge in which potatoes, etc. are grown.
Still tide	a tide flowing imperceptibly, without violent current or waves.
Stint	an allotted amount or measure, here a customary allowance, the limited number of cattle, according to kind, allotted to each definite portion into which pasture or common land is divided, or to each person entitled to the right of common pasturage; also, the right of pasturage according to the fixed rate. Also, a portion of land allotted for pasturing a limited number of sheep or cattle.
Tartarian Oat	Of or pertaining to Tartary, a region now usually called Inner or Central Eurasia; the Tartarian oat, *avena orientalis*, (generally, certainly by the 19thc, acquired from France rather than Asia) has contracted one-sided panicles, and produces a small grain, grown largely for horse feed.
Task work	work done at a fixed price for completion of the whole task or for each piece, ie work for which an employee is paid according to the amount produced, rather than receiving a fixed wage.
Tithe	A tenth of annual produce or earnings, taken as a tax (originally in kind) for the support of the parish church and clergy. Where the church belonged to a religious house, the house might install a vicar, to whom the lesser (vicarial) tithe was due, whilst retaining the greater tithes as rector. At the reformation, the right to tithes often passed into lay hands, and lay rectors (lay impropriators) continued to collect the tithe, which in some places was commuted either to a fixed money rent or to a modus.
Trefoil	see clover
Wether	a male sheep, a ram, especially a castrated ram.
Wire Worm	the slender hard-skinned larva of a click beetle (family Elateridae), which is destructive to the roots of plants. Also: the similar larva of various other insects, esp. the leatherjacket grub of a crane fly.
Wormwood	The bitter-tasting plant (*Artemisia absinthium*) whose leaves and tops are used in medicine as a tonic and vermifuge, and for making vermouth and absinthe.
Yean	to bring a young sheep to lamb.

Bibliography

Manuscript Sources

Cambridgeshire Archives L70/35, 36 draft lease and surrender of the Rev N C Lane's Carlton farm (from the online catalogue).

Cambridge University Library, Doc.656, No 16. Documents relating to the Parliamentary Enclosure of Swaffham Prior.

Cambridge University Library, Add.6075 Book of proprietors for Swaffham Prior.

The National Archives, HO42/54/46 agriculture questionnaires (digital image, downloaded)

Printed Sources

A Practical Farmer, *The Complete English Farmer, or a Practical System of Husbandry.* Newbery, London (1771).

Anon. *A Defence of the Land Owners and Farmers of Great Britain; and an Exposition of the Heavy Parliamentary Taxation under which they labour.* (1814) Bickerstaff, London.

Anon. *The Gentleman farmer, being an attempt to improve agriculture by subjecting it to the test of rational principles.* Creech, Edinburgh (1776).

A Society of Gentlemen. *The Complete Farmer: or a General Dictionary of Husbandry in all its Branches.* Baldwin, London. (1769).

Betham-Edwards, M. Ed. *The Autobiography of Arthur Young with selections from his correspondence.* Smith, Elder & Co. London. (1898).

Board of Agriculture. *Correspondence with the Board.* 1796-1808. Bulmer & Co. London. (6 volumes).

Board of Agriculture. *Agricultural State of the Kingdom, in February, March and April, 1816; being the substance of the replies to a Circular Letter sent by the Board of Agriculture to every part of the Kingdom.* (1816) McMillan, London.

G. Cooke, The Complete English Farmer: or Husbandry made perfectly easy, in all its useful branches. London. (1770).

H.C. Darby, *The Draining of the Fens.*

E.S. Delamer, *Flax and Hemp, their Culture and Manipulation.* Routledge, London. (1854).

R.W. Dickson, *Practical Agriculture: or a Complete System of Modern Husbandry with the Methods of Planting and the Management of Live Stock.* (2 volumes). Richard Phillips, London. (1805).

T. Dyche, *A New General English Dictionary; Peculiarly Calculated for the Use and Improvement of such as are Unacquainted with Learned Languages.* Seventeenth Edition, London. (1794).

L. Earnle, *English Farming Past and Present.* 6th Edition. Heinmann, London. (1961).

H. S. A. Fox, 'Vancouver, Charles', *ODNB* 2004, https://doi.org/10.1093/ref:odnb/28061 accessed 27 November 2021.

G.E. Fussell, English Agriculture: From Arthur Young to William Cobbett. *The Economic History Review.* Vol. 6, No. 2 (1936).

G.E. Fussell, My Impressions of Arthur Young. *Agricultural History*, Vol. 17, No.3 (1943).

J. Gazley, Arthur Young, Agriculturalist and Traveller, 1741-1820. Some biographical sources. *Journal of the Royal Agricultural Society*, lxxxv (1925)

J. G. Gazley, *The Life of Arthur Young, 1741-1820.* American Philosophical Society. (1973)

Rev. W. Gooch, *General View of the Agriculture of Cambridgeshire*. Sherwood, Neely and Jones, London. (1811).

A.D. Hall, (Ed.) *English Farming Past and Present by the Right Honble. Lord Ernle.* Longmans, Green and Co. London. 5th Edition (1936)

H. Home, Lord Kames, *The Gentleman Farmer. Being an attempt to Improve Agriculture by subjecting it to the Test of Rational Principles*. Cadell, London. (1776).

House of Commons. *Select Committee on the Sale of Corn. (1834).*

J. Johnstone, *An Account of the most approved method of Draining Land according to the system practised by Mr. Joseph Elkington.* Edinburgh (1797).

Home Office: Acreage Returns. *List and Index Society*, London, Vols. 189, 190, 195 and 196. Swift (P&D) Ltd, (1982-3).

R. J. P. Kain, J. Chapman and R.R. Oliver, *The Enclosure Maps of England and Wales 1595-1918: A Cartographic Catalogue.* Cambridge University Press, (2004).

E. Kerridge, *The Agricultural Revolution.* George Allen & Unwin ltd., London. (1967).

W. Marshall, *Review of the Northern Reports*. Longman, Hurst, Reese and Orme, London (1808).

W.E. Minchinton, Agricultural Returns and the Government during the Napoleonic Wars. *The Agricultural History Review.* Vol. 1, No. 1 (1953).

G.E. Mingay, (Ed.) *Arthur Young and his Times*. MacMillan Press Ltd. London. (1975).

G.E. Mingay, *The Agricultural Revolution: Changes in Agriculture 1650-1880.* Documents in Economic History. Black, London.(1977).

R. Mitchison, The old Board of Agriculture (1793-1822). *The English Historical Review.* (1959), vol. 74, No.290, pp. 41-69.

S. Moor, *Suffolk Words and Phrases*. Hunter, London, (1823).

Sinclair. *Communications with the Board of Agriculture*. Bulmer and Co. London. (1796).

The Farmers Magazine. London, Vol. 6 (1837).

C. Vancouver, *General View of the Agriculture of Cambridgeshire; with observations on the means of its improvement.* Smith, London. (1794)

J. Tull, *Horse-Hoeing Husbandry: or an Essay on the Principles of Vegetation and Tillage.* Fourth Edition, Millar, London. (1762).

A.P.M. Wright, (Ed.) *The Victoria History of the Counties of England: The History of Cambridgeshire and the Isle of Ely.* Vols. iv, vi, ix Institute of Historical Research, London.

A. Young, *The Farmers Guide in Hiring and Stocking Farms.* Stahan and Nicholls, London. (1770).

Young, A. *The farmers Tour of the East of England, being the Register of a Journey through various Counties of the Kingdom, to enquire into the State of Agriculture, &c.* Strahan and Nicholl, London. (1771)

A. Young, *Observations on the Present State of the Waste Lands of Great Britain.* Nicholls, London. (1773)

A. Young, *The Annals of Agriculture and Other Useful Arts*, (45 volumes)

A. Young, *General Report on Enclosures.* Board of Agriculture (1808).

Online Sources

(Accessed 2021)

ACAD a Cambridge alumni database, *https://venn.lib.cam.ac.uk/*

Ancestry *https://www.ancestry.co.uk*

Cambridge University Library on-line catalogue i-discover *https://www.lib.cam.ac.uk/collections/special-collections/catalogues*

Cambridgeshire Archives online catalogue *https://calm.cambridgeshire.gov.uk/*

CCEd Clergy of the Church of England Database, *www.theclergydatabase.org.uk*

Oxford Dictionary of National Biography, *www.oxforddnb.com*

Index of Persons and Corporate Bodies / Colleges

Where possible, persons have been identified and their first names provided. Sources used were VCH Cambs, ODNB, Venn's Cambridge register (online version), the Church of England Clergy online database, Ancestry website, Cambridge University Library online catalogue, H C Darby's The Draining of the Fens. *For details, see bibliography.*

A

Adeane, Col. James Whorwood of Babraham, 7, 13, 133, 159, 180, 195, 240, 245, 253.
Adeane, Robert Jones of Babraham, 7.
Adeane Thos esq, 240.
Alern, Rev. (See Perne)
Armstrong Col John, (report 1724), 221n, 231.
Atkins (Atkyns), Commissioner of Sewers, (maps 1604, report 1618), 220, 230.

B

Bakewell, Robert, of Dishley, Leics, 87.
Banks Sir Joseph, 187.
Barker, James, esq, of Swaffham Bulbeck 12, 158, 162.
Barker, Benjamin esq, of Little Swaffham, 195.
Bateman, Mr. of Chatteris, 232.
Beaufort, Margaret, countess of Richmond and Derby (d.1509), 221.
Beaumont, Mr. of Whaddon, 170, 171, 180.
Bedford, Duke of , earl of, see Russell.
Bell, Mr. 232.
Bendyshe, ['Bandish' or Benditche] Richard, of Barrington, 54, 169.
Berguer, the Rev Daniel, Rector of Carlton, 163.
Blith ('Blyth'), Walter, writer on husbandry (1605-54), 160.
Bossmore, of Doncaster, threshing machine manufacturer, 158.
Bouch, Samuel, 120.
Boyce, Mr. of Whittlesey, 158, 196, 200, 201, 242, 247.
Boyce, John, 264.
Brame, Thomas of Lynn (see also Brome), 119.
Briggs, Rev Thomas, rector of Little Gransden, 265.
Britton and Brayley, historians, 221n
Brome, Thomas, of Lynn, 226n, 227n.
Brown, Rev Thomas, Rector of Conington, 157, 163, 168, 169, 179, 242, 247, 264.
Bull, Seth, of Ely, 212.
Bunn, Mr. of Burwell, 176.
Burleigh, Mr. of Barnwell, 242, 246, 249n.
Burwell, threshing machine manufacturer of Thetford, 159.
Butts, the Rev William, rector of Little Wilbraham and vicar of Grantchester, 162, 163, 239.

C

Cartwright Rev. Dr. Edmond of Doncaster, 253.
Carey, perhaps John Cary, Mr, 122.
Casborne, Mr. of Coton 179, 235.
Causton, Mr. of Chippenham, 239.
Charter House, 41.
Clare College, Cambridge, Dullingham, 25.
Coke, Thomas William (afterwards 1st earl of Leicester), of Holkham, Norfolk, 8, 133, 157.
Cook, of Essex, agricultural machines, 158.
Cole, Mr. William of Quy, 242.
Cooper, Mr. of Isleham, 176.
Cooper, Mr. of Ely, 245.
Cotton, Sir Charles, of Madingley, 158, 172, 177, 186, 192, 235, 245.
Cotton, Sir John Hind, of Madingley, 57.
Couch, of Harlston, near Northampton, 158.

Creasey, Mr. 231.
Cust, the Hon Henry Cockayne, rector of Cockayne Hatley, Bedfordshire, 264.
Custance, William, surveyor, Cambridge, 153, 232, 239, 257, 265.

D

Darnton, Humphrey. of Babraham, 7, 158, 176, 177, 180, 186, 187, 188, 192, 193, 195, 196, 197, 198, 199, 200, 241, 242, 243, 245, 253.
Downing College, Trustees of, Tadlow, 50.
Dugdale, Sir William, 220, 221 .
Dugmore, Mr. 166, 177.
Dunham, William, 119.
Dunn, Mr. Salisbury, of Burwell, 246.

E

Eaton, Mr., of Stetchworth, 199.
Edis, Edes, John, of Wisbech, 7, 153, 158, 159, 177, 185, 187, 188,189, 191, 193,195, 197, 200, 201,202, 213, 232, 239, 244, 246, 247, 248, 265,
Edmunds, Sir Clement, of Preston Deanery, Northamptonshire, 230.
Ely, Bishop of, see Yorke, James.
Ely Cathedral, Dean and Chapter, Kennet, 27.
Elstobb/Elstebb/Elsteb, Mr., 220, 228, 229.
Elster, Mr., (see Elstobb).

F

Field, Fields, Mr., of Upwell. 199 - 202.
Filby, Mr., of Snailwell, 158.
Fisher, the Rev Edmund, of Linton, 39.
Fiske, the Rev Robert, of Fulbourn, 152.
Folks, Sir Martin, bt. Of Hillington, Norfolk, 229.
Fowler, Mr, of Oxfordshire, 87.
Francis, Mr., of Childerley, 177, 180, 187, 198, 207, 221, 239, 242, 245, 247, 249.
Fryer, Mr., of Chatteris, 185, 187, 194.
Fuller, Mr., of Isleham, 243.

G

Gardner, Gardener Mr., of Chatteris, 170, 222n, 232, 239.
Gardiner, Mr. 1120.
Gaunt, John of , 221.
Godfrey, Mr., of Kennett , 242.
Golburn, Golborne Mr., of Ely, 222n, 229, 231, 239.
Golborne, Mr John, 225.
Golborne, Mr James, 225.
Gorges Lord, 2nd baron gorges of Stetchworth, 231.
Gough, Mr., 221.
Ground, Mr., of Whittlesey, 187, 201, 222, 231, 232, 233, 239.
Guildford, see North.

H

Haighton, Rev. R. Rector of Long Stow, 162.
Hall, General Thomas, of West Wratting, 25.
Hall, Rev. Joseph, rector, Bartlow, 39, 219.
Hammond, Mr., of Ashley, 199.
Lord Hardwicke, 7, 12, 52, 53, 133, 149, 150, 151, 158, 170, 171, 177, 188, 192, 194, 199, 200, 201, 206, 214, 220, 227, 232, 243, 257.
Harris, James, 264.
Hart, of Brinkley, threshing machine manufacturer, 159.
Hart, Mr., of Swaffham, 3, 176, 187.

Harvey, Robert, of Wimpole, 52, 239.
Harwood Prof. Busic, of Bartlow, 168, 188, 198, 199, 218, 242, 260.
Hatton Thomas Dingley Esq, of Long Stanton, 64.
Hatton, Harriet Lady Hatton, Long Stanton, 64.
Heighton, see Haighton, 158.
Hemington, John and his father or son, of Denny Abbey, Waterbeach, 66.
Hicks, Rev. James of the Temple, Great Wilbraham, 188.
Hodgkinson, Mr., 226n, 228, 229.
Holworthy, Rev M, Rector of Elsworth, 163.
Houghton / Houlton, Mr, Weston Colville, 164, 187.
Hudson, Mr. 227, 229.
Huntingdon, Henry of, 221.
Hurrell, Mr., of Foxton, 47.
Hustler, Mr., 239.

I

Ingle, Mr., of Little Swaffham, 187.

J

Jenyns/ Jennyns, the Rev George Leonard JP, 7, 8, 133, 150, 159, 186, 197, 201, 213, 218, 247.
Jobson, the Rev Abraham, curate March, 157, 161, 164.
Johnson, Mr., Whittlesey, 245, 246, 248.
Jones, John, 265.

K

Keene, Benjamin, of Linton, 39.
Kinderley, Charles, drainage engineer, 226
Kinderley, Nathaniel, drainage engineer, 226, 229, 232.
King, Mr., Bottisham, 152, 197.
Knight, Samuel, of Milton, 67.

L

Labelye, Charles, drainage engineer, 229, 229.
Lagden, Rev Henry Allen, of Weston Colville, 161.
Lambert, Mr., of Risington Wyck, Rissington, Gloucestershire, 236.
Lane, Rev. Newton Charles, of Carlton, 150, 158, 167,178,179, 186,187, 196, 199, 235, 242, 245, 250.
Lawton, Mr., Wisbech, 177, 179, 185, 193, 194, 203.
Leeds, Sir George bt, of Croxton, 264.
Leworthy the Rev. William, vicar of Harston, 7, 158, 162, 172, 177, 180, 186, 187, 188, 189, 192, 193, 194, 195, 197, 198, 235, 242, 24, 249, 250.
Lutt, Edward jnr., 2125.

M

Macclesfield, Earl of, see Parker
Mackie, Mr., of Norwich, agricultural contractor, 218.
Malin, Thomas, of Southery, 233.
Malmsbury, William of (c1090-after 1142), monk, 221.
Manners, John Henry, 5th Duke of Rutland, 85.
Metcalf, Rev. William, minor canon of Ely Cathedral, 12, 200.
Middleton, John, 217,
Middleton, Mr., Pilot, Kings Lynn, 119.
Milne, see Mylne
Mortlock, John of Great Abington, 7, 13, 14, 133, 158, 186, 187, 192, 193,194 , 245, 246, 249, 263.
Moscrop, Mr., of Longstowe, 194.
Mules, Rev Charles, perpetual curate of St Mary's, Ely, 212.
Mylne, Robert, drainage engineer, 224, 229, 231.

N

Nasmith, Dr., of Leverington, 152,177, 202, 204n.
Nichols, Mr., of Elm, 228, 232, 239.
North, Lord of Kirtling, 23

P

Page, Jonathan, John, Ely 13,151, 159, 176, 244, 263.
Page, Thomas, Ely 212.
Page, Sir Thomas Hyde, 224, 228, 229, 231.
Pallavicino, 240, 241.
Parker, George, 4th Earl of Macclesfield, 61.
Partridge, Mrs. 123.
Patteson, Mr, of Wimpole, 149.
Pears, Thomas, sluice keeper, Gunthorpe sluice, 120.
Pemberton, Christopher, 176, 177, 218.
Perne, Rev. Andrew, Rector of Abington Pigotts (1770-72), 161.
Peyton, Sir Henry, of Doddington, 150.
Philips, Mr., of Bourn-bridge 157n, 188, 198, 247.
Philips, Mr., of Babraham, 195.
Phipps, Mr., Inn keeper, 180, 241.
Pooley, Mr., 222.
Popham, Sir John fen investor, 230.
Portland, Earl of, see Weston.
Powell, see Pownall
Pownall, Thomas of Saltfleetby, 245.

Q

Quintin, Mr., of Hatley St George, 50, 51, 61.

R

Rayner and Hardwick, of Wisbech, 233.
Rasbrick, Rev. J., of King's Lynn, 220.
Rennie, threshing machine manufacturer, 158.
Rennie, Mr., Water Engineer, 226, 229.
Richmond, Countess Margaret, see Beaufort.
Rutland, Duke of, see Manners

S

Saffery, Edemund, Downham Market, Norfolk, 232, 239.
Saffory (Safory), Mr., of Elm, 184.
Sampson, -, 122.
Sanxter, William, of Horseheath, 198, 199, 213, 246.
Savory, Mr. E. jun, of Downham, Norfolk, 234.
Sawyer, Mr., of Cheveley, 152, 213.
Scott, Rev. Joseph senr. Baptist Minister, Chatteris, 7,140, 177, 183, 187, 193n, 196, 201, 203, 206, 240, 242, 257, 264.
Shearing, Mr., of Soham, 239.
Shepherd, Mr., of Chippenham, 7, 107,152, 157, 172, 187, 188, 189, 190, 192, 193, 195, 196, 197, 202, 239, 245, 248.
Simpson, Mr., of Nowton, Suffolk, 190.
Smeaton, Mr., 228, 229.
Smith, Humphrey, 228.
Smith, Mr., of Chatteris, 236,
Smith Mr. W, 241.
Stevenson, Rev. John, of Wilbraham, 162.
Stirtland, Mr., of Steeple Morden, 235.
Stone, Edward of Leverington,4, 81, 151, 153, 240, 242.
Stone, Thomas, of Greys Inn, Middlesex, enclosure commissioner, 166, 177.

Strickland, John, of Steeple Morden, 50.
Slutter, James, of Bury St Edmunds, 190.

T

Tattershall, Edmund of Ely and Littleport, 71, 207.
Tharp, John, of Chippenham, 7, 13, 107, 135, 141n, 158, 171, 172, 218, 234, 235, 245, 247, 257.
Thomson / Thompson, Rev. Robert of Longstowe, 14, 180, 194, 263, 264.
Townley, Richard Greaves, of Fulbourn, 34.
Trant, the Rev Edmund, rector of Toft, 62.
Treslove, Joseph of Trumpington, 150, 169, 177, 187, 235, 245.
Trinity College, Cambridge, 22.
Turner, Rev., vicar of Burwell, 149, 186.
Turpin, John of Wisbech, 120.

V

Vince, Rev Samuel, curate of Milton, 163.

W

Waddelow, Mr., of Littleport, 247.
Watford, Alexander, 166.
Watte, John, drainage engineer, 124, 226n, 229, 231.
Wattie see Watte.
Waudby, William, of March and Wisbech, 153, 185, 188, 193, 222, 238.
Wedd, Nathaniel, of Ansty Hall, Trumpington, and of Soham, 7, 153, 177, 178, 185, 186, 187, 188, 189, 196, 200, 201, 239, 242, 244, 245, 246, 249.
Wedge, Charles, of Westley Waterless, 7, 158, 159, 169, 177, 179, 184n, 187, 188, 191, 192, 193, 197, 198, 199, 237, 238, 242, 246, 249, 263.
Weston, Charles, 3rd Earl of Portland, 221
Wing, John, of Thorney, 8, 180, 181,182, 220, 237 247, 265 .
Worledge, Mr., of Ingham, Suffolk, 190.

Y

Yellowly, agricultural machine manufacturer, 159.
Yorke, James, Bishop of Ely, 176.
Yorke, Philip, 3rd Earl of Hardwicke, 7
Young, Arthur, of Bradfield, Suffolk, agricultural reformer, 1, 2, 3, 4, 6, 7, 8, 9, 12, 149, 151, 152, 158, 170, 172, 176, 177, 178, 185, 186, 188, 189, 191-197, 199, 201, 202, 209, 211, 218, 220, 221, 222n, 231, 233, 235, 236, 237, 239, 240, 257, 261.

Index of Places

Note:- The surveys contain a great variation of spellings for places. In this index the modern place name is given first and variations in square brackets.

A

Abington Pigotts [Abbington], 11, 16, 48, 92, 96, 144
Abington [Abbington], Great and Little, 9,11, 16, 38,92, 96, 142, 164.
Aldreth, 74, 147, 148.
Apeshall, 71, 94, 97, 147.
Arrington, 16, 52, 92, 96, 105.
Ashley cum Silverley [Silvery], 4, 11, 16, 21, 22, 24, 29, 53, 92, 96, 140, 199, 247, 248.

B

Babraham, 7, 13, 16, 37-38, 92, 96, 142, 158,159, 176, 177, 180, 186, 187, 188, 192, 193, 195-200, 214, 240-243, 233-235, 245, 253, 261.
Badlingham (in Chippenham), 16, 28, 92, 96, 248.
Balsham, 11, 16, 38, 41, 92, 96, 142, 143, 169.
Barnwell, 35, 92, 96, 142, 242, 246, 249n.
Barrington, 11, 16, 53-54, 92, 96, 145, 152, 162, 164, 169, 248.
Bartlow, 16, 39, 92, 96, 168, 188, 218, 219, 242, 260.
Barton, 16, 55, 56, 92, 96, 145.
Barway [Barraway], 69, 92, 97, 147
Bassingbourn, 11, 16, 47, 92, 96, 144.
Benwick, 6, 11, 16, 127.
Bottisham, 4, 7, 11, 16, 30-31, 32, 92, 96, 141, 150, 152, 159, 169, 174, 197, 201, 213, 218, 227.
Bourn, 6, 11, 16, 62.
Bournbridge, 38, 142, 240, 241, 247.
Boxworth, 16, 58-59, 94, 97, 146.
Brinkley, 6,11, 16, 25, 140, 160.
Burrough Green,6, 11, 16, 25, 140.
Burwell, 11, 12, 16, 30, 92, 96, 141, 149, 176, 186, 187, 191, 192, 246, 253.

C

Caldecote [Coldicot], 16, 62.
Cambridge, 16, 35, 95, 129, 152, 172, 209,210, 215, 235, 243, 256, 261.
Carlton cum Willingham,6, 9, 11, 16, 25,140, 150, 152, 158, 163, 167, 179, 235.
Castle Camps, 16, 40, 92, 96, 143.
Caxton, 16, 60, 61, 92, 96, 103, 146, 248, 256.
Chatteris, 7, 9,11, 16, 75-76, 94, 97, 101, 140, 148, 169, 170, 177, 178, 183, 185, 186, 187, 193n, 194, 196, 196, 199, 201, 202, 203, 2096, 213, 219, 222n, 232, 236, 239, 240, 242, 251, 252, 254, 255, 256, 257, 258, 259.
Cherry Hinton, 6, 11, 16, 35, 36, 142, 256.
Chesterton, 16, 35, 68, 94, 97, 147.
Cheveley, 16, 22, 92, 96, 140, 152, 213, 240.
Childerley [Childersley], 16, 58, 63-64, 94, 97, 99, 146, 173, 176, 177, 180, 198, 207, 235, 239, 242, 245, 247, 249.
Chippenham, 7, 11, 13, 16, 26, 28-29, 92, 96, 107, 141, 151, 157, 158, 161, 171, 180, 185, 187, 188, 189, 190, 192, 195, 196, 197, 201, 202, 210, 217, 234, 239, 244, 253, 257.
Chittering [Chillerin], 66.
Cockayne Hatley, see Hatley, Cockayne
Coldham Common, 35, 142.
Comberton, 6, 16, 55, 145.
Conington, 4, 6, 11, 16, 58, 59, 127, 256, 264.
Coton, 11, 16, 56, 94, 97, 145, 152, 163, 169, 179, 235.
Cottenham [Chittenham], 13, 16, 65-66, 94, 97, 146n, 147, 152, 176, 192, 211, 243, 244, 248.
Coveney, 4, 6, 16, 72, 76, 151.
Croxton, 11, 14, 16, , 60, 94, 97, 146, 248, 263.
Croydon cum Clopton [Crowdon], 6, 16, 51, 144.

D

Denny Abbey, 66, 94, 97, 147, 149.
Doddington, 6, 16, 76, 78, 94, 97, 149, 151, 165.
Downham, Little, 16, 72, 94, 97, 117, 147, 151, 210, 232, 239.
Downham Market, 234, 256.

Drayton, Dry, 11, 16, 57-58, 94, 97, 146, 248.
Drayton, Fen [Fenny Drayton], 65, 149.
Dullingham, 11, 16, 23, 24-25, 92, 96, 140, 248.
Duxford, 16, 44, 45, 46, 92, 96, 143.

E

East Hatley, see Hatley, East.
Elm, 11, 16, 76-77, 77, 79, 89, 94, 97, 101, 148, 179, 184, 186, 219, 232, 239, 247, 248.
Elsworth, 6, 11, 16, 59, 146, 152, 163, 167.
Eltisley [Eltsley], 14, 16, 59, 60, 94, 97, 146, 248, 263.
Ely, 6n, 7, 12, 13, 16, 27, 70-71, 94, 95, 97, 103, 105, 118, 147, 149, 150, 151, 152, 159, 179, 191, 200, 202, 208, 209, 210, 212, 217, 222, 228, 230, 231, 239, 244, 251, 256,
Ely, Isle of, 135, 227, 230.
Eversden, Great and Little, 11, 16, 54, 55, 92, 96, 145, 178.

F

Fen Ditton [Fenny Ditton], 11, 16, 33, 92, 142, 243.
Fen Drayton, see Drayton, Fen.
Fordham, 11, 16, 26-27, 28, 92, 96, 141, 190, 191.
Fordham Abbey, 26.
Fowlmere [Foulmire], 43, 46, 47, 92, 96, 102, 143, 144.
Foxton, 6, 16, 43, 46, 54, 143, 144.
Fulbourn [Fulburn, Fulburne], 11, 16, 34, 92, 96, 142, 152, 178.

G

Gamlingay, 11, 16, 61, 94, 97, 146.
Gedney, 84.
Girton, 11, 16, 64, 94, 96, 146.
Gorefield, 16, 85.
Gransden, Little, 6, 11, 14, 16, 61, 263,
Gransden, Great (Hunts.), 14, 263.
Grantchester, 11, 16, 55-56, 92, 96, 145,146, 150, 152, 163, 169.
Graveley, 4, 6, 11, 16, 58, 146.
Guyhirn, 77, 88, 126, 148, 202.

H

Haddenham, 16, 74, 94, 97, 147, 151, 178, 227.
Hardwick, 6, 16, 62-63, 94, 94, 99, 146, 173.
Harlton, 6, 11, 16, 145.
Harston, 6, 7, 11, 16, 46, 143, 158, 162, 172, 187, 188, 189, 235.
Haslingfield, 6, 11, 16, 54, 145.
Hatley, Cockayne, 264.
Hatley, East, 6, 16, 255, 263.
Hatley St George, 14, 16, 50, 92, 96, 144, 263.
Hauxton, 6, 7, 11, 16, 145n, 162, 172.
Hildersham, 16, 38-39, 92, 96, 142.
Hinxton [Hingston, Hinkeston], 16, 42-43, 92, 96, 143.
Histon, 6, 11, 16.
Horningsea, 11, 16, 33, 92, 96, 142.
Horseheath, 6, 16, 41.

I

Ickleton, 11, 16, 43, 92, 96, 143.
Impington, 11, 16, 68, 94, 97, 147.
Isleham, 11, 16, 26, 29, 92, 96,103.

K

Kennett, 11, 16, 27, 92, 96, 141, 248.
Kingston, 11, 16, 54, 61-62, 94, 97, 105, 145, 146, 178, 257.

Kirtling, [Catlidge], 11, 16, 22-23, 24, 92, 96, 140.
Knapwell, 6, 11, 16, 58, 63, 99, 146, 152, 161, 164, 170, 176, 261.
Kneesworth, 11, 16, 47, 52, 92, 96, 144.

L

Landbeach, 11, 16, 94, 97, 147, 176.
Landwade, 6, 16, 26, 27, 141, 190, 191, 199.
Leverington, 12, 16, 79, 81, 82, 85, 87-88, 94, 97, 101, 106, 148, 151, 179, 219.
Linton, 16, 38, 39, 92, 96, 102, 103, 142, 241, 256.
Litlington, 16, 47-48, 92, 96, 144.
Littleport, 16, 117, 149, 178, 185, 227.
Little Thetford, 16, 75, 94, 97, 148, 151.
Longstanton [Long Stanton], 11, 16, 58, 64-65, 94, 97, 147 .
Longstowe, [Long Stowe], 6, 11, 14, 16, 61, 162, 188, 248, 263, 264.

M

Madingley, 16, 57, 146.
Manea, 4, 6, 11, 16, 72, 76, 202.
March [Merch], 2, 6, 11, 16, 76, 105, 150, 151, 152, 161, 162, 165, 199, 202, 209, 210, 213, 222, 256.
Melbourn, 6, 16, 46, 47, 144.
Meldreth [Meldrith], 6, 11, 16, 47, 144.
Mepal, 6, 16, 128, 147, 151, 178, 211, 251, 252, 254, 255, 256, 258, 259.
Milton, 11, 16, 67-68, 94, 97, 147, 152, 163, 169.

N

New Barns Farm, Ely, 208, 209.
Newton, 6, 16, 46, 143.
Newton in the Isle, 11, 16, 79, 81, 83, 94, 97, 148.
Nornea [Nornery], 70.

O

Oakington [Hoggington], 16, 94, 97, 147.
Oddisey [Odissey], 48, 92, 96, 144.
Orwell, 6, 16, 52, 54, 145.
Outwell, 16, 79, 94, 97, 117, 126, 148, 179, 207, 213, 256.
Over, 16, 65, 178.

P

Pampisford, 7, 9, 11, 16, 42, 143, 163, 164.
Papworth Everard, 6, 11, 16, 59, 146.
Papworth St Agnes, 6, 16.
Parson Drove, 16, 87, 88, 94, 97, 101, 106, 148, 179, 219, 250.

Q

Quaney, 70.

R

Rampton [Rumpton], 16, 65.
Reach, 227, 256, 257.
Rectory Farm, Ely, 13.

S

Salters Lode, 117, 118.
Sawston, 11, 16, 41-42, 92, 96, 143, 169.
Shelford, Great and Little, 6, 11, 16, 41, 241, 250.
Shepreth [Sheperheath], 11, 16, 43, 46, 1449.

Shingay, 16, 50, 51, 92, 96, 144.
Shudy Camps, 16, 40, 59, 92, 96, 143, 240.
Snailwell, 11, 16, 26, 92, 96, 141, 190.
Soham [Soame], 13, 16, 69, 94, 97, 151, 177, 178, 185, 186, 188, 199, 200, 213, 217, 227, 239, 244, 256, 259.
Spinney Abbey, 94, 97.
Stapleford, 11, 16, 36, 92, 96, 142.
Steeple Morden, 11, 16, 49-50, 92, 96, 144, 235.
Stetchworth [Stachworth], 11, 16, 92, 96, 140, 199, 218.
Stow cum Quy, 16, 33, 34, 92, 96, 142, 235.
Stretham, 16, 75, 94, 97, 148, 149, 150, 151, 178.
Stuntney, 70.
Sutton, 16, 73-74, 84, 94, 97, 147, 151, 211.
Swaffham Bulbeck [Little Swaffham], 6, 11, 16, 162, 167, 187.
Swaffham Prior, 7, 8, 11, 16, 187.
Swaffham's, 6, 11, 12, 16, 30, 141, 158, 176, 187, 192, 227.
Swavesey [Swasey], 16, 58, 65.

T

Tadlow, 16, 50, 92, 96, 144, 248.
Teversham [Taversham], 11, 16, 32, 34, 92, 96, 142.
Thorney, 8, 16, 89, 90, 94, 97, 101, 106, 148, 151, 180, 186, 213, 219, 220, 221, 248, 250, 259.
Thorney (Ely), 70.
Thriplow [Triplow], 16, 44, 46, 92, 96, 143, 144.
Toft, 11,, 16, 62, 94, 97, 146.
Toseland (Hunts.), 14, 263.
Trumpington [Trompington], 12, 35, 36, 92, 96, 142, 150, 152, 169, 246, 248.
Tydd St Giles [Tid St Giles], 11, 16, 80, 81, 82, 83, 84, 94, 97, 116, 148, 237, 259.

U

Upwell, 11, 16, 78-79, 94, 97, 148, 178, 200, 202, 204, 213, 251, 252, 254, 255, 258, 259.

W

Waterbeach, 11, 16, 94, 97, 103, 147, 151, 153, 176, 185, 188, 211, 235.
Wendy [Wyndee], 11, 16, 51-52, 92, 96, 145.
Wentworth, 6, 16, 75, 151.
West Wickham, 6, 12, 40, 138.
West Wratting, 6, 12, 25.
Westley Waterless [Westley Bottom], 6, 16, 169.
Weston Colville, 11, 16, 161, 164, 257.
Westwick, 6, 16, 94, 97.
Whaddon, 6, 16, 52, 145, 170, 171, 180.
Whittlesey [Whittlesea], 16, 94, 97, 90, 126, 127, 149, 151, 178, 184, 188, 192, 193, 199, 200, 201, 209, 210, 213, 221, 222, 231, 233, 242, 252, 253, 256,
Whittlesey dyke, 90, 126,127.
Whittlesey Meer, 231.
Whittlesford [Wedford], 12, 41, 43-44, 90, 94, 139.
Wicken [Wickin or Wichin], 16, 69, 94, 97, 147, 178, 192.
Wilburton, 16, 74, 94, 97,148, 151, 227.
Willingham, 16, 65.
Wimblington [Wimlington], 6, 16, 151, 165.
Wimpole, 7, 9, 12, 13, 16,145, 149, 180, 188, 197, 200, 201, 206, 260.
Wisbech, 4, 12, 16, 81, 94, 97, 148, 149, 150, 179, 184, 185, 193, 203n, 203, 213, 217, 219,221, 231, 232, 233, 242, 246, 253, 256.
Wisbech canal, 233.
Witcham, 6, 16, 151, 178.
Witchford [Wickford], 6, 14, 16, 75, 151.
Woodditton, 11, 16, 23, 24, 92, 96, 140.

Subject Index

Note:- *Some items appear in great frequency in the text, for example Barley. Such items have been omitted, except where they appear as a dedicated section.*

A

Agricultural Society, 1, 2, 3n, 133.

B

Barley, 191-192,
Barley-big, 78, 79, 85, 88, 204, 205, 207.
Beans, 12, 193-194.
Bears Muck, 77, 79, 90, 116.
Blacksmiths, 85, 258, 259.
Board of Agriculture, 1-2, 3, 4, 7, 12, 19, 113, 135, 152, 153, 156, 165, 181, 183, 187n, 234, 236, 237, 238, 249, 251, 254, 255, 258, 259, 23-266.
Bullocks, 78, 133, 171, 200, 213, 244-245.

C

Cabbages, 201-202.
Canals, delph's, dykes, leam's and lodes, 256.
Carpenter, 85, 259.
Carrot, 12, 77, 201.
Cart, 83-84, 107, 158.
Cattle, see Cows.
Cheese, 12, 39, 65, 166, 243, 244, 253, 256, 258.
Climate, 135-140.
Clover, 197-198.
Coleseed or Rape, 195-196.
Collar Maker, 259.
Common, 135, 143, 145, 151, 152, 161-163, 164, 165, 166, 167, 169, 170, 171, 172, 176, 186, 219, 222,
Commonable House, 168, 170.
Commoners, 85 170, ,257,
Common Field, 8, 9, 20,21, 24, 25, 29,32, 35, 36, 38, 41, 44, 45, 46, 47, 49, 54, 55, 65, 68, 73, 75, 90, 99, 141, 161, 162, 163.
Common Meadow, see Common.
Common Right, 66, 69, 76, 165, 166, 167, 168, 169, 170, 172.
Cottages, 38, 59, 84, 88, 90, 151, 164, 165, 166, 167, 172, 257.
Couch Barn, see Barn.
Cows, 103-104, 243-244.
Cow Common, see Common.

D

Debt, 255.
Deer, 53, 260.
Drainage, 117-129, 233-236.,
Drainage Tax, 165, 222, 263.
Dyking, 12, 196, 199, 204.

E

Eau Brink Cut, 1, 6, 8, 113, 124, 224, 225, 229, 232, 236.
Embanking, 180, 221, 229, 236-237.
Enclosure, 1, 2, 4, 8, 9-11, 25, 52, 99-100, 160-154.
Entercommon, see Intercommon.

F

Fairs, 256.
Fen common, see common.

Flax, 76, 77, 78, 79, 82, 96, 97, 107, 205-207.

G

Gardens, 7, 12, 151, 164, 217.
Grass, 100-101, 212-217 .

H

Half Yearly Meadow Land, 38, 39, 41, 43, 45, 93, 95, 98, 102, 108, 151.
Heath, 21, 22, 23, 24, 27, 37, 93, 95, 98, 102, 160-163, 164, 186, 218, 219-220.
Hemp, 12, 78, 79, 96, 97, 107-108, 202-205.
Hogs - see Pigs.
Horses, 13, 105, 248-250.
Horse Common, see Common.

I

Implements, 1, 4, 8, 83, 106-107,157-160.
Imprisonment, 14, 191.
Improvement, 219-233, 258.
Innovation, 4, 13, 34, 99.
Intercommon, 42, 142, 171.
Irrigation, 2403-242, 261.

K

Kale (Scotch), 199.

L

Labour, 193, 251-256.
Lentils, 29, 31, 207.
Livestock, 12,13.
Lodes, see Canals
Lot Grass, 168.

M

Meadow, 9, 93, 95, 98, 101, 108, 168.
Manufacturing, 39, 71, 84, 256-259.
Manure, 4, 12, 186, 193, 195, 196-197, 198, 199, 200, 201.
Markets, 29, 203, 204, 205, 256.
Masons, 259.
Moor common, see Common.
Mustard, 79, 86, 154, 207-208.

O

Oats, 96, 97, 192-193.
Oil Seed see Coleseed.
Orchards, 217.
Outwell Canal Scheme, 126.
Oziers, 211-212.

P

Paring and Burning, 22, 40,101, 237-240, 253.
Parsnips, 12, 201.
Peas, 194-185.
Pigeons, 13, 251.
Pigs, 13, 75, 250-251.
Plough's, 13, 157-158, 236.
Poor, 8, 153, 165, 166, 167, 168, 169, 170, 191, 257-258.
Poor rate, 4, 13, 14, 153, 265.

Population, 1, 4, 25, 52, 70, 76, 82, 84, 86, 88, 104-105, 163, 165, 166, 167, 169, 170, 171,172, 182, 258.
Potatoes, 12, 199-200.

R

Rape, see Coleseed.
Reed, 210-211.
Rent, 13-14, 92, 93, 94, 95, 98, 151-152.
Roads, 166, 167, 256.
Rye, 193.

S

Sainfoin, 189, 198, 237, 245.
Sedge, 210.
Seed wheat, 30, 39, 186, 187.
Sheep, 245-248.
Sluice, 117, 118, 124, 125, 127, 128.
Soil, 1, 4, 8, 12, 20, 140-149.

T

Tares, 195.
Thatchers, 259.
Thatching, 210, 253.
Threshing, 2, 13, 85, 100, 150, 151, 158, 159, 160, 175n, 252.
Threshing machine, see Threshing.
Tillage, 176.
Timber, 24, 51, 65, 75, 104, 114, 218, 220.
Tithe, 13-14, 151, 152-153, 156, 164,165, 166,167, 168, 169, 171, 175, 263, 264.

W

Wages, 13, 84, 85, 105, 251-256.
Waste, see Common.
Wash Common, see Common.
Water Meadow, 241, 242.
Weeds, 259.
Weights and Measures, 245, 258.
Wheat, 178, 186-191.
Woad, 12, 13, 84, 86, 154, 207-209.
Woods, 217.